# Pharmacy Law
## for California Pharmacists

### Fifth Edition

**William L. Marcus**
**Marsha N. Cohen**

For ordering information, contact Hastings College of the Law Bookstore
(415) 565-4610 or (800) 925-1679

ISBN 0-9713734-2-6

# Preface

*Pharmacy Law for California Pharmacists* presents an overview of the law governing the practice of pharmacy in this state. Included is discussion of statutes, regulations, and, where relevant, judicial decisions affecting pharmacy practice. Also included, through the last chapter and in hypothetical questions in the course of the text, is discussion of a pharmacist's ethical obligations, especially when they create a potential conflict with the law.

**W**hy do pharmacists need to understand the law, especially pharmacy law? Many aspects of our lives are, whether we like it or not, subject to some legal regulation. And of all the professions, pharmacy is one of the most highly regulated. In fact, all aspects of the manufacture and sale of prescription drugs are subject to significant legal scrutiny. In order to recognize your legal obligations, as well as your ethical obligations to patients, and to know how to deal with those situations in which your obligations appear to be in conflict, you must understand the legal context within which you are practicing pharmacy.

**Y**ou do not need to be a lawyer to understand pharmacy law as it applies to your professional life. This text is not intended to give you complete knowledge of pharmacy law, as a lawyer with this specialty would be expected to have. It is intended to describe what "law" is, to describe the key provisions of the law affecting pharmacy practice, to acquaint you with how the legal system works in respect to your pharmacy practice, and to give you the confidence to know when you understand what the law requires and when you ought to seek additional advice.

**I**n this book we have not attempted to include entire statutes and regulations; we paraphrase and often quote from them. The full text of the major statutes and regulations governing California pharmacy practice is available on the website of the California State Board of Pharmacy (www.pharmacy.ca.gov/laws_regs/index.htm); you can also purchase this material, in print or on CD-ROM, through LawTech Publishing Co.

(www.lawtech-pub.com/webstore/page4.html). Before beginning the practice of pharmacy, and periodically as long as you practice, you ought to review the actual language of the pharmacy statutes and regulations, including the laws governing controlled substances, to keep abreast of changes.

**H**ow should you use this text? Use it as a primer to acquaint yourself with the law and how to find, read, analyze, and apply the law to the very real situations that face you in pharmacy practice. Pharmacy law differs from virtually all other aspects of pharmacy practice because in other areas there generally are single clear answers to questions. In the law, in contrast, you may often find that there is no clear answer, that the precise problem you raise has not been contemplated. The law and regulations give you a framework, but not specific direction. Although common sense in applying the words of the law frequently supplies the best answer, in some situations you need to analyze several laws and regulations that may overlap and even appear to conflict. The process of applying the law is often confusing and frustrating; we have tried, in this text, to show you how to steer the course under such circumstances.

**A** number of the text's chapters are important to all pharmacists (such as those on drug classification, licensure, scope of practice, prescriptions, and record-keeping). Others address law that will not necessarily affect you on a day-to-day basis, but of which you need to be aware (for example, those on the Board of Pharmacy and on other law relevant to pharmacy practice).

**W**e hope this text helps to solve the problem that the language of laws and regulations is not always easily understood. We have attempted, without oversimplifying, to make the legal requirements as comprehensible as possible by discussing them in "plain English" rather than "legalese," and by references backward and forward to related materials. We have posed questions in each chapter to help you get used to the process of legal analysis, and consideration of ethics, that will help you when faced with similar problems in the practice of pharmacy.

Even where we do not quote the language of a statute or regulation, we generally include a citation. That citation is a reference to the original source – whether it be a statute, regulation, court decision, or other legal writing – that supports the statement made in the text. The citation will enable you to find the full text of that source. We have modified standard legal citation practice to make our references to source documents as clear and simple as possible. The note, "Understanding Legal Citations," on page v, explains the citation system used throughout the book; a glossary, on page vii, decodes abbreviations in citations as well as in the text. Most of the law that we cite is available on the Board of Pharmacy's website and in the print form of the law book. Other sources – including federal laws and regulations governing prescription drugs and controlled substances and California's food and drug laws – may be found at various Internet sites or in a school of pharmacy library or a county or university law library.

For this fifth edition, we have limited our coverage of drug and device use in facilities other than pharmacies, of enforcement functions and actions of the Board, and of other agencies and monitoring systems. We made these choices to make space available to cover the increasing complexity in more basic areas of pharmacy law. We expect to continue to compile developments in the law annually, and post them at w3.uchastings.edu/cohen/pharmacy.htm, which you might wish to bookmark and check periodically, particularly at the beginning of each new year.

As in previous editions, we have highlighted here the most significant changes and developments affecting California pharmacy practice that have occurred between the publication of the last edition in 2002 and December 2004, when this edition went to press. We have also added, in this edition, a guide (Appendix A) indicating where in this book you will find discussion of each of the items that the Board has indicated it is testing in the new California Pharmacist Jurisprudence Examination (CPJE).

Learning the law is not just a one-time requirement to obtain a pharmacy degree and pass the licensure examination. Recognizing and applying the law is a daily part of pharmacy practice for everyone in the profession. We hope this book helps to make learning and application of pharmacy law easy for you.

---

### Recent legal developments?

Check for a memo each January
until a new edition is published:
w3.uchastings.edu/cohen/pharmacy.htm

---

# About the Authors

**W**illiam L. Marcus, a California deputy attorney general for 25 years, was counsel to the California State Board of Pharmacy from 1982 to 2001. He is currently a part-time administrative law judge with California's Office of Administrative Hearings and is on the faculty of the University of California at San Diego's School of Pharmacy, where he has taught Pharmacy Law and Ethics since the school opened in 2002. He is a past president of both the National Association of State Controlled Substance Authorities (NASCSA) and the Council for Licensure, Enforcement and Regulation (CLEAR), the United States and international organization of agencies and people involved in professional and occupational licensure and regulation. He has been a member of the executive committee of The Council of State Governments and was an official advisor to the National Conference of Commissioners on Uniform State Laws during the 1986-1990 revision of the Model State Controlled Substances Act.

**B**ill has long been active in the field of pain management law and policy. He proposed, and co-coordinated, California's 1994 Summit on Effective Pain Management, was a founding member of the board of directors and chair of the regulatory affairs committee of the Southern California Cancer Pain Initiative, and is currently a member of the steering committee of the Northern California Pain Initiative and co-chair of its professional education committee. He lectures on such subjects as drug and pharmacy law, pain management law and policy, evidence, and administrative law; practices pharmacy law; and is an Assistant Clinical Professor at the University of California at San Francisco School of Pharmacy. He is a theatre arts graduate of the American University (Washington, D.C.) and received his J.D. from the University of San Francisco School of Law.

**M**arsha N. Cohen is Professor of Law, Hastings College of the Law, University of California. She teaches courses on torts, food and drug law, and administrative agency law. She served for two terms as a member of the California State Board of Pharmacy and was its first nonpharmacist president. While a Board member she repeatedly drafted proposed legislation and regulations on such subjects as patient consultation, continuing education, and hypodermic deregulation.

**M**arsha has served on a number of federal government advisory committees, including the Food Advisory Committee (FDA), the Device Good Manufacturing Practices Advisory Committee (FDA), the National Advisory Environmental Health Sciences Council (NIEHS/NIH), and the Review Panel on New Drug Regulation (HEW). She was a member of the Food Forum of the National Academy of Sciences Institute of Medicine from 1996 to 2001, and served as a member of the Institute's committees that produced the reports *Ensuring Safe Food from Production to Consumption* (1998) and *Scientific Criteria to Ensure Safe Food* (2003).

**S**he writes and lectures in the areas of government regulation, pharmacy law, and food and drug law, and is the co-author (with Prof. Michael Asimow of UCLA School of Law) of *California Administrative Law* (2002).

**A**fter serving as a law clerk to the Hon. Raymond L. Sullivan of the Supreme Court of California, Marsha worked as a staff attorney in the Washington, D.C., advocacy office of Consumers Union, publisher of *Consumer Reports*. She is a graduate of Smith College and the Harvard Law School.

# Notice to Reader

The law is constantly evolving. Newly-adopted statutes and regulations and new court decisions may apply to issues discussed in this book. The authors have made diligent efforts to provide information within this work that is accurate and consistent with the body of law existing at the time of the copyright date. *It remains the responsibility of every practitioner to be mindful of the possibility of new developments in the field, and to take them into account.* This work is not intended to provide legal advice, for which a licensed attorney should be consulted.

# Acknowledgments

We would especially like to thank Dean Lorie Rice of the UCSF School of Pharmacy for the original suggestion some 12 years ago that we collaborate on what became this text, and for her support and assistance in bringing the original edition to fruition. We also thank Dean Mary Anne Koda-Kimble and Dr. Gary McCart of the UCSF School of Pharmacy for their editing and other suggestions and assistance in the initial years. The authors also thank the past and present members and staff of the California State Board of Pharmacy, and the many others in government, pharmacy associations, and the private sector, whose service, thoughts, comments, and involvement in the ongoing process of defining and developing pharmacy practice in California have contributed to their understanding of and deep respect for the practice of pharmacy and pharmacists.

We are grateful for the excellent research assistance of Michael Maffei, Class of 2005, and Andrew Chew, Class of 2006, of Hastings College of the Law, in the production of this edition. Thanks also go to Cecilia Bruno, Barbara Topchov, and supervisor Stephen Lothrop of the Hastings Faculty Support Unit, for their assistance in the production of the manuscript; to Andrew Watters Graphic Design, for cover design; and to Isac Gutfreund, Allan Jaffee, and the staff of Somerset Printing for making a computer file into a book.

Bill Marcus thanks his sons Berek and Benjamin for their patience and understanding during the preparation of this text, in this and the preceding editions, and his former supervisor, Assistant Attorney General Ronald F. Russo, for his consistent encouragement and support for over 25 years. He also thanks the many wonderful Board members, inspectors, and staff of the California State Board of Pharmacy for the opportunity to work with and for them for 20 years, but especially the past and present executive officers, Claudia Foutz, Lorie Rice, and Patricia Harris; the current assistant executive officer, Virginia Herold; and the Board's chief supervising inspector, Bob Ratcliff.

Marsha Cohen thanks the Feyer men (Bob, Dan, Steve, and Jon) for their patience and assistance during her triennial December disappearance.

We also thank the students at UCSF School of Pharmacy who have used previous editions of this book, Bill Marcus's classes at the UCSD School of Pharmacy, and many colleagues who have reviewed all or parts of the manuscript for their helpful suggestions and corrections. All remaining errors are our responsibility. Please address comments, corrections, or suggestions to Prof. Marsha Cohen, Hastings College of the Law, 200 McAllister Street, San Francisco, CA 94102, or to cohenm@uchastings.edu, or to Bill Marcus at billnopain@aol.com.

# Understanding Legal Citations

California statutes generally are cited by their code name and section number. We have chosen to use very simple abbreviations in this book for California code names. We use B&PC for the California Business and Professions Code and H&SC for the California Health and Safety Code. All of the state statute citations in this book are to California codes, so the state designation always will be omitted. Similarly, references to "state law" (except in the context of reference to the law of all states) are to the law of California.

A large percentage of the citations in the book are to the California Business and Professions Code. All cited sections with numbers between 4000 and 4426, unless another code name appears, are from Chapter 9 of Division 2 of the California Business and Professions Code, which is known as the Pharmacy Law. For those sections, the citation abbreviation for the Business and Professions Code (B&PC) will always be omitted. We have attempted to use the designation "Pharmacy Law," with capital letters, to refer to this chapter of the Business and Professions Code, in contrast to "pharmacy law," a reference to the broader body of state and federal laws and regulations that affects the practice of pharmacy.

State administrative regulations, found in the California Code of Regulations, generally are cited by their title and section number, for example, 16 CCR §1356.3 (Title 16, California Code of Regulations, section 1356.3, defining a "secure" area for storage of drugs by dispensing physicians). Most of the administrative regulations cited in these materials are from Title 16. All cited sections with numbers between 1703 and 1793.7 are from Title 16, the Board of Pharmacy's regulations; for those sections the title number and reference to the code will always be omitted. Thus a citation concerning the supervision of technicians could be: §4115(f), §1793.7(b). The first number is the citation to the section of the Business and Professions Code (the statute), which sets forth the supervision requirement; the second number is the citation to the section of the California Code of Regulations (the regulation) which contains the Pharmacy Board's addition to the legislative requirement.

Federal statutes are cited by their code and section numbers, for example, 21 USC §824 (Title 21, United States Code, section 824, a section of the federal Controlled Substances Act). Federal regulations, found in the Code of Federal Regulations, are cited by their title and section number, for example, 21 CFR §1301.21 (Title 21, Code of Federal Regulations, section 1301.21, persons required to register to manufacture, distribute, or dispense controlled substances).

Citations to the published opinions of courts are somewhat complex. For example, consider the following citation: *Californians for Safe Prescriptions v. California State Board of Pharmacy*, 19 Cal. App. 4th 1136, 1151 (2d Dist. 1993). The case name indicates the parties, here "Californians for Safe Prescriptions" and "California State Board of Pharmacy." The "v." stands for "versus"; generally, but not always, the first name is the plaintiff and the second the respondent or defendant (sometimes the names are reversed upon appeal).

From the numbers after the names you learn the court that made the decision, the year of the decision, and the reporter, or series of books, in which the decision was published. Here the decision is in Volume 19 of a series called "California Appellate Reports 4th," an official publication of the California courts, starting on page 1136. For simplicity's sake, we have cited to only one of the sets of law reports in which these decisions appear. Typically there is an "official" and at least one "unoffiical" set; both contain the same opinion text. The additional page number citation is to the place in the decision where the court made the statement for which the case is cited in the text. "2d Dist." stands for the

California Court of Appeal for the Second District. (California's trial courts are organized by county; the state is divided into six appellate districts. Federal trial courts are organized by districts within states. The country is divided into 12 appellate circuits, numbered one through eleven plus the District of Columbia Circuit.) The decision was issued in 1993. The most important judicial decisions of each state and the federal government are collected and published.

If you ever need, or are inclined to search for, statutes or regulations, you will find that they are easily available. Although general public libraries are unlikely to have code volumes, each county in California maintains a law library that is open to the public. Books of codes are kept up to date by the inclusion of cumulative annual supplements (called "pocket parts") filed with each volume that has not recently been reprinted in its entirety.

Codes are published by more than one publisher. Titles of individual code sections are unofficial and thus may vary from set to set. The words and section numbers of the laws, of course, will be identical. Most code volumes are annotated; after each section of the law you will find information about the history of the section (including the statute of which it was a part and its amendments), references to related statutes and regulations, citations to legal literature, and annotations of court cases in which the section was cited.

Most legal source materials are now available on the Internet. All California statutes, as well as bills under consideration in the California Legislature, may be viewed at www.leginfo.ca.gov. The California Code of Regulations is online at www.calregs.com. Recent decisions of the California appellate courts are at www.courtinfo.ca.gov.

Federal legal material may be found on a number of sites. The website of the Government Printing Office has links to all branches of the federal government, plus the *Federal Register* and the Code of Federal Regulations; go to www.access.gpo.gov/su_docs/index.html. The website of the United States Congress, http://thomas.loc.gov/, is also helpful. Federal judicial decisions may be located through www.uscourts.gov.

The California State Board of Pharmacy website, at www.pharmacy.ca.gov, is very useful. The Board has its entire law book (the Pharmacy Law and related statutes plus its administrative rules) on line, as well as a link to the publisher of the law book's print and CD-ROM versions (www.lawtech-pub.com/webstore/page4.html). The Board also posts lists of pending legislation of importance to pharmacy, with links to the bills, and all of the supporting materials concerning its proposed and recently-adopted regulations. It also archives its educational materials (including *The Script* and some issues of *Health Notes*), and agendas, minutes, and other materials from Board and committee meetings. The website also contains forms and information about all Board licenses, as well as complaint information. Appendix C of this text lists addresses, phone numbers, and website addresses, where available, for a number of other government agencies important to the practice of pharmacy.

Local ordinances might be difficult to find outside of local law libraries. Often popular codes (such as those important to the building construction industry) are for sale in bookstores close to government offices.

The abbreviations found in citations to codes and judicial decisions, as well as abbreviations used in the text, are decoded in the Glossary.

# Glossary

AB – Assembly Bill (California Legislature)
ACPE – American Council on Pharmaceutical Education
ADA – Americans with Disabilities Act
AIDS – acquired immunodeficiency syndrome
ALJ – administrative law judge
ANDA – Abbreviated New Drug Application
APA – Administrative Procedure Act
APhA – American Pharmacists Association
App. – Appendix
ARCOS – Automation of Reports and Consolidated Orders System
art. – article (as of a Constitution)
BNE – Bureau of Narcotic Enforcement (California Department of Justice)
B&PC – California Business and Professions Code
Cal. – California (Supreme Court) Reports (2d, 3d, 4th indicate set numbers)
Cal. App. – California Appellate Reports (Courts of Appeal reports; 2d, 3d, 4th indicate set numbers)
Cal. Const. – California Constitution
Cal-OSHA – Division of Occupational Safety and Health (California)
CCR – California Code of Regulations
CFR – Code of Federal Regulations
ch. – chapter (California statute designation when passed; see P.L.)
Cir. – Circuit; the United States Court of Appeals is organized by circuit; citations include the number
     of the circuit (such as 2d Cir. or 9th Cir.)
Civ. Code – California Civil Code
Civ. Pro. Code – California Code of Civil Procedure
CMS – Centers for Medicare & Medicaid Services (HHS)
Corp. Code – California Corporations Code
CPG – Compliance Policy Guideline (FDA)
CPJE – California Pharmacist Jurisprudence Examination
CURES – Controlled substance Utilization Review and Evaluation System
D.C. Cir. – District of Columbia Circuit, United States Court of Appeals
DEA – Drug Enforcement Administration (United States Department of Justice)
DHS – Department of Health Services (California)
Dist. – District; the California Court of Appeal is organized by district; citations include the
     number of the district (such as 1st Dist. or 3d Dist.)
D.Mass. – District of Massachusetts, United States District Court
DSHEA – Dietary Supplement Health and Education Act (federal)
EMT – emergency medical technician
Evid. Code – California Evidence Code
F.2d – Federal Reporter, 2d set
F.3d – Federal Reporter, 3d set
Fam. Code – California Family Code
FDA – Food and Drug Administration (federal)
FDAMA – Food and Drug Administration Modernization Act (of 1997) (federal)
FR – Federal Register
F. Supp. – Federal Supplement (law reports from the federal district [trial] courts)
FTC – Federal Trade Commission

GC – California Government Code
GED – General Educational Development exam (high school equivalency)
GHB – gamma hydroxybutyrate
HHS – Department of Health and Human Services (federal)
HIPAA – Health Insurance Portability and Accountability Act of 1996
HIV – human immunodeficiency virus
HMDR – home medical device retailer
H&SC – California Health and Safety Code
ICF – intermediate care facility
IND – Investigational New Drug Application
Ins. Code – California Insurance Code
IPA – Information Practices Act (California)
IPTA – Intractable Pain Treatment Act
JCAHO – Joint Commission on Accreditation of Healthcare Organizations
LAAM – levo-alphacetyl metadol
Lab. Code – California Labor Code
LLC – limited liability company
NABP – National Association of Boards of Pharmacy
NAFTA – North American Free Trade Agreement
NAPLEX – North American Pharmacist Licensure Examination
N.D. Cal. – Northern District of California, United States District Court
NDA – New Drug Application
NDC – National Drug Code
Neb. – Nebraska
NIDA – National Institute on Drug Abuse
N.M. – New Mexico
NRC – Nuclear Regulatory Commission (federal)
OTC – over-the-counter (drugs available without prescription)
P.2d – Pacific Reporter (2d set)
PBM – pharmacy benefit management company
PCP – phencyclidine
Pen. Code – Penal Code
PET – positron emission tomographic drug
PHI – protected health information
P.L. – Public Law (federal statute designation, as passed; see ch.)
PPA – phenylpropanolamine
QA – quality assurance
SAMHSA – Substance Abuse and Mental Health Services Administration (HHS)
SNF – skilled nursing facility
Stats. – statutes (California statute designation, as passed; see P.L.)
THC – delta-9-tetrahydrocannabinol
UETA – Uniform Electronic Transactions Act
U.S. – United States (Supreme Court) Reports
USC – United States Code (organized by title number, as "21 U.S.C.")
USP – United States Pharmacopeia
VIPPS – Verified Internet Pharmacy Practice Sites
Welf. & Inst. Code – California Welfare and Institutions Code

# Table Of Contents

# Chapter I

# Law and the Pharmacist

**What you should know after reading this chapter:**

1.  What are the major sources of law?

2.  What role does each branch of government perform in the creation and enforcement of the law?

3.  What is an administrative rule (or regulation)? What are the differences between statutes and rules?

4.  How can a pharmacist stay aware of developments in the law?

Law is a subject as important to the pharmacist as pharmacology or therapeutics. Our society has set forth its basic governing principles in its laws. Law provides the broad framework of rules that order our lives, and sets forth specific rights, restrictions, and requirements.

Of particular importance to pharmacists, society has registered its concern with the proper distribution and use of drugs by creating a complex regulatory environment for the pharmacy profession. The purpose of this book is to familiarize the pharmacist with that environment.

## What Is "The Law?"

The law that governs our lives is a multifaceted creature that does not all reside within a single shelf of books or at one website. The law encompasses all the standards created and enforced by our society, beginning with the United States Constitution. On the state level, the California Constitution sets forth the basic principles by which California is governed. These charters for government include important and abiding legal principles, including the rights to free speech and freedom of religion in the First Amendment to the United States Constitution and the right to privacy in Article I, section 1, of the California Constitution.

Although the United States and California Constitutions do not directly regulate the practice of pharmacy, they mandate basic protections that are relevant to the pharmacist, such as the right to due process of law in the enforcement of statutes and regulations. Consistent with the constitutional frameworks, federal and state legislative bodies adopt statutes that govern the use of drugs and the practice of pharmacy. Agencies in the executive branch of government adopt administrative regulations to carry out responsibilities conferred on them by statutes passed by the legislature.

Courts play an important role in the development of the law affecting pharmacy in the course of deciding cases in which they interpret the meaning of constitutional law, statutes, and regulations, and determine whether they have been correctly applied.[1]

# Constitutions

The United States Constitution, adopted in 1787, has only 27 amendments, the first 10 of which (the Bill of Rights) were adopted in 1791.  The Constitution sets out the general principles of our federal government.  California's Constitution is substantially more detailed than the federal Constitution, and more easily amended, including by a direct vote of the people.  Constitutional provisions prevail over contradictory provisions of state or federal statutes or regulations.

# Legislation

## *Adoption*

Under the federal and state Constitutions, the basic power to create law through the legislative process is granted to the legislature, with the consent of the chief executive – the President or the Governor – who either may sign or veto any proposed new law, or statute.[2]  The United States Congress creates federal law, such as the Medicare program, the federal Controlled Substances Act, and the Federal Food, Drug, and Cosmetic Act.  The California Legislature is responsible for the laws governing professional licensure in the State of California.  Congress and the California Legislature, then, are the primary sources of the law that governs the practice of pharmacy.[3]  Other legislative bodies – city councils and county boards of supervisors, for example – have the power to make laws that could impact pharmacy practice.  While these local bodies may not modify state or federal statutes concerning pharmacy practice or controlled substances, their jurisdiction over such matters as zoning and public health could result in ordinances that affect a pharmacy.  (The content of such local laws is beyond the scope of this book.)

The creation[4] of legislation starts with a bill introduced by one or more legislators. The bill must be passed by both houses of the legislature.  Generally each bill is the subject of legislative committee hearings and is discussed and amended in committee and in both houses.  Bills, and the

---

[1]  The word "law" is used to refer to any (or all) of the various sources of legal requirements – to constitutions, to statutes, to regulations, and to precedent-setting decisions of appellate courts.  A statute enacted by a legislative body is a "law." Ordinances passed by local government bodies also are referred to as "laws."  The terminology can be confusing.  In this text, we will try to refer to each form of law by its proper name.

[2]  Under certain circumstances, if the President or Governor vetoes a bill or fails to take action upon it, the bill may nevertheless become law without the chief executive's signature.

[3]  In California legislation as well as amendments to the California Constitution may be adopted by a vote of the people when a proposition is placed on the ballot.  Through the initiative process, the people of California at a statewide election may pass a statute or constitutional amendment (CAL. CONST. art. II, §§1, 8). An initiative statute is "superior" to one enacted by the Legislature; that is, where there is a conflict, the provisions of the initiative control.  By referendum the people may vote to reject all or part of a statute enacted by the Legislature (CAL. CONST. art. II, §9).  The Legislature may amend or repeal a referendum statute, but it may not amend or repeal the provisions of an initiative statute unless the terms of the initiative so provide (CAL. CONST. art. II, §10(c)).

[4]  It is possible to track the development of legislation online.  The California Legislature's website, www.leginfo.ca.gov (click on "bill information"), is particularly user-friendly, and allows you to "subscribe" to receive e-mail notification of action concerning any bill you wish to follow.  The Library of Congress maintains a similar website for federal legislation at http://thomas.loc.gov/.

statutes they become when they are adopted, are given unique numbers; occasionally a law becomes known by a popular name given to it by the legislature. For example, the federal law governing manufacture and sale of drugs subject to abuse is the Controlled Substances Act of 1970; California's laws governing pharmacists and pharmacies are known as the Pharmacy Law. Some statutes enact entirely new regulatory programs, while many others make only incremental changes in existing law.

Statutes are compiled into codes, codifications of all adopted legislation. That is, each section is given a place in the federal or state legal code and is assigned a unique number. The government officials responsible for organizing the codes decide where to place new statutory sections. For example, the various sections of the Controlled Substances Act of 1970 were placed in Title 21 of the United States Code, sections 801 to 904; Title 21 includes all the federal laws governing food and drugs, such as the Federal Food, Drug, and Cosmetic Act.

Keep in mind that changes, major and minor, are made to laws over time. For example, the Federal Food, Drug, and Cosmetic Act was adopted in 1938, but substantial amendments since that time, some with their own popular names, have changed many of its original sections. Federal and state code books are updated annually to reflect all changes made in the most recent legislative session.

The California Legislature tends to pass many statutes with a narrow focus; the United States Congress more often passes omnibus legislation covering a whole field. As a result California codes may seem illogically ordered and sections dealing with the same issue may be in several different places. The only cure for this legislative sprawl is periodic recodification and reform. A statute recodifying the Pharmacy Law was passed in 1996, effective in 1997. The result was a more logically organized body of law.

Every year at least some changes, usually additions, are made to the Pharmacy Law or to other laws affecting drugs, controlled substances, and the practice of pharmacy. The most recent significant changes in the law are highlighted throughout the text.

## *Interpretation*

Often the meaning or scope of legislative enactments is not entirely clear. Legislators cannot anticipate all situations that might arise; a statute's application in some unusual situation may seem contrary to the legislative purpose in passing the statute. Sometimes legislators, to get enough votes to pass a statute, knowingly adopt ambiguous language rather than including clear statements about its applicability under certain circumstances. Or legislators will draft a statute that delegates a lot of decisionmaking authority to an executive branch, or administrative, agency to carry out the law's basic intent through promulgating regulations or enforcing the law in individual cases. And, of course, some laws are just poorly written.

When a question arises about the meaning of a law, private parties, regulatory agencies, and, if the matter results in litigation, the courts are forced to interpret the language of the statute. There is a large body of jurisprudence, or legal philosophy, concerning the appropriate methods for courts to use in interpreting statutes. Interpretation generally begins with the language of the statute itself. If the language of the statute, its "plain meaning," is clear, that may be where the analysis stops. If the language could reasonably be read in more than one way, courts often look to legislative history for clues to its meaning. Legislative history includes all the reports of legislative committees, testimony at legislative hearings, and committee and floor debates, which may shed light on the meaning of the language adopted. Courts also may rely on other evidence of meaning, such as the context into which the statute was placed.

The most important thing to recognize is that statutory language that may seem to have an obvious meaning may be interpreted differently when it comes before the courts in a dispute. Fortunately, most statutory obligations of pharmacists are rather clear, either because the statutory language is quite straightforward or because there is an accepted interpretation of long standing.

The ethical pharmacist, faced with apparent ambiguity in regard to a legal obligation, often must decide how to act without much time for contemplation. A pharmacist who is uncertain about what the law requires in a particular instance might be tempted to follow what colleagues or competitors are doing; that impulse, however, could be a trap. That others, even most others, are doing the same thing is no defense to a violation of a statute or regulation.

When faced with a dilemma concerning one's legal obligations, the pharmacist first should look for regulations, policies, or past interpretation or enforcement by government agencies in the area of uncertainty. Articles on confusing issues or new legal developments often appear in the Board of Pharmacy newsletter, *The Script*, or in the journals of the various pharmacy associations. The pharmacist also may seek guidance from a representative of the government agency most responsible for enforcement in the area (Appendix C lists some of those agencies). If still uncertain, and particularly if the issue is likely to arise on a continuing basis, the pharmacist may wish to seek legal advice.

# Administrative Rules and Regulations

As noted above, the federal and state legislatures pass statutes; local bodies' legislative creations often are called ordinances. All of these are "law," but they are not the exclusive source of "law."

Legislative bodies frequently pass laws that delegate great authority in a specific area to specialized governmental bodies, both to fill in the details of the legislative plan and to administer the law on a day-to-day basis. They do so because it is difficult for legislatures to reach consensus on the details of an activity to be regulated and impractical to address every aspect of a complex matter. These specialized bodies, or administrative agencies, to which much regulatory authority is delegated, are generally part of the executive branch of the government, which is responsible for the execution of laws.

The California State Board of Pharmacy is one such administrative agency, with statutory authority to play an important role in the regulation of pharmacy in California (§4001(a)).[5] The Board is charged with the implementation of the licensure and regulation scheme created by the California Legislature. Much of the Pharmacy Law is broad and general, so the Board's authority to interpret and implement the statutory scheme is significant. For example, the Legislature has specifically given the Board the authority to define and implement its laws by adopting "rules and regulations, not inconsistent with the laws of this state, as may be necessary for the protection of the public" (§4005). Rules, or regulations (for the two terms are entirely interchangeable), adopted by the Board are a very important part of "the law" and, unless invalidated by the courts, are binding.

The most important difference between rules and statutes is that only statutes, the product of our elected representatives or the people (through the initiative process), may create wholly new legal rights and responsibilities. No rule is ever valid unless it is authorized by and consistent with statutory

---

[5]  As indicated in "Understanding Legal Citations," p. v, all cited statutory sections with numbers between 4000 and 44276 are from the California Business and Professions Code. Citations ; those rules with numbers between 1703 and 1793.7 are Pharmacy Board regulations, found in from Title 16 of the California Code of Regulations.

law and reasonably necessary to carry out statutory authority. The courts generally accord agencies considerable deference in regard to developing regulations, including deferring to an agency's interpretation of its own statutory authority (*Californians for Safe Prescriptions v. California State Board of Pharmacy*, 19 Cal. App. 4th 1136, 1151 (2d Dist. 1993)). One important limitation is that every regulation, like every statute, must not be in conflict with the state or federal Constitution.

Rules operate within the boundaries of existing statutory provisions, usually to give more precise definition to those provisions. For example, the Board has adopted, and published in the California Code of Regulations, detailed rules imposing on pharmacists the duty to maintain medication profiles (§1707.1), to provide oral consultation to consumers (§1707.2), and to post a notice concerning the availability of retail price information (§1707.2(f)). The Pharmacy Law makes no specific mention of the first two of these duties. However, the Legislature authorized the Pharmacy Board to "adopt . . . rules of professional conduct appropriate to the establishment and maintenance of a high standard of integrity and dignity in the profession." This law is codified as section 4005(c) of the Business and Professions Code and cited as authority for these rules. In section 4122, the Legislature specifically requires the prominent posting in every pharmacy of "a notice provided by the Board concerning the availability of prescription price information," mandating the Board to create the format and wording of the notice, which it accomplished by adoption of section 1707.2(f).

When the Pharmacy Board wants to adopt a regulation, it must follow the procedures mandated for all agencies by the California Administrative Procedure Act (GC §§11346 -11347.3). Those procedures require publication of a notice of the proposal and afford members of the public an opportunity to comment on it (either in writing or, if requested, at an oral hearing). Pharmacy Board proposals must be approved by the Department of Consumer Affairs and by the Office of Administrative Law. To be adopted, regulations must meet statutory standards including necessity, authority, clarity, consistency, and mitigation of impact on small businesses. If an agency believes there is an emergency need for the regulation, the process may be streamlined.

Notice of rulemaking activities in California is published in the *California Regulatory Notice Register*, which is not easily accessible to the average citizen on paper. However, it is online at www.osp.dgs.ca.gov/On-Line+Publications/default.htm; select *California Regulatory Notice Register*. There are many easier ways, however, to keep informed about the proposals of a specific agency like the Pharmacy Board so that you may comment on them. You may ask to be placed on the Board's mailing list; you can read the Board's newsletter or the publications of any of the pharmacy organizations in the state; you can periodically check the Board's website (www.pharmacy.ca.gov), on which it must post this information.[6] Professional associations, such as the California Pharmacists Association, the California Society of Health System Pharmacists, and the California Employee Pharmacists Association, and various other organizations interested in pharmacy issues, such as the National Association of Retail Druggists, the California Retailers Association, Pharmacy Planning Services, Inc., and managed care organizations, frequently comment on Board regulatory proposals on behalf of their members.

There is a similar process by which federal agencies adopt regulations. Federal agencies publish notice of proposed rules in the *Federal Register,* which essentially is the federal government's daily legal newspaper, and virtually all maintain useful websites. The *Federal Register* is available online at www.gpoaccess.gov/fr/index.html. The agencies also maintain mailing lists and send notice at least of important proposals to interested persons. Federal agencies never are required to hold oral

---

[6] If you wish more detailed information than is regularly published through these sources, it is likely to be available on request, upon payment of the costs of copying. The right to most California government records is governed by the California Public Records Act, GC §§6250-6268, and to federal records by the federal Freedom of Information Act, 5 USC §552.

hearings, and rarely do so; anyone may participate in the federal rulemaking process simply by sending comments to an agency. Federal agencies publish their final rules, along with a statement of their basis and purpose that generally summarizes and responds to the most significant comments received, in the *Federal Register.*

California pharmacy law and the regulations adopted by the Pharmacy Board are published annually. In recent years the state has only published the law and regulations online, at the Board's website, www.pharmacy.ca.gov/forms_pubs.htm. If you wish to obtain a copy on paper, LawTech Publishing Co., Ltd. (online at www.lawtech-pub.com or call (949) 498-4815) publishes the law and regulations book in an inexpensive paperbound form. The Board's newsletter (archived online on the same page as the law and regulations) regularly highlights new laws and regulations as well as discussing existing law.

**Suppose that the Pharmacy Board believes that consumers must be alerted to various types of services available in the pharmacy, and proposes to amend its regulation, section 1707.2(f), in a way that you feel will be confusing to consumers or impose unnecessary burdens on pharmacies. What can you do?**

When you learn about the proposed change, you may ask the Board to send you its information packet about the proposal, including the precise language it proposes to adopt. This information also will be available on the Board's website. Then, within the allotted time, you may participate in the process by sending your comments about the proposal to the Board. If there is an oral hearing (which any interested party may request), you may make your comments orally. Unless they are frivolous, your comments must be considered and responded to by the Board when it decides whether to adopt the proposal at all, or whether to adopt it only after making modifications. If you are unsatisfied with the regulation after it is adopted, you may seek review by the superior court. To prevail in court, you need to demonstrate that the Board lacks substantial evidence to support the regulation or that it has not properly followed the procedures for its adoption (*Californians for Safe Prescriptions v. California State Board of Pharmacy,* 19 Cal. App. 4th 1136 (2d Dist. 1993)).

**Suppose a regulation requires you to act in one way and a statute requires you to act differently. Which do you follow?**

A statute is superior to a regulation, so if a regulation requires you to do something that a statute forbids, the regulation should be invalid. However, the regulation is not invalid until it is so declared by a court. If you cannot convince the agency that its regulation is invalid and ought not be enforced (and, in fact, ought to be repealed or modified), you have several options. If you are not faced with enforcement immediately, you may petition the agency to repeal the regulation, arguing that it is invalid because of the conflict with the statute, or you may seek a declaratory decision by the agency concerning the regulation's applicability under the circumstances (GC §§11465.10-11465.70). Whether or not you seek a declaratory decision, you may bring an action in superior court seeking a judgment that the regulation is unenforceable, either in general or in your particular situation. Otherwise, you must choose whether to obey the regulation (ironically, under the facts hypothesized, thereby disobeying the statute) or disobey it and challenge its validity, as is your right, in any proceeding brought against you.

**Suppose a regulation requires you to do something that is not specifically required by a statute. Need you obey it?**

Most such regulations are entirely valid, because the agency usually has the authority to adopt any regulations that are reasonably necessary to carry out the general purposes of its governing statutes; the courts interpret what is "reasonably necessary" quite broadly. It is expensive and risky to disobey regulations and then count on their being held invalid. A preferable course of action is to challenge regulations at the time of adoption or thereafter, in an action seeking a judicial declaration of their invalidity, thus avoiding the need to disobey them and risk penalty. Professional associations or groups of regulated persons or businesses sometimes bring such suits on behalf of interested parties (see, for example, *Californians for Safe Prescriptions v. California State Board of Pharmacy,* 19 Cal. App. 4th 1136 (2d Dist. 1993)).

# Agency Guidance Documents

Regulatory agencies, including the Pharmacy Board, often are asked by regulated parties and others for more specific guidance about rights and obligations than is contained in statutes or regulations. Sometimes it is an agency's own staff members who are anxious for an interpretation of statutes or regulations as they apply to specific facts.

Agencies may, and frequently do, provide their interpretation of obligations under the law, generally in the form of some type of guidance document. Agency guidance is just that – it does not in any way supersede law.[7] Guidance helps agencies assure that their staff members are all applying the law in the same way, and helps regulated parties understand what the regulatory agency believes the law requires and how it is likely to exercise its discretion in enforcement. However, guidance documents of all types cannot be the basis for enforcement action; it is not a violation of law to violate "guidance," only to violate the underlying law or regulation upon which the guidance is based. When a regulated party conforms its activities to guidance by an agency, if the agency later tries to take action against that party for conduct that which was approved by the guidance (but which the agency now believes is in violation of law or statute), reliance on the agency's prior position is likely to be an effective defense against a California agency. (Federal law is, however, much less accepting of this doctrine, which is called equitable estoppel.)

The Pharmacy Board often publishes policy statements or guidelines in *The Script*, along with articles on various aspects of recent or significant laws and regulations. Sometimes the Board's staff or its attorneys will respond by letter to inquiries seeking an interpretation of law. There is also a formal process by which a person may apply to the Board for a declaratory decision as to the applicability to specified circumstances of a statute, regulation, or decision within its jurisdiction (GC §§11465.10-11465.70). If the Board agrees to issue a declaratory decision, it will have the same status and binding effect as any other decision the Board issues in a contested proceeding.

---

[7] In the past, state agencies commonly circumvented rulemaking requirements by relying on policies found only in internal documents, such as inspection manuals or minutes of agency meetings. California law now specifically forbids such "underground" regulations and strictly limits use in the enforcement process of any policies or guidelines that have not been formally adopted as regulations (GC §11340.5).

An agency may still use policies or procedures that have not been adopted by regulation, as long as they are not used as binding standards of general application. For example, agencies may and do utilize internal policies to govern the conduct of inspections, the processing of applications, and the methods of conducting an audit *(Americana Termite Co. v. Structural Pest Control Board,* 199 Cal. App. 3d 228, 233-234 (2d Dist. 1988)).

# Private Standards

Law reform organizations often develop model laws and professional and certifying associations often create codes of professional conduct or institutional standards. These do not have the force of law, but they may be very influential. For example, failure to comply with the standards of the Joint Commission on Accreditation of Healthcare Organizations (JCAHO) may affect an institution's ability to receive financial reimbursement from private and governmental sources. The American Pharmaceutical Association's Code of Ethics for Pharmacists (see Chap. XV: Ethics) may be introduced as evidence from which a jury or a court may determine, in a lawsuit about pharmacy negligence (also called malpractice), what is or is not acceptable professional practice. And such standards may be at least partly the basis for expert opinions that conduct challenged by an agency is "unprofessional," "grossly negligent," or "incompetent" (see Chap. XII, Practice Pitfalls). As a consequence these private standards may have considerable legal influence, although they are not themselves law.

Private associations sometimes offer certification that a practitioner or a practice site meets that association's standards of practice, especially in a specialty area. To obtain the certification, the practitioner might have to provide evidence of education, training, and experience, and sometimes also pass an examination. Such certification generally has no formal legal significance. One example is the VIPPS™ program of the National Association of Boards of Pharmacy, a professional association of pharmacy regulators. This program sets standards for appropriate pharmacy practice on the Internet, and allows certified sites to display its seal. It is intended primarily as guidance for consumers.

Sometimes a government agency (occasionally directed by a statute) formally recognizes certification by a private organization. For example, the Pharmacy Board recognizes, and accepts, continuing education accredited by the American Council of Pharmaceutical Education and the Accreditation Evaluation Service.

# Conflicting Federal and State Laws

Laws at several levels of government (usually federal and state law) sometimes apply to the same situation but are inconsistent with each other. As a general rule, federal law is superior to state law, because of the Supremacy Clause in the United States Constitution.[8] Even a federal regulation is superior to, or preempts, a state law or regulation.

In enacting federal drug and controlled substance laws, Congress has left the states the authority to pass their own laws that are not in "positive conflict" with federal law. Effectively, this means a state's drug law may be more, but not less, restrictive or demanding than federal law. A state may not authorize something barred by federal law or relieve someone from a requirement under federal law. This relationship is the reason why, as discussed in Chapter II: Drug Classifications, state

---

[8]  The California Supreme Court recently reviewed the law of federal preemption in a case in which a warning of reproductive toxicity required by California's Proposition 65 (H&SC §25249.6) conflicted with the warnings allowed by the FDA for certain over-the-counter drug products (*Dowhal v. Smithkline Beecham Consumer Healthcare*, 32 Cal. 4th 910 (2004)). The *Dowhal* court, 32 Cal. 4th at 927-929, found a direct conflict between the federal policy prohibiting any warning other than the ones approved by the FDA and the use of a Proposition 65 warning, even though the latter warning would be truthful. It reached this conclusion even though a "savings" clause in the federal law (21 USC §379r(d)(2)) specifically exempts Proposition 65 warnings from preemption. The Court found that the savings clause only precluded "conflict" preemption (preemption because there is a direct conflict between the federal and state requirements) when the federal requirements are intended to create national uniformity in labeling. Where, as here, there is a consumer health basis for the federal requirement, the state requirement must yield to the conflict with the federal requirement.

medical marijuana initiatives are largely invalid. The states cannot authorize what federal controlled substance law prohibits. Pharmacists therefore must be familiar with applicable state *and* federal laws and regulations. At various points in this text, we explain both state and federal provisions and how to interpret them together, especially when they are or appear to be in conflict.

Each of the states has its own set of laws and regulations, and its own court-made law (discussed below). Although there have been, and continue to be, efforts to conform the provisions of different states on similar subjects, state laws frequently differ. When a transaction involves multiple jurisdictions (for example, where a seller is in one state and the purchaser in another), the outcome of any dispute may well be affected by which state's law will apply. Parties to a contract are usually free to choose the law of a particular state to apply to disputes under that contract. The law governing conflicts of law is complex and confusing. Caution, and perhaps advice of counsel, is appropriate when becoming involved in multi-jurisdiction transactions.

**You are charged with violating state controlled substance law for doing something federal law authorizes. May you raise federal law as a "shield" against the charge?**

No, you may not. Because the state may pass more restrictive controlled substance provisions than are in federal law, the fact that federal law authorizes what you did is no defense.

**You are charged with violating state controlled substance law. May you defend by pointing out that federal law requires you to follow a different procedure?**

It depends. It is a valid defense if you *could not* follow state law without violating federal law. It is not a valid defense if you *could* follow state law without violating federal law.

**What if a federal regulation requires you to do something a California statute forbids?**

A valid federal regulation is just as "superior" to a California statute as a federal statute would be: you have to do what the federal regulation requires.

# The Role of the Courts

## *Judicial Scrutiny of Laws and Regulations*

In addition to federal and state statutes and regulations, there is a third important source of legal obligation that is rather more difficult for the average person to follow. That source is the courts. In the course of litigation of specific disputes, courts frequently develop the law.

Often the issue before a court involves at least some interpretation of a statute or a regulation.[9] While an interpretation by a California trial court usually does not influence other courts because it is not incorporated into a written published opinion, appellate courts frequently publish their written decisions. Their published interpretations of statutes or regulations are binding on the trial courts. Decisions of the California Court of Appeal thus must be followed by the trial courts; when courts of appeal in different appellate districts have ruled in conflict with one another, the trial court must choose among appellate courts' interpretations, generally looking to the most recent opinions on the subject, particularly those in its own appellate district. An interpretation by the Supreme Court of California is binding on all California courts, and an interpretation by the United States Supreme Court

---

[9] A court may also be asked to rule on whether a statute or regulation conflicts with a state or the federal Constitution.

is binding on all federal courts nationwide. Courts often find persuasive the decisions of courts that they are not required to follow, such as courts of another state, especially when there is little or no case law on an issue within their state.

Courts do not literally rewrite laws or regulations. If all or part of a statute is declared unconstitutional, it will remain on the books until repealed by the adopting legislative body, although its continued enforcement is highly unlikely. If a court declares a regulation to be invalid – because it was improperly adopted, not supported by substantial evidence demonstrating its necessity, or inconsistent with applicable statutes – no penalties for its violation will be upheld. In practical effect it will be meaningless, although it will not literally disappear from the code books until officially repealed by the adopting agency. Thus accurate knowledge of legal responsibilities may require research beyond mere reading of legal codes.

An agency may choose to continue enforcing a regulation outside of the jurisdiction of a single lower court that has declared it invalid, whether or not the agency appeals that court's decision. For example, if the United States Court of Appeals for the Ninth Circuit, whose jurisdiction includes California, overturns a particular federal statute or regulation, the agency responsible for its enforcement may treat it as enforceable in every state outside the Ninth Circuit's jurisdiction. The agency may be willing to litigate the validity of the regulation in another case, and it may convince a second court to rule in its favor. Until the United States Supreme Court rules on the issue, the law could be enforced differently in different regions of the country.

As this brief discussion of a complicated subject suggests, the law as created case by case in the courts is a fairly untidy creature. To know "the law" at any given point requires not only reading statutes and regulations but knowing about their judicial interpretations. Fortunately, there are only a few areas of pharmacy law in which significant disputes have arisen, leading to a fairly limited number of court decisions interpreting the law. This book will introduce you to those areas.

It is important to understand that a judicial gloss on the meaning of a statute or regulation might require you to be aware of more than the statute's or regulation's mere words when considering how to fulfill your professional obligations. What may seem clear to you might have a different meaning according to the courts, and what may seem decidedly ambiguous to you might be considered clear by the courts.

## *The Common Law*

Some legal standards are not found in any statute or regulation but have been established by court decisions over the years, sometimes over as long as centuries. In an earlier day, when statutes were few and often inadequate to deal with civil disputes, the courts would consider the facts and the issues of cases that came before them and, by deciding case after case over the years, develop a body of standards for resolving those disputes. The courts would look to decisions in relevant prior decisions (called "precedent") in determining later cases. The standards developed in this manner became known as "common law." This concept and methodology came to America from England (where it began nearly a thousand years ago) with our legal system and continues to grow and develop as individual cases are decided. Today many of the principles and standards developed by the common law have been codified; that is, they have been adopted by a legislative body as statutes. Nevertheless, the common law development of legal standards continues to be very important.

The law of negligence (often called malpractice when a professional is involved) largely developed through common law and is probably the primary example relevant to pharmacy. Negligence today is defined as conduct that "falls below the standard established by law for the protection of others against unreasonable risk of harm" (RESTATEMENT (SECOND) OF TORTS §282 (1990)).[10] A person, or a business, found to be negligent will be liable to pay compensation for the harm caused by that negligence. A person is negligent, it is said, whose conduct fails to meet the standard of care of the ordinary prudent person. When the person whose negligence is at issue is a professional pharmacist, the test would be whether the conduct failed to meet the standard of care of the ordinary prudent pharmacist. The obvious problem with these definitions is that they do not provide any specificity about the behavioral content of the standard that you are required to meet. Ultimately a jury or judge applies these general standards to the facts of each case. That is, for better or for worse, the way of the common law.

In deciding any negligence case, the court will look to relevant precedent (as well as to any applicable statutes or regulations), consider the facts of the case before it (as determined by the jury, where a jury trial is held, or by the judge, when the trial is held only before the judge), and then reach a decision in that case. Lawyers therefore must study prior published decisions of the courts to try to predict the outcome of new cases. Lawyers will argue that the facts of their case either are the same as those in an earlier case, thus justifying the same outcome, or that they are clearly distinguishable from the facts in prior decisions that appear on the surface to be quite similar, thus demanding a different outcome. What the "ordinary prudent pharmacist" must do in particular circumstances, then, cannot be determined merely by reference to a single source.

To decide what that hypothetical "ordinary prudent pharmacist" would have done under the circumstances, the court will look for relevant standards. The court will check if there are any applicable statutes or regulations. If so, has the pharmacist complied? If the pharmacist has not complied, and the harm has flowed from the violation, the likely conclusion will be that the pharmacist was negligent.

Some situations will be considerably more complicated, and there may be no decided cases to provide guidance. If there are no applicable statutes or regulations, the court will look elsewhere for indications of what theat ordinary pharmacist would be expected to do under the circumstances. Government regulators may have adopted guidance documents that cover the subject. The standard practices of the profession also are important; these may be brought before the court in the form of private standards adopted by professional associations or through the testimony of pharmacists deemed sufficiently familiar with practice in the relevant community to be qualified to testify as experts. The manuals, policies, and other instructions of an employer may also be relevant. From all the information brought before the court, a judgment will be made based on the unique facts in the individual case.

Just as most statutes affecting the pharmacist's professional life are not ambiguous, most situations we could hypothesize in which a pharmacist might be charged with negligence do not pose much difficulty. To a significant extent this is because the practice of pharmacy is so highly regulated. A pharmacist's incorrect filling of a prescription – with the wrong drug or the wrong strength – is a perfect example. That pharmacist probably has not exercised ordinary prudence; in addition, a regulation has been violated (§1716).

---

[10] A "Restatement" is an influential treatise published by the American Law Institute, an organization whose members are lawyers, judges, and legal scholars from all over the country; the Institute attempts to organize and "restate" the prevailing American law in the subject area, even though the details of the law vary from state to state.

**Suppose a pharmacist, during a three-day holiday weekend when the patient's physician cannot be reached, gives the patient a three-day supply of phenytoin (Dilantin®) for seizure control, although no refills remain on the prescription. The patient becomes ill; the physician states that, because of test results received just before the weekend, she would not have authorized the refill, and the continued use of the drug caused the harm. The patient sues the pharmacist who provided the drugs without a prescription. Was the pharmacist negligent? What is the basis for your conclusion? What are the applicable laws and regulations? What is the standard of practice in the community? What are the societal expectations and implications of one course of action or another? Consider the arguments you would make on behalf of the patient and on behalf of the pharmacist.**

The outcome of such a case is not easily predictable. If the pharmacist made all the appropriate inquiries of the patient that we would expect a pharmacist to make, made reasonable efforts to contact the prescriber, believed that the patient needed to continue the drug regimen during the weekend to protect his health, and saw no reason why the physician would not continue to maintain the patient on this medication, the conclusion probably would be that the pharmacist acted in accordance with the standard of care expected of him or her. However, suppose the patient knew that his physician was awaiting test results before deciding whether to terminate the medication or to refill the prescription. The patient did not tell this to the pharmacist but the pharmacist also did not ask any questions about why the patient had run out of his maintenance drug. Whether the pharmacist was liable would probably turn on whether the withholding of information by the patient or the failure to inquire by the pharmacist was the key to the injury occurring.

# The Pharmacist's Responsibility

As a society, we have chosen to regulate pharmacy closely to protect the health of patients and to provide protection from the abuse of otherwise-beneficial pharmaceuticals (*Vermont & 110th Medical Arts Pharmacy v. California State Board of Pharmacy*, 125 Cal. App. 3d 19 (2d Dist. 1981)). The pharmacist's primary obligation is to fulfill his or her patient care responsibilities. Pharmacists are not expected to have the legal knowledge of lawyers, but they are required to know about the law governing pharmacy, despite how complex it may appear.

The short course in pharmacy law provided in pharmacy schools introduces pharmacy law, but it cannot provide all the legal knowledge a pharmacist will ever need. This is especially true because the law is dynamic, constantly changing. The pharmacist must stay abreast of changes and recognize the need for thoughtful consideration of his or her obligations. For example, the pharmacist faced with the phenytoin refill in the hypothetical case above needs to know that California law changed a few years ago to expand the pharmacist's discretion in making refill judgments under these circumstances (§4064, see Chap. X: Dispensing and Beyond). The Pharmacy Board supplies some information, especially in its newsletter, *The Script*, and elsewhere on its website, to help pharmacists remain informed; each pharmacist has to obtain or access and read that information. Involvement with professional associations, discussions with colleagues, interactions with inspectors from the Board of Pharmacy and other government agencies, continuing education, and reading publications that cover changes in pharmacy law are all methods that a pharmacist can and should use to keep informed. In addition, an interested pharmacist may attend meetings of the Board of Pharmacy or most of its committees.

A pharmacist who cannot find an answer to a legal concern should seek guidance. Guidance is available from colleagues or superiors, from Board staff, or from a qualified lawyer or a professional association. Acting in ignorance not only risks poor service or actual harm to patients, but also legal liability (see Chap. XII: Practice Pitfalls).

The pharmacist also needs to be willing to change his or her practice habits as laws and standards of care evolve. For example, when patient consultation was first required by law (at the same time it was becoming a standard of practice), pharmacists had to reconsider the flow of prescriptions in their pharmacies so that a pharmacist would be readily available to fulfill the consultation requirement. The informed, ethical, and cooperative pharmacist will not encounter difficulty satisfying the obligations of the law.

## Changing the Law

The individual also may effect change in the law. Regulations, such as those enforced by the Pharmacy Board, are relatively easy to influence. Not only may you comment on proposals set forth by the Board, as described above, but you also may propose to the Board the adoption, repeal, or amendment of any regulation. To do so you need only petition the Board – that is, write to the Board setting forth exactly what change you propose and all the evidence and reasons in support of your proposal, and referring to the Board's authority to take the action you request. You may wish to seek support for your idea from colleagues, professional associations, consumer groups, or others for whom the change would be beneficial. The Board is required to consider your proposal seriously and, within 30 days, either deny the petition, giving reasons, or schedule the matter for public consideration (as discussed above).

Effecting legislative change is more difficult but certainly not beyond the reach of a highly motivated citizen. You need to find a legislator willing to sponsor legislation you propose. The adoption process is considerably more complex than the rulemaking process, but good ideas often garner sufficient support to become law. When there is legislation pending on which you have an opinion, you should communicate with the legislative sponsor, who usually is anxious to learn of public concerns with, or support of, a pending proposal. As groups of voters generally are more influential than individuals, your involvement in the legislative process is more likely to be fruitful if you engage the participation of others who share your views.

**What you should think about after reading this chapter:**

1.  When the obligation of a pharmacist under a statute or a regulation is not entirely clear, what can you do?  What should you do?

2.  When you believe that a statutory provision or a regulation is interfering with, rather than promoting, good patient care or good pharmaceutical practice, what can you do?  What should you do?

3.  What should you do when best serving the needs of a particular patient will violate a law or regulation?

4.  Who should you contact if you don't understand how the law applies to some aspect of your pharmacy practice?

# Chapter II

# Drug Classifications

**What you should know after reading this chapter:**

1. What is a drug, under federal law?

2. What is a "new drug," under federal law?

3. What are the requirements for marketing a prescription drug? What are the requirements for marketing a dietary supplement?

4. Under what circumstances can a drug be marketed as an over-the-counter drug?

5. What makes a drug a "generic" substitute for a brand name drug?

6. What is a device, under federal law?

7. What is a "dangerous" drug or device, under California law?

8. What is a "controlled substance?"

9. May a pharmacist dispense marijuana for medical purposes?

10. Why are chemicals and precursors subject to controls?

The regulatory framework relevant to the practice of pharmacy requires an understanding of how the law classifies substances as drugs or pharmaceuticals. Throughout this text there will be references to regulatory requirements when dealing with certain types of drugs. This chapter provides a basic context for understanding and applying drug law.

## Drugs

The Federal Food, Drug, and Cosmetic Act was passed in 1938 but had its origins in the Food and Drugs Act of 1906. It defines a drug in several ways. First, in recognition of common understanding and professional practice at the time of the Act's passage, it defines as a drug an article recognized in the official United States Pharmacopoeia, official Homeopathic Pharmacopoeia of the United States, or official National Formulary (21 USC §321(g)(1)(A)).[1] Second, a drug is any article

---

[1] The need for reliable reference works and for the standardization of drugs has long been recognized by the medical/scientific community, which supported the creation of compendious works before the adoption of the Federal Food, Drug, and Cosmetic Act. The United States Pharmacopoeia, the Homeopathic Pharmacopoeia of the United States, and the National Formulary are such compendia. At the time of adoption of the Act, these works listed all those drugs

"intended for use in the diagnosis, cure, mitigation, treatment, or prevention of disease" (21 USC §321(g)(1)(B)).  Third, a drug is any article "(other than food) intended to affect the structure or any function of the body" (21 USC §321(g)(1)(C)).[2]

Under the last two definitions, categorization of a product requires consideration of the intent of its seller as to the product's use.  Because that intent is so critical to the classification of an article as a drug, disputes concerning classification often focus on the nature of promotional material and labeling for the product.[3]  California's Pharmacy Law and its Sherman Food, Drug, and Cosmetic Law both incorporate essentially verbatim the federal definition of a drug (§4025, H&SC §109925).

A detailed discussion of how to know when something that appears to be a drug is not considered one under federal law, and when what might appear to be a food or cosmetic is covered by drug laws, is beyond the scope of this text.  However, it is important to know the basic principles involved in the legal classification of substances as drugs.

## New Drugs

A "new drug" is any drug "the composition of which is such that such drug is not generally recognized, among experts qualified by scientific training and experience to evaluate the safety and effectiveness of drugs, as safe and effective for use under the conditions prescribed, recommended, or suggested in the labeling" (21 USC §321(p)(1)).[4]

---

then accepted by the medical/scientific community, and thus provided a convenient means to delineate which then-existing products should be allowed to continue on the market without being subjected to newly adopted standards (regulators say these products are "grandfathered").

[2]   A drug also is any article intended for use as a component of any article meeting any of the other three definitions (21 USC § 321(g)(1)(D)).  These definitions apply to veterinary as well as human drugs.  The drug approval process for both classes of drugs is similar; for veterinary drug approval, sponsors also must demonstrate the safety of any drug residues that might be found in the tissues of food animals.

[3]   For example, these issues were an important focus in the litigation concerning tobacco products.  The Food and Drug Administration (FDA) based its attempt to regulate tobacco on its conclusion that nicotine is a drug, and that cigarettes and smokeless tobacco, as drug delivery devices, are combination products.  However, the United States Supreme Court struck down the FDA regulations on the ground that Congress intended to exclude tobacco products from the regulatory authority granted FDA under the Food, Drug, and Cosmetic Act (*FDA v. Brown & Williamson Tobacco Corp.*, 529 U.S. 120 (2000)).

[4]   The term "new drug" also refers to a drug that has become recognized as safe and effective as a result of clinical investigations but has not been used to a material extent or for a material time other than in investigations (21 USC §321(p)(2)).  Also, there is an exception from the new drug definition for drugs that were subject to the federal Food and Drugs Act of 1906 and at that time were labeled with the same representations as currently in use (21 USC §321(p)(1)).Each time Congress has made the requirements for marketing a new drug more stringent, it has had to determine what to do about drugs already on the market.  When it demanded evidence of safety and then of effectiveness before the marketing of new drugs, Congress did not require products already on the market to prove immediately that they met the new standards.

Old drugs posing safety problems have been subject to individual challenge under the broad prohibition on misbranding (see Chap. VIII: Preparation of Drugs).  When the efficacy standards were added to the law in 1962, Congress mandated that the FDA review all previously-approved prescription and over-the-counter (OTC) drugs.  The OTC Drug Review kept many scientists, attorneys, and regulators busy for decades.  As many as a thousand drugs still sold today were originally marketed prior to modern-day regulation, and thus have not been subject to the NDA process.  FDA published a draft Compliance Policy Guide in October 2003 outlining its views on the status of these drugs, which are essentially illegal but have not been removed from the market.  For an overview of the regulation of OTC drugs, see PETER BARTON HUTT AND RICHARD MERRILL, FOOD AND DRUG LAW: CASES AND MATERIALS 588-614 (2d ed. 1991).  For further explanation of the developments in drug approval requirements and grandfathered exceptions over the years, see generally HUTT AND MERRILL, FOOD AND DRUG LAW, Chapter 3.

Federal law strictly forbids the introduction of any new drug into interstate commerce unless a New Drug Application (NDA) is effective with respect to it (21 USC §355, 21 CFR Part 314 (Applications for FDA Approval to Market a New Drug)). The process of obtaining approval for a new drug application is complex, lengthy, and costly. After laboratory development and animal testing on a promising compound, a sponsor files a "Notice of Claimed Investigational Exemption for a New Drug" (IND); after Food and Drug Administration[5] approval, the drug may be shipped for purposes of human testing (21 USC §355(i), 21 CFR Part 312 (Investigational New Drug Application)).

The sponsor of the drug must do testing in humans using methods deemed appropriate by the Food and Drug Administration (FDA) to demonstrate that there is substantial evidence that a drug is both safe and effective for use under the conditions prescribed, recommended, or suggested in the proposed labeling (21 USC §355(d)). "Substantial evidence" of effectiveness is "evidence consisting of adequate and well-controlled investigations, including clinical investigations, by experts qualified by scientific training and experience to evaluate the effectiveness of the drug involved, on the basis of which it could fairly and responsibly be concluded by such experts that the drug will have the effect it purports or is represented to have" (21 USC §355(d)). It is most important to note that uncontrolled clinical observations are not adequate evidence to support drug approval (21 CFR §314.126).

The human tests proceed in phases, from tests on a small number of healthy volunteers to gather basic safety information, to tests on several hundred patients with the target ailment to obtain more information on safety and to produce data about efficacy, and then to tests on several hundred to several thousand patients to confirm the compound's effectiveness and gather additional safety information, as well as to collect data about optimum dosage amounts and schedules. Thereafter the sponsor may seek approval of the NDA. The process generally costs tens of millions of dollars and it is not unusual for it to consume a decade or more.

There is ongoing tension between pressure to approve drugs more quickly so they will be broadly available and the need for adequate investigation of safety and effectiveness. Largely because of the AIDS crisis, laws and regulations were adopted during the past two decades to provide for accelerated approval ("fast track") of drugs for serious or life-threatening illnesses (§21 USC §356; 21 CFR Part 314, Subpart H (new drugs); 21 CFR Part 601, Subpart E (biological products)). Sponsors of drugs approved under such provisions may be required to complete another phase of post-approval testing. However, even when an NDA is approved after standard testing protocols, only a limited number of people have been exposed to the new drug before it is marketed. In addition, the study population may not include a cross-section of the ultimate users (by age, gender, or other characteristics). Serious side effects, for everyone or a subgroup of users, are frequently discovered only after a drug has been prescribed for millions of people; sometimes a drug is discovered not to be as effective as it first appeared. Because of the paucity of clinical trial information about drug use in children, Congress authorized FDA to require drug testing in children and give manufacturers an increased period of exclusive marketing rights in return (21 USC §355a).

---

[5]   The Food and Drug Administration is part of the Department of Health and Human Services (HHS), a cabinet-level agency. Statutes officially vest authority to take action concerning food and drugs in the Secretary of HHS; that authority has always been exercised, for all practical purposes, by the FDA Commissioner. In 1988 the FDA was recognized officially in statute, provision made for its Commissioner (who thenceforth would be appointed by the President with the advice and consent of the Senate, rather than by the HHS Secretary), and the Secretary's responsibility for executing food and drug laws recognized as being exercised "through the Commissioner" (21 USC § 393(a),(b)). In these materials we will refer to the FDA's powers and authority rather than attributing them, as the statutes still do, to the Secretary of HHS.

Recent experiences with a number of widely-used medications have illustrated the difficult problem of providing reasonable assurance of drug safety and effectiveness.  (See, for example, Marc Kaufman and Brooke A. Masters, *FDA Is Flexing Less Muscle; Some Question Its Relationship With Drugmakers*, WASHINGTON POST, Nov. 18, 2004, p. A01; Gina Kolata, *Merck and Vioxx: The Overview; A Widely Used Arthritis Drug Is Withdrawn*, NEW YORK TIMES, Oct. 1, 2004, p. A1; David Willman, *How a New Policy Led to Seven Deadly Drugs*, LOS ANGELES TIMES, Dec. 20, 2000, p. A1).  Drug approval and drug recall have major financial implications for drug company sponsors as well as for the public health.  Questions have been raised recently about the appropriateness of FDA's oversight of the drug approval process (Phil B. Fontanarosa, Drummond Rennie, Catherine D. DeAngelis, *Postmarketing Surveillance–Lack of Vigilance, Lack of Trust*, JOURNAL OF THE AMERICAN MEDICAL ASSOCIATION, Vol.  292, No. 21, Dec.  1, 2004, p.  2647; Gardiner Harris, *F.D.A.'s Drug Safety System Will Get Outside Review*, NEW YORK TIMES, Nov. 6, 2004, p. A11).  Such questions have emerged and been studied multiple times in the past (e.g., the 1977 reports by the Review Panel on New Drug Regulation, Norman Dorsen and Jeffrey M. Miller, *The drug regulation process and the challenge of regulatory reform*, ANNALS OF INTERNAL MEDICINE, Vol.  91, No.  6, Dec. 1979, p. 908).

Manufacturers and distributors of drugs (as well as devices and biologics) are required to document and report to the FDA significant adverse incidents involving their products.  Health care professionals and consumers are asked to report any problems with FDA-regulated products; forms for this purpose are available at www.fda.gov/medwatch/report/hcp.htm.

**Suppose you have filled a prescription for a newly-approved drug.  The patient's spouse notifies you that the patient died after taking the drug as directed.  What should you do?**

You should review your records of the prescription, including the patient's profile, the preparation and labeling of the drug, and any records of consultation, to determine whether there was a medication error that must be analyzed through the pharmacy's quality assurance program (§4125; see Chap. IV: Licensing Pharmacies).

**Should you make sure the prescriber is aware of the problem?  Should you report the death to the manufacturer?  To the FDA?**

There is no legal requirement that you report what could possibly be a serious adverse drug requirement to FDA, the manufacturer, or to the prescriber.  However, unless medical professionals share their observations of isolated clinical events, knowledge of what could be an important aggregate problem will be delayed.  FDA encourages voluntary reporting by health professionals and consumers (www.fda.gov/medwatch/report/hcp.htm); the information would be helpful to the manufacturer and to the prescriber.  Such reporting should be considered as an ethical rather than a legal obligation (see Chap. XV: Ethics).

To assure drug quality, federal drug law first broadly defines and then forbids misbranding (21 USC §352) and adulteration (21 USC §351) of drugs and devices.  For example, if a drug's label fails to contain adequate directions for use and adequate warnings, it is considered misbranded (21 USC §352(f)); its sponsor is subject to the penalties provided in the law (21USC §§332-334; see Chap. VIII: Preparation of Drugs).  If a drug has deteriorated so that it no longer has the potency stated on the label, it is adulterated (and can also be challenged as misbranded).

All drugs sold (except those originally marketed before modern-day regulation) must be covered by an NDA, whether or not they are restricted to sale on prescription of a medical professional.  Prior to the time of dispensing, drugs limited by federal law to sale upon prescription must bear on their label at minimum the symbol "Rx only" (21 USC §353(b)(4)).  Formerly prescription drugs had to carry the statement, "Caution: Federal law prohibits dispensing without prescription." This federal "caution" label or "legend" requirement was the reason some still refer to prescription drugs as legend or prescription legend drugs.

## *Off-Label Uses*

Federal law does not allow a drug to be marketed for a use (including a dosage or length of therapy) not included in the approved labeling.[6] However, drug manufacturers may, under certain limited circumstances, disseminate written information about the safety, efficacy, and benefits of a use not described in the labeling to health care practitioners, among others (21 USC §360aaa). The FDA has long recognized that the practice of medicine is regulated by the states. Physicians may choose to prescribe, and pharmacists thus may dispense, approved drugs for what are called "off-label" uses, uses not included in the approved labeling, if there is a recognized medical basis for those uses.

Frequently drug manufacturers have done research supporting off-label uses, but have not submitted their results to FDA to change the drug's labeling. They may have terminated these investigations when the drug was approved for other uses, because the costs of the additional research were no longer financially worthwhile, or they may not yet have sufficient data to support the labeling change.[7] Clinicians in academia may have conducted, and reported, research using drugs successfully for unapproved uses. Reports of promising overseas use of drugs for unlabeled indications also fuel American off-label usage. A physician may also base prescribing for off-label uses on his or her own clinical observations.

Depending upon the strength of the scientific support for the off-label use, the prescriber may need to provide the patient with information about the nature of the evidence on which he or she is relying, and may need to obtain the patient's informed consent. When a pharmacist has a concern about the use of a drug, he or she may, and should, contact the prescriber to inquire about it. While the decision to prescribe a drug off-label is properly for the prescriber, the pharmacist's inquiry could avert an unintended, erroneous use of a drug.

## *Generics*

A generic version of an approved drug has the same active chemical ingredients, in the same strength, quantity, and dosage form, as a brand name product (see §4073(a)). Federal law provides a simplified drug approval process for sponsors who wish to market generic versions of previously-

---

[6]  Federal officials have increased their prosecutorial activity for improper drug company promotion of off-label uses. A unit of Pfizer agreed to pay hundreds of millions of dollars in fines to settle criminal charges of illegal marketing of Neurontin® for unapproved use. Such unapproved uses were estimated to represent 90 per cent of the drug's $2.7 billion sales in 2003 (David Armstrong and Anna Wilde Mathews, *Pfizer Case Signals Tougher Action on Off-Label Drug Use*, WALL STREET JOURNAL, May 14, 2004, p. B1).

[7]  The failure to report clinical trial results that do not support either approved or off-label uses has recently sparked significant controversy, and led to calls for a national database of clinical trial information and an international clinical trial registry. Under pressure from New York State prosecutors, several manufacturers announced plans to create such a database for their own data and to support a public trial registry (Barry Meier, *Spitzer Asks Drug Maker for Off-Label Use Material*, NEW YORK TIMES, Aug. 4, 2004, p. C2). The major medical journals have announced they will no longer publish a study that is not registered in a publicly-accessible database, to assure that negative as well as positive results are known to researchers and the public (*Journals' stand to improve drug data*, TORONTO STAR, Sept. 18, 2004, p. L06).

approved drugs. The sponsor must demonstrate, in its Abbreviated New Drug Application (ANDA), that the generic version is bioequivalent to the previously-approved drug (21 CFR §314.94).[8]

Marketing permission cannot be obtained for a generic drug until the rights of the original sponsor to exclusive manufacture of the drug have expired by the passage of time or in response to a legal challenge. Once a generic version of a drug reaches the market, the price of the brand name drug inevitably drops significantly. Because of the financial benefits of marketing exclusivity, brand name manufacturers are vigorous in protecting their patent and other marketing rights. Companies have tried various strategies in recent years to prevent the loss of market share to generic competition. For example, they have taken advantage of a provision of federal law granting six additional months of patent protection in return for testing already-marketed drugs in children (sometimes testing drugs with little, if any, application to pediatric practice). Some have apparently paid generic drug companies in return for their not marketing, or delaying the introduction of, competing generic drugs, and have been the subject of antitrust lawsuits as a consequence. (See, for example, Melody Petersen, *Suits Accuse Drug Makers of Keeping Generics Off Market*, NEW YORK TIMES, May 10, 2001, p. C1.)

Under current law, the holder of a drug patent can prevent a competing generic drug from coming to market for 30 months simply by filing a patent infringement claim against the generic company. After patent holders found ways to obtain multiple 30-month stays, FDA adopted new rules to allow only one automatic 30-month stay under these circumstances (see 68 FR 36676 (June 18, 2003), amending 21 CFR Part 314). The law also gives generic applicants willing to challenge patents an incentive of 180 days of market exclusivity if the patent challenge is successful (21 USC §355(j)(5)(B)(iv)). To circumvent this market exclusivity for successful patent challengers, patent holders have been licensing their patent-protected products to generic manufacturers, creating "authorized" generic versions. Their purpose is to reduce the incentive for other generic companies to challenge their patents; the patent-holder benefits from the licensing fee which it would otherwise not receive (Hollister H. Hovey, *Big Pharma Courts Copycats' Rivals*, WALL STREET JOURNAL, Aug. 11, 2004, p. A8). FDA ruled that this practice is pro-competitive and promotes lower drug prices; the generics industry disagrees. A court challenge is underway, claiming that the practice improperly circumvents the statutory 180-day exclusivity provision. There is a significant amount of ongoing antitrust and patent infringement litigation involving pharmaceutical companies, with very high financial stakes.

The financial consequences of the availability of generic drugs are quite significant to the economy, as well as to individuals. In this decade, patents are expiring on about two dozen popular brand name drugs worth billions of dollars to their manufacturers. The Pharmacy Board has long encouraged consumers to ask about lower-cost generic drugs through its mandated "Notice to Consumers," which must be posted in every pharmacy (§1707.2(f)).

## *Over-the-Counter Drugs*

A prescription is not required when the safety of a drug approved for sale does not depend upon patient supervision by a prescriber; such drugs are popularly known as "over-the-counter" (OTC) drugs. The criteria used by the FDA to determine whether a drug should be limited to sale upon prescription are found at 21 USC 353(b).

---

[8]   The FDA's "Orange Book" (APPROVED DRUG PRODUCTS WITH THERAPEUTIC EQUIVALENCE EVALUATIONS) lists therapeutically-equivalent products and the standards for and categories of therapeutic equivalence. Its Patent and Exclusivity Information Addendum identifies drugs that qualify under the Drug Price Competition and Patent Term Restoration Act (Hatch-Waxman Amendments) for periods of exclusivity, during which certain generic drug applications will not be granted. The Electronic Orange Book is accessible at www.fda.gov/cder/ob.

Newly-approved drugs typically go on the market as prescription drugs. Sponsors or others may later seek OTC status for a drug, or any formulation of it; they must demonstrate that it is safe and effective for use in self-medication and prescription requirements are not necessary for protection of the public health (21 CFR §310.200(b)).[9] FDA regulations now require OTC drugs to bear a "Drug Facts" label to provide consumers clear, simple, and readable information. In some states, transitional requirements have been applied to drugs when they switch from prescription to OTC status; California has not adopted any such restrictions.

The Pharmacy Law does not generally apply to nonprescription drugs that are sold in the manufacturer's or distributor's original container and labeled in compliance with federal and state drug requirements (§4057(a)). Sometimes physicians prescribe OTC drugs, primarily to enable the patient to obtain insurance reimbursement for them; in filling those prescriptions, all prescription requirements apply, including packaging, labeling, and consultation. If a pharmacy repackages or relabels an OTC drug not pursuant to a prescription, that is manufacturing subject to all state and federal requirements governing manufacturers, including registration.

**What if a customer purchases an OTC drug and then asks the pharmacist to repackage it (for example, to place its contents in a more-easily opened container or to add an auxiliary label with the physician's dosing instructions)?**

These actions are unlikely to be considered manufacturing. However, the pharmacist must use care in repackaging or relabeling, just as in handling prescription drugs.

Although pharmacists are not obliged to oversee the OTC drugs or dietary supplements used by their patients, it may be advisable, and in some cases necessary, to inquire about their use in order to give proper counsel about prescription drugs. Information about the interactions between prescription drugs and OTC drugs and supplements is increasingly available. In addition, pharmacists are likely to be asked to recommend, or for advice about, OTC or dietary supplement products. While there is no obligation to provide such information or recommendations, in doing so a pharmacist will be expected to meet the standard of a professional knowledgeable about pharmacology.

# Biologics

FDA is also responsible, under the Public Health Services Act, for the licensing of biological products, which must be demonstrated to be "safe, pure, and potent" (42 U.S.C. §262(a)(2)(C)). FDA has assigned the regulation of most therapeutic biologics, which also fall within the drug definition, to its Center for Drug Evaluation and Research, which is also responsible for review of new drugs. Traditional biologics have included vaccines, blood, and other tissue products; in this category are such products as monoclonal antibodies, proteins intended for therapeutic use, immunomodulators, and growth factors. Human gene therapy products (of which none has yet been approved for sale) also fall into this category. FDA is actively overseeing the ongoing study of gene therapy products by manufacturers and medical researchers.

---

[9] Some examples of drugs formerly available only on prescription and now approved for sale over the counter, at least in some formulations, are cimetidine (Tagamet®), ibuprofen (Advil®), minoxidil (Rogaine®), nicotine polacrilex (Nicorette®), and loratadine (Claritin®). The request for OTC status for Claritin® was made not by its manufacturer, but by health insurers, which rarely cover OTC drugs and generally do not cover prescription drugs if there is a similar OTC product available. OTC status is likely to be sought for statins, anti-cholesterol drugs; Great Britain recently approved a change for one such drug (Lizette Alvarez, *Britain to Start Direct Sale of an Anti-Cholesterol Drug*, NEW YORK TIMES, May 15, 2004, p. A10).

# Devices

Under federal law, a device is "an instrument, apparatus, implement, machine, contrivance, implant, in vitro reagent, or other similar or related article, including any component, part, or accessory" recognized in the official National Formulary or United States Pharmacopoeia, and intended for use in the diagnosis of disease or other conditions, or in the cure, mitigation, treatment, or prevention of disease, or to affect the structure or any function of the body (21 USC §321(h)). In contrast to a drug, a device "does not achieve its primary intended purpose through chemical action within or on the body of man" and is "not dependent upon being metabolized for the achievement of its primary intended purposes" (21 USC §321(h)). Some devices are used with drugs (for example, hypodermic syringes) and some products are drug-device combinations (for example, a prefilled syringe or a wound dressing with an antimicrobial agent).

California's definition of a device, adopted years before the Medical Device Amendments to the Federal Food, Drug, and Cosmetic Act, is less sophisticated, but the differences should have no regulatory impact. In California a device "means any instrument, apparatus, . . . or contrivance, including its components, parts, products, or the byproducts of a device, and accessories that are used or intended for either of the following: (a) Use in the diagnosis, cure, mitigation, treatment, or prevention of disease . . . [or] (b) [t]o affect the structure or any function of the body . . . (§4023)." Contact lenses and nonprescription prosthetic and orthopedic devices are expressly excluded from California's definition of "device" (§4023); contact lenses nevertheless may only be dispensed upon prescription (§4124).

The universe of medical devices is vast, ranging from tongue depressors, thermometers, and bedpans, on one end, to heart-lung machines, implantable pacemakers, and breast implants on the other. Unlike drugs, devices need not all be tested for safety and efficacy before marketing. Devices are classified into three groups, and the regulatory controls differ for each.

- Class I devices, which present minimal harm to the user, are subject only to general controls, such as avoidance of adulteration or misbranding.
- Class II devices are those where general controls are not sufficient to provide reasonable assurance of safety and efficacy; these devices may be subject to performance standards, postmarket surveillance, patient registries, and guidelines for development and dissemination.
- Class III devices are used to support or sustain human life, have substantive importance in preventing impairment of human health, or present a potential unreasonable risk of illness or injury. This class of devices is subject to premarket approval. (See 21 USC §360c for details.)

Even Class III devices are not specifically subject to prescription requirements. However, FDA may restrict a device to prescription sale when, "because of its potentiality for harmful effect or the collateral measures necessary to its use," there cannot otherwise be reasonable assurance of its safety and effectiveness (21 USC §360j(e)). While many Class III devices by definition would fit this description, many are purchased not by patients but by hospitals or other health care providers.

No state may regulate devices in a way that is in conflict with federal law; a state, may, however, seek approval of a state provision that is stricter than federal law (21 USC §360k).

# "Dangerous" Drug or Device

The terms "dangerous drug" and "dangerous device" are creatures of California law, defined in section 4022 as follows:

"Dangerous drug" or "dangerous device" means any drug or device unsafe for self-use in humans or animals,[10] and includes the following:

a. Any drug that bears the legend: "Caution: federal law prohibits dispensing without prescription," "Rx only," or words of similar import.

b. Any device that bears the statement: "Caution: federal law restricts this device to sale  by or on the order of a _____," or words of similar import, the blank to be filled in with the designation of the practitioner licensed to use or order use of the device.

c. Any other drug or device that by federal or state law can be lawfully dispensed only on prescription or furnished pursuant to Section 4006.

Consistent with federal regulations, California law considers any drug or device "unsafe for self-use" to be a "dangerous" drug or device; all prescription drugs and devices fall in this category (§4022(a), (b)).  In addition, if either federal or state law requires a drug or device to be dispensed only on prescription, that drug or device also would fall into the "dangerous" category (§4022(c)).  In essence, California's "dangerous" drug or device terminology simply describes what are called "prescription" drugs or devices under both federal and state food and drug laws.  Section 4022 of course encompasses prescription controlled substances.

The Pharmacy Board may adopt regulations restricting the furnishing of any particular drug "upon a finding that the otherwise unrestricted retail sale of the drug . . . is dangerous to the public health or safety" (§4006).  If it did so, that drug would become a "dangerous drug," and be subject to regulation as such.  This authority could be used to restrict the sale of so-called transitional drugs, those that have just been moved from prescription to OTC status by FDA, if the Board were to deem such action appropriate to protect the public.[11]

# Controlled Substances

The concerns that led to general restrictions on the marketing of drugs were primarily the protection of the public from quackery and from impure, unsafe, or otherwise unreliable drug products.  The concerns that led to the more specific regulation of controlled substances were addiction, drug abuse, and diversion for street sales.  Concern about the abuse of and addiction to powerful drugs, especially narcotics, has existed in many parts of the world for centuries.  Many countries have far more restrictive laws, particularly as to opioids, than the United States.  In the early part of the 20th century, this concern in the United States led to severe restrictions on such narcotics as opium and derivatives such as cocaine, heroin, and morphine.

Drugs are subjected to controlled substances requirements because of their potential for abuse.  They are governed by more stringent regulatory controls than other drugs to assure that they are only produced and distributed through proper channels and for proper medical purposes.  As Chapter VIII:

---

[10] Until 2004, drugs labeled for veterinary use were not included in the definition of "dangerous drugs."  The elimination of that exemption gives the Pharmacy Board jurisdiction over anyone in possession of these drugs (see Chap. XIII: Board of Pharmacy).

[11] The American Pharmacists Association (APhA) is recommending a new category of OTC drugs that could be sold only in an outlet that contains a pharmacy.  As more drugs for chronic and asymptomatic conditions are being considered for a switch to OTC status (for example, the statins), APhA argues that the "pharmacy care OTC" designation would assure the availability of professional counseling (Sandra Levy, *Make room for "Pharmacy Care OTCs": APhA*, DRUG TOPICS, Nov. 22, 2004, www.drugtopics.com).

Preparation of Drugs by a Pharmacy and Chapter IX: The Prescription Process: From Receipt to Labeling will make clear, the regulatory framework for the sale of all controlled substances is considerably more complex than that for other dangerous drugs.

The federal law concerning controlled substances, the Drug Abuse Prevention and Control Act of 1970, is more commonly known as the Controlled Substances Act (21 USC §§801-971). It divides all "drugs of abuse" into five "schedules" of what are called "controlled substances." The federal schedules are found in 21 USC §812(c). Additional drugs may be added to the schedules by regulation; the complete list is in 21 CFR §§1308.1-1308.15. Most scheduling changes at the federal level are made by regulation. Regulatory authority over these drugs under federal law is given to the Drug Enforcement Administration (DEA), an agency of the federal Department of Justice, headed by the Attorney General of the United States. As new drugs of abuse are identified, they are added to the schedules. Occasionally a drug that is legal to prescribe is moved, because of massive abuse, to Schedule I and therefore outlawed, as was methaqualone (Quaalude®) in the 1980s. Other drugs may be added to, removed from, or moved within the schedules because of new medical or scientific information[12] or because of obligations under treaties governing narcotics and psychotropics.

Drugs are determined to be drugs of abuse by applying the following 8 criteria:

1. actual or relative potential for abuse;
2. scientific evidence of the drug's pharmacological effect, if known;
3. state of current scientific knowledge regarding the drug or other substance;
4. history and current pattern of abuse;
5. scope, duration, and significance of abuse;
6. risk, if any, to the public health;
7. psychic or physiological dependence liability; and
8. whether it is an immediate precursor of a substance already controlled (21 USC §811(c)).[13]

If a drug has a high potential for abuse but no accepted and safe medical use, it is placed in Schedule I. If it has a high potential for abuse, but is recognized as safe and effective for medical use, it is placed in Schedule II. Schedule III, IV, and V controlled substances are also recognized as safe and effective for medical use, with a declining potential for abuse and dependence in each schedule group.[14]

---

[12] Often that new information is about a drug's potential for abuse, and responds to fads in choice of drugs of abuse. For example, gamma hydroxybutyrate (GHB), used as a "date-rape" drug, became a federal Schedule I drug in 2000; California made it a Schedule I drug in 2002, except when it is in an FDA-approved pharmaceutical, in which case it is in Schedule III (H&SC §§11054, 11056).

[13] The Model Uniform Controlled Substances Act of 1990, which is followed by most states, contains these same criteria for determining whether to schedule a drug and in which schedule (§§ 201-208). Oddly, California has never adopted any criteria for its scheduling decisions although it incorporated many of the other provisions of the model act into state law.

[14] The federal statutory language governing placement of drugs in the schedules is as follows:

Schedule I: there is a high potential for abuse, no currently accepted medical use in treatment in the United States, and a lack of accepted safety for use of the drug under medical supervision (21 USC §812(b)(1)).

Schedule II: there is a high potential for abuse, a currently accepted medical use, and abuse may lead to severe psychological or physical dependence (21 USC §812(b)(2)).

Schedule III: there is a potential for abuse less than for Schedule I or II substances, a currently accepted medical use, and abuse may lead to moderate or low physical dependence or high psychological dependence (21 USC §812(b)(3)).

In general, a Schedule I controlled substance is illegal and cannot be manufactured, prescribed, dispensed, or used, except for investigatory purposes approved by the government (21 USC §823(f), H&SC §11212). Other scheduled drugs may be manufactured, prescribed, dispensed, and used in accordance with law if they are prescribed and dispensed for a valid medical purpose of each particular patient (see Chap. IX: Prescriptions: Receipt to Labeling and Chap. XII: Practice Pitfalls).

By its terms, the federal law does not supersede state law in this field (21 USC §903). The states may apply, and some do, different and more complex rules for the sale and use of these drugs, but a state cannot authorize what federal law prohibits. For example, California long required the use of a preprinted triplicate prescription form, not required by federal law, for the prescription of Schedule II controlled substances. The triplicate has now been replaced by a controlled substance prescription form for Schedule IIs, a requirement still more stringent than federal law mandates (see Chap. IX: Prescriptions: Receipt to Labeling). Also, a state may place a drug in a different schedule than under federal law or choose not to schedule it at all. If a state restricts a drug more than the federal government does, its more restrictive status will apply in that state. However, if a drug is not scheduled by a state, or is subject to lesser restrictions by the state than by federal law, it remains subject to the more stringent federal requirements.

California law defines a "controlled substance" as any substance listed in the California Uniform Controlled Substances Act (§4021). The formidable schedules in the California law, found in Health and Safety Code sections 11054 to 11058, list all the drugs by generic name or chemical composition that are covered by this law. These schedules are frequently changed (by statute, rather than by regulation) to incorporate federal changes or to include substances posing a problem in California. The federal and state schedules are quite similar, but not identical.

## The Case of "Medical Marijuana"

As is obvious to any observer of the American drug scene, some controlled substances that at least in some forms are recognized as safe and effective for medical use are frequently manufactured, distributed, and used illegally; cocaine, methamphetamine, and phencyclidine (PCP) are just three examples. Legally manufactured drugs are illegally diverted for improper uses; some drugs are diverted in large quantities.

When legitimate medical uses are found for a Schedule I controlled substance, it may be moved to a lower schedule, but the political opposition often is significant. In the 1980s legalization of heroin (for legitimate medical use) was proposed but defeated. Levo-alphacetylmetadol (LAAM) was moved from Schedule I to Schedule II in 1993 to allow its legal use in approved drug treatment programs as a substitute for methadone.

---

Schedule IV: there is a low potential for abuse relative to Schedule III substances, a currently accepted medical use, and abuse may lead to limited physical dependence or psychological dependence relative to drugs or substances in III (21 USC §812(b)(4)).

Schedule V: there is a low potential for abuse relative to those drugs in Schedule IV, a currently accepted medical use, and abuse may lead to limited physical dependence or psychological dependence relative to those [drugs] in [Schedule] IV (21 USC §812(b)(5)).

Drugs with a potential (but not a "high potential") for abuse, and no currently accepted medical use in treatment, are not expressly covered by the scheduling scheme. DEA has consistently taken the position that such substances also belong in Schedule I.

Efforts to reschedule marijuana from Schedule I to Schedule II to allow its use for such purposes as to alleviate nausea in persons undergoing chemotherapy have been rejected by the DEA, even though they have received support from respected medical practitioners.[15] Dronabinol, a synthetic, oral form of the active ingredient in marijuana, was approved by FDA in 1985 and placed in Schedule II by DEA, making it available on prescription, in 1986. DEA rescheduled dronabinol to Schedule III in 1999; California followed suit in 2000.

An initiative measure intended to legalize marijuana in all forms for medical use was adopted by California's voters, as Proposition 215, in November 1996.[16] Similar initiatives or legislation have passed in other states. [17] The initiative affected Health and Safety Code section 11357, relating to the possession of marijuana, and section 11358, relating to the cultivation of marijuana, by making them inapplicable to "a patient, or to a patient's primary caregiver, who possesses or cultivates marijuana for the personal medical purposes of the patient upon the written or oral recommendation or approval of a physician" (H&SC §11362.5(d)). The initiative also provides that no physician "shall be punished, or denied any right or privilege, for having recommended marijuana to a patient for medical purposes" (H&SC §11362.5(c)).

The list of medical conditions for which a physician may recommend the use of marijuana is very broad: "cancer, anorexia, AIDS, chronic pain, spasticity, glaucoma, arthritis, migraine, *or any other illness for which marijuana provides relief*" (H&SC §11362.5(b)(1)(A), emphasis added). Because of the limited amount of research on marijuana as a medicine, the medical basis for using marijuana for either the conditions listed in the California law or for other illnesses is not clear.[18]

The California initiative made no provision for either buying or selling marijuana. Even prior to the passage of Proposition 215, there were some "buyers' clubs" in existence whose purpose was to allow patients access to marijuana for medical purposes. Since the passage of Proposition 215, these clubs have taken the position that they could obtain and sell marijuana to persons needing it for medical purposes. However, this activity is unquestionably illegal under federal law, no matter how well-intentioned, and whether or not prosecutors are taking legal action.

The buyers' clubs argue that inherent in Proposition 215 is a means for people to obtain marijuana other than growing it themselves. In the alternative, they have claimed to be "primary caregivers" who, under Proposition 215, may grow marijuana for people for whom they are providing

---

[15] A petition to reschedule marijuana as a Schedule II controlled substance was filed in 1972; the DEA did not issue its final ruling rejecting the request until 1994. That decision was challenged in the courts but upheld (*Alliance for Cannabis Therapeutics v. Drug Enforcement Administration*, 15 F.3d 1131 (D.C. Cir. 1994)). Another rescheduling petition filed in 1995 was denied in 2001 (66 FR 20038 (Apr. 18, 2001). The editors of The New England Journal of Medicine called for reclassification of marijuana in an editorial published in January 1997 (Glen Martin, *Medical Journal Blasts U.S. on Marijuana for the Sick; Editorial calls drug policy "misguided,"* SAN FRANCISCO CHRONICLE, Jan. 30, 1997, p. A1).

[16] The adoption of Proposition 215 was widely discussed in the media (see, e.g., Glen Martin, *Both Sides Say 215 Decriminalizes Pot Use,* SAN FRANCISCO CHRONICLE, Nov. 7, 1996, p. A17; Eric Bailey, *New Pot Law Brings Turmoil, Concerns,* LOS ANGELES TIMES, Nov. 7, 1996, p. A3).

[17] Those states are Alaska, Arizona, Colorado, Hawaii, Maine, Montana, Nevada, Oregon, Vermont, and Washington. Maryland has not legalized marijuana for medical use, but has made proof of medical use a defense to criminal prosecution for possession. Canada adopted regulations in 2001 allowing, and financially supporting, medical use of marijuana for a limited set of indications.

[18] The federal government has controlled the legal supply of marijuana for research purposes, and over the years resisted most researchers' requests for access. Policy changes in 1999 eased access, so an improved research base concerning the medical use of marijuana is likely to be available soon (see Marsha N. Cohen, *Breaking the Federal/State Impasse Over Medical Marijuana: A Proposal,* 11 HASTINGS WOMEN'S LAW JOURNAL 59-60, 70 (2000)).

care.  Although a trial court initially accepted that position, the California Court of Appeal has held that California law continues to prohibit sale and possession for sale of marijuana, even by sellers not profiting from their transactions, and that cannabis buyers' clubs do not qualify as "primary caregivers" of their thousands of patrons (*People ex rel. Lungren v. Peron*, 59 Cal. App. 4th 1383, 1389-1390 (1st Dist. 1997)).[19]

Federal law enforcement officials have both initiated prosecutions relating to Proposition 215 and been sued by those seeking protection from federal prosecution.  Not long after the passage of Proposition 215, the federal government promulgated a policy declaring that a physician's recommendation of a Schedule I controlled substance to a patient was inconsistent with the public interest and would lead to the revocation of the physician's DEA registration, the license to prescribe controlled substances.  Physicians and patients brought suit, and obtained an injunction protecting the First Amendment right of physicians to make such recommendations.  However, the court noted that this injunction does not "limit the government's ability to investigate doctors who aid and abet the actual distribution and possession of marijuana" (*Conant v. Walters*, 309 F.3d 629, 632 (9th Cir. 2002)).  In other words, while a physician may discuss, and even recommend, the medicinal use of marijuana, he or she cannot provide it or direct the patient to a source, because that would amount to distribution of marijuana or aiding and abetting its distribution.  The court's statement that the physician would be aiding and abetting if he or she "intends for the patient to use [the recommendation] as the means for obtaining marijuana" (*Conant v. Walters*, 309 F.3d at 635) is somewhat difficult to understand.  Under California law, any recommendation (even oral) from a physician is sufficient for the patient to obtain and use marijuana for medical purposes.  The line between exercising First Amendment rights and aiding and abetting marijuana distribution is hard to comprehend in this context, and the court decision is not as protective as it may appear.

The federal courts and the California courts have generally agreed that distribution of marijuana by cannabis buyers' clubs is illegal under federal law.  In some California counties individuals involved with distribution of marijuana through clubs have been prosecuted.[20]  The California Legislature has amended California law to require the provision of identification cards to patients and their primary caregivers, to identify them as medical marijuana users to law enforcement personnel; to define a primary caregiver; and to establish an amount of marijuana and a number of plants that a patient or his or her caregiver may possess, among other things (H&SC §§ 11362.7-11362.83).  However, it has not amended the law to specify how a patient could obtain medical marijuana by purchase, or to provide for sellers of medical marijuana.  A number of California cities and counties have established programs through which patients may be supplied medical marijuana, including by clubs approved by the city or county.  However, federal law prohibiting use of marijuana for any purpose has remained unchanged.

The most significant federal court battle concerning medical marijuana arose when federal prosecutors took action to shut down a number of northern California medical cannabis clubs.  The federal government won the first round, when the trial court held that the federal prohibition against the distribution of marijuana was in direct conflict with, and overrode, Proposition 215.  It also held that a claim of "medical necessity" was not a defense to the government's action seeking to shut down permanently the operations of the clubs (*United States v. Cannabis Cultivators Club*, 5 F. Supp. 2d 1086, 1102 (N.D. Cal. 1998)).  On appeal, the federal appeals court asked the trial judge to reconsider whether clubs should be allowed to distribute marijuana to those patients for whom it is a medical

---

[19] An earlier state court decision had determined that Proposition 215 does not give a patient the right to possess an unlimited amount of marijuana or provide an automatic defense to charges of illegal transportation of marijuana (*People v. Trippet*, 56 Cal. App. 4th 1532, 1549-1550  (1st Dist. 1997)).

[20] See Daniel Yi, *O.C. Cannabis Club Activist Found Guilty*, LOS ANGELES TIMES, Nov. 20, 1998, p. A1.

necessity (*United States v. Oakland Cannabis Buyers' Cooperative*, 190 F.3d 1109, 1115 (9th Cir. 1999)). Medical marijuana proponents celebrated this decision as a triumph, but it was short-lived. In May 2001, without any dissenting votes, the United States Supreme Court held that there can be no medical necessity defense to a charge of manufacturing or distributing marijuana, because of the clear legislative prohibition of those activities in the federal Controlled Substances Act (*United States v. Oakland Cannabis Buyers' Cooperative*, 532 U.S. 483 (2001)). After this Supreme Court decision, the federal government started significant new enforcement actions, focusing its efforts in California (Greg Winter, *U.S. Cracks Down on Medical Marijuana in California*, NEW YORK TIMES, Oct. 31, 2001, p. A12).

Medical marijuana proponents took a different legal approach in a more recent case and won a split decision by the federal appeals court. In *Raich v. Ashcroft*, 352 F.3d 1222 (9th Cir. 2003), marijuana users and growers successfully argued that the federal government could not constitutionally prosecute an individual for cultivation or use of marijuana as authorized by California law, as long as the activity was entirely intrastate and noncommercial, because to do so would violate the Commerce Clause of the United States Constitution. The United States Supreme Court agreed to review this decision, heard oral argument in November 2004, and will issue its opinion by June 2005.[21]

If the United States Supreme Court accepts the Commerce Clause argument in the *Raich* case, the states would be able to adopt controlled substances laws less restrictive than the federal law, at least to govern entirely intrastate, noncommercial activity. Such laws could govern other substances as well as marijuana. One concern that is likely to be important in the Court's consideration is the ease with which substances legal only in one state can pass across boundaries into another.

Unless a court rules otherwise, marijuana remains illegal in California and in the other states which have adopted similar medical marijuana laws, even for personal medical use, because it is illegal under federal law. Federal prosecutors can take action against anyone within California violating federal law, even if that person would have a defense to a California violation based upon Proposition 215. However, federal drug enforcement generally focuses upon large-scale violators of drug laws, rather than small offenders, making it unlikely that individual Californians growing and possessing limited amounts of marijuana within the boundaries approved by Proposition 215 will be the targets of prosecution. Federal enforcement actions have mostly targeted large cannabis clubs, large-scale marijuana gardens, and clinics supplying medical marijuana, although there have been some actions against small growers, including a patient, a plaintiff in the *Raich* case, growing six plants for her personal medical use. State and local enforcement officials are highly unlikely to take action against anyone whose conduct complies with California law. Many county law enforcement officials in California announced their cooperation with Proposition 215 soon after its passage. Their major concern, the ability to distinguish legitimate medical users from other users of marijuana, has been eased by the identification card legislation. In any case, local enforcement of marijuana laws against casual users for marijuana possession has not been vigorous for many years; Proposition 215 has surely reduced even that low level of state prosecutorial activity.

**Could a cancer patient using marijuana that she cultivated be convicted of illegal possession and cultivation in a California court? In federal court?**

---

[21] California filed a brief in support of plaintiffs in the *Raich* case, for itself and for the states of Maryland and Washington, which both have laws concerning medical marijuana. The states of Alabama, Louisiana, and Mississippi also filed a brief in support of plaintiffs, because of their position in support of state autonomy ("states' rights") (see list of briefs filed in the *Raich* case at www.supremecourtus.gov/docket/03-1454.htm; Bob Egelko, *State backs medical pot case before U.S. Supreme Court; Attorney general files brief supporting two Californians,* SAN FRANCISCO CHRONICLE, Oct. 14, 2004, p. A5).

If marijuana use was recommended to the patient by a physician for her medical condition, and she possessed and was cultivating a quantity of the drug consistent with personal use, Proposition 215 would protect her from conviction in California courts. She is, however, at risk of conviction in federal court, because the cultivation and possession of marijuana, for whatever purpose, remain illegal under federal law. The *Raich* case will determine whether the federal government has the right to prohibit this intrastate, noncommercial use of marijuana. As noted above, federal law enforcement officials do not have as a high priority finding and prosecuting individuals who cultivate and possess marijuana but do not sell it.

**Suppose a patient comes to you and says she needs marijuana for her chemotherapy-related nausea. You ask her if she has a physician and she says she does. You ask her if she has tried dronabinol (Marinol®), a synthetic, capsule form of marijuana that is a Schedule III controlled substance. She has tried it but has trouble swallowing it. May you help her obtain marijuana?**

For many reasons you may not. First, she has no prescription. Second, even if her physician wrote a prescription (which would be in violation of federal law), you would have no proper source of the drug. A pharmacy must get its drugs and components from which it compounds drugs from recognized, identifiable sources and in a form legally approved for retail distribution. There is no source because marijuana (or its active ingredient, delta-9-tetrahydrocannabinol (THC)) has not been approved by the FDA as safe and effective for any medical use, other than in the form of dronabinol. Third, and most important, marijuana still is illegal. A pharmacist who becomes involved in illegal distribution – even for humanitarian reasons and without profiting from the distribution – risks not only a criminal record and prison time, but also the loss of the license to practice pharmacy and the forfeiture of assets, including the pharmacy.

From the perspective of the pharmacist, Proposition 215 did not change any relevant law in respect to marijuana. It did not provide any proper source of the drug (except for cultivation), even for those allowed to possess it. Its purchase and sale remain illegal, even for patients, under California law. The possession, sale, and cultivation of marijuana remain illegal under federal law for everyone. Distributing marijuana continues to violate many sections of California law respecting pharmacies. In addition, federal authorities could take criminal and disciplinary action against you; the disciplinary action would be revocation of your pharmacy's DEA registration, without which no controlled substances may be sold. The pharmacy's privileges to participate in the Medicare and Medicaid programs could also be revoked.

Only if the patient is part of an approved investigational project and your pharmacy is approved to be in the distribution system may you distribute marijuana. You then would be restricted to the approved source and subject to strict compliance with the approved investigational protocols.

**Assuming that you know how to get in touch with people who continue to make marijuana available to patients who want to try it to relieve nausea or for AIDS wasting syndrome, may you provide your patient with that information? Will you be guilty of aiding and abetting the violation of the drug laws by your patient and his or her suppliers, or are you merely exercising your First Amendment rights?**

There are no court cases precisely on this point. This is a similar issue to that raised by the physicians in *Conant v. Walters*, who wanted to recommend marijuana to their patients without risk of the loss of their federal prescribing privileges. As noted above, the federal court agreed with the physicians that DEA had no right to threaten their licensure merely because they recommended marijuana. Under the *Conant* case, a pharmacist who simply told a patient about the continued existence of some cannabis buyers' clubs would appear to be exercising First Amendment rights. Providing specific instruction on their location, however, might be considered crossing the line to aiding and abetting a violation of federal law. Given the risks to a pharmacist of involvement in controlled substance transactions, caution is certainly appropriate.

**Will marijuana ever be available for prescribing and dispensing?**

The prestigious Institute of Medicine of the National Academy of Sciences concluded, in a 1999 report entitled MARIJUANA AND MEDICINE: ASSESSING THE SCIENCE BASE,[22] that marijuana might be efficacious for some purposes. It urged that additional research be undertaken, and in the meantime, that smokeable marijuana be made available for some conditions until the drug could be available in another, safer form. While the political pressure exerted by the passage of state medical marijuana laws (as well as the Academy's recommendations) has helped to reduce federal opposition to making marijuana available for medical research, there remain formidable barriers to commercializing any findings of marijuana's safety and effectiveness for medical purposes. A sponsor would need to present the safety and efficacy evidence to FDA using the NDA process, and would also need to convince DEA to reschedule the drug, at least in the form it wishes to commercialize, from Schedule I to Schedule II. Although a sponsor might be able to secure patent protection for a novel method of introducing marijuana into the body, such patent protection would not be available for marijuana itself. The lack of potential for significant profit, along with the possible political risks and the security concerns of being a marketer of marijuana, might well deter investment in making marijuana products available for medical uses.

# Dietary Supplements

Although not classified by federal law as drugs and specifically exempt from the Pharmacy Law (§4057(e)), dietary supplements can have significant effects on the body. Increasing numbers of patients are likely to be using dietary supplements at the same time they are taking prescribed drugs, magnifying the potential for interactions. Reference works on dietary supplements therefore should have a place on the pharmacy shelf alongside the reference works on pharmaceuticals.

Prior to the passage of the Dietary Supplement Health and Education Act (DSHEA) by Congress in 1994, making a health claim in connection with the sale of a vitamin, mineral, herbal, or botanical product caused that product to be regulated as a drug. DSHEA amended the Federal Food, Drug, and Cosmetic Act to recognize dietary supplements as a new category of regulated products. The new law greatly liberalizes the labeling of these products, enabling sellers to make the kind of claims that previously would have triggered premarket approval requirements, including proof of safety and efficacy.

Statements on dietary supplements may not claim to diagnose, mitigate, treat, cure, or prevent a specific disease or class of diseases. However, they may claim a benefit related to a classical nutrient deficiency disease if the prevalence of such disease in the United States is disclosed, describe the role of a nutrient or dietary ingredient intended to affect the structure or function in humans, characterize the documented mechanism by which a nutrient or dietary ingredient acts to maintain such structure or function, or describe general well-being from consumption of a nutrient or dietary ingredient. The manufacturer of the dietary supplement must have substantiation that the statement is truthful and not misleading, and the statement must prominently display the disclaimer, "This

---

[22] The material in the report has been reissued in a format directed to the lay audience (Alison Mack and Janet Joy, MARIJUANA AS MEDICINE?: THE SCIENCE BEYOND THE CONTROVERSY, National Academies Press, 2000).

statement has not been evaluated by the Food and Drug Administration. This product is not intended to diagnose, treat, cure, or prevent any disease" (21 USC §343(r)(6)(C)).

The distinction between forbidden drug claims and the structure/function and general well-being claims allowed on dietary supplement labels under DSHEA is at best confusing to the public. There are no restrictions on pharmacy sale of dietary supplements; most pharmacies today carry a large selection of such products. Pharmacists should be able to explain to patients the difference between the level of scrutiny given by the FDA to drugs and to dietary supplements, and the contrast between drug labeling, all of which is approved by the FDA, and dietary supplement labeling, which is not subject to government approval.

DSHEA was passed with significant support both from a politically-active dietary supplement/herbal remedy industry and from consumer and practitioner proponents of alternatives to standard medical treatment. The law gives FDA no premarket approval authority over these products, and allows FDA to remove them from the market for adulteration or misbranding only after bearing a significant burden of proof. However, the problems that have arisen in respect to dietary supplements containing ephedra,[23] for example, may lead Congress to re-examine the regulatory scheme. In the meantime, it appears that FDA has recently directed greater regulatory attention than in prior years to safety problems and misleading promotional claims involving this category of products.

# Chemicals and Precursors

Both federal and state law now require reporting of sales of certain chemicals and precursors often used in the illicit manufacture of drugs (21 USC §830, H&SC §11100; see 11 CCR §§800-808).[24] These laws were passed in response to the appearance of designer drugs (or controlled substance analogs) in the 1980s, in California and elsewhere. Street chemists, and occasionally a licensed pharmacist or drug company employee, would synthesize a drug with only slight variations from a recognized controlled substance, hoping to avoid prosecution under the law.

Very common chemicals, such as ephedrine, pseudoephedrine, norpseudoephedrine, and phosphorus, have been used to make these new street drugs, particularly street versions of methamphetamine. Pharmacists need to be aware of the reporting requirements and sales restrictions and alert to unusual or suspicious purchases or sales of reportable chemicals.

Very broad laws covering chemicals, precursors, and analogs of existing controlled substances were passed to monitor and control these "designer drug" activities (21 USC §§802(32), 813; H&SC §11055(e)(3)(C)(analogs of phencyclidine)). Other laws were amended to allow federal and state agencies to rapidly schedule analogs to existing controlled substances and to respond to efforts by

---

[23] Dietary supplement products (but not drugs) containing ephedrine group alkaloids became illegal in California in 2004, under newly-adopted H&SC §§110423.100-.101, except when prescribed or used by practitioners to treat patients other than for weight loss, body building, or athletic performance enhancement. These products may be sold to a licensed pharmacist for resale on prescription. In December 2003 FDA issued a consumer alert advising consumers to stop buying and using dietary supplements containing ephedra, and gave notice of its intent to publish a rule stating that these supplements present an unreasonable risk of illness or injury. The final rule (supported by a 363-typescript-page document) was published on February 11, 2004 (69 FR 6788) and became effective 60 days later. Several legal challenges to the rule are underway, but the rule has gone into effect (see www.fda.gov/bbs/topics/NEWS/2004/NEW01050.html).

[24] Failure to comply can be costly. A manufacturer of pseudoephedrine that repeatedly failed to comply with the requirement to report sales, and 34 million of whose tablets were discovered at methamphetamine labs, was fined $2 million and prohibited from further manufacturing or distributing pseudoephedrine (*Advance Pharmaceuticals, Inc. v. United States*, 2004 U.S. App. Lexis 24919 (2d Cir., Dec. 3, 2004).

dealers, anxious to avoid being subject to felony enforcement, to market potent drugs that are slightly different, chemically or structurally, from scheduled drugs.

The California laws governing reporting and sales of certain chemicals that can be used in the illicit manufacture of methamphetamine were tightened in 2000 (H&SC §§11100-11107.1).  These provisions affect common products sold to promote weight loss and for relief of allergies, asthma, colds, and sinus problems, including those containing ephedrine, pseudoephedrine, norpseudoephedrine, and phenylpropanolamine (PPA).[25]  In general, manufacturers, wholesalers, pharmacies, and other retailers must report all sales and transfers of such substances, or products containing them, including OTC products and sales.[26]  No more than three packages of a product containing such substances and, in any event, no more than nine grams of active ingredient, may be sold in any single retail transaction.

Sellers of these chemicals other than licensed pharmacies, wholesalers, or manufacturers registered with the DEA and licensed either by the Board or the Department of Health Services (DHS), and retailers that sell in face-to-face transactions with walk-in customers must obtain a Precursor Business Permit from the Bureau of Narcotic Enforcement (BNE).  The sale of an amount exceeding the three package/nine gram limit is a misdemeanor; an unlicensed sale may be punished as a felony.[27]

Neither the state sales limits nor the reporting requirements apply to a pharmacist who dispenses pursuant to a prescription, to sales of certain pediatric liquid products containing less than one fluid ounce, to wholesalers licensed by the Board and manufacturers licensed by DHS (if they obtain a letter from the purchaser or recipient that includes certain information about the company and how the product is to be used), or to transfers for the purpose of lawful disposal as waste.

The federal requirements under the Comprehensive Methamphetamine Control Act of 1996, P.L. 104-237, are somewhat different.  Records are required to be kept for two years of retail transactions involving these same precursors that exceed certain amounts (more than 24 grams of pseudoephedrine, PPA, or combination ephedrine or more than zero grams of a single-entity ephedrine drug product).  Proof of identity is required from customers under these circumstances; suspicious transactions involving such quantities must be reported immediately to DEA.  The 24-gram threshold does not apply to blister packs of pseudoephedrine and PPA.  Of greatest practical importance, given the stringent California law, is the federal requirement that all transactions, regardless of size, involving ephedrine, pseudoephedrine, and PPA(except those to DEA licensees) that are sent by mail or carrier

---

[25] FDA proposed the withdrawal of all NDAs for drugs containing phenylpropanolamine for safety reasons several years ago (66 FR 42665 (Aug. 14, 2001)).  No final action appears to have been taken, but FDA has requested that manufacturers stop marketing products containing PPA and has advised the public to avoid such products (see www.fda.gov/cder/drug/infopage/ppa/default.htm).

[26] The law also forbids possession of these substances by minors and furnishing or selling these substances to minors.  While on its face the law would thus prohibit a minor from purchasing many OTC drug products, the Bureau of Narcotic Enforcement believes that this was not the law's intent and it is not applying it to prohibit those sales.  The law also excludes from the sales and reporting requirements retail sales of OTC products containing these substances that are not in "solid or liquid" form.  However, it appears that no such products are currently marketed.

[27] California is not alone in responding to this problem with regulation.  Because of methamphetamine addiction, Oregon has recently required that pharmacists keep OTC cold remedies containing pseudoephedrine behind the counter and obtain photo identification before selling them; sales by supermarkets and other retail outlets have been banned (www.pharmacy.state.or.us/PE%20Rule/PE%20Temp%20Rule.pdf, Oregon Board of Pharmacy press release, Oct. 14, 2004).

must be reported to DEA on a monthly basis.  The federal rules may be found in the DEA Pharmacist's Manual, pp. 37-41.[28]

---

**What you should think about after reading this chapter:**

1.  Why are some drugs designated as "controlled substances?"

2.  What are some of the factors that affect whether a generic version of a drug is approved for marketing?

3.  What role should the pharmacist play with respect to products other than prescription drugs?

4.  What is a pharmacist's responsibility with respect to sales of OTC products containing ephedrine or pseudoephedrine?

---

[28] The DEA Pharmacist's Manual (8th ed. 2004) is an important reference for pharmacists and is frequently cited in this text. While DEA cautions that it does not substitute for the laws and regulations, it provides valuable guidance with respect to federal controlled substances.  It is available at www.deadiversion.usdoj.gov/pubs/manuals/pharm2/pharm_content.htm.

# Chapter III

# Licensing Pharmacists and Other Individuals

**What you should know after reading this chapter:**

1. What are the requirements for obtaining a license as a pharmacist?

2. What types and length of experience do you need to obtain to fulfill the internship requirement?

3. Your license to practice pharmacy expires while you are living overseas writing the Great American Novel. Four years later you return to California. What will you need to do to resume the practice of pharmacy?

4. What is the continuing education requirement for pharmacists? Can you get credit for a course entitled *Successful Approaches to Obesity?* For *Giving Painless Immunizations?* For *Managing a Small Business?* For a course on managing diabetes approved by the Board of Registered Nursing?

5. When a technician is filling prescriptions in a community pharmacy, what are the supervising pharmacist's responsibilities? What about in a hospital pharmacy?

6. What ratios of technicians to pharmacists are permissible?

7. To what extent may a technician participate in compounding?

8. What is an exemptee? A designated representative?

State governments impose restrictions on the performance of certain acts to assure public health and safety in the delivery of health care. California, like all other states, requires persons who wish to engage in the pharmacy profession to obtain permission to do so, in the form of a license or a permit.[1] Statutes and regulations set forth the substantive standards and the procedures by which such permission may be obtained, the conditions for maintaining the license, and those that could cause it to

---

[1] The 1996 reorganization of the Pharmacy Law defines the term "license" to include "any license, permit, registration, certificate, or exemption" issued by the Pharmacy Board (§4032). It thereafter uses the term "license" predominantly, but not exclusively. For example, section 4110(a) refers to the requirement of a pharmacy *license,* whereas section 4110(b) speaks of the issuance of a temporary *permit.* Under federal law, the permission to engage in controlled substances transaction is a "registration" (21 USC §823). Regardless of the terminology, each of these is a grant of permission from the government to engage in some regulated activity. Traditional terms undoubtedly will continue in popular use: the pharmacist will have a license and the pharmacy a permit. Regardless of the terminology, each is a grant of permission from the government to engage in some regulated activity. Following the lead of the drafters of the 1996 reorganization, this book will primarily use the term "license" to refer to such permission.

be revoked.  This chapter, Chapter IV: Licensing Pharmacies, and Chapter V: Other Pharmacy Board Licensees describe the many categories of license held by those involved in the practice of pharmacy and the pharmaceutical industry, from the retail pharmacist to the veterinary food-animal drug retailer. This chapter focuses on individual licensees: pharmacists, interns, technicians, and exemptees (and their successors, designated representatives).  Chapter IV focuses on pharmacies; Chapter V focuses on other premises licensed by the Board where drugs and devices are found.  In addition, Chapter VI, Scope of Practice, mentions additional settings in which pharmacists must or may play a role in connection with drug ordering and use.

The applicant for any license must file the proper application, provide required information, and cooperate with reasonable follow-up requests and investigation of the application.[2]  The Board has broad authority to investigate applicants, including to request any information the Board deems necessary to properly evaluate the applicant (§4207).  The applicant for any type of license must be notified in writing of its denial; within ten days thereafter the applicant may petition the Board and a hearing process concerning the propriety of the denial will follow (§4310).  The application review process is discussed in more detail in Chapter XIII: The Board of Pharmacy and Other Agencies.

Licenses, once issued, must be periodically renewed (see §§4401-4403).  The Board may refuse to renew any license, other than that of a pharmacist, which is not renewed within 60 days of its expiration (§4402(e)).  A pharmacist's license may not be renewed, restored, or reinstated and shall be cancelled by the Board if it is not renewed within three years following its expiration date (§4402(a)). If a pharmacist's license is cancelled for nonrenewal, he or she must reapply, retake and pass the licensure examination (§4402(b)(1)), and meet any other conditions the Board may impose to restore the license (§4402(b)(2)).

# The Pharmacist

## *Criteria for Licensure*

The most important license to the pharmacy student, of course, is that which makes him or her a "pharmacist."[3]  Under California law the requirements are straightforward: the applicant must be at least 18 years of age and have completed the prescribed course of study, satisfactorily completed the internship, and passed the licensure examination (§4200).

For most students, completion of all requirements for graduation from a school of pharmacy accredited by the American Council on Pharmaceutical Education (ACPE)[4] or recognized by the Board is the path to the licensure exam (§4200(a)(2)(A), §1719(a)).  The law also requires all

---

[2]  All California agencies are mandated to process applications for licenses and permits of all sorts in a timely fashion. Practically speaking, a court is highly unlikely ever to order the issuance of a license, but when it finds agency action unreasonably delayed it may well order the agency to act on the application and impose costs of filing suit.  The Pharmacy Board has adopted a regulation, section 1706.1, in which it has committed itself to certain maximum processing times for the various licenses it grants

[3]  The pharmacy student formerly wished to become a "registered pharmacist."  "Registered pharmacist" was both a traditional and a legal term describing a person who had been issued a pharmacist's license; that term has been eliminated from the law.  A person may be educated as a pharmacist, and may be licensed by another state or country, but only someone who holds a current California license is a "pharmacist" within the meaning of the Pharmacy Law (§4036).

[4]  Graduation from a school of pharmacy given candidate status by ACPE will be acceptable if the Board adopts a regulation proposed in November 2004.

applicants to have completed 150 semester units of collegiate study, or about five years, at least 90 units of which must have been in a school or college of pharmacy, and to have earned at least a baccalaureate degree in a course of study devoted to the practice of pharmacy (§4200(a)(3),(4)). Beginning in 2005, graduates of foreign pharmacy schools must be certified by the Foreign Pharmacy Graduate Examination Committee of the National Association of Boards of Pharmacy to be eligible for licensure (§4200(a)(2)(B), §1720.1 (amendments proposed November 2004 to conform to new statute)).

Any statement or representation an applicant makes as part of the application process must be as accurate as possible.  Making false representations or committing fraud to obtain a license is a crime (§4322); knowingly making a false statement required to be revealed in the application for licensure is a ground for denial of the application (B&PC §480(c)).

To comply with federal law that limits the eligibility of aliens for certain public benefits, including occupational licensure, the Board must not issue or reissue a license to anyone who cannot establish legal residency in the United States.

## The Internship

The internship requirement mandates that each applicant have 1,500 hours of pharmaceutical experience (§§4200(a)(5), 4209) in compliance with regulations adopted by the Board or the Standards of Curriculum established by the ACPE.  The internship must include at least 900 hours in a pharmacy (§1728).  The law now requires that applicants for licensure have completed 1,500 internship hours before applying to take the examination (§4209(a)).

Prospective interns first must obtain an intern card from the Pharmacy Board.  Under a statute new in 2005, intern cards are issued for one to six years for current pharmacy students, two years to pharmacy graduates who have applied to become licensed in California (including foreign graduates who have met the educational requirements for licensure), and for one year to pharmacy graduates who have failed the licensure examination four times and have reenrolled in a school of pharmacy to satisfy the educational requirements to retake the exam (§4208).  An intern who is no longer enrolled in a school of pharmacy must return his or her intern license to the Board within 30 days (§4208(d)).

Interns may perform all acts pertaining to the practice of pharmacy, in accordance with Board regulations, including acts restricted by law to a pharmacist, as long as they are done "under the supervision of a pharmacist" whose license is in good standing with the Board.  A law change effective in 2005 allows the pharmacist to supervise two interns, rather than only one (§4114).  The supervising pharmacist is obliged to provide the experience necessary for an intern to become proficient in the practice of pharmacy (§1726(b)).

New law also clarifies that an applicant for California licensure who has been licensed as a pharmacist in any state for at least one year, as certified by that state's licensing agency, may submit that certification in satisfaction of the internship requirement (§4209(c)).

The Board proposed, in November 2004, to eliminate all regulatory references to preceptors; interns could be supervised by any pharmacist whose license was in good standing (§4114(a)).  Since a pharmacist did not need a separate license to be a preceptor, the impending change is of little consequence.  The supervising pharmacist, like the preceptor, will be responsible for all professional activities performed by the intern under his or her supervision (proposed §1726(a)).  Misconduct by an intern remains grounds to revoke the authority to be an intern and to deny a subsequent application to become licensed as a pharmacist.

Although there is little mandated structure to the internship, there are some areas of experience that are prerequisite to licensure. All applicants must demonstrate experience in both community and institutional pharmacy practice settings. The regulations currently in effect mandate experience of the following types:

- receiving and interpreting the prescription,
- patient medication profiles,
- prescription preparation,
- consultation,
- record-keeping,
- over-the-counter (OTC) products, and
- drug information (§1728(b)).

Proposed regulations would substitute for these detailed requirements that the intern receive "[p]harmacy practice experience that satisfies the requirements for both introductory and advanced pharmacy practice experiences established by the Accreditation Council for Pharmacy Education" (proposed §1728(a)(1)(D)).[5]

At the Board's discretion, an applicant may be granted up to 600 intern hours for other types of experience that substantially relate to the practice of pharmacy (current §1728(a)(2),(3), proposed §1728(a)(1)(B)).[6] It appears that the internship still must be served under the supervision of a pharmacist rather than another category of professional, whatever the setting (§4209(b)). The Board has also proposed to eliminate the 250-hour limitation on intern hours during the first year of pharmacy school that could only be earned in a school-sponsored program (§1728(a)(1)).

### How closely must a pharmacist supervise the intern's work?

Neither the Pharmacy Law nor Board regulations provide more specificity than the requirement of "supervision." However, as discussed below, the law provides for "direct supervision and control" of technicians by pharmacists, and in many settings requires the technician to work within view of the pharmacist. This contrast suggests that the level of supervision of an intern is within the discretion of the pharmacist, who should use judgment based upon the intern's experience, demonstrated skills, and competence, and the nature and complexity of the acts being performed. The pharmacist should be motivated to supervise interns with care because the pharmacist as well as the intern will be responsible for any errors made by the intern.

**Suppose you are working as an intern in a very busy pharmacy. Your supervising pharmacist, who has been filling prescriptions next to you, decides to leave the pharmacy for a little while to buy some lunch. There is another pharmacist and one other intern working in the pharmacy. Before leaving, your supervisor reviews the next eight prescriptions in your pile; all are clearly written and for standard dosages of common medications. The expectation is that you will work on filling those prescriptions during your supervisor's absence. Is it legal to do so?**

---

[5] Unless otherwise stated, "proposed" regulations are proposals that were pending, but not finally adopted, at the time of publication.

[6] The Board has long granted intern hours for experience outside the pharmacy setting, although the Pharmacy Law itself seemed to require that internships be served in a pharmacy. Amendments effective in 2005 have removed that apparent conflict.

The law requires supervision of the intern by the pharmacist. Under new law effective in 2005, a pharmacist may supervise two interns. When one pharmacist leaves the pharmacy, the other pharmacist may legally supervise both interns. However, the fact that the ratio is not exceeded is not the only test; the other pharmacist must actually engage in supervising the intern whose primary supervisor has left for lunch.

**You are an intern in a pharmacy where technicians are employed. You check the work of the technician. Your supervising pharmacist checks some, but not all, of those prescriptions. Is this legal?**

An intern may, under the supervision of a pharmacist, perform any function of a pharmacist, which would include checking an order prepared by a pharmacy technician (§4114, §1727(e)). A pharmacy technician may perform packaging, manipulative, repetitive, or other nondiscretionary tasks only while assisting and under the direct supervision and control of a pharmacist (§4115(a)). Reconciling these provisions, what is required is sufficient supervision of the intern by the pharmacist.

"Supervision" does not necessarily require that every prescription dispensed by an intern be physically reviewed, even where the intern has reviewed the technician's work. While an intern must work under the supervision of a pharmacist, a technician must work under the *direct supervision and control* (§4115(a),(f)) or the *immediate, personal supervision and control* of the pharmacist (§4115(f)). In other words, the level of supervision required of an intern is more general than that required of a technician. The pharmacist must ensure that the intern is doing work properly and professionally, and receiving the training that the internship is intended to provide. The pharmacist should exercise professional judgment about the level of supervision a particular intern needs when that intern is checking the work of a technician.

**Suppose you work full-time as an intern at a community pharmacy after taking the licensure examination. For two hours of each eight-hour shift you are assigned to work the cash register at the front of the pharmacy. An occasional prescription sale is rung up there; most sales at this register are of OTC drugs, cosmetics, and sundries. Are those reportable internship hours? Suppose a pharmacist employed by a life sciences research corporation offers you the opportunity to be her intern. Are those reportable internship hours?**

Under new law and proposed Board regulations, the type of pharmacy practice experience that qualifies for internship credit is that which satisfies requirements for pharmacy practice experiences established by the ACPE. Performing purely retail functions not requiring the skills and knowledge of a pharmacist, other than as an incidental part of pharmacy practice, is unlikely to meet those standards. The position with a research corporation, depending upon the functions you perform, could be reportable as internship hours counting toward the maximum of 600 hours of credit for work "substantially related" to the practice of pharmacy.

## *"Character" Requirements*

In order to protect the public, the Board may deny a license to a prospective pharmacist or a permit to any applicant who has been convicted of a crime or done any act involving dishonesty, fraud, or deceit, if the crime or act is substantially related to the qualifications, functions, or duties of the pharmacy profession (B&PC §480(a)). A crime or act is "substantially related" to the practice of pharmacy "if to a substantial degree it evidences present or potential unfitness of a licensee or registrant to perform the functions authorized by his license or registration in a manner consistent with the public health, safety, or welfare" (§1770).

**Should a convicted bank robber be allowed to be a pharmacist or own a pharmacy? What about an embezzler? An arsonist? A sex offender? Someone convicted of assault with a deadly weapon? Someone convicted of a drug-related crime? (Does it matter what drug is involved?) What about multiple convictions for driving under the influence of alcohol? Which of these convictions are "substantially related" to the practice of pharmacy?**

There are no published guidelines on this subject beyond the Board's regulation, quoted above, and no published judicial decisions involving the Board of Pharmacy. There are court cases on the meaning of "substantially related" in licensure cases involving other professions that the Board uses to guide its decisions (see Chap. XII: Practice Pitfalls).

Even applicants who have been convicted of a substantially related crime may be eligible for licensure if they demonstrate rehabilitation (B&PC §480(b)) and if public protection can be assured (§4313). The Board has specific criteria for determining whether rehabilitation has been established (§1769(a)). The Board also may choose to issue a probationary license, subject to appropriate probationary conditions, to any applicant for licensure who is guilty of unprofessional conduct (§4300(c), B&PC §488).

An applicant for any license must report to the Board, on his or her application, all criminal convictions, other than minor traffic offenses. Criminal convictions that have been set aside or expunged under Penal Code section 1203.4 nevertheless must be reported to the Board and any other local or state agency in response to a direct question on a licensure application.

Note that it is a misdemeanor for any person to make false representations on his own or another's behalf to become licensed as a pharmacist or for a non-licensed person to hold himself or herself out to be a pharmacist (§4322). A license may be denied if an applicant knowingly makes a false statement of any fact required on a licensure application (B&PC §480(c)). A license may also be denied for any act that, if done by a licensee, would be grounds for suspension or revocation of that license (B&PC §480(a)(3)).

## The Pharmacist Licensure Exam

California adopted the North American Pharmacist Licensure Examination (NAPLEX), used by virtually all other states, in 2004.[7] In addition, California requires applicants to pass the Board's own test, called the California Pharmacist Jurisprudence Examination (CPJE) (§4200(a)(6)). Both examinations may be taken on computers at test centers open six days a week all year. An applicant must pass both examinations to be licensed. Information about the examinations is available at the Board's website (www.pharmacy.ca.gov/naplex_info.htm). An exam handbook, sample questions, and a content outline are available to explain the new CPJE. Although the CPJE is styled a "jurisprudence" exam, the Legislature specifically authorized the Board to include questions pertaining to clinical aspects of the practice of pharmacy (§4200.2), and the content outline makes it evident that the Board intends to do so. The content outline for the CPJE, with references to the pages of this text and to materials available on the Board's website that cover each subject, may be found in Appendix A.

It is a crime to subvert the security of the licensure examination in any way (B&PC §123), and of course such conduct is grounds for disqualification from the examination (§1723.1) and denial of licensure (B&PC §496). In addition to the obvious behaviors that constitute cheating, subversion of

---

[7] Information about NAPLEX is available at the National Association of Boards of Pharmacy (NABP) website, http://www.nabp.net/.

the examination process includes aiding the unauthorized reproduction of any portion of the licensure examination and paying to reconstruct portions of the examination, for such purposes as preparing students to take the examination (B&PC §123). The Board's regulation adds that conveying or exposing all or part of an examination to any other person, with or without compensation, or removing all or part of the qualifying examination from an examination room or area, may disqualify an applicant from licensure (§1723.1) An applicant for examination who engages in dishonest conduct during the examination will not have his or her examination graded, will not be approved to take the examination for twelve months from the incident, and will have to surrender his or her intern card until he or she is again eligible to take the examination. The applicant also may not obtain a pharmacy technician license until he or she is again eligible to take the examination (§1721).

A candidate who fails to pass the licensure examination in four attempts may not retake it until successful completion of 16 additional semester units of pharmacy education in an ACPE-accredited or Board-approved pharmacy school (§4200.1, §1725). To count toward these units, each course must require a final examination (§1725). While the grading of individual licensure examinations is not subject to review by the Department of Consumer Affairs, the Department may investigate allegations of misconduct or violations of criminal law in the examination process (B&PC §109). For a fee, the Board will regrade the CPJE at the applicant's request. Although some appeals to licensure boards concerning individual examinations have been successful, courts are generally wary about becoming involved unless a violation of protected rights is alleged.

**Are review or refresher courses for the licensure examinations legal? May the instructor discuss questions that were on a prior examination? May the instructor ask students to remember questions from the examination and report about them to the instructor?**

Examination security and confidentiality and security of examination questions are further discussed in Chap. XII: Practice Pitfalls. There is nothing illegal about refresher or review courses for the examinations. However, the instructor should not have questions from a prior examination unless they were released by the Board or discussed by someone who took a prior examination. Requesting or soliciting questions from a prior or future examination, especially for compensation, is subversion of the examination process and a violation of law, just as is conveying that information to the solicitor of it (B&PC §123).

## *Recognition of Out-of-State Licensure (Reciprocity)*

A California pharmacist's license only authorizes its holder to practice within the State of California. Some states have agreements to grant licenses to each other's licensees without further examination or investigation. California does not currently participate in any such reciprocal arrangement. It has not had reciprocity with other states in large part because it did not use the NAPLEX examination, used by nearly all states. If you wish to practice pharmacy in any other jurisdiction, you must consult that jurisdiction's pharmacy regulators about practice requirements. New California pharmacists who have passed NAPLEX are likely not to have to retake that examination for licensure elsewhere.

Additional legislation would be necessary for California to adopt reciprocity. At the present time, applicants who have passed the NAPLEX prior to 2004 for licensure elsewhere must retake NAPLEX for California licensure. All applicants also need to pass the CPJE. It remains to be seen what position California will take in respect to implementing the requirements of the North American Free Trade Agreement (NAFTA) that provide for a measure of professional mobility internationally, among the United States, Canada, and Mexico.

## *Licensure Fees*

There is a $155 fee to apply for pharmacist registration; the biennial renewal fee is $115 (§4200(c), §1749(d),(f),(g)). There are additional costs to take NAPLEX and the CPJE, and for out-of-state applicants for fingerprint analysis.

The Board of Pharmacy, like the administrative agencies governing other licensed occupations and professions in California, is funded almost entirely by the fees it is allowed by statute to collect from those it regulates (§§4400, 4407). Current fees set by Board regulation are in sections 1749 and 1750. These fees, rather than general funds collected by state taxation and other revenue sources, pay for the licensure, examination, investigation, and discipline functions of the Board. When the costs of regulating the profession increase, the fees borne by holders of licenses must be increased to meet them. Some efforts have been made in recent years to shift the very substantial costs of investigating and taking regulatory action against wrongdoers to them, through administrative fines and cost recovery (B&PC §§125.3, 125.9; also see Chap. XIII: Board of Pharmacy).

## *Unauthorized Practice of Pharmacy*

Leaving nothing to chance or interpretation, the law makes abundantly clear that the practice of pharmacy is limited in California to the licensed pharmacist. One statutory section makes it "unlawful for any person to manufacture, compound, sell, or dispense any dangerous drug or device . . . unless he or she is a pharmacist" (§4051(a)). Another makes it a misdemeanor if any person who is not a pharmacist "takes charge of or acts as manager of any pharmacy or . . . compounds or dispenses a prescription or furnishes dangerous drugs" (§4329). The law authorizes exceptions from these broad proscriptions (for manufacturers, wholesalers, hypodermic dealers, and veterinary food-animal drug retailers) in circumstances where the public health and safety can be adequately protected through less restrictive means, as detailed in Chapter V: Other Pharmacy Board Licensees.

In recent years unauthorized, and thus illegal, sales of prescription drugs have been increasing at swap meets, flea markets, unlicensed store front clinics, and some small retail outlets. The small criminal penalties for violations did not justify the use of limited Board resources for this problem, even though the activity is patently illegal. Calling these illegal sales "a significant threat to the health, safety, and welfare" of Californians, the Legislature enhanced the penalties several years ago (H&SC § 11352.1), and both state and local officials have recently increased enforcement actions.

Although there are many legitimate pharmacy websites, considerable Internet commerce in prescription drugs is properly described as the unauthorized practice of pharmacy; that problem is discussed in Chapter X: The Prescription Process: Dispensing and Beyond.

## *Responsibilities After Licensure*

**In General.** The pharmacist's primary responsibility after licensure, of course, is to act as a careful, ethical, and informed professional at all times. Every applicant for any license issued by the Board must acknowledge that he or she has read and will follow the rules of professional conduct adopted by the Board (§4206).

The law mandates additional, specific responsibilities. Fees must be timely paid for biennial pharmacist license renewal (§4401). Pharmacists must report changes of their name or address to the Board within 30 days (§4100, §1704); similar requirements apply to technicians, exemptees, and interns.

A pharmacist who no longer wishes to practice pharmacy but wants to maintain a license may choose inactive license status. The fee requirements remain the same, but continuing education is not required (B&PC §462). To restore an inactive license to active status, the pharmacist must pay the renewal fees and complete 30 hours of continuing education (B&PC §704). A pharmacist in good standing may also choose to obtain a retired license, for which there is a one-time fee. A pharmacist with a retired license may not practice pharmacy. To return to active status a retired pharmacist must retake and pass the licensure exam (§4200.5).

**Knowledge of Laws and Regulations.** It is the responsibility of every pharmacist to know the federal and state laws and regulations governing his or her practice. A pharmacist who fails to comply with any law governing pharmacy or engages in unprofessional conduct may be disciplined, and is subject to the revocation of his or her license to practice pharmacy (§§4300-4301). Indirect as well as direct violations, conspiracies to commit violations, and aiding or abetting violations by others all subject the pharmacist to risk. A pharmacist serving as the pharmacist-in-charge may also be responsible for violations by others (§ 4113(b)). Unprofessional conduct and discipline are explored at length in Chapter XII, Practice Pitfalls, in which the serious civil, monetary, disciplinary, and criminal consequences for failure to follow the law are outlined.

Pharmacists are expected to comply with the requirements of laws and regulations. If there is a conflict between what the law, regulations, or professional standards dictate and what a pharmacist is asked or directed by another to do, the pharmacist has a clear obligation to follow the law. The only exception would be a true case of immediate medical necessity; such situations are rare, and it would be the pharmacist's burden to demonstrate that the facts supported the pharmacist's conclusion that there was a necessity.

Fortunately most pharmacists are motivated to follow the law by common sense, self-respect, a fundamental sense of morality, and a good work ethic. The responsibility to know what the law requires is an ongoing one, as laws and regulations frequently change.

**Responsibility to Prevent Theft, Fraud, and Drug Diversion.** Pharmacists are legal caretakers of stocks of drugs that, in addition to their importance medically, are highly valued for criminal use. Thus pharmacists have a special responsibility to prevent theft, fraud, and drug diversion. Pharmacists may not engage, under the guise of practicing pharmacy, in the diversion of drugs or fill prescriptions that they know or ought to know are not for a legitimate purpose (§4301(d), §1761(b), H&SC §11153, 21 CFR §1306.04(a); see Chap. XII: Practice Pitfalls). This responsibility involves more than the avoidance of intentional misconduct; it includes exercising due diligence in evaluating the validity of prescriptions before filling them (§1761(b); see *United States v. Kershman*, 555 F.2d 198 (8th Cir. 1977)).

While drug diversion generally calls to mind controlled substances, there is also a substantial black market for prescription drugs that are not controlled substances, such as antibiotics. Although less stringent prescription requirements apply to these drugs, the obligation remains the same: to remain vigilant and not fill prescriptions that the pharmacist knows, or ought to know, are not for a legitimate purpose. That the purchasers want to send drugs overseas for what appear to be medical reasons does not make such transactions legal.

The pharmacist's attention and concern also must be directed to prescriptions of uncertain legitimacy, to the risk of counterfeit drugs, and to drugs sold as being of one strength when they are weaker or have been diluted.

**Responsibility for Other Personnel.** Pharmacists frequently work in settings where they are responsible for the supervision and control of interns (§4114), technicians (§4115(f), §§1793-1793.2), other pharmacists, and unlicensed personnel (§4116(a), §1793.3).  The pharmacist, especially a pharmacist-in-charge, is generally responsible for ensuring that unlicensed persons are not improperly on the licensed premises in the absence of a pharmacist and that interns, technicians, and other nonpharmacists are properly supervised and not performing tasks beyond their legal authority or their individual capability.

Each pharmacist who supervises interns, technicians, or technician trainees in any setting must be sure that the supervision is adequate to meet the requirements of the law and to assure safe practice.  Legal requirements for that supervision are discussed elsewhere in this chapter.

Pharmacists employed in health care settings other than pharmacies may have responsibility for supervising or generally overseeing the conduct of personnel such as nurses or other health care aides who may be handling drugs, as discussed in Chapter VI: Scope of Practice for Pharmacists.

**Continuing Education.**  To be a careful, ethical, and informed professional, a pharmacist must keep abreast of current developments affecting the practice of pharmacy.  To encourage pharmacists to consider a lifetime of learning as their professional responsibility, the Legislature has mandated continuing education.  Each pharmacist is required to complete 30 clock hours of approved continuing pharmaceutical education in each two-year renewal cycle (other than the first two-year period following graduation from pharmacy school), and to retain course completion certificates for four years (§4231, §1732.5(a),(b)).  The only exceptions to the fulfillment of the continuing education requirement are in cases of demonstrable emergency or hardship, such as illness or full-time enrollment at a health professional school.  An exception may be sought by written application to the Board (§4234, §1732.6).

Approved continuing education course work is available in a wide variety of formats and on a broad spectrum of subjects.  To satisfy the requirement, course work must be relevant to the practice of pharmacy and related to the scientific knowledge or technical skills required for the practice of pharmacy, to direct or indirect patient care, or to the specific management and operation of a pharmacy practice.  All continuing education course work must be:

- accurate and timely;
- presented in an orderly fashion conducive to the learning process;
- complete and objective, and not reflecting predominantly the commercial views of the provider or of anyone giving financial assistance to the provider;
- specifically applicable and pertinent to the practice of pharmacy; and
- based on stated educational goals and objectives (§1732.1(c)).

Anyone who wants to provide continuing education courses for California pharmacists first must seek recognition as a provider and must comply with various requirements designed, among other things, to assure at least the minimum educational quality of the course work offered.  The Board will now accept courses that have been approved by the Medical Board of California, the Board of Dental Examiners, the Board of Podiatric Medicine, or the Board of Registered Nursing.  In addition, pharmacists who attend a full-day Board meeting are eligible for six hours of continuing education credit (see www.pharmacy.ca.gov/about/earn_ce.htm).  The Board's extensive regulations on the subject of continuing education are found in sections 1732 to 1732.7; the Board recently proposed amendments to the regulations that appear to be of greater significance to CE providers than to pharmacists.

# The Pharmacy Technician

## *History and Background*

People have acted as pharmacy technicians for many years, but regulation of this category of personnel was not adopted by the Legislature until 1991. Before that time there was tacit acceptance of pharmacy technicians performing drug dispensing[8] functions in hospital pharmacies, but technicians were strictly forbidden in community pharmacies. When the Pharmacy Board first initiated proposals to require patient consultation more than 20 years ago, discussions about technicians increased in significance. It was thought that the full training and education of the pharmacist should be employed in the service of patients, especially out front at the pharmacy counter, and that ancillary personnel could be entrusted, as they had long been in hospitals, with counting and pouring under the pharmacist's supervision. Because of the major economic impacts on the profession both of required consultation and of licensing technicians, and public health and safety concerns about increasing non-pharmacist involvement in the dispensing process, the debate took considerable time to resolve.

Patient consultation now is mandatory for most new prescriptions for most outpatients (§1707.2, see Chap. X: Dispensing and Beyond),[9] and a technician statute and regulations are in place.[10] Section 4038 defines a pharmacy technician as an individual who assists a pharmacist in a pharmacy in the performance of his or her pharmacy-related duties. Section 4115 is quite specific about the duties that may be delegated to the technician and about the level of required supervision. To implement the statute, the Board has issued detailed regulations (§§1793-1793.7).

## *Registration Requirements*

There are multiple pathways to becoming a technician. All applicants must now have a high school degree or equivalent (GED) (§4202(a)). Applicants also must have earned an associate of arts degree in pharmacy technology (§4202 (a)(1)), *or* successfully completed a training course specified by the Board (§4202(a)(2), §1793.6), *or* be eligible to take the California pharmacist licensure examination (§4202(a)(3)), *or* be certified by the Pharmacy Technician Certification Board (§4202(a)(4)). The Board must do a criminal background check on each applicant (§4202(c)).

Within 30 days, applicants must be notified of any deficiencies in their applications and how to correct them; the Board must notify applicants of the decision within 60 days after an application is

---

[8]  "Dispense" (or "dispensing") can have several meanings, depending on how it is being used. In general, dispensing refers to the processing of an order for a drug or device, from receipt of the order to delivery to the patient or patient's agent. But it also can mean the act of providing the completed, packaged order to the patient; it also can refer to the act of a physician or other prescriber who provides drugs for take-home use to a patient from stock maintained by the prescriber. Section 4024 addresses the multiple uses of the word "dispense." Chapter X: The Prescription Process: Dispensing and Beyond covers the most common use of "dispensing," the entire processing of an order from receipt to delivery.

[9]  The patient consultation requirement is a regulation, not a statute. However, the Legislature's tacit recognition and approval of the requirement are reflected in the law governing registration of nonresident pharmacies (see Chap IV: Licensing Pharmacies), which requires that any rules on consultation be equivalent for resident and nonresident pharmacies. Patient consultation also is consistent with section 4074, which mandates drug warnings to patients. Furthermore, federal law now demands, for participation in the Medicaid program, that each state adopt a drug use review program for outpatient drugs to assure that prescriptions are appropriate, medically necessary, and not likely to result in adverse medical outcomes (42 USC §1396r-8(g)(1)). This requirement encompasses both oral consultation and maintenance of patient profiles, among other patient services (42 CFR §456.705(c),(d)).

[10]  A legal challenge to the validity of the technician regulations was rejected by the courts *(Californians for Safe Prescriptions v. California State Board of Pharmacy,* 19 Cal. App. 4th 1136 (2d Dist. 1993)).

complete (§1793.5(c)). The registration fee and the biennial renewal fee are $50 (§1749(c)). There are no continuing education requirements for technicians.

Technicians working in state correctional institutions or facilities operated by California's Departments of Mental Health, Developmental Services, or Veterans Affairs are exempt from registration requirements until they have worked for a year at any one facility (§4115(e)(2)).

**Suppose one of the two technicians in a community pharmacy, although adequately trained, is not registered as a technician with the Board.**

That technician, no matter how capable, may not be employed to do the work of a pharmacy technician in a community pharmacy. The only exception would be for a technician working solely on prescriptions for inmates of correctional facilities, and only during that employee's first year of employment as a technician filling inmate prescriptions.

## *Functions*

The technician may perform "packaging, manipulative, repetitive, or other nondiscretionary tasks" but "only while assisting, and while under the direct supervision and control" of a pharmacist (§4115(a)). Nondiscretionary tasks that a technician may perform include:

- removing the drug or drugs from stock;
- counting, pouring, or mixing pharmaceuticals;
- placing the product into a container;
- affixing the label or labels to the container; and
- packaging and repacking (§1793.2).

Specifically forbidden to the technician is the performance of any act "requiring the exercise of professional judgment by a pharmacist" (§4115(c), see Chap. VI: Scope of Practice). These requirements apply equally to community and hospital pharmacies.

Pharmacy technicians must wear identification clearly identifying them as technicians, and pharmacies must have written policies and procedures and job descriptions adequate to ensure that their personnel comply with the technician law. The pharmacy must maintain for three years records that establish that it is complying with this law (§1793.7(c),(d)). Even a pharmacy that employs a single pharmacy technician must describe in writing the respective roles of technician and pharmacist, ascertain that its personnel understand the job descriptions, and maintain notes that indicate how and when its personnel were trained in this regard.

**May a pharmacy technician participate in the compounding of prescriptions?**

"Mixing pharmaceuticals" would seem to be broad enough to encompass some compounding under a pharmacist's supervision and control, and neither section 4115 nor the technician regulations, sections 1793 to 1793.7, limit the technician to the dispensing of individual prescriptions, as opposed to other pharmacy tasks. However, if the actions in the compounding process are at all sophisticated, and involve judgment, discretion, or pharmaceutical or pharmacological training, they would appear not to be the type of tasks authorized by the technician law and regulations.

**May a technician fill or dispense a prescription for a controlled substance?**

Effective in 2005, section 11207 of the Health and Safety Code has been amended to acknowledge that a technician, under the supervision of a pharmacist, may perform the same tasks with respect to controlled substance prescriptions as with all others.

# Responsibility of Pharmacy and Pharmacist for Technicians

Both the pharmacy and the pharmacist have responsibilities with respect to technicians. The pharmacy must, under regulations effective in October 2004, develop a job description for the technician and written policies and procedures adequate to assure that the pharmacy is in compliance with laws and regulations governing technicians; records to establish compliance with these rules must be maintained for three years (§1793.7(d)). The pharmacist is responsible for the work of the technician under his or her supervision. The technician's tasks must not allow for the exercise of discretion that would in any way change a prescription order. A technician engaged in compounding therefore cannot make any changes in process, amounts, formulation, or packaging; or be entrusted with any sophisticated actions requiring the expertise of a pharmacist. The pharmacist must assure that his or her instructions to the technician are clear and complete, and that the technician's activities are "performed completely, safely and without risk of harm to patients" (§1793.7(e)).

The pharmacist is required to verify and document in writing functions performed by technicians in connection with prescription dispensing. Except in the hospital inpatient or correctional facility settings, that verification must be made by initialing the prescription label before the medication is provided to the patient (§1793.7(a)) or by other verification procedures that the Board might adopt by regulation. Although the Board has sought legislation to change the law, it remains illegal for a technician, rather than a pharmacist, to verify the work of another technician ("tech-check-tech") in any setting in lieu of the pharmacist doing so (§1793.1(f)).[11]

The supervision requirements for technicians are somewhat different for persons employed to assist in filling prescriptions for inpatients of hospitals and inmates of correctional facilities than they are for all other technicians. *All* technicians must work under the direct supervision and control of a pharmacist (§4115(a)) who must be on duty (§4115(b)). Except when the technician is filling prescriptions for hospital inpatients or correctional facility inmates, the supervising pharmacist must also be on the premises.[12] Technicians must work in a relationship in which the pharmacist is fully aware of all activities involved in the preparation and dispensing of medications, including the maintenance of appropriate records (§1793.7(b)). Technicians filling prescriptions for patients other than hospital inpatients and inmates must work "only under the immediate, personal supervision and control" of the pharmacist and within his or her view (§4115(f)). The pharmacist need not actually

---

[11] In 1995, after proposing but not adopting amendments to the technician regulations that would have allowed technicians to check the work of other technicians in general acute care hospitals, the Board established a committee to review and propose modifications of the technician regulations. An experimental program to evaluate the use of "tech-check-tech" for unit dose medications in hospital settings was approved by the Board in 1998. The final committee report, in January 2001, showed that the technician "checkers" provided a slightly better rate of accuracy than the pharmacists. The study authors also found a dramatically increased (almost tripled) usage of pharmacists by prescribers for clinical drug therapy management activities in the three-year period of the study, making the freeing of pharmacist time more critical. The pharmacist would remain responsible for prescriptions prepared and checked only by technicians. Following its receipt of this report, the Board has voted repeatedly to allow the study protocol to continue (the latest extension was until December 2004), and it has supported legislation to authorize "tech-check-tech" in the settings and under the circumstances in the study.

[12] Since the pharmacist also must be fully aware of the activities the technician is performing, it is hard to imagine circumstances where the distinction between "on duty" and "on the premises" would make a meaningful difference.

watch every act the technician undertakes, but the technician must work where the supervising pharmacist is able to observe whatever the technician is doing.

The supervision regulations do not address every conceivable situation that might arise when a technician works with a pharmacist. It seems unlikely that it would be considered a violation of the regulations for a technician to continue working while the supervising pharmacist is using the restroom. However, the technician should not work during the pharmacist's lunch hour, except in strict conformance with the Board's temporary absence regulations (§1714.1, see Chap. XIV: Other Relevant Law).[13] If a pharmacy has two technicians and two pharmacists and one of the two pharmacists is absent, as opposed to elsewhere on the pharmacy premises, only one technician may work as a technician, except if both are filling prescriptions for inpatients of licensed health facilities, patients of a licensed home health agency, inmates of correctional facilities, or persons receiving treatment in various state-operated facilities (§1793.7(f)).

**If there are two pharmacists and two technicians on duty, must each technician be working within view of the particular pharmacist responsible for that technician's supervision? Or is it sufficient if the technician is working within view of either pharmacist on duty (such as when one pharmacist is in a stock room and cannot view the work of the technician)?**

The language of the law appears to require that each technician work within the view of his or her pharmacist supervisor. However, the Board takes a more practical and reasonable approach: as long as the pharmacy's operations are otherwise in compliance with law, both technicians may continue working as technicians if at least one of the two pharmacists has both in view at all times.[14]

## Ratios

A major issue in the technician debate has been how many technicians any one pharmacist would be allowed to supervise. Not surprisingly, pharmacists pressed for no more than one technician per on-duty pharmacist. Pharmacy owners supported higher ratios of technicians to pharmacists. Currently the ratio in community pharmacies is one technician if there is only one pharmacist on duty; two technicians are allowed for each additional pharmacist on duty. Thus, where there is a single pharmacist on duty, one technician is the maximum; where there are two pharmacists, three technicians are allowed; with three pharmacists working, five technicians will be allowed (§4115(g)(1)). These ratios are subject to the right of the pharmacist asked to supervise more than one technician to object, as discussed below.

The Board, by regulation, may establish ratios for licensed health facilities and home health agencies, as long as those regulations allow at least as many technicians as the statute allows for community pharmacies (§4115(g)(2)). At the present time the Board's regulations establish a maximum ratio of two technicians to one pharmacist in those practice settings (§1793.7(f)). The law continues to set no limit on the number of technicians a pharmacist may supervise when filling prescriptions for inmates of correctional facilities or persons receiving treatment in facilities operated by the State Departments of Mental Health, Developmental Services, or Veterans Affairs

---

[13] The statute authorizing the temporary absence of a pharmacist for breaks and lunch periods provides that the technician "may, at the discretion of the pharmacist, remain in the pharmacy but may only perform nondiscretionary tasks" (§4115(h)). This language is ambiguous because, even in the presence of a pharmacist, technicians may only perform nondiscretionary tasks (§4115(a)).

[14] This interpretation was confirmed in a May 21, 2004, conversation with the Board's chief supervising inspector.

(§4115(g)(1)).[15]  If a pharmacy fills prescriptions for inmates as well as for a regular patient population, it must comply with the technician to pharmacist ratio for community pharmacies when filling prescriptions for its regular patients; the unlimited technician to pharmacist ratio applies solely to the filling of inmate prescriptions.  A pharmacy that fills prescriptions for different populations and multiple settings may use the ratio allowed for that population or setting, but not when filling prescriptions for its regular community pharmacy patients.

The law allowing pharmacists (except those working solo) to supervise two technicians in a community pharmacy provides that a pharmacist scheduled to supervise a second pharmacy technician may refuse to do so "if the pharmacist determines, in the exercise of his or her professional judgment, that permitting the second pharmacy technician to be on duty would interfere with the effective performance of the pharmacist's responsibilities."  The pharmacist assigned to supervise two technicians must notify the pharmacist-in-charge in writing of this determination, specifying his or her concerns, within a reasonable period, not to exceed 24 hours, after the posting of the relevant work schedule.  The pharmacist's timely notification is protected: "No entity employing a pharmacist may discharge, discipline, or otherwise discriminate against any pharmacist in the terms and conditions of employment for exercising or attempting to exercise in good faith [this] right" (§4115(g)(3)).  The effectiveness of this protection for pharmacists of course remains to be seen.

Ancillary personnel performing clerical functions, inventory control, housekeeping, maintenance, or similar functions for which the pharmacist's education, experience, training, and knowledge are not reasonably required are not technicians, and these ratios therefore do not apply to such personnel (§§4007(b), 4115(g)(1)).  A recent regulatory change has removed the limit that each pharmacist on duty could supervise only one nonlicensed clerical employee performing the tasks of typing prescription labels, entering prescription information into computerized record systems, or requesting and receiving refill authorization.  The new regulation allows a pharmacist to supervise as many non-licensed personnel engaged in these tasks as the pharmacist determines "does not interfere with the effective performance" of his or her responsibilities (§1793.3(b)).  Like the protection noted above for pharmacists asked to supervise two technicians, a pharmacist may refuse to supervise the number of non-licensed personnel scheduled by the pharmacy by notifying the pharmacist-in-charge of his or her specific concerns within 24 hours after the posting of the schedule; the pharmacy may not penalize any pharmacist who in good faith exercises this right (§1793.3(c),(d)).  The responsibility for the accuracy of the prescription information and the prescription as dispensed remains with the pharmacist who initials the prescription or prescription record (§1793.3).

In addition to any technicians supervised by the pharmacist, a pharmacist may simultaneously supervise two pharmacy interns and any number of nonlicensed clerical employees.  And there also may be a technician trainee (discussed below).  So for every pharmacist on duty there could be multiple people other than technicians engaged in some aspect of prescription-filling: two interns, a technician trainee, and one or more clerks.  The first pharmacist may only supervise one technician, for a total of four ancillary personnel plus clerks; each additional pharmacist may supervise two technicians, for a total of five ancillary personnel plus clerks.  Furthermore, the pharmacist at the same time may also supervise an unlimited number of personnel who are not engaged in functions for which a pharmacist's knowledge is required (such as working the cash register or cleaning the premises).  However, no pharmacist should supervise or be responsible for more personnel than he or she actually can manage safely, even if that supervision is allowed by law.

---

[15] Dispensing in the settings where there are no limitations on the technician to pharmacist ratio is obviously no safer than elsewhere.  The Legislature continues to treat those settings, and prescriptions for inmates, differently to control the prescription costs that will be borne by the State of California.

**Suppose a community pharmacy has one pharmacist on duty plus two people who have been registered as technicians. One wears a badge designating him as a technician; the other is designated a pharmacy clerk. Is this legal?**

On its face this arrangement is legitimate, as long as the clerk trained and registered as a technician is truly functioning only as a clerk and not engaging in functions like counting and pouring for which you need to be a technician. If the pharmacy and pharmacist are taking advantage of the training of both employees as technicians, using them simultaneously as technicians, and the designation of the second as a clerk is a subterfuge, all licensees involved – the pharmacy, the pharmacist, and the technician – are responsible for the violation of the law. A pharmacy that switches the responsibilities of the two technicians back and forth during the course of a work shift is likely to be scrutinized very closely by the Board.

**Suppose a community pharmacy has two pharmacists on duty plus three people who have been registered as technicians, all working as technicians. Is this legal?**

If a second pharmacist is on duty, up to three licensed technicians may work for the two pharmacists. A pharmacy that adds a second pharmacist on a part-time basis may add up to two additional technicians, but only when that pharmacist is on duty.

A pharmacy with multiple pharmacists and multiple technicians and interns must take into account, when creating its work schedules, the need to maintain the legal ratios between the pharmacists and the technicians and interns.

**Suppose that both technicians working in a pharmacy are engaged in prescription-filling activities, although only one pharmacist is present. Half of the pharmacy's business is filling prescriptions for home health agencies. Is it in compliance with the law?**

Both technicians may engage in activities requiring registration as a technician under the supervision of a single pharmacist as long as they are filling home health agency prescriptions. However, if they are filling other prescriptions they, the supervising pharmacist, and the pharmacy are all in violation of the law. The ratio does not depend on the general type of pharmacy, but on the nature of the prescriptions being filled. The differing ratios of technicians to pharmacists depending upon the type of patient make personnel scheduling tricky; caution must be observed to avoid violating the law.

**A pharmacy in a federal Veterans Administration facility has five pharmacy technicians on duty for every pharmacist on duty. Does this violate California's ratio laws?**

A federal Veterans Administration pharmacy is generally not subject to licensure or control by the Board. Even though it is located within California, a federal facility (whether it is military, Veterans Administration, or a correctional facility) or a Native American reservation is considered federal land. It is not subject to state law unless it chooses to be licensed by the Board or seeks to serve California consumers other than those entitled by federal law to the pharmacy's services. While the ratio of technicians to pharmacists would violate California law, the pharmacy is not subject to California law.

## *Technician Trainees*

The technician trainee may perform an externship in a pharmacy while enrolled in a technician training program operated by an approved educational institution (§4115.5(a)).

The trainee must be under the immediate, personal supervision and control, and in the view, of a pharmacist, who must be on the premises (§4115.5(b)(1)). The supervising pharmacist is directly responsible for the trainee's conduct (§4115.5(b)(2)) and must verify each prescription prepared by the trainee by initialing its label before it is dispensed (§4115(b)(3)).

A pharmacist may supervise only one trainee at a time (§4115.5(b)(4)), in addition to whatever pharmacy technicians and interns are permitted under his or her supervision. The trainee must wear a badge identifying him or her as a student (§4115.5(e)).

The externship is limited to 120 hours in a community pharmacy (§4115.5(c)(1)). If the trainee also works at a hospital, the externship may last up to 320 hours, provided no more than 120 hours are served in any single department within the hospital pharmacy (§4115.5(c)(2)). The externship also cannot last more than six consecutive months (§4115.5(d)). The supervising pharmacist must certify both trainee attendance and compliance with the institution's educational objectives (§4115.5(b)(5)).

# Exemptees/Designated Representatives

Certain categories of businesses that handle drugs (such as wholesalers, veterinary food-animal drug retailers, and licensed laboratories) have long been exempt from the law's command that only pharmacists may lawfully manufacture, compound, sell, or dispense prescription drugs or devices (§§4051, 4053(a)). That exemption has been premised upon their employment of "sufficient, qualified supervision . . . to adequately safeguard and protect the public health" (§4053(a)), in the form of a Board-certified "exemptee." Without a qualified exemptee in place, these entities were required to employ a pharmacist. For many years the Board had an exemptee examination; that requirement was eliminated in 2002, but specific training requirements remain. A statute adopted in 2004 that becomes fully effective only in 2006 makes some changes in this regulatory scheme. Instead of exemptees, there will be "designated representatives" and "designated representatives-in-charge" (§4022.5), subject to a similar set of licensure requirements as now exist for exemptees (§4053).[16]

There is currently no examination for exemptees, but there are specific training requirements. The exemptee must be a high school graduate or equivalent (GED) and have a minimum of a year of paid work experience related to the distribution or dispensing of dangerous drugs or devices or have met all the requirements to take the pharmacy licensure examination (§4053(b)). The exemptee must have completed a training program approved by the Board that addresses a list of specific subjects, including knowledge of the laws concerning dangerous drugs and controlled substances, of quality control systems, of safe storage and handling of drugs, and of prescription terminology (§4053(b)(3)). The Board has the discretion to require training programs to include additional material (§4053(b)(4)). The pharmacist or exemptee must be present and in control of the premises during the conduct of business (§1781(a)); operations must cease if no such person is available. To assure that the company always has a qualified exemptee available to operate the facility, the Board recommends to wholesalers and others who require an exemptee on duty that they qualify more than one of their employees as an exemptee to supervise operations.

Under the new law, effective January 1, 2006, federally-licensed laboratories will no longer be required to have a pharmacist or exemptee on their premises. Manufacturers, previously covered by the exemptee law, have been left out of the change to designated representatives (see Chap. V: Other Board Licensees ("Manufacturers")). Veterinary food-animal drug retailers and wholesalers will be required to have a "designated representative" on their premises if a pharmacist is not present.

---

[16] Existing exemptee certificates will remain valid until their expiration dates or January 1, 2007, whichever is earlier (§4053.1).

The requirements for licensure as a designated representative are very similar to those for an exemptee. However, the year of work experience must be *recent*, defined as within the last three years, and it must be *paid* work experience. The training program requirements are the same. As of now, business cannot be conducted by the entities covered by this law without the presence either of a pharmacist or the alternative – as of 2006, a "designated representative" rather than an "exemptee." The new law also specifies that only a pharmacist or designated representative may prepare and affix labels to veterinary food-animal drugs (§4053 (c)(d), effective January 1, 2006)).

---

**What you should think about after reading this chapter:**

1. What kinds of tasks involved in the receiving and filling of prescriptions require professional judgment that a technician cannot exercise? In what ways do the different professional settings in which pharmacists and technicians work affect your answer?

2. How much supervision is desirable from the perspective of the intern? How much supervision should the supervising pharmacist expect or want to provide?

3. In a pharmacy that fills a mix of prescriptions, what considerations must be taken into account in scheduling pharmacy personnel and handling prescriptions?

4. What factors affect the ability of the pharmacist to supervise ancillary personnel safely and efficiently?

5. What are the benefits and detriments of allowing a technician to perform a final check of prescriptions prepared by another technician? As the pharmacist responsible for the technicians' work product, what should your expectations and concerns be about such a change in the law?

6. When might a second pharmacist on duty wish to refuse to supervise a second technician? Ask to limit other personnel for which he or she is responsible?

---

# Chapter IV

# Licensing Pharmacies

**What you should know after reading this chapter:**

1. Who is allowed in a community pharmacy when a pharmacist is not present? In a hospital pharmacy?

2. What constitutes the licensed pharmacy?

3. What may an intern do in a pharmacy in the absence of the supervising pharmacist?

4. What security requirements must be met by a pharmacy?

5. Who may own a pharmacy? Who may not?

6. What is the "quality assurance" program?

7. Under what circumstances may a pharmacy sell drugs to a prescriber or to other entities?

8. What policies must a pharmacy have for any pharmacy technicians it employs? For what else must a pharmacy have policies and procedures?

9. For what is the pharmacist-in-charge responsible?

10. What requirements must a Nevada pharmacy meet to mail or otherwise deliver prescription drugs to California?

11. What requirements must be met by pharmacies compounding sterile injectables?

12. Who may deliver dialysis supplies to patients at home? What requirements must be met?

13. What is the so-called "chart order exemption?"

14. How does the hospital pharmacist's responsibility for security differ from that of the community pharmacist?

# The Pharmacy

Public protection requires regulatory control over the premises where pharmacy is practiced, as well as over the individuals engaged in that practice. The pharmacy itself is subject to licensure and must comply with a variety of requirements. The Board has broad authority to investigate applicants for pharmacy licenses, as discussed below. There are no separate classes of pharmacy licenses, although the practices of community pharmacies, institutional pharmacies, and specialty pharmacies are quite different. The law does separately define "hospital" pharmacy (§4029), and there are some special requirements applicable to pharmacies that serve different types of patients or prepare certain specialized types of drugs.[1]

## *Pharmacy Premises*

Most people use the term "pharmacy" to apply to the entire store in which they receive their prescription drugs. Although in some circumstances the "pharmacy" encompasses the entire premises, under the law the "pharmacy" subject to licensure usually is much smaller. The law defines "pharmacy" as the "area, place, or premises . . . in which the profession of pharmacy is practiced and where prescriptions are compounded" (§4037(a)). It is not necessarily the entire retail space (including where OTC drugs and other products are merchandised), and often is just the pharmacy-practice area. The licensed "pharmacy" is that which is described in the pharmacy's permit (§4037(a)). It is illegal to conduct a pharmacy in California without a license; a separate license is required for each of the premises of an owner that operates multiple pharmacies (§4110(a)). A new statute bars a single site from having a license both for a pharmacy and for another entity licensed by the Board, such as a wholesaler (§4107), although a licensed pharmacy may have the additional license required for sterile compounding. The holder of a pharmacy license may sell and dispense hypodermics without the separate permit generally required before someone without a pharmacy license can sell them (§4205).

No building in California may display any sign that suggests a pharmacy is therein unless a pharmacy holding a valid license is in fact in the building. The words "pharmacy," "drugstore," "apothecary," and the characteristic prescription sign (Rx) are among the forbidden words, as are all others of similar import (§4343, §1706).

The licensed pharmacy includes the storage area as well as the compounding, repackaging, and dispensing areas of premises from which prescription drugs or devices are furnished, sold, or dispensed at retail ((§4037(a)). A neighborhood pharmacy retailer's entire premises may well be licensed as the pharmacy; in contrast, only the pharmacy area of a supermarket or large retail store will be described in and subject to the license.

## *Building Requirements*

The Board's building regulation (§1714) for pharmacies simply mandates that, at the time of initial licensure and upon renewal, the licensee certify that it meets the section's various requirements (§1714(f)). Section 1714(b) generally requires that the pharmacy maintain its facilities, space, fixtures, and equipment so that drugs are prepared, maintained, secured, and distributed safely and properly. It also requires that the pharmacy be of sufficient size and unobstructed area to accommodate the safe practice of pharmacy.

---

[1] The ordering, maintenance, preparation and disposition of drugs and devices by a pharmacy is discussed in Chapters VII: Ordering, Receipt, Maintenance, and Transfer of Drugs and Devices; Chapter VIII: Preparation of Drugs by a Pharmacy; and Chapter IX: The Prescription Process: From Receipt to Labeling.

Section 1714(c) requires the pharmacy, including its fixtures and equipment, to be maintained in a clean and orderly fashion, dry and well-ventilated, free from rodents and insects, and properly lighted. It also requires that the pharmacy be equipped with a sink with both hot and cold running water for pharmaceutical use. Section 1714(d) provides for pharmacy security, as discussed below. Section 1714(g) specifically requires that a pharmacy maintain a readily accessible restroom with a toilet and washbasin supplied with running water.

Finally, consistent with the Board's mandate of patient consultation for most new prescriptions, section 1714(a) requires that pharmacies, except for hospital inpatient pharmacies that solely or predominantly furnish drugs to inpatients, contain an area suitable for confidential patient counseling.[2]

If the applicant falsely certifies that it is in compliance with the building requirements (§1714(f)), either at time of licensure or renewal, the pharmacy and those involved in the deception are likely to face disciplinary charges. At any time, if a pharmacy is not maintained in a clean and orderly fashion or its security, space, or equipment are inadequate to safely conduct its practice, it may be found in violation of section 1714.

## *Pharmacy Security*

In addition to requiring that pharmacy premises be designed with an eye toward security (§1714(b)), the law prohibits anyone other than a pharmacist, an intern, an authorized prescriber, or a law enforcement officer from being in the licensed area. Anyone else who is present must be there for a pharmacy-related purpose and is the responsibility of the pharmacist present in the pharmacy (§4116(a)).

The pharmacy that maintains DEA registration (as virtually every pharmacy does), and each pharmacist on duty, must provide effective controls to guard against theft and diversion of controlled substances (21 CFR §1301.71, §1714(d)), including the secure storage of its stock of controlled substances (21 CFR §1301.75). One important responsibility of a DEA registrant pharmacy is to notify the DEA's local field office immediately of any theft or significant loss of controlled substances on a DEA form specifically intended for that purpose (21 CFR §1301.76(b)). The pharmacy owner must also notify the Board within 30 days of discovery of any loss of controlled substances, including their amounts and strengths (§1715.6).

The DEA requires that an employee of a registrant pharmacy that has any knowledge of drug diversion by a fellow employee is obligated to report that information to the employer; a failure to report such information "will be considered in determining the feasibility of continuing to allow an employee to work in a drug security area." The employer is required to inform all employees about this policy (21 CFR §1301.91). California law requires each pharmacy to have procedures to deal with circumstances involving licensed employees (pharmacists or technicians) who are chemically, mentally, or physically impaired, or who have engaged in theft, diversion, or self-use of prescription drugs. The Board may choose to require that incidents of this type be reported (§4104), but has not yet done so.

A pharmacy that is a DEA registrant may not employ anyone who has been convicted of a felony related to controlled substances or who has had discipline imposed against his or her DEA registration. Thus, a registrant may inquire about prospective employees' past criminal convictions or

---

[2] The Board also has the authority to waive any licensing requirement for good cause (§4118). Notwithstanding some assertions that this section authorizes the Board to waive any requirement of Pharmacy Law, the history of this statute and its location in the article of Pharmacy Law on general requirements for pharmacies reflect its considerably narrower scope, allowing the Board to waive only building requirements.

pending criminal charges (21 CFR §1301.90); it may request a waiver to employ a person who has a criminal conviction or charge (21 CFR §1307.03)).

Consistent with long-standing Board policy, the pharmacy security regulation, section 1714(d), provides that only a pharmacist may have possession of a key to the pharmacy area where dangerous drugs and controlled substances are stored; an exception is discussed below. Building regulations no longer include detailed security requirements, such as making the locking of doors and barriers to the pharmacy when no pharmacist is present the specific responsibility of the pharmacist. Section 1714's more general requirement that the pharmacist provide effective controls against drug theft or diversion undoubtedly encompasses the responsibility for locking the premises and for taking whatever other measures are needed for security at the particular pharmacy.

The security requirement mandating that a pharmacist be on the premises at all times is both quite literal and enforced. If the pharmacy clerk is the first to arrive at the pharmacy in the morning, he or she must await the pharmacist to enter the premises. If the pharmacist leaves the pharmacy premises at any time during the day and no other pharmacist is present, all other personnel must leave the licensed premises, except under the limited exception made to accommodate breaks and lunch periods in a single-pharmacist pharmacy (§4116(b)(2), §1714.1; see Chap. XIV: Other Relevant Law). Discipline may be imposed on the pharmacist, as well as the pharmacy, if the pharmacy is left open for any period of time, however short, without a pharmacist present (*Brodsky v. California State Board of Pharmacy*, 173 Cal. App. 2d 680, 691-693 (2d Dist. 1959) (45-minute absence)).

If the prescription department of a community pharmacy is not separate from the rest of the store, that pharmacy may be open for business only when a pharmacist is present, even if the only business actually conducted is the sale of sundries. If the prescription department is secured adequately against theft or diversion, business may be conducted outside that area in the absence of a pharmacist.

An important part of pharmacy security is having a pharmacist-in-charge. The holder of the pharmacy license has the responsibility to assure that a pharmacist is in charge of the pharmacy (§4113(a),(b)). If that license holder permits the compounding, dispensing, or furnishing of dangerous drugs in the pharmacy other than by a pharmacist, he or she is guilty of a misdemeanor (§4330(a)), and the pharmacy license is subject to immediate suspension or revocation (§4305(b)). Any person who is not a pharmacist who engages in managing a pharmacy or compounding, furnishing, or dispensing a dangerous drug (except as provided elsewhere in the law) also is guilty of a misdemeanor (§4329).

**May the pharmacist's spouse or nonpharmacist business partner have a key to the pharmacy? May the landlord of the building have a key? May the manager of the supermarket in which the pharmacy is located have a key? May the burglar alarm company have a key?**

The pharmacy owner, the building owner or store manager, or a family member of a pharmacist owner – but only one of them, and no one else – may possess a key to the pharmacy. This key must be in a tamper-evident container; the signature of the pharmacist-in-charge must be on the container so that a pharmacist to whom it is provided can readily determine if the key has previously been removed. This key is only to be used for delivery to a pharmacist or to provide access when necessary in an emergency; an emergency, for purposes of this section, includes fire, flood, or earthquake (§1714(e)). In other words, this key is not for a personal emergency, such as when the pharmacist does not arrive.

## *Restrictions on Pharmacy Business*

The primary business of pharmacies is to prepare and dispense drugs and devices on prescription. Through the years pharmacies have also sold a certain amount of both commercially-prepared and compounded drugs to other licensed entities or persons, and it has been legal for them to do so.  In other words, pharmacies have sometimes served in part as wholesalers, but have not been required to be licensed as wholesalers to do so.

Effective in 2005, the authority of pharmacies to engage in resale of commercially-prepared dangerous drugs has been severely restricted.  A pharmacy may now sell drugs (other than to retail patients on prescription) only to the wholesaler owned or under common control by the wholesaler from which the drugs were obtained, to the manufacturer from which the drugs were obtained, to a licensed wholesaler acting as a reverse distributor, to another health care practitioner that is not a pharmacy but is authorized to purchase dangerous drugs, or to another pharmacy under common control with the selling pharmacy.  Otherwise, a pharmacy may only sell drugs to another wholesaler or pharmacy to alleviate a temporary shortage of a drug, and only in an amount necessary to alleviate the shortage and thereby avoid denial of care (§4126.5).  In other words, a pharmacy may not be a general supplier of drugs to pharmacies and wholesalers.  This provision was part of a statute (Stats. 2004, ch. 857) aimed at curbing perceived abuse in the wholesaling of prescription drugs (see Chap. V: Other Board Licensees).

## *Quality Assurance*

Every pharmacy must establish a quality assurance (QA) program to, at a minimum, document medication errors attributable, in whole or in part, to the pharmacy or its personnel (§4125(a)).[3]  The purpose of the requirement is to assure that pharmacies assess their errors to help them avoid repeating them (§1711).

Pharmacies are expected to make an "essential cause examination" of any medication error.  That examination means a "process for identifying the basic or causal factors that underlie the occurrence . . . of a medication error."  The examination is intended to focus on systems and processes, rather than individual performance, and to identify potential improvements in processes or systems that would tend to decrease the likelihood of such events in the future (§1711(d)).  A pharmacy may arrange, by contract or otherwise, for a third party to run the required quality assurance program, as long as it determines that the third party has the necessary skill or expertise to do so (§1711(h)).

The pharmacy must have written policies and procedures for its quality assurance program, and maintain them in the pharmacy in a readily retrievable form (§1711(c)).  When a pharmacist determines that a medication error has occurred in which the drug was administered to the patient or has resulted in a clinically significant delay in therapy, the pharmacist must, as soon as possible, both communicate to the patient or patient's agent that the error occurred, and the steps necessary to avoid or mitigate injury and communicate to the prescriber that the error occurred  (§1711(c)(2),(3)).  If the pharmacist learned of the error from the patient, patient's agent, or the prescriber, he or she need not provide notification back to that person (§1711(c)(4)).  The record of a quality assurance review of a medication error must be retained in the pharmacy and be immediately retrievable for one year from its creation (§1711(f)).  The pharmacy's personnel must be informed of any changes to pharmacy quality assurance policy, procedures, systems, or processes (§1711(e))

To encourage candor in the program, all records created and maintained as part of the quality assurance program are considered peer review documents, not subject to discovery in arbitration or any civil or other proceeding.  The records will be available to the Board to protect public health and safety or to any government agency that alleges fraud by the pharmacy (§4125(b)).  The protection from discovery is solely for records actually generated for the QA program.  Compliance with section 1711

---

[3]  A different and more extensive quality assurance program is required for pharmacies that engage in sterile injectable compounding (see below).  That program is required to assure ongoing quality and compliance with sterile compounding requirements, not just to respond to medication errors.

will be considered by the Board as a mitigating factor in any disciplinary investigation that arises from a medication error (§1711(g)).

## *Policies and Procedures*

It is often advisable for management to establish policies and procedures to govern various aspects of business, and this is especially true in pharmacy, where there are many detailed types of processes for staff members to implement. A well-managed pharmacy might have policies and procedures for most aspects of operations, from ordering and handling drugs to the prescription process, to maintenance of patient profiles and consultation. In addition to the advisability of maintaining policies and procedures, a significant number are specifically required by law, or required by implication to comply with law. These include:

- Regarding pharmacy technicians (§1793.7(d), Chap. III: Licensing Pharmacists)
- Governing employee drug diversion, reports by fellow employees to employer (§4104(a), Chap. IV: Licensing Pharmacies)
- Sterile injectable compounding (§1751.02(a), Chap. IV: Licensing Pharmacies)
- Disposal of infectious material or cytotoxic residue (§1751.6, Chap. IV: Licensing Pharmacies)
- Regarding portable drug storage containers (§1751.11(d), Chap. IV: Licensing Pharmacies)
- Secure storage facilities for after-hours deliveries to the pharmacy (§4059.5(f), Chap. V: Other Board Licensees)
- Repackaging other than for prescriptions (§§4033(c), 4052.7; Chap. VII: Ordering Drugs)
- Maintaining privacy and security of common electronic files (§1717(d),(e), Chap. X: Dispensing and Beyond)
- Operation of pharmacy during temporary absence of pharmacist (§1714.1(f), Chap. XIV: Other Relevant Law)

## *Pharmacy Personnel*

Pharmacy personnel are obviously crucial to the appropriate operations of the pharmacy. Some of those personnel are mandated by law. A pharmacy must be under the direction of a pharmacist-in-charge and in the charge of at least one on-duty pharmacist at all times it is in operation. In addition, a pharmacy today is likely to have a variety of other employees. These include interns, pharmacy technicians, and technician trainees (see below and Chap. III: Licensing Pharmacists), each of whom is licensed by the Board. In addition, there are likely to be clerk-typists, cashiers, and other clerical staff to perform other functions related to the pharmacy, as well as persons performing janitorial or maintenance work and bookkeeping and claim-handling functions. Pharmacy management must know the limitations on what each category of personnel may do and the supervision required for this personnel, including limits on numbers of people other categories of people may supervise. This topic is discussed below and, with respect to interns, technicians, and technician trainees, in Chapter III: Licensing Pharmacists and Other Individuals.

Nonlicensed persons may type prescription labels and enter prescription information into a computer. At the pharmacist's direction, they may also request and receive refill information (§1793.3(a)). The only limit to the number of nonlicensed persons that the pharmacist may supervise is his or her own judgment that the supervision does not interfere with the effective performance of the pharmacist's responsibilities. As with technicians (see Chap. III: Licensing Pharmacists ("Ratios")), the pharmacist may notify management if he or she feels that there are too many nonlicensed persons scheduled to work than can be safely supervised (§1793.3(d)). Regardless of the number and type of ancillary personnel, the responsibility for the accuracy of the prescription information and the medications as dispensed still rests with the pharmacist who initials the prescription or prescription record.

# *Pharmacy Ownership*

**Types of Ownership.**  In pharmacy, as in numerous other professions, laws once restricted all aspects of the practice to licensed professionals.  Pharmacy ownership, for example, was at one time restricted to pharmacists in most states.[4]  Pharmacists could hire other pharmacists to work for them, but nonpharmacists could not obtain a pharmacy license and hire pharmacists to run the pharmacy.  Logical arguments can be mustered both for and against such stringent limitations.  On the one hand, proponents argue that the health and safety of the public are best assured when pharmacists are in full control of the site of their practice, the pharmacy.  The contrary argument has prevailed in pharmacy: the public benefits most from an atmosphere in which competition in the provision of goods and services flourishes, and that requires minimizing restrictions on who can own a pharmacy.  The public is still protected because each pharmacy must be run by a pharmacist, regardless of its ownership.[5]  Thus for many years nonpharmacists have been granted pharmacy licenses, and many pharmacists are employed by nonpharmacists.  Some pharmacies are owned by pharmacists, but many more are not.

A pharmacy may be owned by any legal entity capable of ownership.  That is, partnerships, unincorporated associations, limited liability companies (LLCs), or corporations, as well as individuals, may apply for pharmacy licenses.[6]  The license application requires the name, address, usual occupation, and professional qualifications, if any, of the applicant.  When the applicant is other than an individual, the application must provide that information for all persons who have a beneficial interest in – that is, who stand to profit from – the pharmacy.  For a partnership or unincorporated association, that is each partner or member; for a corporation (other than a nonprofit corporation), that is each officer, director, and stockholder.  If there are more than five partners, members, or stockholders, the information is required only concerning the five partners, members, or stockholders with the largest interests in the applicant entity.  The Board has the right to request information about other partners, members, or stockholders (§4201(a)-(c)).

Any change in the beneficial ownership interest of the pharmacy or in corporate officers must be reported to the Board within 30 days (§4201(i), §1709) and may require an application for a new license.  In addition, upon request of the Board a pharmacy owner or manager must provide the names of all owners, managers, and employees of the pharmacy, and a statement of the capacity in which persons are employed by the pharmacy (§4082).  The pharmacy license must be renewed annually (with the timely payment of fees) (§4201(f)).  One section of the law states that a pharmacy license "shall not be transferable" (§4201(f)); another gives the Board authority to adopt a regulation determining the circumstances under which a pharmacy license "may be transferred" (§4110(a)).  As the Board has not adopted any such regulations to date, pharmacy licenses are not transferable.

The pharmacy license, like all facility licenses issued by the Board, must be displayed on the licensed premises so that it may be read by the purchasing public (§4058).  A pharmacy license that is not renewed within 60 days of its expiration may be cancelled by the Board (§4402(e)).  If an owner

---

[4]  In 1973, the United States Supreme Court upheld the right of a state legislature to restrict the ownership of pharmacies to pharmacists in *North Dakota State Board of Pharmacy v. Snyder's Drug Stores, Inc.*, 414 U.S. 156 (1973).

[5]  A similar argument still rages in California in regard to optometry.  The commercial practice of optometry is essentially illegal in California; optometrists may not be employed by non-optometrists (B&PC §3103), and there are restrictions on branch offices that are not optometrist-owned (B&PC §3077).  The Federal Trade Commission adopted regulations in 1989 barring such limitations on optometry practice, but they were struck down by the courts on the ground that the FTC did not have the statutory authority to regulate the acts of the states in this regard (*California State Board of Optometry v. Federal Trade Commission*, 910 F.2d 976 (D.C. Cir. 1990)).  The same debate goes on over lay control of medical practices.

[6]  The Board may also register a nonresident pharmacy organized as an LLC in its home state, if it is legal for that state's LLCs to hold professional licenses (§4112(b)).

wishes to sell a pharmacy, the new owners must apply to the Board; the Board, in its discretion, may ease the transition by granting a temporary license for up to 180 days, subject to terms and conditions it deems in the public interest (§4110(b)).

Each pharmacy permit application requires "a statement to the effect that the applicant has not been convicted of a felony and has not violated any of the provisions" of the Pharmacy Law; an applicant that cannot make this statement must disclose the violation (§4201(d)). When the applicant is a corporate-type entity, this section requires disclosure of felonies of the major partners, members, officers, managers, or stockholders, as well as of the applicant itself.[7]

The Board is required to make a "thorough investigation" of a pharmacy license applicant and the premises proposed for licensure. It must "investigate all matters directly related to the issuance of the license which may affect the public welfare" because of the furnishing, sale, or dispensing of drugs and devices (§4207(a)). Of necessity, the Board may request financial records from an entity seeking a license, as well as any other information ". . . it deems necessary to complete the application investigation required" by law (§4207(d)).

Purely retail-related concerns (such as parking, congestion, or noise) are not within the Board's jurisdiction. The Board must deny an application if the applicant or the premises "do not qualify" (§4207).

A pharmacy owner is at significant risk if the pharmacy is not operated in compliance with the law. Just as a pharmacist is subject to discipline, including loss of license, for violations of the law, so too is the pharmacy, as discussed at length in Chapter XII: Practice Pitfalls. The pharmacy risks discipline for virtually any misconduct occurring there, regardless of whether the pharmacy owner knew about it.

In addition, the Board may void the license of a pharmacy (or a wholesaler or veterinary food-animal drug retailer) simply for remaining closed (§4312(a)). For these purposes "closed" means not open for business at least one day per week during any 120-day period; the Board may act sooner if there is good cause to do so (§4312(a),(e)). Consider the public safety need for the Board to have this power: the drugs stored on the premises are subject to theft and to deterioration (if only by the passage of time) when the business is not in active operation. The law requires the rapid transfer of the drug stock from a discontinued business for the same reason (§4312(b)); knowing failure to comply is a misdemeanor (§4321(a)). The Board has the power to seek a court order to transfer the drug stock in the case of owner noncompliance (§4312(c)).[8]

All license holders – pharmacy, wholesaler, or other – are required to contact the Board before transferring or selling any of their drug, device, or hypodermic inventory as a result of termination of their business or bankruptcy proceedings, and to follow instructions then given them by the Board (§1708.2).[9] In addition, any pharmacy, wholesaler, or manufacturer that files a petition in bankruptcy, enters into any creditor compromise agreement, has a receiver appointed, or enters into any liquidation

---

[7]   The statute does not limit the felonies an applicant must disclose to those substantially related to ownership of a pharmacy; the Board, not the applicant, decides whether felonies disclosed by applicants are substantially related to the license sought. It is interesting to note that the authority of the Board under its statute is narrower than the authority granted to licensing boards generally, by section 480 of the Business and Professions Code, to deny a license based on any crime (not just a felony) that is substantially related to the license sought.

[8]   The initial impetus for the provision was to deal with people who "stockpiled" pharmacy licenses, without operating most of their licensed premises, unless or until their primary pharmacy was facing revocation or other discipline.

[9]   A pharmacy that either terminates or transfers its business must also comply with DEA requirements (see DEA Pharmacist's Manual, pp. 7-8).

or other arrangement that might result in the sale or transfer of drugs, devices, or other goods that can be sold only by a pharmacist must notify the Board immediately in writing (§1705). The drugs may only be transferred to an entity legally entitled to possess them. It is not legal to move them to a place that has applied for, but not yet received, a license. It is not legal to turn the drugs over to a bankruptcy trustee who lacks the proper licensure. Both the transferor and the transferee must make and retain appropriate records. These requirements protect the public when the license holder is in financial distress; they assure that drugs remain at all times under the control of an entity licensed to handle them.

**Ownership Restrictions.** By law, no California prescriber may directly own a pharmacy (§4111(a)(1)). The concerns behind this restriction are financial as well as health-related. If prescribers own pharmacies, they might be tempted to steer patients to their pharmacies and even to write more prescriptions than are necessary for the health of their patients. If prescriber ownership were widespread, nonprescriber-owned pharmacies would have a difficult time competing. Without competition, economists tell us, prices rise, to the disadvantage of consumers.

A pharmacy license may not be issued to a corporation if a prescriber controls it or if prescribers own ten percent or more of its stock (§4111(a)(3)). The Board considers it "control" when a prescriber is in a position of authority (such as president or chief executive officer) or when prescribers constitute a majority of a quorum of the board of directors. The prohibition against pharmacy ownership also extends to any person who shares a community (marital) property or other financial interest in the license with a prescriber (§4111(a)(2)). A pharmacist whose spouse is a prescriber would need to eliminate the spouse's community or other financial interest in the pharmacy (by assuring that it is the pharmacist's separate property) before obtaining a license. The restriction does not apply to inpatient hospital pharmacy licenses issued to the owner of a hospital (§4111(b)) or to a person licensed, before August 1, 1981, under the Knox-Keene Health Care Services Plan Act of 1975. These restrictions apply equally to non-profit corporations. The Board will scrutinize the names of those holding interests in corporations to ensure that physicians are not exercising prohibited control or holding interests hidden by layers of ownership.

**May a nurse practitioner who furnishes drugs under authority of Business and Professions Code section 2836.1 own or have an interest in a pharmacy permit? May a physician assistant who issues delegated orders under authority of Business and Professions Code section 3502.1 own or have an interest in a pharmacy permit?**

What nurse practitioners and physician assistants do in respect to drugs has never been called prescribing, at least not using that term. Thus one might conclude that a nurse practitioner or a physician assistant could own or have an interest in a pharmacy permit. However, the ownership restrictions in section 4111 apply to a person authorized to prescribe or write a prescription as specified in section 4040 (§4111(a)(1)), and section 4040 defines a prescription as an oral, written, or electronic transmission order that is issued by, among others, a physician assistant (pursuant to B&PC §3502.1) or a nurse practitioner (pursuant to B&PC §2836.1). So for purposes of the ownership prohibitions and restrictions of section 4111, nurse practitioners and physician assistants are prescribers.

**May a husband who is a pharmacist own a pharmacy next door to the office of his wife, who is a physician? Is this arrangement legal as long as the pharmacy does not fill prescriptions written by the physician wife?**

If the physician wife has any direct interest, which would include a community property interest, in the pharmacy, or control of the pharmacy, the husband could not own the pharmacy. But the simple fact that the husband and wife have adjoining or neighboring businesses or practices does not violate the law if the wife has no direct interest in or control over the pharmacy. Nor is it required, if the wife has no interest in the pharmacy, that her prescriptions be filled elsewhere. Regularly filling prescriptions issued by one's spouse, regardless of where his or her office is located, would raise potential issues of conflict of interest or lack of independent judgment by the pharmacist. A pattern of filling one's spouse's prescriptions for commonly-abused controlled substances in significant volume would raise concerns about possible drug diversion and abuse. If the Pharmacy Board is aware that the pharmacy owner's spouse practices medicine next door, it will want to know who owns the property and to review any lease.

**The Pharmacy Corporation.** Another legal form in which a pharmacy may be owned is the so-called "pharmacy corporation." This entity is a corporation authorized to render professional services, in accordance with the Moscone-Knox Professional Corporation Act (Corp. Code §§13400-13410). Only licensed pharmacists may hold stock or major offices in a pharmacy corporation (Corp. Code §13406(a)). Advantages in areas not related to their professional practices, such as taxes, have led various groups to seek the legal right to practice their professions in a corporate form. Sections 4150 to 4156 of the Business and Professions Code allow pharmacists to take advantage of the Moscone-Knox Act but, according to the Board of Pharmacy, pharmacists rarely, if ever, do so.

**Management Firms.** People continue to explore new forms in which to operate businesses.[10] One form that has been appearing in pharmacy practice, particularly in health care facility settings, is the pharmacy management firm. The firm's principals may or may not be pharmacists. The pharmacy owner (and holder of the pharmacy license) contracts with the management firm to handle the day-to-day operations of the pharmacy, which may include everything from accounting to drug ordering and record-keeping to hiring and firing pharmacy personnel. There appears to be no direct obstacle in the law to such an arrangement. However, the pharmacy owner, and license holder, remains responsible for any violations of law or regulation committed by the management firm. Similarly, the responsibility of the pharmacist-in-charge or any employee pharmacist is no different because that person is employed by the management firm rather than the pharmacy owner.

The important question is whether the Board has any control over the management firm and its personnel, including its officers or other top staff. The management firm is not licensed by the Board and its key staff may or may not be pharmacists (but in any case will be giving direction to pharmacists). The Board has existing authority under section 4307 to prohibit participation in responsible positions in pharmacy management firms by any individual who had knowledge of or knowingly participated in any conduct for which a pharmacy license of any sort was denied, revoked, or suspended. If principals of a management firm are themselves pharmacists, the Board has the option to proceed against their pharmacist licenses for activity in violation of the law. However, since running a pharmacy management firm does not require a pharmacy license, this control may not prove too effective.

Should you become part of a management firm or be employed in a pharmacy managed by such a firm, the fact that the law is not clear about the role of management firms does not relieve you of responsibility for complying with all the law relevant to pharmacy practice.

---

[10] Some pharmacies or other entities licensed by the Board may use the power of attorney as a management tool. By granting a power of attorney to an individual or an entity, the pharmacy allows that individual or entity to exercise control over one or more aspects of the pharmacy's operation. There must still be a designated pharmacist-in-charge, and the pharmacy owner is still responsible for the conduct of anyone to whom he or she has delegated authority to operate or manage the pharmacy. A power of attorney can either be broad (for example, giving the grantee complete control over the pharmacy's financial affairs) or narrow, limited to very specific acts. The use of powers of attorney is specifically recognized by federal regulations that authorize a DEA registrant to grant such powers to an individual to order controlled substances on behalf of the registrant (21 CFR §1305.07). Too broad a grant of authority under a power of attorney may amount to a transfer of the pharmacy permit, of a beneficial interest in the pharmacy, or both. The Board will scrutinize closely any power of attorney granted by a licensee to ensure that it is legal.

**Pharmacy Benefit Management Companies.** Health plans and other health care benefit payors today commonly contract with pharmacy benefit management companies (PBMs) to help contain drug costs and to improve drug therapy. PBMs negotiate with manufacturers and wholesalers, using the size of their potential purchases to obtain the lowest possible prices. According to a 1997 federal government report on cost containment and potential patient outcomes, financial imperatives driving managed care arrangements can compromise the quality of pharmacy programs. In 1993, 40 percent of the United States population – or 100,000,000 people – had their benefits managed by PBMs. As of 1995, the five largest PBMs managed 80 percent of all health plan enrollees served by PBMs. By 1997, three of the five largest PBMs were owned by drug companies.[11] Obviously the implications of this dramatic shift in control over prescription drug services are significant. Because the largest PBMs are owned by or financially allied with drug manufacturers, there is a serious potential for conflicts of interest in determining what drug or brand of drug ought to be dispensed. In addition, there are significant risks of improper use of patient information.

Existing laws prohibiting kickbacks, rebates, referrals, and so forth (see Chap. XII: Practice Pitfalls) will likely be employed to challenge the use of formularies and/or financial incentives for selecting or promoting certain products. Antitrust laws are available to attack what are perceived as monopolistic practices.[12]

There are ongoing concerns about the relationships of PBMs to other entities involved in drug manufacturing or distribution, including pharmacies. For example, a majority of mail order pharmacies are owned by the three largest PBMs, making it likely that patients will be under increasing pressure to switch from community pharmacies to mail order pharmacies. Fueling this trend, especially for patients on Medicare, is the fact that the new Medicare prescription drug benefit that begins in 2006 (see Chap. X: Dispensing and Beyond ("Prescription Pricing")) will largely be administered by PBMs, and nothing in that law restricts the use of mail order pharmacies (Martin Sipkoff, *The New Showdown, Community pharmacies are pulling out all the stops to derail mandatory mail-order plans*, DRUG TOPICS, Apr. 19, 2004, www.drugtopics.com).

## The "Pharmacist-in-Charge"

Protection of the public when a pharmacy is owned by a nonpharmacist is assured by the requirement that every pharmacy be in the charge of a pharmacist. Pharmacy owners must designate a "pharmacist-in-charge," who is responsible for the pharmacy's compliance with all laws and regulations relating to pharmacy practice (§4113(a), (b)). The owner must vest the pharmacist-in-charge with adequate authority so he or she can assure such compliance (§1709.1(b)).

Each pharmacy's pharmacist-in-charge must complete a biennial self-assessment of the pharmacy's compliance with federal and state pharmacy law (§1715). This self-assessment must be completed before July 1 of every odd-numbered year (§1715(a)) and kept on file in the pharmacy for three years (§1715(d)). A new assessment must be prepared within 30 days of the employment of a new pharmacist-in-charge or whenever a new pharmacy permit is issued (§1715(b)).

---

[11] US Department of Health and Human Services, Office of Inspector General, *Experiences of Health Maintenance Organizations with Pharmacy Benefit Management Companies*, April 1997, OEI-01-95-00110, pp. 2-4.

[12] When the nation's four largest drug wholesalers announced plans to merge to create two larger companies, public attention was called to the impact of the increasing relationships among drug manufacturers, health care facilities, health plans or insurers, and pharmacies. Because the Federal Trade Commission feared the two wholesaler mergers would cause drug prices to increase, it went to court to block them. After a federal court granted a preliminary ruling prohibiting both mergers, Cardinal Health, Inc. withdrew its offer to acquire the Bergen Brunswig Corporation for $2.8 billion, and McKesson Corporation dropped its plan to buy the Amerisource Health Corporation for $2.3 billion (*Company News; 4 Big Drug Wholesalers Drop Merger Plans*, NEW YORK TIMES, Aug. 8, 1998, p. D3).

Pharmacies must complete their self-assessment using the Board's forms. At the end of 2004 the Board was in the process of adopting new forms (Form 17M-13 for Community Pharmacy & Hospital Outpatient Pharmacy and Form 17M-14 for Hospital Pharmacy) to substitute for the January 2001 versions (§1715(c)). The appropriate versions of the forms should be available for downloading at www.pharmacy.ca.gov/app_forms.htm. The self-assessment requires answers to questions about all aspects of pharmacy practice; when the answer to any question is "no," the pharmacy is required to explain its corrective action or action plan to bring its practice into compliance.

The pharmacist-in-charge must be a pharmacist employed at that location and is responsible for the daily operation of the pharmacy. The pharmacy owner is required to give the pharmacist-in-charge adequate authority to assure compliance with pharmacy law (§1709.1(b)). A regulation effective in October 2004 allows a pharmacist to be the pharmacist-in-charge at two pharmacies, as long as they are not separated by a driving distance of more than 50 miles (§1709.1(c)). Previously a pharmacist could be pharmacist-in-charge at a second pharmacy only if the two did not have overlapping business hours and if he or she was the only pharmacist at each pharmacy. A pharmacist may not be the pharmacist-in-charge of a pharmacy while also serving as the exemptee-in-charge[13] for a wholesaler or veterinary food-animal drug retailer (§1709.1(d), see Chap. III, Licensing Pharmacists).

A pharmacist may refuse to be the pharmacist-in-charge at a second pharmacy if he or she believes that to assume that responsibility would interfere with the effective performance of his or her responsibilities. In refusing the assignment, the pharmacist must notify the pharmacy owner in writing about the concerns that have led to the refusal; the pharmacist's employer is forbidden to penalize the pharmacist for a good-faith refusal (§1709.1(f),(g)).

In recognition of the potential for conflict between an employee pharmacist responsible for compliance with the law and an owner who may be insensitive to legal requirements or, worse, opposed to compliance, the Legislature has provided that "[a]ny nonpharmacist owner who commits any act that would subvert or tend to subvert the efforts of the pharmacist-in-charge to comply with the laws governing the operation of the pharmacy is guilty of a misdemeanor" (§4330(b)). This provision affords some leverage to pharmacists in their dealings with nonpharmacist bosses who may need education about the importance of compliance with pharmacy law. Because the pharmacist-in-charge is jointly responsible with the owner for the accuracy of pharmacy record-keeping (§4081(b)), it is prudent to insist upon a complete drug inventory the day you begin employment as a pharmacist-in-charge and the day that you leave. In addition, a pharmacist-in-charge who reports a violation to the Board is now offered some protection in a disciplinary proceeding. While the fact of reporting does not preclude discipline, if the pharmacist-in-charge did not engage in or encourage the conduct he or she reported, the fact of the report must be considered as a mitigating factor (§4306.6).

Pharmacy owners are required to notify the Board within 30 days of the termination of employment of their pharmacist-in-charge; that pharmacist has an independent duty to notify the Board within 30 days of leaving such employment (§§4101(a), 4113(c), 4305). A Board regulation underscores the permit holder's notification requirement and also requires the pharmacist-in-charge to be listed on the pharmacy permit (§1709(a)). These notice requirements are designed to ensure that each California pharmacy is at all times under the supervision of a pharmacist known to the Board who assumes legal responsibility for the pharmacy's compliance with the law.

A pharmacy may designate an interim pharmacist-in-charge for not more than 120 days from among the pharmacists who are employees, officers, or administrators of the pharmacy or the entity that

---

[13] A new statute changes the terminology of "exemptee" to "designated representative," effective in 2006. The prohibition in this regulation will presumably apply to a pharmacist serving as the "designated representative-in-charge" under the new statute (§4022.5).

owns the pharmacy.  The interim pharmacist-in-charge must be actively involved in the management of the pharmacy on a daily basis or be practicing pharmacy there.  The owners must be able to document, upon request of the Board, that the interim pharmacist-in-charge is involved adequately with the pharmacy and that efforts to obtain a permanent pharmacist-in-charge are underway (§1709.1(e)).

## *The Hospital Pharmacy*

All hospitals[14] and many other health care facilities require ready access to pharmaceuticals for use in the treatment of their patients.  All hospitals with 100 or more beds must maintain at least one licensed pharmacy on the premises (22 CCR §70263(a)).  In addition to filling prescriber orders for drugs for particular patients, hospitals need to have drugs accessible to staff in emergency rooms and on patient floors for immediate administration.  Differences between the community and the hospital (or other health facility) setting suggest the need for differences in regulatory approach, and such differences exist.  Keep in mind that where a statute or regulation applies to the practice of pharmacy, but does not refer to or make exceptions for a particular practice setting, it is applicable in every setting.

A "hospital pharmacy" is a pharmacy licensed by the Board that is located either within a hospital or within any of the buildings that are part of the consolidated hospital license issued by the DHS (§4029).[15]  While all legal requirements described above for a community pharmacy license apply to the hospital pharmacy, the Board may waive requirements concerning equipment, space, sanitary facilities, or any other licensing requirements, if the Board determines that a "high standard of patient safety, consistent with good patient care" can be met (§4118(b)) and, when a waiver is granted, the pharmacy so licensed may furnish drugs only to patients registered for or obtaining treatment on an inpatient or outpatient basis at the hospital (§4118(b)).  That is, the pharmacy that has received a waiver may not fill prescriptions for "walk-in" customers.

The restriction on prescriber ownership of pharmacies does not apply to inpatient hospital pharmacies owned by the hospital in which they are located (§4111(b)).  However, to avoid the prescriber ownership restriction such a pharmacy must furnish drugs solely or predominantly to inpatients of that hospital; no more than one per cent of its prescriptions may be for others (§1710(b)).

Security is important for hospital pharmacies, as it is for all others.  However, the limitations on access to the licensed premises for pharmacies whose permit is issued to a hospital differ in significant respects from the parallel limitations for community pharmacies.  First, additional categories of persons are allowed access, namely registered nurses and licensed vocational nurses (§4117).  Second, whereas section 4116, governing all other pharmacies, contemplates the physical presence of the pharmacist at all times when others enter the permit area (and whenever the pharmacy is open), section 4117,

---

[14] For purposes of the Pharmacy Law, a "licensed hospital means an institution, place, building, or agency that maintains and operates organized facilities for . . . the diagnosis, care, and treatment of human illnesses to which persons may be admitted for overnight stay" (§4028).  It includes any institution that the California Department of Health Services classifies as a general or specialized hospital, maternity hospital, or tuberculosis hospital, but does not include a sanitarium, rest home, nursing or convalescent home, maternity home, or institution for treating alcoholics (§4028, H&SC §1250).

[15] The law includes within the definition of "hospital pharmacy" a pharmacy outside the hospital itself but within a physical plant that is covered by the hospital's DHS license.  This law recognizes the growing administration of what formerly were inpatient treatments, including intravenous drugs, to outpatients at hospital clinics not physically connected to the main hospital building.  Those treatments are simplified by being within the framework of hospital pharmacy because, among other things, the chart order exemption for Schedule II prescriptions (see text below) may be used.  Such a pharmacy may provide pharmaceutical care only to registered hospital patients on the premises of that physical plant, and the services rendered by the pharmacy must be related directly to the services or treatment plan administered in the physical plant (§4029(b)).

governing access to the hospital pharmacy, on its face limits the categories of persons allowed access but does not seem to make the same demand for the pharmacist's continual presence. It does require, however, that any person's presence in the permit area to perform clerical, inventory control, housekeeping, delivery, maintenance, or similar functions relating to the pharmacy be "authorized" by the pharmacist-in-charge; in the community pharmacy such persons are the "responsibility" of the pharmacist-in-charge (a distinction perhaps without significant difference).

The issue of where a pharmacist must be and what, if anything, may be done in a hospital pharmacy in his or her absence is a matter that gives rise to substantial discussion in pharmacy. That a pharmacist must be on the premises of the hospital and on duty at all times that the pharmacy is in operation seems unassailable.[16] But a pharmacist on duty may have a need to be elsewhere in the hospital for purposes of consultation, checking ward stock, or other legitimate duties; the difficult question is what the technicians in the pharmacy may do in the pharmacist's absence or whether at least one pharmacist must remain in the hospital pharmacy at all times. The Board has had this issue under consideration for some time, and once held hearings on a regulation that would have required a pharmacist to be present at all times when the hospital pharmacy was open, but took no further action. Even though it appears that the pharmacy need not be closed when the only pharmacist on duty is elsewhere in the hospital, the pharmacist's responsibility for ancillary personnel suggests that such absences should be kept to a minimum. The pharmacist is responsible for the operation of the pharmacy whether or not he or she is present.

Even in the absence of a regulation, the hospital pharmacist must use his or her professional judgment to determine what types of work the technicians may do without the pharmacist present, considering both the need to maintain patient safety and the pharmacist's ultimate responsibility for the accuracy of the technician's work. So a pharmacist could allow the technicians to engage in order-filling activities that are easily checked visually, but could not allow them to fill orders involving mathematical calculations or not subject to visual confirmation of accuracy. Current law clearly does not permit drugs to leave the pharmacy until the final product has been checked by a pharmacist (§4115(a),(b),(f); §1793.1(f)). That requirement generally would require the pharmacist's presence at the time drugs leave, although there could be circumstances in which orders approved by the pharmacist are picked up when he or she is elsewhere in the hospital.

While public health and patient safety are obviously important, a major reason for limiting who is present in the pharmacy and assuring supervision by a pharmacist is security. Because of the less-stringent limitations on access to hospital than to community pharmacies, the pharmacist-in-charge of a hospital pharmacy may need to exercise greater vigilance to assure the integrity of drug stocks. Even though under current interpretation and practice the hospital pharmacist need not be physically present in the pharmacy area at all times, he or she remains responsible to account for the pharmacy's handling of all drugs (§4081(b)). In all settings the pharmacist must be personally involved in and knowledgeable about maintaining pharmacy security; federal controlled substances law specifically demands that a pharmacy maintain a system to prevent the theft or loss of controlled drugs (21 CFR §1301.71). Careful monitoring by the pharmacist, required by law, may deter illegal behavior, to the benefit of the pharmacy and the individuals deterred.

The most dramatic difference between community and hospital pharmacy practice is what often is referred to as the "chart order exemption." In essence, an "order" entered on the chart or medical record of an emergency room or admitted hospital patient by or on order of an authorized prescriber is adequate authorization for administration of a drug within the facility and is the equivalent of a

---

[16] The regulation (§1714.1) allowing for the temporary absence of the pharmacist for breaks and meal periods, without requiring that the pharmacy be closed, applies only when the pharmacy is staffed by a single pharmacist, which will rarely be the case with a hospital pharmacy.

prescription if the drug is furnished to the patient by a pharmacy. The chart must contain all the information required by section 4040 or 4070 for any other prescription, and the order must be signed by the prescriber at the time of his or her next visit to the hospital or by the attending physician responsible for the patient's care at the time the patient receives the drugs (§4019). This exemption applies to all drugs, including controlled substances (H&SC §11159).

Section 4019 has been used by some hospitals to justify a wide and rather surprising variety of practices under the "chart order exemption." Pharmacists must be aware that the chart order exemption actually is fairly limited; they should be cautious when the only basis a superior or colleague cites for doing something that appears to be illegal is a vague, "it's under the chart order exemption." It probably is not.

**Filling After-Hours Orders.** Ordinarily the drugs in a hospital pharmacy must be dispensed by a pharmacist. However, effective in 2005, a prescriber in a hospital may dispense a dangerous drug, including a controlled substance, from hospital pharmacy stock to an emergency room patient even though the pharmacy is closed and there is no pharmacist available. There are a number of conditions: the prescriber must reasonably believe no outside pharmacy is available and must determine it is in the best interests of the patient that the drug regimen either commence or continue; the drug must have been acquired in the hospital pharmacy; the quantity is limited to that necessary to maintain uninterrupted therapy while pharmacy services are not available, but not to exceed a 72-hour supply; the information about the dispensing must be recorded and provided to the pharmacy when it reopens; the pharmacy must retain that information and, where a Schedule II or III drug was dispensed, send the information on to the CURES program (see Chap. IX: Prescriptions: Receipt to Labeling); the label on the dispensed drug must comply with section 4076 (see Chap. IX: Prescriptions: Receipt to Labeling); and the prescriber is responsible for any errors or omissions related to the dispensing (§4068).

**Small Hospitals and Drug Room Permits.** Small hospitals (100 or fewer beds) that do not employ a full-time pharmacist and cannot maintain a hospital pharmacy may obtain a license from the Board to allow them to purchase drugs from wholesalers that are needed for administration, or limited dispensing, by physicians to hospital patients (§4056, 22 CCR §70263(a)). There are application and fee requirements; the license is subject to revocation for violation of the law (§4056(c)-(e)); the hospital must keep records of all drugs purchased and administered under this authority. Holders of these licenses may also purchase drugs for dispensing by physicians to registered hospital inpatients or, if they are in rural areas, to certain outpatients §4056(a)). The latter "rural hospital" authorization applies when the physician determines it is in the best interest of the patient to commence or continue treatment immediately and reasonably believes there is no pharmacy located outside the hospital which is available and accessible at the time of dispensing within 30 minutes (measured by the patient's intended mode of transportation) or within a 30 mile radius of the hospital. The quantity of drugs that may be dispensed is limited to the amount needed to maintain therapy during the time when outside pharmaceutical services are unavailable, but no more than a 72-hour supply (§4056(f)). The hospital must obtain, and update annually, information regarding the hours of operation of each pharmacy located within 30 minutes/30 miles (§4056(g)). Each holder of a section 4056 license must retain a consulting pharmacist to monitor and review the pharmaceutical services provided by the hospital to inpatients and the dispensing by physicians to outpatients (§4056(h)).

## *Nonresident Pharmacies*

A nonresident pharmacy is one that ships, mails, or delivers drugs or devices into California (§4112(a)).[17] Until 1988 California's pharmacy law made only limited reference to nonresident

---

[17] A foreign pharmacy would seem to fit within the definition of nonresident pharmacies, except that the importation of prescription drugs – currently a subject of significant controversy – is illegal under federal law (see Chap. VII: Ordering Drugs).

pharmacies doing business in the state. As more and more consumers were restricted by their group health plans to the use of mail order pharmacies, at least for their chronic disease medications, two concerns about nonresident (or out-of-state) pharmacies increased. First, if the goal of California pharmacy law is protection of consumer health and safety, consumers should have the same protection whether they purchase their prescriptions down the block or from a pharmacy a thousand miles away. Second, in-state pharmacies appropriately complained that they operated at an economic disadvantage because they were subject to regulations from which nonresident pharmacies appeared to be exempt.[18] At the same time, nonresident pharmacies objected to what they characterized as undue interference with interstate commerce.

A state has the authority to regulate out-of-state distributors (*Pharmaceutical Manufacturers Assn. v. New Mexico Board of Pharmacy*, 525 P.2d 931, 936 (N.M. 1974) (imposing minimum standards on manufacturers and requiring registration of out-of-state drug distributors)), but the Interstate Commerce Clause of the United States Constitution limits such controls to those that evenhandedly effectuate a legitimate local public interest and do not unduly burden interstate commerce (*Pike v. Bruce Church, Inc.*, 397 U.S. 137, 142 (1970)). The California Legislature's solution was mandatory registration of each nonresident pharmacy.

To register with the Pharmacy Board, each nonresident pharmacy must disclose information about its locations, principal corporate officers, and pharmacists. It must indicate that it has a valid license in its home state, complies with all lawful directions and requests for information by its licensing agency and by the California Board, and maintains its drug and device prescription records in such a way that records of products dispensed to California patients may be readily retrieved. In order to register, the pharmacy's most recent home state inspection report must be submitted to the Board (§4112(d)). And, of course, it must pay a fee; the fee is the same as that charged a resident pharmacy (§§4112(h), 4400(a)).

One of the major complaints of California pharmacies about out-of-state competitors was the absence of a consultation requirement for the latter. The law facilitates patient communication with out-of-state pharmacies by requiring that those pharmacies offer a toll-free telephone service to call their pharmacists during their business hours, but not fewer than six days per week and at least 40 hours per week. The toll-free telephone number must be on the label of each prescription container shipped into California (§4112(f)). The consultation requirement of a California mail order pharmacy, like any pharmacy in the state that ships or delivers prescriptions, is met by giving all patients written notice of the right to oral consultation and a telephone number (§1707.2(b)(2)). The law requires the Board to apply the same oral consultation requirements to out-of-state pharmacies as apply to in-state pharmacies that ship, mail, or deliver prescriptions to patients in California. It is forbidden to mandate face-to-face consultation in any shipping or delivery context or adopt regulations that would result in unnecessary delays in patients receiving their medication (§4112(g)).

Nonresident pharmacy licenses may be denied, revoked, or suspended only for violations of the specific sections of California pharmacy and controlled substances law made applicable to them

---

[18] Community retail pharmacies in particular have felt challenged financially by the growth of nonresident pharmacies, and mail-order pharmacies in general. The new Medicare prescription drug benefit (see Chap. X: Dispensing and Beyond) will likely rely heavily on mail order pharmacies, as do an increasing number of insurers and employers that provide prescription drug benefits. Community pharmacies, including some chains, are resisting this movement, including by refusing to participate in drug plans that mandate that maintenance drugs be purchased through the mail (Martin Sipkoff, *The New Showdown, Community pharmacies are pulling out all the stops to derail mandatory mail-order plans*, DRUG TOPICS, Apr. 19, 2004).

(§4303).[19] When nonresident pharmacies cause harm to Californians through their negligence or errors committed in their home state, the home state licensing board is the primary investigatory agent. Every state licenses pharmacies, so each nonresident pharmacy registered in California is subject to regulation by its home state. California law provides that the California Board may take action against the nonresident pharmacy registration "for conduct which causes serious bodily or serious psychological injury" to a Californian if the Board has referred the matter to the home state licensing authority and it has not begun an investigation within 45 days of the referral (§4303(b)).

It is unlawful for an unregistered nonresident pharmacy to advertise its services in California or for any Californian to advertise the pharmacy services of an unregistered nonresident pharmacy with the knowledge that the advertisement will or is likely to induce Californians to use that pharmacy to fill their prescriptions (§4340). Knowing violation of this statute, like knowing violation of other sections of the Pharmacy Law for which no other penalty is provided, is punishable under the criminal law as a misdemeanor; violation without proof of knowledge is an infraction punishable by a fine (§4321). Anyone acting as a principal or agent for an out-of-state pharmacy that is not licensed by the Board must register with the Board before selling or distributing dangerous drugs or dangerous devices within California (§4162(a)) and is subject to discipline (§4162(c)).

In recent years a large number of prescription drug sellers have opened for business on the Internet. The Board's position that Internet pharmacies are subject to the nonresident pharmacy law seems well supported by the language of section 4112(a), which applies by its terms to *any* pharmacy that ships, mails, or delivers drugs or devices into California. How the pharmacy obtains its business, and whether or not it utilizes computer technology to interact with patients, appears irrelevant. Internet pharmacies pose the same concerns as do other nonresident pharmacies. Additional concerns arise, for both pharmacy and medical regulators, because some Internet pharmacy sites offer to connect the inquiring consumer to a physician who will write a prescription for the desired drug, and many of these sites offer not full pharmacy service but only a few "lifestyle" prescription drugs. For discussion of California's attempt to regulate this practice, see Chapter X: The Prescription Process: Dispensing and Beyond.

## *Specialty Pharmacies*

Pharmacy law was written with the general practice pharmacy and the hospital pharmacy in mind. Many pharmacies today, however, are engaged in specialties or operating in ways that were not contemplated when the law first went into effect. Using its broad authority to protect the health and safety of the public, the Pharmacy Board has adopted regulations governing some specialty practices. The Board has also had to respond to new practices adopted by the pharmacy profession in the pursuit of efficient operations and customer service.

**Radiopharmacy.** Radioactive drugs are widely used for both diagnostic and treatment purposes. Because of their radioactivity, this category of drugs (defined in section 1708.3) potentially poses special dangers necessitating careful handling. In part because there is little documentation of significant risk or injury, the Board's regulatory controls are fairly simple, focusing primarily on the competence of the pharmacist handling the drugs.

---

[19] Section 4303(a) provides that violations of sections 4112 (nonresident pharmacy registration requirements), 4124 (refills of contact lens prescriptions), and 4340 (unlawful advertising), and Health and Safety Code section 11164 (controlled substance prescription requirements), may be punished by actions against the nonresident pharmacy registration, as may be "significant or repeated" violations of sections 4074 (warnings) and 4076 (labeling).

Licensure alone is insufficient to qualify the pharmacist for the handling of radioactive drugs.[20] He or she must be competent in the "preparation, handling, storage, receiving, dispensing, disposition and pharmacology of radioactive drugs" (§1708.4). The radiopharmacist must have completed a nuclear pharmacy course, acquired experience in Board-approved programs, or attained equivalent education and experience in nonapproved programs.

Pharmacies that exclusively furnish radioactive drugs are exempt from compliance with the consultation area requirement (§1708.5). Whenever furnishing of radioactive drugs occurs, a pharmacist qualified under section 1708.4 must be present in the pharmacy. Also, all personnel involved in furnishing radioactive drugs must work under the *"immediate and direct supervision"* (§1708.5) of that qualified pharmacist.

**Dialysis.** Patients on home dialysis require drugs and supplies delivered to them. For several decades it has been legal for nonpharmacy providers (including manufacturers, wholesalers, and others), as well as pharmacies, to distribute dangerous drugs and devices directly to dialysis patients, in accordance with regulations adopted by the Board (§§4054, 4059(c)).

The Board's regulations specify the drugs and devices that may be distributed under this authority: dialysate; heparin 1000 u/cc; sterile sodium chloride 0.9% for injection; needles; syringes; and dialyzers, delivery systems, and their accessory equipment necessary for chronic dialysis. These items must be distributed in case or full shelf package lots (§1787(a)).

These specified products may be distributed on the basis of a written or oral order received from a licensed prescriber; oral orders may be transmitted directly to a pharmacist or the licensed nonpharmacist employee (an "exemptee" or "designated representative," see Chap. III: Licensing Pharmacists) of the manufacturer, wholesaler, or other supplier. Orders may be refillable for up to six months (§1787(c)).

In addition to the manufacturer's label, each case or full shelf package must have the patient's name conspicuously affixed to it. The shipment also must include the patient's name and address; the name, strength, dosage size, and quantity of each dangerous drug or device in the shipment; the name

---

[20] The DHS has the overall responsibility for setting standards of competence for the use of radiopharmaceuticals. Section 107155(d)(3) of the California Health and Safety Code exempts from DHS regulations in this area pharmacists who handle radioactive drugs in accordance with the regulations adopted by the Pharmacy Board.

There also are federal controls concerning radiopharmaceuticals imposed by the federal Food and Drug Administration and the Nuclear Regulatory Commission. After a number of years of confusion about FDA regulation of this field, Congress clarified the regulatory scheme. First, FDA was required to adopt regulations governing the approval process for radiopharmaceuticals. "Regulations for In Vivo Radiopharmaceuticals Used for Diagnosis and Monitoring" were adopted in May 1999 (64 FR 26657, 21 CFR Parts 315 and 601). The regulations clarify the evaluation and approval of in vivo radiopharmaceuticals used in the diagnosis or monitoring of diseases, describe the indications for which FDA may approve diagnostic radiopharmaceuticals, and include criteria that FDA will use to evaluate the safety and effectiveness of diagnostic radiopharmaceuticals. The new law and regulations make it clear that producers of radiopharmaceuticals must comply with all drug producer requirements, including registration, under federal law. Second, the law exempts from the new drug approval process positron emission tomographic (PET) drugs compounded by or on the order of a state-licensed practitioner that are not adulterated. Adulteration is defined largely by reference to the standards adopted by the United States Pharmacopeia. This section, for the first time in federal drug law, recognizes the practice of compounding of PET drugs by pharmacists or other practitioners.

The NRC has authority to establish by regulation standards and instructions to govern the possession and use of special nuclear material, source material, and byproduct material, as the Commission may deem necessary or desirable to protect health or to minimize danger to life or property (42 USC §2201(b)). The NRC has adopted extensive regulations under this authority that apply to nuclear medicine and pharmacy (see, for example, 10 CFR Part 30, Rules of General Applicability to Domestic Licensing of Byproduct Material; Part 32, Specific Domestic Licenses to Manufacture or Transfer Certain Items Containing Byproduct Material; and Part 35, Medical Use of Byproduct Material).

of the prescriber; the name and address of the supplier; the date of assembly of the shipment; and appropriate directions for use (§1791).

A record included in the patient's shipment must include the name, quantity, manufacturer's name, and lot number of each drug or device; the date of shipment; and the name of the pharmacist or exemptee who supervised and was responsible for the distribution. A copy of this record must be provided to the prescribing physician. The supplier must maintain for three years copies of these records for all orders shipped (§1790). Upon delivery of these supplies, the supplier must obtain the signature of the patient or the patient's agent, who may note discrepancies, corrections, or damage (§1792).

If the Board finds any dialysis drugs or devices distributed directly to patients to be ineffective or unsafe for their intended use, it may institute an immediate recall (§4059(c)).

Home dialysis patients may not receive these drugs or devices unless they have received a full course of home training given by a dialysis center. The prescriber is required to submit to the supplier proof that the patient has completed the program (§4059(d)).

**Pharmacies Compounding Injectable Sterile Drug Products.** In response to a death blamed on an injectable sterile drug product supplied by a northern California pharmacy, the Legislature adopted a statute in 2001, effective in 2003, increasing regulatory control over this practice. The statute gives the Board authority to order a pharmacy to cease compounding injectable sterile drug products when the Board has a reasonable belief, based on information obtained during an inspection or investigation, that the pharmacy's practice poses an immediate threat to the public health. The order can remain in effect for up to 30 days or until a hearing seeking an interim suspension order, whichever is earlier (§4127.3(a)). The Board must give the owner immediate notice of the order, specifying the acts or omissions upon which it was based (§4127.3(b)). The owner may, within 15 days, request a hearing before the president of the Board to contest the cease and desist order (§4127.3(c)). These provisions go into effect when the Board is allocated positions for its implementation (§4127.6).

Mandated regulations updating standards for compounding injectable sterile drug products in a pharmacy finally went into effect on October 29, 2004 (§1751-1751.9). A new statute effective July 1, 2005, further restricts compounding of these products by a pharmacy to one of the following environments: an ISO class 7 cleanroom (with a positive air pressure differential relative to adjacent areas) with an ISO class 5 laminar airflow hood, an ISO class 5 cleanroom, or a barrier isolator that provides an ISO class 5 environment for compounding (new §4127.7). The regulations further define, in considerable detail, the required environment and the need for annual certifications, largely by reference to standards in Title 24 of the California Code of Regulations (§1751).

The pharmacy must have detailed written policies and procedures for all the sterile injectable products it prepares and dispenses, covering compounding, filling, labeling, equipment and supplies, staff training, procedures for handling cytotoxic agents, a quality assurance program, and record-keeping (§1751.02(a)). The policies and procedures for pharmacies that compound sterile injectable products from one or more non-sterile ingredients must cover a significant number of additional elements, including process validation, cleaning and disinfection, and enhanced environmental control concerns; pharmacies that do sterile batch compounding must have policies and procedures in addition for master formulas, work sheets, and appropriate documentation (§1751.02(c)). In short, there are significant requirements for engaging in these practices that must be encapsulated in written documents that must be immediately available to all personnel engaging in these activities as well as to Board inspectors (§1751.02(b)(1)). Needless to say, all personnel must read the policies and procedures before compounding sterile injectable products; any changes to the policies and procedures must be communicated to all those personnel (§1751.02(b)(2)). For environmental protection, there must also be policies and procedures for disposal of materials that are infectious or contain cytotoxic residues (§1751.6); these must conform to the public health requirements of the local jurisdiction.

Before compounding, the ingredients and compounding for each preparation must be determined in writing and reviewed by a pharmacist (§1751.02(c)).  The pharmacy may not compound these products if it knows, or reasonably should know, that the compounding environment does not meet the criteria in its written policies and procedures (§1751.01(a)).

Detailed records are required for all such products when compounded from one or more non-sterile ingredients, including records of training and competency evaluation of employees in sterile product procedures (§§1751.3, 1751.5(c)).  The records must be retained for three years.

When compounding sterile injectable products for a prescriber's future office use pursuant to section 1716.1, the pharmacy must maintain records showing the name, lot number, and amount provided to the prescriber, and the date provided (§1751.3(a)), in addition to records required by section 1716.2 to be kept for all compounding for a prescriber's office use.

In addition to the quality assurance program required of all pharmacies, a sterile injectable compounding pharmacy must have a separate QA program to cover the various critical aspects of this process, including personnel performance, equipment, and facilities.  The end products must also be periodically sampled to assure they meet specifications (§1751.7(a)).  In addition to covering such issues as sanitation and documentation of proper storage, the QA program must consider actions to be taken in the event of a drug recall and written justification for choice of product expiration dates (§1751.7(a)(1)-(4)).  Batch-produced sterile injectable drug products compounded from one or more non-sterile ingredients must be quarantined until end product testing confirms their  sterility and acceptable levels of pyrogens; this testing must be documented (§1751.7(c)).

There are training requirements for personnel involved in sterile injectable compounding that require each person to successfully complete a validation process on technique.   Other sections limit access to the cleanroom to properly-attired personnel (§§1751.01(b), 1751.4(b),(c)) and mandate that the equipment be easy to clean and disinfect (§1751.01(c)), and be disinfected weekly and after any unanticipated event that could increase the risk of contamination (§1751.01(d)).  The regulations describe in detail the validation and annual revalidation process, and also require revalidation whenever the QA program yields unacceptable results, improper aseptic techniques are observed, or there are changes in process, facilities, or equipment (§1751.7(b)).

The pharmacist-in-charge is responsible for ensuring that all pharmacy personnel engaging in sterile injectable compounding have training and demonstrated competence in the safe handling and compounding of these products, including cytotoxic agents if used (§1751.5(b)).

As with any prescription medications, there are labeling and consultation requirements.  The label of compounded sterile injectable products must include all the information required for other prescription drugs, plus the name and concentration of its ingredients, instructions for storage and handling, and, unless dispensed to inpatients of a hospital pharmacy, the pharmacy's telephone number.  If cytotoxic agents are involved, there must be a special label reading, "Chemotherapy – Dispose of Properly" (§1751.2).  Consultation must be available to the patient and his or her primary caregiver as to the proper use of these products and related supplies the pharmacy furnishes (§1751.5(a)).

As extensive as is this description of the more than six pages comprising these regulations, it is necessarily incomplete.  Any pharmacy considering engaging in sterile injectable compounding, the licensure requirements for which are discussed below, must study all the regulations in great detail, and be able to ensure full compliance.

The law requires a pharmacy to get an additional license, with a $500 annual fee, to compound injectable sterile drug products (§§4127.1(a), 4127.5).  The license may only be issued or renewed after the pharmacy is inspected and found in compliance with Board regulations; this provision means these pharmacies will have to be inspected annually (§4127.1(b), (c)).  Nonresident pharmacies also require a license to compound injectable sterile drug products (§4127.2(a)); obtaining or renewing the license is contingent upon the Board receiving a current (within 12 months) inspection report by the pharmacy's licensing agency or an approved accrediting agency documenting the pharmacy's compliance with Board regulations (§4127.2(b)).

There are some exceptions to this licensure scheme.  Pharmacies operated by entities licensed by the Board or DHS, and accredited by the Joint Commission on Accreditation of Healthcare Organizations or other private accreditation agencies approved by the Board, are exempt from the licensure requirement (§4127.1(d)); they are not, however, exempt from the new compounding environment statute noted above (§4127.7).  Also, reconstituting a sterile powder does not require a license if the sterile powder was obtained from a manufacturer and the drug is reconstituted for administration to patients by a health care professional licensed to administer drugs by injection in California (§4127.1(e)).

Violations of the sterile injectable drug law or regulations are punishable by a fine of up to $2,500 per occurrence, through the Board's cite and fine program (§4127.4, see Chap. XIII: Board of Pharmacy).

In addition to the new Board regulations on sterile compounding, new USP sterile compounding regulations (Chapter 797) took effect in 2004.  Key provisions of those regulations are discussed in Sandra Levy, *Home Care, Get Ready for New Sterile Compounding Regulations*, DRUG TOPICS, Nov. 17, 2003.

**Pharmacies Dispensing Parenteral Solutions.**  Before it adopted its extensive regulations for sterile injectable drug products, the Board had a simpler set of regulations for pharmacies dispensing parenteral solutions, also designated sections 1751-1751.12 of the Board's regulations.  The same set of regulations, described above, now essentially governs both practices.[21]

Consistent with section 4052(5)(A)(iv) and the regulations on sterile compounding (§§1751-1751.12), the pharmacist may carry and furnish to a patient at home dangerous drugs (other than controlled substances) and devices for parenteral therapy for which the patient has a current prescription.  This provision enables pharmacies to maintain outside the pharmacy (usually in a lock box at the pharmacist's home) a supply of drugs and devices that patients receiving parenteral therapy may need on an emergency basis.  As long as the patient has an ongoing prescription, the pharmacist may supply the needed drug or device item immediately and follow up with the pharmacy and home health agency paperwork thereafter to ensure continuity of therapy.

If a pharmacy were to compound drugs for sale to another pharmacy it probably would constitute manufacturing, making the pharmacy subject to the laws regulating manufacturers (see Chap. VIII: Preparation of Drugs).  The Legislature has made an exception in the case of pharmacies that, on prescription, compound drugs for parenteral therapy and deliver them to another pharmacy for furnishing at retail to the patient.  There are limitations: neither the parenteral solutions nor their components may be prepared in any way before the receipt of a prescription for an individual patient (§4033(b)).  Also, any pharmacy that contracts to compound a drug for parenteral therapy for delivery to another pharmacy must report to the Board within 30 days its contractual arrangement for those services (§4123).

---

[21] Much of Article 7 of the Board's regulations, described above, commencing with section 1751, now specifically refers to sterile injectable compounding.  Much, if not all, of parenteral drug compounding will be subject to those provisions, as well as to the requirements set forth in this section of this text.

Patients requiring parenteral solutions today often remain at home and have their medical needs filled by home health agencies or hospices. Both types of organizations are granted only a limited exemption under statute to allow them to purchase, store, furnish, or transport drugs (§4057(c)). The Board's regulations, sections 1751.11 and 1751.12, reflect the same concerns that are seen throughout the law affecting pharmacy: the protection of the integrity and security of drugs and the assurance that prescriptions are filled accurately for the protection of patients.

The regulations allow pharmacies to furnish to licensed home health agencies or licensed hospices for parenteral therapy those dangerous drugs named in the regulation (§1751.11(b)). The drugs are supplied in a portable container for the purpose of furnishing these drugs to patients at home for emergency treatment or for adjustment of ongoing parenteral therapy. The pharmacy retains ownership of and responsibility for the portable containers. It must ensure that each container is: furnished by a pharmacist; sealed with a tamper-proof seal that must be broken to gain access to the drugs; kept under the effective control of a registered nurse, pharmacist, or delivery person at all times when not in the pharmacy; labeled on the outside with a list of its contents; maintained at an appropriate temperature according to United States Pharmacopeia (USP) standards; and protected at all times from extreme temperatures that could damage the contents (§1751.11(a)).

The pharmacy must ensure that the home health agency's or hospice's policies and procedures list the specific drugs and quantities to be included in its portable containers (§1751.11(b)(5)). The pharmacy may not supply such a container to an organization that does not implement and maintain policies and procedures for the appropriate storage, transportation, and furnishing of the drugs and a treatment protocol for the administration of each medication (§1751.12).

The receiving organization also must have its policies, procedures, and protocols reviewed and, if needed, revised annually by a group of professionals that includes a physician, a pharmacist, and a registered nurse, or it cannot be supplied with the portable container (§1751.11(c)(2)). The furnishing pharmacy must maintain a copy of these policies, procedures, and protocols from each organization to which it furnishes a portable container (§1751.11(d)). In addition, the furnishing pharmacy must have written policies and procedures for the contents, packaging, inventory monitoring, labeling, and storage instructions of the portable container (§1751.11(g)) and must maintain a current inventory of all items placed into and furnished from the portable container (§1751.11(i)).

When a home health agency or hospice administers a drug from the container to a patient based on an oral order, the oral order must be written down immediately by the registered nurse or pharmacist and communicated in writing by copy or fax within 24 hours to the furnishing pharmacy. A prescriber-signed copy must be forwarded to the pharmacy within 20 days (§1751.11(e)).

The pharmacy must ensure that within seven days after its seal has been broken the portable container is returned to the pharmacy by a registered nurse employed by the home health agency or hospice. The furnishing pharmacy must inventory the container and restock and reseal it before returning it to the organization. At least every 60 days the container must be returned to the pharmacy for verification of product quality, quantity, integrity, and expiration dates (§1751.11(h)).

Section 1751.12 underscores the obligation of the pharmacy furnishing portable containers to do so only while the home health agency or licensed hospice is in full compliance with section 1751.11.

**"Refill" Pharmacies.** Some pharmacies and health care entities have proposed or established "refill" pharmacies to handle oral, faxed, or electronically transmitted refill orders for multiple pharmacies by contract, or as part of a unified health care entity. These pharmacies dispense from the refill pharmacy's drug stock, but label the prescription with the name of the originating pharmacy, either mailing the prescription to the patient or returning it to the originating pharmacy for patient pickup. Although no statute recognizes refill pharmacies, the Pharmacy Board has concluded that the concept is legal and adopted regulations to govern them.

A pharmacy may both operate as a "refill" pharmacy for other California pharmacies and handle new prescriptions (§1707.4(a),(b)). The refill pharmacy must either have a contract with the pharmacy whose refills it is handling or be under the same ownership as that pharmacy (§1707.4(a)(1)). In addition to the label information required for all prescriptions, the label must clearly show the name and address of the refill pharmacy or the name of the pharmacy that will receive the refilled prescription for dispensing to the patient (§1707.4(a)(2)). The patient must be provided written information, either on the prescription label or with the prescription container, that explains which pharmacy to contact if the patient has any questions (§1707.4(a)(3)).

Both the pharmacy that received the refill request and the refill pharmacy must maintain complete and accurate records of the refill, including the name of the refilling pharmacist, the name of the refill pharmacy, and the name of the pharmacy that received the refill request (§1707.4(a)(4)). Both pharmacies are responsible for ensuring that the order has been properly filled (§1707.4(a)(5)). The pharmacy that received the refill request is responsible for compliance with the Board's patient profile and patient consultation requirements (§1707.4(a)(6)).

A related concept, not yet formally recognized by the Board, is the "central" pharmacy, which would purchase its own stock for use in filling prescriptions from member pharmacies, pharmacies that have contracted to participate in such a centralized program. The central pharmacy would handle prescriptions for which there was no acute need; the receiving pharmacy would handle prescriptions needing immediate filling. Prescriptions requiring special equipment or expertise could be handled by member pharmacies capable of filling them.

DEA adopted central fill pharmacy regulations for controlled substances in 2003 (68 FR 37405 (June 24, 2003)). A pharmacy may transmit controlled substance prescriptions to another pharmacy for filling if the pharmacies are under common ownership or have a contractual relationship for this purpose. The originating pharmacy must also verify the DEA registration of the filling pharmacy. Each pharmacy must keep complete and accurate records of the transactions; both have a corresponding responsibility (21 CFR §1306.04(a), see Chap. XII: Practice Pitfalls) to assure the legitimacy of prescriptions. The central fill pharmacy is responsible for the drugs it dispenses and ships until they are received, and must report any losses to the DEA. The prescription label must show the originating pharmacy's name and address and some unique identifier to indicate it was filled at another pharmacy. The originating pharmacy may transmit the order to the central fill pharmacy by fax or electronic transmission. The originating pharmacy must maintain complete records that show "central fill" on the order for two years. The central fill pharmacy also must maintain complete records of the transaction. All information required for controlled substance prescriptions remains mandatory, even when the originating pharmacy has the prescription filled at a central fill location.

**"Call-in" Centers.** In a "call-in" center, pharmacists would receive prescription or refill orders, which they would then transmit to a pharmacy for filling. The center would maintain no drugs and fill no prescriptions itself. The center would provide consultation to patients and clinical advice to other practitioners. Other health care practitioners, such as nurses and physicians, might provide clinical advice from the same geographical location, possibly from a common database, at least where the center was part of a health care entity such as a health maintenance organization. This concept has significant potential for increasing the availability of quality clinical services to patients in a cost-effective manner; the question is whether it would require a license as a pharmacy. Because pharmacists now are allowed to provide clinical advice or consultation outside the confines of a pharmacy, as long as they have access to appropriate patient information and assure the security of that information (§4051(b), see Chap. VI: Scope of Practice), the answer is not clear. The Board is considering its response to call-in centers.

**Pharmacy Service Centers.**  The Board has recognized a new category of community pharmacy, the "pharmacy service center."  These centers will hold a standard community pharmacy license but will not have physical possession of drug stock.  The center's purpose is to receive orders by fax or digital imaging from a hospital when the hospital pharmacy is closed.  The center's pharmacist will be able to access the hospital computer system to review orders, perform prospective drug utilization review, and approve the orders within an hour.  The pharmacist will also be available by telephone to answer medication questions from nursing and other hospital staff.  The authority for such a pharmacy comes from section 4071.1 and Health and Safety Code section 11164.5, both pertaining to transmission of electronic orders to a hospital or a hospital pharmacy computer.  The pharmacy service center could handle assessment and paperwork functions for entities and situations where no pharmacist is required for dispensing, as well as to ease the burden for pharmacists where their presence is required by law.

**"Drive-through" Pharmacies.**  The "drive-through" pharmacy enables the patient, as at a fast-food restaurant, to drive up to a window where the pharmacist either is present, visible and audible behind protective glass, or "present" through an interactive audio-visual system (where the window is, for example, in the same building but separate from the pharmacy).  In the latter case, drugs are delivered through some secure system such as a pneumatic tube.  Consultation must still be offered, and provided by a pharmacist.  A drive-through system offers convenience to consumers, especially those who have small, ill children or are disabled.  However, this system would seem to encourage the patient in a hurry to forego consultation.  Nevertheless, the Board now recognizes the use of drive-through windows as long as security, availability of patient consultation, and maintenance of patient privacy and confidentiality are assured.

**Remote Pharmacy Sites.**  Some pharmacies asked the Board to approve the operation of remote sites where automated devices stocked and monitored by a pharmacist would dispense labeled prescription containers based on an electronic authorization from a pharmacist working for the "parent" pharmacy.  The containers would be physically dispensed by an on-site pharmacy technician or other licensed health care provider, and two-way audio/video consultation would be available at the time of dispensing.

New law authorizing the licensure of such remote sites became effective in 2002; however, the provisions of new section 4186 are more limited than those sought by the Board.  It allows automated drug delivery systems to be located in any clinic licensed by the Board under section 4180 and operated in accordance with written policies and procedures "to ensure safety, accuracy, accountability, security, patient confidentiality, and maintenance of the quality, potency, and purity of drugs" (§4186(a)).  Drugs may be removed from the system only upon pharmacist authorization, and after the pharmacist has reviewed the prescription and the patient profile.  The drugs removed from the system must be provided to the patient by a licensed health professional (§4186(b)).  The stocking of the system must be done by a pharmacist (§4186(c)).  Review of the drugs and the system as a whole is the responsibility of the clinic, which must assure monthly review by a pharmacist, including physical inspection of the drugs in the system, inspection of the machine for cleanliness, and review of transaction records to verify the system's security and accountability (§4186(d)).  Patient consultation with a pharmacist must be made available when required by law via a telecommunications link that has two-way audio and video (§4186(e)).  The pharmacist operating the system must be located in California (§4186(f)), and all the drugs dispensed must be properly labeled (§4186(g)).

The authority to employ automated drug dispensing systems was expanded, effective in 2005, to skilled nursing facilities and intermediate care facilities.  A pharmacy is responsible for the operation of the system, including inventory, training of facility personnel, and general oversight (§4119.1, H&SC §1261.6).

**Dispensing Kiosks.** At the end of 2004, using its authority to grant waivers of the regulation prohibiting "depoting" (§1717(e)), the Board granted requests by several chain pharmacies to install 24-hour prescription drop kiosks not on the licensed premises and to use automated devices to dispense prescription medications when the pharmacy is not open. The latter contemplates a device much like an automated teller machine at a bank; the patient would have a code, and could use it to pick up the filled prescription and written information. This expansion of depoting obviously could have a significant impact on direct patient contact. The Board is in the early stages of considering a regulation that would allow such machines generally. An independent pharmacy in Utah has had such a machine for two years (Carol Ukens, *Dispensing kiosk raising eyebrows in California*, DRUG TOPICS, Dec. 23, 2004).

---

**What you should think about after reading this chapter:**

1. As a pharmacy owner employing pharmacists, technicians, clerks, and interns, how may you best ensure that your employees know, and will comply with, their proper roles?

2. Are requirements of law and regulation concerning security adequate? Too stringent? How, if at all, would you change them?

3. How do the responsibilities of a pharmacist-in-charge differ from those of any other pharmacist?

4. Are patients who need sterile injectables, parenteral solutions, or dialysis supplies adequately protected and allowed appropriate access to pharmacy services under existing laws and regulations? How, if at all, would you modify the laws and regulations?

5. As pharmacist-in-charge of a pharmacy with nonpharmacist owners, if you are frustrated in your efforts to meet all requirements of the law by demands and directives of the owners what can you do? What should you do?

6. Are recent innovations in delivery of pharmacy services a benefit to patients? Why or why not?

# Chapter V

# Other Pharmacy Board Licensees

**What you should know after reading this chapter:**

1. What is manufacturing?

2. Who licenses (or registers) manufacturers? What authority does the Board have over manufacturers?

3. What obligations do wholesalers have in regard to examining drugs that they receive or ship? What is their responsibility when they find drugs unfit for sale?

4. Where may a wholesaler store its stock?

5. Who may own or operate a wholesaler? A manufacturer? A veterinary food-animal drug retailer?

6. When is a prescription required for sale of hypodermic needles and syringes? When is it not required? Under what circumstances may someone sell or possess hypodermic needles and syringes without either a prescription or a license?

7. What are clean needle exchange programs?

8. What clinics have the authority to dispense drugs? What drugs may they dispense?

The Board of Pharmacy has at least some authority over most persons and entities by whom drugs and devices are created or through whom they reach the marketplace, in addition to its primary role in regulating pharmacies (Chap. IV: Licensing Pharmacies) and pharmacists, technicians, and exemptees (Chap. III: Licensing Pharmacists). This chapter addresses the Board's relationship with, and authority over, those other persons and entities.

## Manufacturers

Manufacturing, defined below, comprises all aspects of the creation of drugs. Federal and state registration are required for all acts and conduct constituting manufacturing unless otherwise allowed by law.[1]

The drug distribution system has multiple levels. Manufacturers create their products, generally using components purchased from suppliers, and distribute them either directly to retail

---

[1] Pharmacy compounding is the most important example of an act that appears to be manufacturing but is not regulated as manufacturing. Compounding is discussed below and in Chapter VIII: Preparation of Drugs by a Pharmacy. Even a pharmacy's ordinary handling of drugs and devices is technically manufacturing, but not treated as such when within the scope of pharmacy practice.

customers, such as pharmacies, hospitals, and health practitioners, or, more commonly, through a wholesaler. Many such products are sold to a wholesaler, which then sells to retail customers.[2] Regulation of all the major elements in the drug distribution system is intended to protect the integrity of drugs from their creation to their use by the consumer. As discussed below, new requirements for manufacturers, wholesalers, and pharmacies have been introduced to enhance that protection.

## *Regulation of Manufacturing*

**Definition of Manufacturer.** The Pharmacy Law defines a manufacturer as one who "prepares, derives, produces, compounds, or repackages any drug or device" (§4033(a)). California Department of Health Services (DHS) regulations define a manufacturer a bit differently, as any person who prepares, compounds, propagates, processes, or fabricates any drug, including anyone who repackages or otherwise changes the container, wrapper, or labeling of any drug in furtherance of its distribution (17 CCR §10377(i)); federal law is similar (21 USC 360(a)).

**Licensing.** Manufacturers are not licensed by the Board of Pharmacy, but are nevertheless regulated by it.[3] They are regulated extensively by the California Department of Health Services, FDA, and, as to controlled substances, DEA. Those who manufacture a drug or device in California must have a license granted by the California DHS (H&SC §111615, 17 CCR §10376) and must comply with both federal and state laws and regulations (17 CCR §10377.8(a)).[4]

Drug and device manufacturers must register each of their establishments with FDA (21 USC §360(b)-(e), see Chap. II: Drugs). Manufacturing establishments are subject to federal inspection (21 USC §§360(h), 374). Registrants are required to file lists with the agency of all drugs and devices they manufacture (21 USC §360(j)) and comply with Current Good Manufacturing Practices for Finished Pharmaceuticals (21 CFR Part 211) and detailed provisions governing labeling and

---

[2]  In the past the manufacturer/wholesaler/retailer relationship was the same in the drug business as it is for other products: the manufacturer sold to wholesalers, which then sought retail customers to whom it resold products for a profit. Today, at least the largest wholesalers, which control the overwhelming majority of wholesale distribution, operate differently. Wholesalers purchase their stock from manufacturers for a set wholesale price. Retail customers (such as pharmacies and hospitals) contract to purchase drugs from the manufacturer, and a price is set between them. The retailer contacts the wholesaler, with a copy of the purchase order, to arrange delivery. If the purchaser is getting a special discount of some kind, the wholesaler sells the drugs to that purchaser for that special price and then is reimbursed by the manufacturer to reflect the difference between what it paid and the lower price it had to offer the retailer and still make a profit.

Some purchases fit the traditional pattern: that is, the deal is between the retailer and a wholesaler which has previously purchased (or contracted to purchase) goods from the manufacturer. But these "traditional" deals now occur primarily when retailers are buying from wholesalers without formal relationships with drug manufacturers or from small wholesalers that depend on "spot" purchases to obtain their stock. These small wholesalers generally purchase on the "secondary" market, buying from, for example, institutions that have over-purchased certain drugs and wish to resell them before they are too old for sale or use. They aim to purchase drugs they believe will be in demand in other markets, hoping to resell at a higher price. While many such spot or secondary wholesalers are legitimate and ensure the legitimacy of their products, others have not been reliable; experience with the latter has led to tighter controls on wholesalers generally.

[3]  For example, a license is required for each sales or distribution outlet of any out-of-state manufacturer that is not itself licensed by the California Board (§4160(b)).

[4]  The licensing process is similar to that for licenses granted by the Board, involving an application, separate licenses for each place of manufacture, fees, annual renewal, prelicensure inspection, and facilities and personnel requirements (H&SC §§111620-111640).

advertising. Other regulations (for example, 21 CFR Parts 226 and 250) apply to the manufacturing of specific pharmaceutical products.[5]

In addition, every person or business that manufactures, distributes, or dispenses any controlled substance must register with the DEA (21 USC §822, 21 CFR §1301.11).[6] Manufacturers are not free to produce as much of any controlled substance as they wish; quotas are set by the DEA for Schedule I and II controlled substances (21 CFR §1303.21). The regulations provide the processes for determining production amounts, increasing those amounts to meet need during any calendar year, and challenging quota limits, among other things (21 CFR Part 1303). There also are detailed inventory requirements for manufacturers (21 CFR §1304.11) and others in the chain of distribution and use of controlled substances, as well as extensive reporting and other requirements (21 USC §§821-828, 21 CFR §§1304-1305).

**Board Authority over Manufacturers.** Although manufacturers are not licensed by the Board, they are subject to many provisions of the law that it enforces. For example, they are subject to the provisions of sections 4080 and 4081 concerning record-keeping and inspection, and, until January 1, 2006, must report excessive sales of drugs subject to abuse (§4164, §1782).

Manufacturers located or with a site in California were, until 2005, like some other entities in the distribution chain such as wholesalers, exempt from the Pharmacy Law's command that only pharmacists may lawfully manufacture prescription drugs or devices (§§4051, 4053(a)) if they employed "sufficient, qualified supervision . . . to adequately safeguard and protect the public health" (§4053(a)) in the form of a Board-certified "exemptee" (see Chap. III: Licensing Pharmacists). The Pharmacy Law no longer provides that an exemptee, rather than a pharmacist, may take charge of a manufacturer's premises.[7] That change might suggest that manufacturers now require a pharmacist to be in charge. However, another amendment to the law effective in 2005 exempts entirely from this supervision requirement any manufacturer that is licensed either by the FDA or the Food and Drug branch of the California Department of Health Services and only ships dangerous drugs or dangerous devices of its own manufacture; those entities also do not require wholesaler licenses (§4160(f), until 2006; thereafter §4160(e)).

Drug manufacturers which have obtained a license from the DHS or are applying for one must submit to the Board of Pharmacy such information as the Board deems reasonably necessary to carry out the Board's responsibilities, including, for example, information on drug inventories or controlled substances. The manufacturer's failure to submit information to the Board in a timely fashion is grounds for the DHS to deny, suspend, or revoke the manufacturer's license (H&SC §111645). The Board may examine drug stock (§4080) and records (§4081) of California manufacturers. The Board may obtain records of drug transfer and sale from out-of-state manufacturers relating to California transactions, and may cite, fine, or issue an order of abatement against a manufacturer for failure to provide such records or other documents within a reasonable time (§4165).

---

[5] An FDA initiative to improve product quality regulation by focusing on companies that make the riskiest products and using new technology ("Pharmaceutical cGMPs for the 21st Century: A Risk-Based Approach") is described at www.fda.gov/oc/guidance/gmp.html.

[6] Employees of a registered business (such as pharmacists) do not need to register separately (21 CFR §1301.22).

[7] The Board's regulation, section 1781, still includes that requirement, but to the extent it conflicts with the newly-adopted law it is no longer authorized. The new law's intent was to eliminate the requirement for a manufacturer to have either a pharmacist or an exemptee, but the statutory language did not make this result entirely clear. It is likely the Board will move to amend section 1781 early in 2005 to eliminate the reference to a manufacturer.

Both manufacturers and wholesalers are required to avoid furnishing drugs to unauthorized persons, a duty necessary for maintaining security of the drug distribution system (§4163; see *People v. Kessler,* 250 Cal. App. 2d 642, 647 (2d Dist. 1967)). A Board regulation imposes a duty on manufacturers and wholesalers to know their customers and that they are legitimate (§1783). Drugs or devices may only be furnished to an "authorized person" (§1783(a)). "Authorized person" means a person to whom the Board has issued a license permitting the purchase of drugs or devices for use within the scope of that license and includes any other person authorized to be furnished the drugs or devices by California law, applicable federal law, and the law of the jurisdiction in which the purchaser is located (§1783(b)). If the customer is not known, the manufacturer or wholesaler must contact the Board or other agency by which the customer is purportedly licensed to confirm its licensure (§1783(a)). Until January 1, 2006, manufacturers must also report certain "excessive sales" of drugs (§4164), as discussed below under "Wholesalers."

Drugs or devices are to be delivered only to the premises listed on the recipient's license, although an authorized person or agent of the purchaser may pick up the purchase at the manufacturer's or wholesaler's premises if both the identity and authorization of the person or agent are established and such a pickup is used only to meet the immediate needs of a particular patient of the purchaser (§1783(c)), except as provided in Chapter IV: Licensing Pharmacies. Only an owner of the purchaser, its chief executive officer, or its chief financial officer, as listed on its license, may pay for the drugs or devices or may have its credit used to establish an account for purchases, and the account itself must be in the name of the licensee (§1783(d)). Consistent with section 4081, records of such furnishing by a manufacturer or wholesaler must be preserved for three years and be open to inspection during business hours by authorized officers of the law at the premises from which the drugs or devices were furnished (§1783(e)).

## *The Pharmacy Exemption*

The Health and Safety Code exempts licensed pharmacies from its manufacturer licensing provisions where the pharmacy is operating in conformity with pharmacy law, is regularly engaged in dispensing drugs or devices on prescription, and does not manufacture for sale other than in the regular course of dispensing (H&SC §111655(a)). A pharmacy may also provide drugs to a person licensed to administer those drugs in the course of professional practice or to another pharmacy to meet a temporary inventory shortage, without being licensed as a manufacturer (H&SC §111655(c)).[8]

Pharmacies that regularly dispense prescription drugs or devices but only manufacture or compound in the regular course of the business of dispensing drugs at retail are exempt from registration as manufacturers under federal as well as state law (21 USC §360(g)(1)). The FDA long has taken the position that a hospital pharmacy is exempt unless it repacks or relabels beyond the usual conduct of dispensing or sale at retail (FDA Compliance Policy Guideline Manual, Ch. 4, §460.100 (CPG 7132.06)). The exemption extends to compounding an end product that has not received FDA approval, at the direction of a physician. The first federal statute to define compounding and regulate it was struck down as containing an unconstitutional restriction on commercial free speech (*Thompson v. Western States Medical Center*, 535 U.S. 357, 377 (2002)); current compounding guidelines are detailed in Chapter VIII: Preparation of Drugs by a Pharmacy.

---

[8]  Persons licensed to prescribe or administer drugs who manufacture drugs for use in their own professional practice are also exempt, as are licensed wholesalers, persons who manufacture for use in nonclinical research, teaching, or chemical analysis and not for sale, and registered dispensing opticians (H&SC 111655(d)-(f),(h)). The DHS may exempt by regulation any other class on a finding that licensure is not necessary to protect the public health (H&SC§111655(g)).

DHS regulations exclude from the definition of manufacturer a retailer who repackages from a bulk container at the time of sale to the ultimate consumer, which is precisely what a pharmacy does (17 CCR §10377(i)(1)). In addition, a pharmacy may repackage previously-dispensed prescription drugs, at a patient's request, without becoming, under the law, a manufacturer (§4033(c)). Under the Pharmacy Law, when a pharmacy manufactures on the immediate premises from which the drug or device is sold to the ultimate consumer, it is not considered to be a manufacturer (§4033(a)). This exception allows a pharmacy to compound a prescription for a patient without becoming, under the law, a manufacturer. The limits to the exception are discussed in Chapter VIII: Preparation of Drugs by a Pharmacy.

# Wholesalers

A wholesaler is an entity that sells dangerous drugs or devices for resale or negotiates for their distribution. Wholesalers include jobbers, brokers, wholesale merchants, agents, or any other entity or person, regardless of the title it uses, that engages in the above activity. Reverse distributors, which receive, inventory, and manage the disposition of outdated or nonsaleable dangerous drugs as agents for pharmacies, manufacturers, and other entities, are also wholesalers (§4043). An e-commerce entity that never touches drugs, but acts as a middleman in transactions through which it orders drugs for pharmacies, is also a wholesaler. All wholesalers must be licensed by the Board (§4160(a)).[9] A new law effective in 2005 bars the issuance of a business license by a county or municipality to a wholesaler without a current wholesaler license from the Board (§4168). Wholesalers from out of state that sell drugs into California must also be licensed by the Board, as is discussed below.

Wholesalers buy from manufacturers (or sometimes from other wholesalers) and handle the process of redistributing on order to the large number of retail outlets. When the product involved is pharmaceuticals, assurance of public health and safety necessitates that the entire chain of distribution of the product be subject to close control. For example, at the wholesale level there is a need to assure that drugs are stored properly so their quality and effectiveness are not impaired, they remain properly labeled, and they are distributed legally only to authorized recipients (see §1783, discussed above). A wholesaler (or manufacturer) may not furnish dangerous drugs or dangerous devices to unauthorized persons, and every recipient of dangerous drugs or dangerous devices must acquire them from a person or entity authorized to possess and furnish them. When a wholesaler first acquires such drugs or devices from a person or entity, its obligation is "limited to obtaining confirmation of licensure" (§4163(b)); the phrasing of this requirement, effective in 2005, was carefully negotiated by drug wholesalers.

Although the conditions for obtaining a wholesaler license from the Board are not stringent, the holder of the license must comply with the law or be subject to revocation of the license. The statute sets out few details of the licensure process, other than the annual fee requirement (§4160(a)). It does mandate a separate license for each place of business owned or operated by a wholesaler (§4160(c)). With the exception of a veterinary food-animal drug retailer license, no location may have a wholesaler license and another Board license (§4107).

---

[9] A pharmacy that wishes to engage in wholesaling must obtain a separate license as a wholesaler; this function is not covered by the pharmacy license. The exceptions in section 4059(b) to the ban in section 4059(a) on furnishing a dangerous drug or device without a prescription are intended simply to recognize that various entities in the drug distribution system sell to each other without prescriptions. Other than sales on prescription, the pharmacy's right to distribute drugs under its license has always been limited. Pharmacies have been allowed to sell to other pharmacies, return drugs to a distributor, or, to a limited extent, furnish drugs to a prescriber for use in his or her practice (§4052(a)(1); see Chap. VI: Scope of Practice). As of 2005, even that limited authority has been further restricted; see Chapter IV: Licensing Pharmacies.

A wholesaler's stock must be stored on the licensed premises (§4043); wholesalers are forbidden to order drugs for which they do not have adequate secure storage on those premises (§4167). Some major wholesalers have in recent years placed their stock in pharmacies, while retaining title to the drugs; the pharmacy only takes title and pays the wholesale price for the drugs when they are sold. This consignment sale technique is of questionable legality, because it results in the pharmacy acting as one of the wholesaler's premises, but without a wholesaler license. It also raises questions about which entity would be responsible for accounting for the stock.

The wholesaler remains responsible for orders it fills until the drugs reach the purchaser (§4166). Effective in 2007, under California law neither a wholesaler nor a pharmacy may acquire or distribute a dangerous drug without a "pedigree" (§4163(c),(d)).[10] A pedigree is a record, in electronic form, that contains information on every transaction changing the ownership of a drug, from its first sale by a manufacturer to its final sale to a pharmacy or other person who will furnish, dispense, or administer the drug to a patient (§4034(a)). The new law details the information required in the pedigree (§4034(b)). FDA has had the power, under the Prescription Drug Marketing Act of 1987, as amended in 1992, to impose on all wholesalers that are not manufacturers or authorized distributors of a drug (but not on pharmacies) the requirement to obtain and maintain information showing the pedigree of the drugs they handle. FDA adopted regulations to effectuate this law in 1999, but their effective date has repeatedly been delayed, most recently until December 1, 2006 (69 FR 8105 (Feb. 23, 2004)).

Difficulties and costs of maintaining a paper pedigree have been a major reason for the delays in FDA issuing its regulations. The expectation that electronic track and trace technologies (such as radio frequency identification) will soon be available, reliable, and reasonable in cost has been cited by FDA as a reason for pushing off the effective date of its regulations. The federal law imposing pedigree requirements, however, is already in force, and in mid-2004 FDA obtained some guilty pleas in criminal prosecutions brought for failure to comply with them (*FDA Gets Significant Guilty Pleas*, FDA Press Release, Aug. 27, 2004, www.fda.gov/bbs/topics/news/2004/NEW01109.html).

Dangerous drugs and devices may only be ordered by a licensee and delivered to a licensed premises, except as the law otherwise specifically authorizes, and they must be signed for and received by the pharmacist-in-charge, a pharmacist designated by the pharmacist-in-charge, or an exemptee at the licensed premises (§4059.5(a)). There are exceptions for hospital pharmacies and after-hours deliveries to pharmacies, as discussed in Chapter IV: Licensing Pharmacies.

The transfer, sale, or delivery of dangerous drugs or devices to persons outside of California must be done in compliance with the laws of the state or country in which the drugs or devices are delivered as well as with California and federal law. Compliance requires that the seller determine that the recipient of the drugs or devices is authorized to receive them by the law of the state or country where they are received (§4059.5(e)).

Like other non-pharmacy sellers of prescription drugs and devices, wholesalers must either employ a pharmacist or provide adequate supervision of their facilities by employing a qualified

---

[10] The California Legislature has specifically stated that, if it determines that electronic technologies to implement the pedigree requirement are not economically and technically feasible by 2007, it may extend the deadline to 2009 (§4163.6).

Increasing concern about drug counterfeiting, as well as the traditional issue of drug purity, has led several states to adopt stricter controls for wholesalers, including pedigree requirements. The National Association of Boards of Pharmacy has proposed a comprehensive model wholesaler licensure law that would include such a requirement, which it would like to see effective throughout the country by 2007 (Carol Ukens, *NABP proposes wholesaler Rx pedigrees to combat counterfeits*, DRUG TOPICS, Jan. 26, 2004).

exemptee (§§4051, 4053; see Chap. III, Licensing Pharmacists). The pharmacist or exemptee must be present and in control of the premises during the conduct of business (§1781(a)); without that person present, the location must cease operations. There also must be an exemptee-in-charge (called "designated representative-in-charge" as of 2006) who, like the pharmacist-in-charge at a pharmacy, is responsible for the wholesaler's compliance with state and federal laws; a wholesaler may not be licensed without designating one (§4160(c)). As with a pharmacist-in-charge, the initial designation of, and any changes in, the exemptee-in-charge must be reported to the Board within 30 days, both by the entity and by the individual (§4305.5(c)). A pharmacist may be designated as the exemptee (§4160(d),(e)).

A wholesaler has a responsibility, similar to that of a pharmacist (see Chap. XII: Practice Pitfalls), to make sure it does not distribute controlled substances to any entity when it knows they are not for a legitimate medical purpose (H&SC §11153.5(a)). As with pharmacists, "know" also means "reason to know" from actually known or readily-available information. Violation of this requirement is criminal under the Controlled Substances Act (H&SC §11153.5(b)). Clearly excessive furnishing in violation of section 11153.5(a) is a ground for discipline by the Board (§4301(e)). As of 2006, a wholesaler will also be subject to discipline for clearly excessive furnishing of dangerous drugs (but not dangerous devices) to a pharmacy that primarily or solely dispenses to patients of long-term care facilities. As in section 4301(e), several factors are set out for judging when the furnishing is "clearly excessive." If a wholesaler has, and uses, a tracking system, as described below, that will be considered in determining whether there are grounds for discipline (§4301(s)).

The Board has long been concerned about the need for wholesaler and manufacturer vigilance in respect to sales of controlled substances. For years it has required that drug distributors, including wholesalers, report "excessive" sales to the Board (§4164, §1782). The Board identifies threshold amounts of certain controlled substances, and sometimes certain dangerous drugs, to be reported, and varies the drugs and amounts as patterns of abuse change. The Board currently requires quarterly reports but has the authority to require reports as often as monthly (§4164, §1782). The Board has the legal right to obtain copies of transaction records concerning any dangerous drug or device that a licensed wholesaler sends into or out of California (§4165).

Commencing in 2006, wholesalers will also need to have in place a system for tracking individual sales of dangerous drugs (but not dangerous devices) at preferential or contract prices to pharmacies that primarily or solely dispense to patients of long-term care facilities. The system must be capable of identifying anomalous purchases; the wholesaler must furnish tracking information to the Board on request (§4164).[11]

Various legislative changes that affect wholesalers respond to the increasing concern about assuring the legitimacy of all dangerous drugs and devices sold, given the known risks of drug counterfeiting and diversion. A new law effective in 2005 provides that a person or entity may not purchase, trade, sell, or transfer dangerous drugs or dangerous devices at wholesale with a person or entity that is not licensed with the Board as a wholesaler or pharmacy, and may not purchase, trade, sell, or transfer drugs or devices that were known or reasonably should have been known to be misbranded, adulterated, or past the beyond use date on their label (§4169(a)). This provision does not apply to a manufacturer licensed by FDA or DHS (§4169(d)). The Legislature has specified that the Board may issue citations and fines, even to nonresident wholesalers, for violations of pharmacy law or regulations. In order to secure the Board's ability to collect any fines it imposes, as of 2006 wholesalers may not receive a license without posting a surety bond (§§4162, 4162.5). Large wholesalers must post a $100,000 surety bond; smaller wholesalers may be allowed to post a $25,000

---

[11] The Legislature has also indicated this deadline could be extended to 2009 (§4163.6).

surety bond (although the Board may demand the $100,000 bond from a wholesaler previously disciplined by a government agency). The Board may make claims against these bonds for unpaid fines. Sections 4162 and 4162.5 will be effective only from 2006 through 2010, unless extended.[12]

The Board has by regulation established a set of minimum standards for wholesalers. To assure the security of its drugs, the wholesaler must store them "in a secured and lockable area"; entry into the area where prescription drugs are stored must be limited to authorized personnel. To assure non-entry, an alarm system is required for after-hours use. Also mandated is a security system that will provide "suitable protection against theft and diversion." When appropriate, the system must afford protection against theft or diversion that would be facilitated or hidden by tampering with electronic records. Adequate lighting of the outside perimeter of the premises also is required (§1780).

To protect the quality of stored drugs, all wholesaler premises, fixtures, and equipment must be maintained in a clean and orderly condition, free from rodents and insects, and adequately lighted. Plumbing must be in good repair, and the temperature and humidity must be monitored to assure compliance with United States Pharmacopoeia Standards (§1780(b)).[13]

Wholesalers are required to examine their goods upon receipt and before shipment.[14] Upon receipt, the required visual examination is of each outside shipping container. The wholesaler must verify the identity of the drugs and check for container damage that would suggest possible contamination or otherwise make the drugs unfit for distribution. Upon shipment, careful inspection must be made to verify the identity of the prescription drug products and to assure that they have not been damaged in storage or held under improper conditions (§1780(d)).

The regulations are quite specific about the wholesaler's duty when handling returned, damaged, and outdated prescription drugs. Prescription drugs that are outdated, damaged, deteriorated, misbranded, or adulterated must be quarantined – that is, kept physically separate from other drugs – until they are destroyed or returned to their supplier. Any prescription drugs whose immediate or sealed outer or sealed secondary containers have been opened or used must be identified as such and quarantined until they are either destroyed or returned to the supplier (§1780(e)). "If the conditions under which a prescription drug has been returned cast doubt on the drug's safety, identity, strength, quality or purity, the drug shall be destroyed or returned to the supplier unless testing or other investigation proves that the drug meets appropriate United States Pharmacopoeia Standards" (§1780(e)(3)).

---

[12] The laws passed in 2004 concerning wholesalers also contain provisions governing to whom sales may take place, adulteration, misbranding, and beyond-use date violations; these are discussed in Chapter VII: Ordering, Receipt, Maintenance, and Transfer of Drugs and Devices.

[13] This regulation refers to the 22nd Revision of those standards, published in 1990; the most current version of the United States Pharmacopoeia Standards is the 28th Revision, dated 2005. The regulation has not been updated in this respect.

[14] The Board's regulation, section 1780(d), actually reads, "[a]ll materials must be examined upon receipt *or* before shipment" (emphasis added). A logical reading of the regulation suggests that examination *both* upon receipt *and* before shipment is required because otherwise the intent of the rule, to assure the integrity of drug supplies, could not be met. Furthermore, federal law mandates that the states adopt regulations governing wholesalers concerning the storage and handling of prescription drugs and the establishment and maintenance of drug distribution records (21 USC §353(e)(2)(B), 21 CFR §205.50). The detailed requirements of the Pharmacy Board's rules about examination of drugs upon receipt (§1780(d)(1)) and before shipment (§1780(d)(2)) otherwise are identical to the FDA's regulations; the federal rules clearly require examination both upon receipt and before shipment (21 CFR §205.50(d)).

**Suppose drugs are returned to the wholesaler because of the bankruptcy of a pharmacy. Is that a condition that casts doubt on the drug's safety, quality, or purity? Suppose drugs are returned to the wholesaler because a pharmacy has gone out of business after a fire in its building. Is that such a condition?**

The answer to the second hypothetical case is obvious: the exposure of drugs to a fire (and therefore to heat, smoke, and water) should at least "cast doubt" on the integrity of the drugs that survived. Bankruptcy less surely casts such doubt, but the wholesaler should at minimum inquire whether the financial condition of the pharmacy exposed the drugs to less than optimal conditions of storage. If the bankruptcy of a particular pharmacy occurred suddenly, in the context of an ongoing business (for example, the financial problems were related to difficulties in a distant corporate structure), there may be no reason to question the integrity of the drugs. On the other hand, if financial stress had been directly impacting the operations and maintenance of a particular pharmacy, greater inquiry might be in order.

Wholesalers must have written policies and procedures, available to the Board upon request, to follow in regard to the "receipt, security, storage, inventory and distribution of prescription drugs, including policies and procedures for identifying, recording, and reporting losses or thefts, for correcting all errors and inaccuracies in inventories, and for maintaining records to document proper storage" (§1780(f)(1)). These records must be kept in accordance with section 205.50(g) of Title 21, Code of Federal Regulations, the federal rules for wholesaler prescription drug records, and maintained for three years after the disposition of the drugs.

Wholesalers must maintain lists of the names, duties, and qualifications of their officers, directors, managers, and other employees in charge of wholesale drug distribution, storage, and handling. It is the responsibility of each wholesaler to provide adequate training and experience to assure that all its personnel comply with licensing requirements (§1780(f)(3),(4)).

# Home Medical Device Retailers

Under long-standing law, only a pharmacist could dispense a dangerous drug (§4051) and the definition of a dangerous drug included devices available only on prescription (§4022). However, many sales of prescription devices were occurring illegally outside the pharmacy setting; policymakers recognized that there was a need for broader availability of prescription devices while still assuring adequate consumer protection. The result was a comprehensive regulatory program, adopted in 1987, for which enforcement responsibility for the category of medical device retailer was placed with the Pharmacy Board. That law was repealed in 2001, and what are now called "home medical device retailers" were placed under the primary jurisdiction of the California Department of Health Services. A home medical device retailer (HMDR) is subject to very similar provisions under DHS as it was under the Pharmacy Law; the entity still has to be in the charge of a pharmacist or exemptee, although DHS, rather than the Pharmacy Board, has the responsibility for registering HMDR exemptees (H&SC §111656.4).

Basically, the HMDR may furnish prescription devices from its premises, and may deliver, install, and maintain such devices, and give instruction in their use (H&SC §§109948.1(a), 111656). Pharmacies do not need a home medical device retailer license because pharmacists are authorized to manufacture, measure, fit to the patient, sell, repair, and furnish instructions about the use of prescription devices (§4052(a)(6)). The HMDR may not operate without a pharmacist or exemptee on the premises, but the law allows DHS to provide, by regulation, that HMDRs may set up a locked storage system for emergency or after-hours furnishing of prescription devices. If DHS regulations so allow, an HMDR employee could furnish devices after hours from this locked storage upon the direction of the pharmacist or exemptee (H&SC §111656.4 (b),(e),(f)). The HMDR may also furnish prescription devices to licensed health care facilities for storage in secured emergency pharmaceutical supplies containers (H&SC §111656(e)).

The law sets forth storage, security, and sanitation standards for licensees (H&SC 111656.2). This law does not apply to a wide range of licensed health care facilities that supply home medical devices or services (including hospitals, home health agencies, hospice programs, nursing homes, emergency medical services providers, and breast feeding support programs), nor does it apply to manufacturers, wholesalers, pharmacists and pharmacies, or to prescribers, including dentists and veterinarians, unless the home medical devices or services are supplied through a separate business entity (H&SC §11656(f)). In other words, in a large hospital corporation, the hospitals themselves could supply medical devices without obtaining an HMDR license, but a subsidiary that is in the business of acting like an HMDR must obtain a license for that activity.

# Unlicensed Out-of-State Manufacturers and Drug Distributors

The intent of the Pharmacy Law and related Health and Safety Code provisions is to assure that at every level the commercial chain of distribution of dangerous drugs is, through close legal control, safe and secure. In general, California's jurisdiction stops at its borders. Nevertheless, California requires nonresident pharmacies doing business in California to register (Chap. IV: Licensing Pharmacies). The California Legislature also has given the Board authority to require registration of two other categories of out-of-state businesses.

Section 4161 requires anyone who ships, mails, or delivers dangerous drugs or devices into California at wholesale to be licensed. Until 2006, these entities are called out-of-state distributors; thereafter, they are called nonresident wholesalers. A prior exemption for wholesalers which sold only to California-licensed wholesalers has been repealed. A separate license is required for each place of business that sells or distributes dangerous drugs or devices to a site in California (§4161(c)). Other provisions of section 4161 set out, among other requirements, the information that must be provided to the Board and records that must be kept.

The Board has explicit authority to deny, revoke, or suspend these licenses for violations of the Pharmacy Law and related laws (§4304).

# Hypodermic Dealers

Controversy has long surrounded the limitations placed by pharmacy law on the sale of hypodermic needles and syringes. In California, it generally has been illegal to possess or distribute hypodermics without a prescription, although only four other states still have prescription requirements for syringes (Jordan Rau and Nancy Vogel, *Governor OKs Over-the-Counter Sale of Syringes; He signs a bill sought by AIDS activists that lets pharmacists sell needles without a prescription*, LOS ANGELES TIMES, Sept. 21, 2004, p. B1). Resistance to changing California law has been largely based on concerns about promoting drug abuse. However, dirty and shared needles, frequently used by drug addicts with no access to clean needles and syringes, often are contaminated with the hepatitis and acquired immunodeficiency syndrome (AIDS) viruses. Because these needles are a significant source of the spread of those diseases among drug addicts and their family members and sexual contacts, there have been widespread community and public health efforts to provide clean needles and syringes. The funding of needle exchanges is a contentious political issue; there is a ban on using federal funds for this purpose. Nevertheless, legal and underground needle exchange programs distributed more than 17.5 million syringes nationwide in 1997, and many of those syringes were distributed in California, notwithstanding the illegality of the activity.[15]  Police in several California cities arrested people conducting "needle swaps"– exchanging clean needles and syringes for those already used by drug addicts – and brought criminal prosecutions against them, although apparently without achieving convictions.[16]

Efforts by the Legislature to legalize clean needle exchanges, stymied by gubernatorial opposition through two administrations, came to fruition in 1999.  Upon finding that there is a local emergency due to a critical local public health crisis that requires the authorization of a clean needle program, a public entity may now approve such a program for that locality without risk of criminal prosecution (H&SC §11364.7(a)).  The law does not limit which government agencies may make such a declaration, so that means a local, county, or state agency could do so.  Every major California city has made the requisite finding of a local public health emergency to authorize a clean needle program.  Subsequent efforts to expand the authority for clean needle exchange programs were repeatedly vetoed.

Effective in 2005, a new law creates the Disease Prevention Demonstration Project in which pharmacies will collaborate with state and local health officials; the pharmacies will be allowed to sell or furnish up to ten hypodermic needles or syringes for human use to a person 18 years of age or older without a prescription.  This authority will continue through 2010, while the results are studied (Stats. 2004, ch. 608 (SB 1159)).  The pharmacy must register with the participating local health department, and certify that it will provide, along with the needles and syringes, written information or verbal counseling on how to access drug treatment, how to access testing and treatment for HIV and hepatitis C, and how to safely dispose of used needles.  In addition, the pharmacy is required to store the needles and syringes so they are accessible only to authorized personnel, and provide an option to customers for the safe disposal of needles and syringes (H&SC §121285(d)).

It remains illegal to furnish hypodermic needles or syringes without a license from the Board for each location at which sales will be made (§§4141, 4205(d)).  The licenses held by pharmacies, home medical device retailers, wholesalers, and out-of-state drug distributors include authorization for the sale of hypodermics (§4205(a)).  License requirements do not apply to wholesale sellers, such as drug and surgical instrument manufacturers, that supply pharmacies, physicians, dentists, podiatrists, veterinarians, or licensed resellers of hypodermics (§4143).  Every licensed entity that may sell hypodermics must comply with all requirements for ordering, handling, dispensing (on prescription or otherwise), record-keeping, and disposal of the hypodermics.  Licenses may be issued authorizing the sale of hypodermic syringes and needles for veterinary use (§4205(b)).

Although the law continues to require a prescription for the retail sale of hypodermic needles or syringes (§4142), exceptions virtually swallow the rule.  Without a prescription, a pharmacist or physician may now furnish needles and syringes for human use if the person is known to the furnisher and has previously provided a prescription or other proof of a legitimate medical need; this is a broadening of the prior authority to furnish syringes without a prescription for human use in the administration of insulin or adrenaline (§4145(a)(1)).  A pharmacist or veterinarian may continue to furnish needles and syringes for use on animals to a purchaser who can properly establish his or her identity (that is, present proper identification).  The requirement of recording these transactions in a

---

[15]  David Perlman, *Needle Exchange Programs Proliferate; 17.5 Million Syringes Distributed Last Year Despite Funds Ban,* SAN FRANCISCO CHRONICLE, Aug. 19, 1998, p. A9.

[16]  It appears that all those who were prosecuted for involvement in clean needle exchange programs (notably in San Mateo and Alameda counties) were acquitted by juries.  No pharmacists have been involved in any of these prosecutions.

hypodermic register (§4146) has now been repealed. The same law eliminated the requirement of a register for non-prescription sales.

**You work in a pharmacy in a locality where a local emergency has been declared under Health and Safety Code section 11364.7. The authorizing public agency wants to contract with a pharmacy to administer the program (to purchase the stock and distribute or supervise the distribution of the needles and syringes). May the pharmacy legally enter into such a contract?**

The clean needle exchange law merely exempts certain people, under stated circumstances, from the threat of criminal prosecution for engaging in the otherwise-illegal behavior of distributing needles and syringes, but it does not specify how a needle exchange program should operate. Acting as an agent of the public entity, the pharmacy and pharmacist would be safe from criminal prosecution for their activity. It makes sense for pharmacies and pharmacists, who are familiar with medical devices, to be involved in needle exchange programs. However, the Pharmacy Law was not amended by the passage of section 11364.7; a pharmacy could not literally comply with the Pharmacy Law and participate in the needle exchange program. Under the Pharmacy Law, hypodermics may be furnished without a prescription only under the conditions set forth in section 4145. While non-prescription sales authority was somewhat broadened as of 2005, outside of the Disease Prevention Demonstration Project sales without a prescription may be made only to people known to the pharmacy to have a medical need for syringes (as evidenced, for example, by an earlier prescription for insulin or adrenaline). The repeal of the hypodermic register requirement eliminates one factor that may have deterred some addicts from obtaining their syringes from a pharmacy, even under a needle exchange program. While the needle exchange law did not fully consider conflicts with the Pharmacy Law for participating pharmacies and pharmacists, the creation of the new law specifically involving pharmacies in needle exchange surely reflects legislative intention that pharmacies participate in the prior as well as the new needle exchange program.

**A person comes into a pharmacy or a hypodermic dealer with a prescription for 200 needles and syringes. Is this legal? A person without a prescription wants to purchase 200 needles and syringes for injection of insulin. Is this legal?**

There is nothing inherently illegal about a prescription for a large number of hypodermic needles and syringes; however, the dealer or pharmacy must be alert to signs indicating that the prescription is not legitimate or the devices not intended for a legitimate purpose. The diabetic patient's request should be evaluated with respect to his or her insulin prescription and its directions. For some patients, 200 needles and syringes could be an enormous number; for others, it may be only about a month's supply.

**A person comes into a pharmacy and requests hypodermic needles and syringes to administer medication to his pet dog. Is this legal?**

The law allows a pharmacist or veterinarian to furnish needles and syringes for use on animals, and does not exclude pets. The person furnishing the needles and syringes is obliged to confirm the identity of the person requesting them, and to obtain reasonable assurance that the items will be used for the purpose stated.

**Must a pharmacy or hypodermic dealer sell syringes only by the box?**

Nothing in the law requires sales of hypodermic needles and syringes by the box.

Section 4144, which allows the sale or receipt of hypodermic needles and syringes without a prescription or a license for uses that the Board determines are industrial, is an additional exception.

At the present time the Board allows firms to determine for themselves if they are eligible for the industrial use exemption, in which case they need not seek Board approval for their hypodermic sale or possession.

A person who possesses any hypodermic needle or syringe acquired other than in a legal manner is in violation of section 4140; such violations are punishable as misdemeanors (see *People v. Fuentes*, 224 Cal. App. 3d 1041 (6th Dist. 1990)). It is a misdemeanor to obtain hypodermic needles or syringes by fraud, forgery, misrepresentation, or otherwise in violation of the law (§4326(a)), or to obtain hypodermic needles or syringes legally and use or allow them to be used for any purpose other than that for which they were purchased (§4326(b)). Stocks of hypodermic needles or syringes found outside the licensed premises of a license-holder and in the possession or control of a person not entitled to their possession "shall be confiscated" (§4148).

The law also mandates proper disposal of hypodermic needles and syringes, in accordance with sections 117600 to 117780 of the Health and Safety Code (§4147). This provision was added to the law because of the haphazard way many health facilities and practitioners were disposing of medical waste, including hypodermics. Amendments effective in 2005 specifically make it illegal to discard or dispose of a hypodermic needle or syringe on the grounds of a playground, beach, park, or any public or private elementary, vocational, junior high, or high school (except in an appropriate container for that purpose).

**Suppose a pharmacy customer confesses that she is addicted to narcotics and regularly injects them intravenously. She is concerned about the risks of contamination from repeated use of the same needles and syringes and about infectious diseases, including AIDS, from their shared use. If this customer asks to purchase hypodermic needles and syringes, may you sell them to her?**

The law is clear that you cannot do so. It is a crime, for which you can be prosecuted, to provide these items without a prescription except under the circumstances described above, none of which apply to an addict, unless you are part of an authorized clean needle exchange program. Your violation of the law will subject you to discipline by the Board of Pharmacy. If you violate the law – even if you and most practitioners disagree with it and even with the noblest of intentions – you must be prepared to face the penalties. The fact that the law has now made provision for legal needle exchange programs reduces the power of any claim of necessity the pharmacist charged with the violation might make.

**May you tell the customer what you know about a needle exchange program in your community?**

Assuming the needle exchange program is a legal one, you certainly may tell the customer about it.

# Veterinary Food-Animal Drug Retailers

The veterinary food-animal drug retailer is an entity that has a license as a wholesaler, which obtains a special license to dispense veterinary drugs for food-producing animals at retail on prescription by a veterinarian (§4041). Veterinary food-animal drugs are those prescription drugs intended for use in food-producing animals (§4042).

The law borrows much from licensing schemes for other premises. The application for licensure is subject to the same requirements as those for a pharmacy (§4201); each separate location must be licensed (§4196(a)).[17] The licensee must inform the Board of changes in beneficial ownership in a timely manner (§4201(i)), the Board may grant a temporary license upon transfer of ownership (§4196(b)), and the license may be voided by the Board if the retailer remains closed (§4312). The licensee's stock and records are subject to inspection (§§4080-4081), adequate records must be kept (§4081), and the names of owners, managers, and employees must be revealed upon request (§4082). No person other than a pharmacist, exemptee (or, as of 2006, designated representative), licensed prescriber, authorized officer of the law, or a person performing clerical, inventory control, housekeeping, delivery, maintenance, or similar functions is permitted in the licensed premises (§4196(c)).

The veterinary food-animal drug retailer, like other nonpharmacy premises that deal with dangerous drugs, must be in the charge of a pharmacist or an exemptee (or designated representative) (§§4053(b), 4196(c)). Veterinary food-animal drug retailers as well as wholesalers must designate an exemptee-in-charge (or designated representative-in-charge) with responsibility for the firm's compliance with state and federal law. The initial designation of, and any changes in, the exemptee or designated representative-in-charge (who may be a pharmacist) must be reported to the Board within 30 days both by the entity and the individual (§§4196(d), 4305.5). Prescriptions must be dispensed only by a pharmacist or exemptee (or designated representative) except where otherwise provided (§4331(c)), and only they may prepare and affix the label to veterinary food-animal drugs (§4053(d)). The label must meet all the requirements of Pharmacy Law (§4199(a)). The licensee may dispense, furnish, transfer, or sell these drugs only to a veterinarian's client by prescription for food-producing animals, or to a veterinarian, a pharmacy, or another veterinary food-animal drug retailer (§4059(h)). Prescription records must be kept for three years (§4199(b)).

Each licensed retailer must store its drugs in a secure, lockable area and maintain its fixtures and equipment in a clean and orderly condition and its premises in a dry, well-ventilated, and adequately lighted condition (§4197(a)). The Board may impose by regulation other minimum standards pertaining to acquisition, storage, and maintenance of drugs or other goods, or to maintenance or condition of the premises (§4197(b)). The Board may waive any of these or other licensing requirements where it determines that a high standard of animal safety and care can be provided (§4197(c)).

Each licensee must have written policies and procedures related to handling and dispensing veterinary food-animal drugs. These written policies must cover training of staff; cleaning, storage, and maintenance of drugs and equipment; record-keeping requirements; storage and security requirements; and quality assurance (§4198(a)). Each licensee must prepare records of training and demonstrated competence for each employee and maintain them for three years after the last date of employment (§4198(b)). In addition, each licensee must have an ongoing, documented quality assurance program that monitors personnel performance as well as storage, maintenance, and dispensing of drugs (§4198(c)). Its training, competence, and quality assurance records must be available for inspection by authorized officials during business hours (§4198(d)).

Further, each licensee must have a consulting pharmacist who visits the premises at least quarterly to assure compliance with the law. The consulting pharmacist must review, approve, and revise the licensee's policies and procedures and assure compliance with all laws governing labeling, storage, and dispensing. At least twice a year, the pharmacist must certify in writing that the licensee is in compliance with pharmacy law; the most recent certification must be submitted with the veterinary food-animal drug retailer's license renewal application (§4198(e)).

---

[17] The same site may be licensed both as a wholesaler and as a veterinary food-animal drug retailer; this is one exception to a new law barring two or more Board licenses from being granted for the same premises (§4107).

The Board has adopted regulations for veterinary food-animal drug retailers which are in addition to those required of all wholesalers. They include the following:

- Drugs may be dispensed only for use on food-producing animals, and only on the basis of an order (written, oral, or electronic) from a licensed veterinarian (§1780.1(a),(d));
- Prescriptions may be refilled only if the initial prescription specifies the number of refills, and in no case more than six months after the original issue date (§1780.1(g));
- Repackaging of case lots is allowable, as long as no seals on individual containers are broken (so dosages may not be counted out or measured) (§1780.1(b));
- Returned drugs must be treated as damaged or outdated, stored in the quarantine area, and not returned to stock or redistributed (§1780.1(c));
- Controlled substance container labels must be countersigned by the prescribing veterinarian (§1780.1(e));
- If drugs are ordered by multiple veterinarians for the same client's production class of farm animals, the veterinarians must be contacted for authorization before dispensing (§1780.1(f)); and
- Labels must contain the information specified in section 1780.1(h), which includes all the information required for a human's prescription plus the name of the client, the species of food-producing animals for which the drug is prescribed, and withdrawal time.

The regulations also set out the training requirements for the "vet retailer exemptee," the person other than a pharmacist who is allowed to dispense drugs for use on food-producing animals (§1780.1(m)). Presumably these regulations will become applicable to the new category of designated representative.

# Clinics

Physicians practicing in their own private offices have always been able to purchase drugs to administer or dispense to their own patients (§4170(a)); physicians who work in clinics also may order drugs in their own names for use by their own patients. However, except for those types of clinics that have been given express authority to do so, it is not legal for a clinic to order drugs or to pool the drugs ordered by individual physicians. Notwithstanding the inefficiency and expense of doing so, each practitioner must order separately, maintain and keep records of use separately, and dispense or administer from his or her own stock.

**Nonprofit Community or Free Clinics.** In the mid-1980s the Legislature adopted statutes to allow clinics to order drugs for their physicians' use. First it allowed licensed nonprofit community clinics or free clinics, as defined in sections 1204(a)(1) and (2) of the Health and Safety Code, to receive licenses allowing them to purchase drugs at wholesale for administration or dispensing to registered clinic patients.[18] Then it allowed nonprofit multispecialty clinics, defined in section 1206(*l*) of the Health and Safety Code, the same privilege (§4180).[19] The same privileges are now also granted to:

- primary care clinics owned or operated by a county,

---

[18] Community clinics and free clinics both are run by tax-exempt nonprofit corporations; a community clinic sets its charges based on the patient's ability to pay, whereas a free clinic does not charge for its services (H&SC §1204(a)(1)(A),(B)).

[19] A nonprofit multispecialty clinic engages in medical research and health education and provides health care with a staff of at least 40 independent contractor physicians and surgeons (at least two-thirds of whom work full time at the clinic), representing no fewer than ten board-certified specialties (H&SC §1206(l)).

- clinics operated by a federally recognized Indian tribe or tribal organization,
- clinics open no more than 20 hours a week that are operated by a primary care community or free clinic on separate premises from a licensed clinic, and
- student health center clinics operated by public institutions of higher education.

The license application process (including the payment of fees) is similar to that for other types of licensed premises. The Board is required to make a "thorough investigation" to determine whether the applicant and the premises qualify; the investigation is limited to matters relating to the furnishing, sale, or dispensing of drugs or devices (§4203(b)). The application must include, among other things, whether the applicant is licensed as a primary care clinic and the names of its professional director, administrator, and consulting pharmacist (§4203(a)); the professional director must be a physician (§4182(c)). The Board may inspect the clinic for compliance with the law at any time and may revoke or suspend its license for violations of law (§§4185, 4300). Each location that a clinic maintains must have its own license (§4180(b)).

Before being issued a clinic license, the applicant clinic must be in compliance with all DHS-enforced laws and regulations relating to drug distribution, to ensure that inventory control, security, training, protocol development, record-keeping, packaging, labeling, dispensing, and patient consultation are handled properly. The clinic is required to have policies and procedures to ensure compliance; the policies and procedures must have been developed and approved by the clinic's consulting pharmacist, professional director, and administrator (§4181(a)). The policies and procedures are to include a written description of the method for development, approval, and revision of those policies (§4181(b)).

Drug dispensing in these clinics may be done only by a physician, a pharmacist, or other person lawfully authorized to dispense drugs, and only in compliance with applicable laws and regulations (§4181(c)).

The professional (or medical) director of a clinic is responsible for the "safe, orderly, and lawful" provision of pharmacy services. To fulfill that responsibility, the director must retain a consulting pharmacist (volunteer or paid) to participate in the development and approval of policies and procedures and to visit the clinic regularly (at least quarterly) to monitor compliance (§4182(a)). At least twice a year the consulting pharmacist must certify in writing that the clinic is in compliance with the law; the most recent certification must be submitted with the clinic's license renewal application (§4182(b)).

A licensed clinic itself may not dispense any Schedule II controlled substance, but this limitation does not prohibit employee physicians from dispensing Schedule II controlled substances purchased and maintained separately by them for administration or dispensing to their own patients in accordance with the law (§4184). Effective in 2005, when an order for a controlled substance other than a Schedule II is issued for a clinic patient by a clinic licensed pursuant to section 4180, the order is exempt from the usual requirements for a controlled substance prescription (see Chap. IX: Prescriptions: Receipt to Labeling). A written entry on the patient's chart, signed by the prescriber, is sufficient if it has the name and quantity of the controlled substance, the amount actually furnished, and the date. That record must be maintained for seven years. The clinic must maintain a separate record of the controlled substances it furnishes for review by authorized persons (H&SC §11159.1).

Clinics that have permits under section 4180 authorizing them to purchase drugs at wholesale for administration or dispensing are not allowed to charge Medi-Cal any professional dispensing fee (§4183). Notwithstanding that limitation, a community or free clinic with a section 4180 permit that is eligible for discount drug purchase prices (see Chap. VII: Ordering Drugs ("Authorized Discount Purchases")) may charge Medi-Cal's Family FACT program (Family Planning, Access, Care, and

Treatment Waiver program for low-income families) a fee between $12 and $17 over the clinic's purchase price (or its usual charge to the general public, whichever is lower), as long as the net cost does not exceed the Medi-Cal pharmacy reimbursement rate (Welf. & Inst. Code §14132.01).

Automated drug delivery systems may be used in clinics eligible, under section 4180, for the purchase of drugs at wholesale (§4186, see Chap. IV: Licensing Pharmacies ("Specialty Pharmacies/Remote Pharmacy Sites")).

**Surgical Clinics.** Surgical clinics (as defined in section 1204(b)(1) of the Health & Safety Code) are required to obtain licenses from the Board to purchase drugs at wholesale for administration or dispensing, under direction of a physician, to registered patients (§4190). In contrast to nonprofit community or free clinics, which may choose not to obtain a clinic license from the Board if they do not want to pool drugs for administration and dispensing, the law provides that "[n]o surgical clinic shall operate" without such a license (§4190(c)).

A surgical clinic may dispense a maximum 72-hour supply of drugs to its patients, but only for the control of pain and nausea. Although the clinic is subject to this stringent limitation, the physicians working in the clinic may dispense from their own supplies as they could before the clinic had the authority to dispense, for any purpose or duration. The clinic also may administer any drugs for a patient's immediate needs, including drugs that are directly applied to the patient's body by injection, inhalation, ingestion, or other means (§4190(b)).

The procedures and standards for surgical clinics to obtain a license are virtually identical to those described above for other clinics (compare §4204 with §4203; compare §§4191-4192 with §§4181-4182). Upon initial application by a surgical clinic, a consulting pharmacist is required to certify that its drug distribution policies and procedures are consistent with public health and safety (§4204(b)), but quarterly visits and semi-annual certification of compliance by a consulting pharmacist do not appear to be required (compare §4192 with §4182). Neither type of clinic may itself dispense Schedule II controlled substances. Although the language of the two statutes differs slightly (no Schedule II controlled substances shall be dispensed *by* a nonprofit or free clinic; none shall be dispensed *in* a surgical clinic), physicians in both types of clinic may dispense Schedule II drugs from their own stock in compliance with federal and state controlled substances law (compare §4194 with §4184). Schedule II drugs may be administered on the premises of a surgical clinic (§4194).

Other provisions discussed for free and nonprofit clinics (for example, ineligibility to receive Medi-Cal dispensing fees (§4193) and Board authority to inspect (§4195)) are the same for the surgical clinic. Both nonprofit and surgical clinics are required to retain for *seven* years records of the kind and amounts of drugs purchased, administered, and dispensed (§§4180(a)(2), 4190(a)). Contrast this requirement with the three years that pharmacy prescription records are required to be maintained (§4081(a)).

**Veterinary hospitals.** Although not licensed by the Board, veterinarians in veterinary teaching hospitals operated by an accredited veterinary medical school may, as of 2005, dispense and administer dangerous drugs and devices from a common stock. A pharmacist is responsible for ordering the drugs, security, training of personnel, inventory, and other drug-related responsibilities (§4170.5). The Board has the authority to inspect such facilities.

# Other Institutions

The Pharmacy Law takes note of the use of dangerous drugs by research, teaching, and testing laboratories. These laboratories, which use drugs for scientific or teaching purposes but do not sell them, are required to maintain an established place of business and to keep purchase records. The law states that they are "subject to the jurisdiction of the board," but does not mandate the acquisition of a license (§4031). A similar exemption appears in federal law (21 USC §360(g)(3)). If the laboratory is using an unapproved drug for human experimentation it must do so in accordance with FDA provisions governing investigations of new drugs (21 CFR §§312.1-312.160).

The Pharmacy Law is virtually silent about the various other health care facilities in which pharmacists may work and to which pharmacies deliver or dispense drugs. These include physicians' offices, intermediate and long-term care facilities, and juvenile or correctional institutions, among others. Most of these facilities are regulated by the Department of Health Services. The roles pharmacists may, or must, play in or in connection with some of these facilities are described in Chapter VI: Scope of Practice for Pharmacists.

---

**What you should think about after reading this chapter:**

1. Why do we need to regulate drug manufacturers? Wholesalers? Are current laws and regulations adequate to address those needs?

2. Why do we permit manufacturers, wholesalers, home medical device retailers, and veterinary food-animal drug retailers to operate without a pharmacist present?

3. What should the education, training, and exam requirements be for a person to become an exemptee or a designated representative?

4. Should hypodermic needles and syringes be regulated? How?

5. What would be the optimal way to organize a clean needle exchange program? What role could pharmacists legally play in such a program? What role should pharmacists play in such a program?

6. Should clinics and group medical practices be given broader authority to purchase, administer, and dispense drugs? Why or why not?

---

# Chapter VI

# Scope of Practice for Pharmacists

---

**What you should know after reading this chapter:**

1.  What role must a pharmacist play in the prescription drug dispensing process?

2.  What information must a pharmacist provide to a consumer and under what circumstances?

3.  What information may a pharmacist provide to consumers or health care professionals?

4.  Are there any limitations on what clinical advice or patient consultation a pharmacist may provide to a patient or health professional?  On the settings in or from which the pharmacist may provide such advice or consultation?

5.  What clinical or diagnostic functions may a pharmacist perform and in what settings?

6.  When may a pharmacist provide emergency contraception for a consumer without a prescription?

7.  When may a pharmacist perform or analyze a laboratory test for a consumer?  Check a patient's blood pressure or other vital signs?  Administer an immunization?

8.  In what other roles in the health care industry would the education, skills, and training of a pharmacist be useful?

---

## The Changing Role of the Pharmacist

The role of the pharmacist in the drug making and distribution process has changed over the years.  In the 20th century, until the mid-1970s, the pharmacist was largely a dispenser of premixed drugs who reduced them from stock obtained from a manufacturer or wholesaler and relabeled and dispensed them to a waiting patient.  Little compounding was necessary, and exchange with patients and dialogue with prescribers limited.  Everyone, it seemed, wanted the pharmacist to fill orders mechanically and without question, despite the fact that it has always been the pharmacist who, among health care providers, has had the best practical and theoretical knowledge of the nature and effect of pharmaceuticals.

Over the last few decades, at first slowly and now with great speed, there have been major changes in the nature of the pharmacist's work, and increased recognition both of the pharmacist's knowledge and essential role in clinical judgment pertaining to drugs and devices and ability and opportunity to provide information to patients.  In California, this recognition has been reflected in a statute specifically noting that pharmacy is a profession (§4050(a)) and a "dynamic patient-oriented health service that applies a scientific body of knowledge to improve and promote patient health by means of appropriate drug use, drug-related therapy, and communication for clinical and consultative purposes" (§4050(b)). Pharmacists employ their knowledge about drugs and devices in various health care settings, not just in the pharmacy.[1]

As the role of pharmacy has been evolving, there have been dramatic changes in all aspects of the delivery of health care. Nonpharmacists are performing or assisting in performing more tasks in the pharmacy, enabling pharmacists to spend more time counseling patients, conferring with other health care professionals, and making decisions about sophisticated aspects of pharmacy operations.[2] Thus, as to many nondiscretionary aspects of drug preparation, packaging, and labeling, the pharmacist's role is increasingly that of manager and supervisor of others carrying out those functions. In addition, pharmacists may now perform certain patient assessment and testing procedures without physician supervision or specialized training and may perform numerous functions in virtually any setting with appropriate medical supervision, as discussed below.

The pharmacist is still most commonly engaged in the traditional functions of retail compounding, furnishing, selling, and dispensing of dangerous drugs and dangerous devices (§§4037(a), 4051(a)). Some of these functions remain restricted to pharmacists; some are shared with other professionals or entities or are delegated to nonpharmacist staff, working under pharmacist supervision.[3]

Only a pharmacist or an intern acting under the supervision of a pharmacist may do the following:

- Receive a new prescription orally from a prescriber or other person authorized by law,
- Consult with a patient or a health care professional or his or her agent regarding a prescription (before or after dispensing) or any medical information in the patient's record,
- Identify, evaluate, or interpret a prescription,
- Supervise the packaging of drugs and check the packaging procedure and product upon completion, or
- Perform any pharmacy-related function requiring professional judgment (§1793.1).

# Compounding and Dispensing

Compounding – the creation of a medication from component parts in accordance with a prescription for a particular patient – is a traditional function of a pharmacist. Although the resulting medications are drugs that lack approval by the FDA, both state and federal policymakers recognize the continuing need for custom preparations for particular patients, and the ability of pharmacists to meet this need. Pharmacists may compound to fill a prescription order for a particular patient or to furnish a reasonable quantity of compounded medication for a prescriber's office use (§4052(a)(1)). While compounding is legal for a pharmacist, the difficult issue has been defining the line between

---

[1]  While the pharmacist's predominant role is in connection with drugs for human use, the recent establishment of a pharmacy residency in clinical veterinary medicine by the University of California at Davis recognizes the role of the pharmacist in respect to animal health.

[2]  The role of other members of the health care team is, of course, also expanding. For example, see the descriptions of the roles of nurse practitioners, physician assistants, and others in issuing orders for prescription drugs in Chapter IX: The Prescription Process: From Receipt to Labeling.

[3]  For example, while traditionally a pharmacist dispenses a prescription, prescribers may do so under certain conditions (§§4051(a), 4170-4175). Pharmacists may manufacture, measure, fit to the patient, sell and repair dangerous devices, and furnish instruction to the patient or the patient's representative as to the use of such devices (§4052(a)(6)); the home medical device retailer, now regulated by the Department of Health Services rather than the Pharmacy Board, may do so as well (H&SC §§109948.1,111656; see Chap. V: Other Board Licensees).

pharmacy compounding and manufacturing, for which additional federal and state licenses (and approval of any new compounds) are required.  That issue is covered in Chapter VIII: Preparation of Drugs by a Pharmacy.

# Emergency Contraception

In general a pharmacist can dispense a prescription drug only upon receipt of an order from a licensed prescriber (§4040); however, there are exceptions, such as in a public emergency or in the case of emergency refills (see Chap. X: Dispensing and Beyond).  Another exception is the dispensing of emergency contraception drugs.

A course of prescription drugs begun as soon as possible and optimally within 72 hours after unprotected sexual intercourse can prevent the implantation of a fertilized egg, thus preventing pregnancy.  Because there is such a short time to begin this therapy, the Legislature has made an exception to the  requirement that a patient obtain a prescription before obtaining drugs from the pharmacy.  Under section 4052(a)(8), a pharmacist may furnish emergency contraception drugs either under a standardized procedure developed with a prescriber acting within his or her scope of practice or under standardized procedures developed and approved by the Pharmacy and Medical Boards (§4052(a)(8)(A)(i),(ii)).

A regulation adopted in 2004 (§1746) requires the protocol to provide access to emergency contraception medication within required time limits,  and to ensure the patient receives sufficient information to successfully complete the therapy (§1746(b)).  The pharmacist must ask the patient requesting emergency contraception if she is allergic to any medications and inform her that timing is essential to the product's effectiveness.  He or she must explain the need to begin the drugs as soon as possible after unprotected intercourse and no more than five days or 120 hours thereafter, that the effectiveness of the treatment declines over those five days, and that its use will not interfere with an already-established pregnancy.  The pharmacist must provide a standardized fact sheet developed by the Pharmacy Board that includes indications for use of the drug, the appropriate method of use, potential adverse effects, the need for medical followup, and other relevant information (§4052(b)(3), §1746(b)).  (The fact sheet is available at www.pharmacy.ca.gov/publications/emer_contraception.pdf in English and nine other languages.)  The pharmacist must review any patient questions, collect required patient profile information (§1707.1), and document the furnishing of the medication (see Chap. X: Dispensing and Beyond).  The pharmacist must also comply with mandatory state laws for reporting of sexual abuse (§1746(b)).

The pharmacist is playing the role of the prescriber, a significant expansion of the pharmacist's usual role.  In all other circumstances where the pharmacist may initiate drug therapy (which is essentially indistinguishable from prescribing), he or she may do so only while working under formal policies and procedures of a facility or physician, and under a physician's supervision, as described below.

If emergency contraception services are not immediately available at the pharmacy or the pharmacist declines to furnish the drugs on the basis of conscience, the pharmacist must refer the patient to a provider who can provide them (§1746(b)).  Emergency contraception drugs may be furnished in advance of need; the pharmacy may also provide up to 12 non-spermicidal condoms to any Medi-Cal or Family FACT client who obtains emergency contraception.

The regulation sets out a list of available products for emergency contraception from which the pharmacist may select; the current list of products must be maintained in the pharmacy.  The list includes adjunctive medications for nausea and vomiting that may also be dispensed with the emergency contraception medication.

To dispense emergency contraception, the pharmacist must have completed a training program that consists of at least one hour of approved continuing education (§4052(a)(8)(B)), §1746(b)).  In dispensing these drugs, the pharmacist may not demand any more information than that required for a patient profile (§4052(a)(8)(D), §1707.1).  The pharmacist may only charge the retail price of the drug and an administrative fee not to exceed $10; the fee may not be charged if the consumer has prescription drug insurance or if such a fee is forbidden by a contract that the pharmacist has signed (§4052(a)(8)(C)).  An FDA panel recommended that these drugs be available OTC throughout the country, but FDA rejected the recommendation in 2004, primarily because the drugs would be available to minors under 16.  The manufacturer has submitted a revised proposal that would limit the OTC status to women 16 or older.  Should the drugs become available over-the-counter, the administrative fee provision will become inoperative (§4052(a)(8)(C)).

# Provision of Information

Pharmacists have always been providers of information to consumers and to medical professionals, even before they were mandated to do so in the form of patient consultation (§1707.2).  The Pharmacy Law specifically recognizes the authority of pharmacists to provide "consultation to patients and professional information, including clinical or pharmacological information, advice, or consultation to other health care professionals" (§4052(a)(7)).

The essential, and constantly growing, role of the pharmacist as the member of the health care team most knowledgeable about drugs and pharmacology was also recognized in legislation that amended section 4051.  As discussed also in Chapter IV: Licensing Pharmacies ("Call-In Centers"), a pharmacist, outside of pharmacy premises, may now provide clinical advice, information, or patient consultation to a health care professional or to a patient as long as he or she has access to prescription, patient profile, and other relevant medical information to inform the consultation and advice, and keeps that information secure from unauthorized access and use (§4051(b)(2),(3)).  Prior to its amendment in 2002, the law provided that pharmacists could provide advice and information outside licensed premises only with respect to patients under the care of a hospital, health care facility, home health agency, or hospice.

In other words, a pharmacist may now go into practice solely as an information provider, essentially as an independent consultant, entirely unconnected to any medical facility or prescriber group.  The law does not restrict pharmacists' provision of advice to face-to-face encounters.  So the practice of "telepharmacy" for providing drug information is legal, whether the pharmacist uses the telephone or the computer.[4]

Business entities, inside or outside of California, providing telephone medical advice to patients at a California address are required to register with the Department of Consumer Affairs (B&PC §4999(a)).  However, this law does not list pharmacists among those covered (B&PC §4999.2) and expressly states that it does not limit the authority of persons licensed pursuant to Division 2 of the Business and Professions Code (which includes pharmacists) to provide telephone medical advice services (B&PC §4999.7).[5]

---

[4]  If a California pharmacist provides information to someone out-of-state, there is the possibility that the other state's laws could define what the pharmacist is doing as practicing pharmacy in that state, for which the pharmacist would need licensure there.

[5]  The issue of prescriptions issued or dispensed through the Internet is discussed in Chapter X, The Prescription Process: Dispensing and Beyond.

Within the pharmacy the pharmacist may be asked for information about prescription drugs by customers not filling prescriptions and about OTC drugs, vitamin and mineral products, and botanicals and herbs by customers with and without prescriptions to fill. Pharmacists have no legal obligation to provide information in these contexts, but for business reasons and to use their knowledge to best serve the public pharmacists have traditionally done so. A pharmacist who chooses to answer customer questions must do so in a professional manner and exercising due care. When the customer's question is outside the boundaries of the pharmacist's expertise, the pharmacist should acknowledge that fact rather than risk providing inaccurate information.

# Clinical Functions

## In A Licensed Health Care Facility

A pharmacist who has received appropriate training, as prescribed in the policies of the licensed health care facility (§4052(b)(1)), may perform the following functions in that facility:

- order or perform routine drug therapy-related patient assessment procedures including temperature, pulse, and respiration (§4052(a)(4)(A));
- order drug therapy-related laboratory tests (§4052(a)(4)(B)) and, if properly trained, perform such tests of up to moderate complexity under the overall operation and administration of a laboratory director (B&PC §1206.5(a)(11), (b)(13));
- administer drugs and biologicals by injection pursuant to a prescriber's order (§4052(a)(4)(C)); and
- initiate or adjust the drug regimen of a patient pursuant to an order or authorization by the prescriber and in accordance with the facility's policies, procedures, or protocols (§4052(a)(4)(D)).

The pharmacist's initiation of the drug regimen in this context is essentially prescribing, albeit within a limited formulary and pursuant to guidelines about when and how much to prescribe. The pharmacist's role is not called "prescribing" because of the resistance of the medical profession to expansion of the authority of so-called "mid-level practitioners" (see Chap. IX: Prescriptions: Receipt to Labeling). The pharmacist is acting as a clinician in this role and others described below; he or she is generally referred to as a clinical pharmacist or, more recently, a primary care pharmacist.

A "licensed health care facility," for these purposes, means a facility licensed by the Department of Health Services under sections 1250 to 1261.5 of the Health and Safety Code. This category is quite broad, encompassing acute care hospitals, intermediate care facilities, skilled nursing facilities, and others set out in section 1250 of the Health and Safety Code, as well as facilities operated by a health care service plan (§4027(b); see App. C: Definitions of Various Health Facilities). The role of a pharmacist in administration and management in these and other organizations is discussed below.

## In Other Health Care Settings

The settings in which a pharmacist may perform clinical activities have been expanded several times in recent years. Once he or she has successfully completed clinical residency training or has demonstrated clinical experience in direct patient care delivery (§4052(b)(2)), the pharmacist may perform virtually all the services authorized to be performed by a pharmacist in a licensed health care facility, set out above, as part of the care provided in the following settings:

- In a health care facility,[6]
- In a licensed home health agency,
- In a licensed clinic in which there is physician oversight,
- For a provider who contracts with a licensed health care service plan to provide services to its enrollees, or
- For any physician (§4052(a)(5)(A)).

In each of these settings, the pharmacist must act in accordance with policies, procedures, or protocols developed by health care professionals. These policies must require that the pharmacist function as part of a multidisciplinary group that includes physicians and direct care registered nurses, that the patient's medical records be available to the prescriber and the pharmacist, and that the procedures performed by the pharmacist relate to a condition for which the patient has first been seen by a physician (§4052(a)(5)(C)).

The initiation or adjustment of a drug regimen must be pursuant to a specific written order or authorization by the prescriber for the particular patient. Adjusting the drug regimen does not include substituting or selecting a different drug, unless authorized to do so by the protocol. The pharmacist must provide written notification to the patient's prescriber, or enter the information in an electronic patient record shared by the prescriber, of any drug regimen initiated under this authority within 24 hours (§4052(a)(5)(A)(iv)). The prescriber may prohibit any such adjustment or change in the drug regimen by written instruction (§4052(a)(5)(B)).

When the clinical pharmacist is working in the home health agency or physician's office setting, the above clinical functions must be performed in accordance with a written, patient-specific protocol approved by the treating or supervising physician. Any change, adjustment, or modification of an approved pre-existing treatment or drug therapy must be provided, in writing, to the treating or supervising physician within 24 hours (§4052(a)(5)(C)(iv)).

## *Immunizations*

Regardless of the setting, whether or not in a health care facility and even in the traditional pharmacy, a pharmacist may administer immunizations under the supervision of a prescriber (§§4052(a)(4)(C), 4052(a)(5)(A)(iii)). The required level of supervision is not defined in the law; it simply requires "supervision," in contrast to other provisions in the Pharmacy Law that mandate "direct supervision and control" or "immediate, personal supervision and control" (§4115(a),(f)). Thus it appears that the law contemplates more general oversight by the prescriber of the pharmacist administering immunizations than is required of the pharmacist supervising technicians. Supervision cannot, however, be merely a formality; the prescriber should be involved, at minimum, in determining what immunizations to make available, in developing the procedures for screening patients to participate, and in formulating the criteria that should cause the pharmacist to decline to immunize a patient. The prescriber should also be available (at least by electronic means) should problems or questions arise.

**A pharmacy wants to offer immunizations to its customers and arranges with a physician to oversee the program. May it do so? May it advertise the availability of this service and charge a fee for it?**

---

[6] A health care facility for purposes of section 4052(a)(5) means a facility operated by a health care service plan and includes an organization under common ownership or control of the health care service plan. A "licensed clinic" for these purposes means one licensed under Health and Safety Code sections 1200 to 1212 (§4027(c), see App. B: Definitions of Various Health Facilities).

Encouraging such programs clearly is one of the purposes of granting this authority to pharmacists. There is no prohibition on advertising the service; doing so would serve the public health by making immunizations more widely available. Since the law does not prohibit charging for the service, a fee may be charged.

**May a school of pharmacy or a pharmacy association offer immunizations to the public at a health fair? May interns do the immunizations?**

A school of pharmacy or pharmacy association may offer immunizations, as long as it follows the standards described above concerning prescriber supervision. Interns may perform any activity restricted to a pharmacist, including providing immunizations, if they do so under the supervision of a pharmacist and in accordance with the two-to-one intern/pharmacist ratio.

## Skin Puncture and Other Patient Assessment Procedures

A pharmacist has been authorized to perform skin puncture for testing purposes for a number of years. The pharmacist may perform skin puncture in the course of performing routine patient assessment procedures. "Routine patient assessment procedures" are those that patients could, with or without a prescription, perform themselves (such as drawing blood to check glucose levels) and clinical laboratory tests that are classified as waived under federal law governing clinical laboratories. In both cases the pharmacist performing skin puncture shall report the results to the patient and to any physician designated by the patient (§4052.1). The pharmacist may perform this function anywhere, not just in a pharmacy.

Under California law governing clinical laboratory personnel, a pharmacist may perform clinical laboratory tests classified as "waived" if under the overall operation and administration of a laboratory director (B&PC §1206.5(a)), as long as the tests are drug therapy-related or are routine patient assessment procedures (B&PC §1206.5(a)(11)). The law does not contemplate a pharmacist performing these laboratory tests in the pharmacy; rather, it enables pharmacists to work in or with a clinical laboratory without additional training. Previous authority for pharmacists to perform tests classified as of moderate complexity has been repealed.

A pharmacist may also take a patient's blood pressure, inform him or her of the results, render an opinion as to whether the reading is low, normal, or high, and advise the patient, if appropriate, to consult the physician of his or her choice. In rendering opinions and referring patients to physicians, the pharmacist must use "commonly accepted community standards" (§4103). This authority is not limited to a particular setting and does not require physician oversight. Therefore, not only may pharmacies offer blood pressure assessment services, but also pharmacists may do blood pressure assessments independently, outside pharmacies, such as at health screening fairs.

Pharmacists do not appear to have the authority to take other vital signs outside clinical settings. By contrast, the pharmacist who is acting as a clinical pharmacist may in any setting perform or order drug therapy-related patient assessment procedures (§4052(a)(4)(A),(5)A)(i)), including temperature, pulse, and respiration. Both in their traditional role and today, with mandatory consultation, pharmacists have long been regularly engaged in patient assessment, if not in the "hands-on" sense, and particularly when consulted about the use of over-the-counter remedies. So while pharmacists may not place thermometers in patient's mouths or ears and then read the results unless they are acting as clinicians, surely in a retail setting or at a health fair they may and do ask patients if they feel feverish, if they are in pain, or how acute their pain is. It is somewhat ironic that pharmacists engage in this "intellectual" process of drug-related patient assessment routinely, but have no legal authority outside the clinical setting to take a patient's temperature, check a patient's pulse, or assess the patient's breathing.

**Suppose that a patient has diabetes, has never had a prescription filled at the pharmacy, and wants you to teach him how to perform skin puncture to draw blood to test his glucose level. May you do so?**

Yes.

**Suppose the patient wants you to perform the skin puncture, not for the purpose of teaching him to do so, but because he does not want to do it himself. May you?**

Yes.

**May the pharmacist provide the testing equipment for performing skin puncture to obtain a blood specimen?**

Yes, the pharmacist may provide such equipment.

**May a pharmacist set up a booth at a health fair and offer to check a person's blood pressure or perform skin puncture to check a person's blood glucose level?**

Nothing in the law limits these activities to a pharmacy setting, just as nothing in the law limits the administration of immunizations by a pharmacist, under a physician's supervision, to a licensed health care facility.

**May a pharmacy student order a test or perform any test that a pharmacist is authorized to perform?**

A pharmacy student may do so once he or she is registered with the Board as an intern. As a pharmacy intern the student may engage in all the functions of a pharmacist, at the discretion and under the supervision of a pharmacist (§4114, §1727(e)). When the law imposes a requirement of "appropriate training" upon a pharmacist, the supervising pharmacist will need to have had that training and assure that the intern does also (§4052(b)). There is no legal barrier to an intern performing skin puncture for patient assessment tests that patients could perform themselves. Similarly interns may give immunizations and test, interpret, and advise patients about their blood pressure, as long as their pharmacist supervisors are willing to supervise and be responsible for their performance of these functions.

**May a pharmacy intern perform the clinical functions authorized to be performed by a pharmacist under section 4052(a)?**

The law does not preclude interns from performing the clinical pharmacy functions set out in section 4052(a), but they would need to meet the specific training requirements of the law before doing so. [7]

**May the pharmacist charge for any of these services?**

If there is a need for these services, and patients are willing to pay for them, there is no legal obstacle to charging for them. Insurance companies are now specifically authorized to reimburse

---

[7] The "appropriate training" required to perform functions under section 4052(a)(4) is either "demonstrated clinical experience in direct patient care delivery" or completion of a clinical residency. Only under unusual circumstances would a pharmacy intern have completed a clinical residency, but an intern might have demonstrated clinical experience from previous work, for example, as a paramedic.

pharmacists for services beyond dispensing, such as monitoring blood glucose, managing anticoagulation therapy, and preventing drug problems by consulting with the patient's physician (H&SC §1368.5; Ins. Code §10125.1). Nor is there any reason not to perform these services for persons who have no prescription or pre-existing relationship with the pharmacy.

# Pharmacists and Health Facility Management

Pharmacists have major responsibilities for the over-all handling of drugs and devices by a variety of health care facilities and in settings where drugs and devices are available to and used by health care professionals and patients (or inmates).[8]

## Acute Care Hospitals

In California, acute care hospitals, those that have facilities for patients requiring acute care to remain overnight, are licensed by the DHS (H&SC §1250(a)). Each acute care hospital must have a pharmacy and therapeutics committee, of which a pharmacist must be a member, to develop written policies and procedures for the hospital's pharmacy practice and to develop a drug formulary; the pharmacist, in consultation with other health professionals and hospital administration, is responsible for development and implementation of those procedures (22 CCR §§70263(c), 71233(c)).[9] The pharmacist has overall responsibility for the hospital's pharmaceutical service, including for obtaining, storing, and distributing all drugs; these responsibilities are to be set out in either a job description or an agreement between the pharmacist and the hospital (22 CCR §§70265, 71235). A hospital with 100 or fewer beds that has a section 4056 drug permit rather than a pharmacy license must employ a pharmacist at least as a consultant (22 CCR §§70265, 71235). Because of the essential, pervasive role drugs and devices play in a hospital setting, the pharmacist has a major role in hospital policy, not just in the operation of the pharmacy itself.[10]

There are circumstances in which hospital facilities obtain and distribute drugs without the involvement of a pharmacist. However, any time a pharmacy touches a drug, it remains the pharmacy's responsibility at least until it leaves the pharmacy's control; use within an acute care hospital is not generally considered to be outside the pharmacy's control. A pharmacist who participates in a facility's management, handling drug purchasing or establishing facility drug policies, will be partly responsible for the facility's drugs and drug records even if the drugs have left the pharmacy or were never in the pharmacy, or even if the facility has no pharmacy.

## Intermediate and Long-Term Care Facilities

There are extensive general regulations governing pharmacy services in intermediate and long-term care facilities, and the role of pharmacists in providing consultation to and oversight in those facilities (22 CCR §§72353-72377 (skilled nursing facilities (SNF)); §§73347-73375

---

[8] The filling of prescriptions for patients of health facilities and furnishing of drugs to such facilities by a pharmacy is discussed in Chapter IV: Licensing Pharmacies and Chapter V: Other Pharmacy Board Licensees.

[9] A recently-adopted law requires each hospital to have a discharge planning policy for all patients and a written policy for ensuring that each patient receives information regarding each medication dispensed at discharge (H&SC §1262.5). Presumably pharmacists will be involved in compliance with these requirements.

[10] The regulations governing pharmaceutical services in hospitals are extensive (see 22 CCR §§70261-70269 (acute care hospitals) and 22 CCR §§71231-71239 (acute psychiatric hospitals)).

(intermediate care facilities (ICF)); §§76387-76413 (intermediate care facilities for developmentally disabled); §§76893-76906 (intermediate care facilities for developmentally disabled–habilitative)).

A SNF must retain a consulting pharmacist to coordinate, supervise, and review the facility's pharmaceutical service committee (22 CCR §72375(a)). A pharmacist must review each SNF patient's drug regimen and report, in writing, any irregularities in the dispensing and administration of drugs (22 CCR §72375(c)).

There must also be emergency supplies readily available at each nursing station (22 CCR §72377(b)). The facility's drug distribution system must be appropriately monitored, and consultative and other services by pharmacists must be available (22 CCR §72355(a)(3),(4)).

Controlled substances must be maintained so they are accessible only to licensed nursing, pharmacist, and medical personnel as designated by the facility (22 CCR §72369(a)). Medications brought into the facility by or with the patient may only be used if the patient's physician or a pharmacist has examined them after the patient arrives and positively identifies their contents or if the medications are transferred from other licensed health facilities (22 CCR §72367). At the time of discharge, unused medications must be destroyed; however, noncontrolled drugs in sealed containers may be returned to the issuing pharmacy for disposition, as long as they are unopened, can be identified by lot or control number, and a proper log is maintained showing their return (22 CCR §72371(d)).

The regulations for intermediate care facilities are similar, but somewhat simpler (see 22 CCR §§73349-73375). There are also similar requirements for ICFs for the developmentally disabled (22 CCR §§76411-76413).[11]

## *Home Health Care*

Pharmacy for home health care patients is a growing and unique practice area. It involves ongoing, often daily, delivery of pharmaceutical care by health care professionals, usually specially trained nurses, to patients in their homes or in a hospice. The care is administered under a set of broad, fairly open-ended physician orders and frequently involves administration of drugs for some length of time, from a few weeks to indefinitely, to patients on parenteral, antibiotic, chemotherapy, or other therapy. Both the pharmacist and the registered nurse involved in the patient's care have a great deal of responsibility for preparing and administering drugs and evaluating (and often adjusting) the drug regimen. In some cases the patient may be ambulatory, taking charge of the daily therapy and picking up and administering his or her own medications. It nevertheless is home health care, because it involves frequent, sometimes daily, home visits to monitor the patient, home administration of what were traditionally drugs administered in a hospital, or both.

The basic prescription rules apply, although there are some special rules governing home health care. For example, narcotic Schedule II prescriptions for direct administration may be faxed as long as the pharmacy prepares an "appropriate" form before the prescription is dispensed and has it signed by the recipient (see Chap. IX: Prescriptions: Receipt to Labeling). As noted in Chapter IV: 3 Licensing Pharmacies, a visiting pharmacist may furnish already-prescribed drugs and devices as needed by such patients and do the prescription paperwork later.

---

[11] The role of pharmacists in additional health facilities is spelled out in Title 22 of the California Code of Regulations: psychiatric health facilities (§§77079.1-77079.13), adult day health centers (§§78075, 78317(*l*)), chemical dependency recovery hospitals (§§79061, 79215(i)), and community care facilities (§§87914-87915, 87919-87920, 87920.1, 87922).

Pharmacists are authorized to furnish dangerous drugs and devices, but not controlled substances, on home visits to patients receiving parenteral therapy, when the drug or device is one currently prescribed for the patient (§1751.10). In this role the pharmacist works with a licensed pharmacy authorized to purchase and resell the drugs.

## *Prescribers' Offices and Clinics*

Drugs are needed in individual prescribers' offices and clinics, for purposes of administration and dispensing to their patients. Although pharmacies and pharmacists have not often been involved in these settings, increasingly pharmacies are found in various clinics and even some individual prescribers' offices. When a pharmacist is engaged to help with the furnishing of dangerous drugs or devices in a prescriber's office or a clinic, he or she must become familiar with the rules governing drug handling in those settings. The laws governing the handling of drugs and devices in clinics licensed by the Board are discussed in Chapter V: Other Licensees.[12]

A prescriber's handling of drugs and devices is governed by sections 4170-4174. Even if he or she employs a pharmacist, a prescriber may not keep a pharmacy, open shop, or drugstore, whether or not it is advertised, for retailing of drugs or dangerous devices (§4170(a)(3)). A prescriber may dispense drugs only to his or her own patients, and may advertise that service; a prescriber may not fill prescriptions from other prescribers, and may not advertise that he or she will do so. The prescriber may furnish or administer drugs or devices to a patient under his or her treatment and may purchase drugs for that purpose from a manufacturer or wholesaler. The prescriber also may purchase quantities of drugs compounded for him or her by a pharmacy (§4052(a)(1), §1716.1, see Chap. VIII: Preparation of Drugs). When furnishing or dispensing, the labeling requirements of section 4076 must be satisfied, except for the prescription number (§4077(b)), as must all Pharmacy Law record-keeping and packaging requirements.

Drugs must be kept in a secure area, which the Medical Board has defined as a locked storage area within the prescriber's office that is secure at all times, with the key available only to authorized staff (§4172, 16 CCR §1356.3). The prescriber may not use a dispensing device unless he or she owns it; the prescriber must personally dispense the drugs (although a registered nurse, and presumably a pharmacist, working for the prescriber may prepare, label, and package the drug and physically hand it to a patient, if the prescriber has checked what the nurse does).

The prescriber may dispense or administer Schedule III-V controlled substances, may administer Schedule II controlled substances, and may dispense Schedule IIs, but only when the patient is not expected to require them for more than 72 hours. The prescriber must also submit information to the CURES system and make records for Schedule II and III dispensing (H&SC §11207). The prescriber may also furnish a limited quantity of free drug samples in their original packaging if the patient is not charged and a record of the furnishing is made in the patient's chart (§4171(a)).

A prescriber may charge a fee for dispensing, although the prescriber must disclose in writing that the patient has the option of taking the prescription elsewhere; for that purpose, the prescriber must offer a written prescription to the patient (§4170(a)(6),(7)).[13]

---

[12] For the role of pharmacists in primary care clinics, see 22 CCR §§ 75007-75009, 75014, and 75032-75039.

[13] Community and free clinics, state, federal or Native American clinics, and narcotic treatment programs, as well as veterinary practices, and prescribers treating cancer are exempt from the prescriber dispensing provisions (§4171(a)).

Pharmacists who are considering involvement in a prescriber's office or clinic must be aware that there are various programs promoted that involve group purchase of dangerous drugs for dispensing from communal stock. Some involve a managing company, independent of the clinic or group practice, that purchases and dispenses drugs for the practice, sometimes through automated devices. Such programs are illegal under California law. Some programs have promoted obtaining and pooling samples to provide "free" drugs to patients. Notwithstanding the "free" aspect of such programs, they too are illegal.[14] The only circumstances in which clinics may make purchases for communal use by the practitioners in a clinic are set out in Chapter V: Other Pharmacy Board Licensees.

## *Correctional and Other Restricted Facilities*

The law requires that emergency and basic health care services, including pharmaceutical services, must be available to correctional facility and juvenile facility inmates (15 CCR §§1200, 1400). There are extensive regulations governing the development of policies and procedures for storage, handling, dispensing, and disposing of pharmaceuticals with which the pharmacist working at those sites must be familiar (15 CCR §§1206(j), 1438(b)(1)-(8)). Pharmacists must be involved in the planning process for the provision of pharmaceutical services at these facilities; consultation involving a pharmacist and the facility administrator for these purposes is mandated (15 CCR §§1216(a), 1438). At least annually a pharmacist must prepare a written report on the status of pharmacy services in the correctional (but not the juvenile) facility (15 CCR §1216(a)(9)). It is interesting to note that regulations specifically provide that psychotropic medications may not be administered for disciplinary purposes (15 CCR §§1217, 1439(d)); when used at all in juvenile facilities, this type of drug must be carefully monitored (15 CCR §1439).

Regulations also require that a mental health rehabilitation center must provide pharmaceutical services (9 CCR §785.00(a)) by making an arrangement for their provision by a California-licensed pharmacy. Each mental health rehabilitation center (see Chap. IV: Licensing Pharmacies) must have a consulting pharmacist to coordinate, supervise, and review at least quarterly the work of the facility's pharmaceutical service committee. The consulting pharmacist is required to review and report upon each patient's drug regimen monthly. That review must include all currently ordered drugs, drug-therapy related information about the patient's condition, medication administration records, and, where appropriate, physician's progress notes, nurses' notes, and laboratory test results. The pharmacist is responsible for reporting to the center director and the nursing service director, in writing, dispensing and administration irregularities and other matters relating to the review of the drug regimen (9 CCR §785.30(b)).

The facility must follow all state and federal laws in dispensing, labeling, storage, and administration of drugs (9 CCR §785.20(b)). The regulations make specific and detailed provision for the maintenance within the center of adequate equipment and supplies necessary for provision of pharmaceutical services (9 CCR §785.31(a)(1)-(5)).

The regulations governing mental health rehabilitation centers specifically require the availability of a range of pharmaceutical services including dispensing, monitoring of the drug distribution system, and provision of consultation and other services by which pharmacists assist in the coordination, supervision, and review of pharmaceutical services within the facility (9 CCR §785.21(a)). The regulations also cover matters of drug labeling, dispensing, storage, and security (9

---

[14] The sample pooling also appears to violate federal law that prohibits the sale or trade of drug samples (21 USC §353(c)(1); see Chap. VII: Ordering Drugs). It is also an abuse of the sample distribution process, which is intended to promote products by familiarizing prescribers with them and easing the initiation of patient therapy, rather than to substitute for traditional drug distribution.

CCR §785.22).[15] Regulations governing pharmaceutical services in correctional treatment centers are similar to those in ICFs, as discussed above (22 CCR §§79645-79665, 79781(d)(3)).

# Other Uses of a Pharmacist's Skills

The pharmacist may play additional roles neither tied to traditional licensed premises nor necessarily requiring a pharmacy license or a license as a pharmacist. Many pharmacists are engaged as consultants to health care facilities, where they engage in drug utilization review, supervise or advise on drug storage and drug handling procedures, and otherwise assist in the proper use of pharmaceuticals. A pharmacist's license may not be required for a person to perform these activities, although a pharmacist's expertise is surely required. Many health care facility regulations, however, require that a pharmacist be engaged for certain functions involving drugs.

Pharmacists may be hired to supervise other licensees of the Board and of DHS, specifically wholesalers, veterinary food-animal drug retailers, and home medical device retailers, each of which must be under the supervision and control of a pharmacist or an exemptee (or designated representative). Many pharmacists work in management positions in pharmacy corporations, hold research or marketing positions with drug companies, and engage in drug utilization review for health care providers, among other career choices. Pharmacists also may be involved in clinical research studies or in other positions in the pharmaceutical industry. For some of these positions, it is also not the license but the expertise of a pharmacist that is critical.

It is important to note that acts or omissions committed by a pharmacist when using his or her education, training, or experience as a pharmacist, even when licensure is not required for the activity, may be considered unprofessional conduct and lead to proceedings by the Pharmacy Board against the pharmacist's license (§4306.5). Whether or not a pharmacist is working within the realm of practice for which a license is required, he or she will be held to the standards expected of all licensees.

---

**What you should think about after reading this chapter:**

1. What does it mean to say that a pharmacist is a professional?

2. What roles may a pharmacist currently play in a licensed health care facility? In other health care facilities? For a physician?

3. For what clinical functions are pharmacists prepared by their education and training?

4. Are pharmacists' skills effectively used in health care facilities? What other functions could they usefully perform? Would it be legal for them to perform those functions?

---

[15] These regulations make specific provision for the disposition at the time of patient discharge of drugs dispensed for inpatient use. If properly labeled for outpatient use, these drugs may be furnished to patients on discharge as ordered by the discharging physician (9 CCR §785.28(a)). If the discharge orders make no provision for disposition of remaining drugs, the drugs are to be furnished to the client unless: the discharging physician specifies otherwise; the patient leaves or is discharged without approval or a physician's order; the patient is discharged to a general acute care hospital, acute psychiatric hospital, or acute care rehabilitation hospital; the drug was discontinued before discharge; or the labeled directions for use are not substantially the same as the most current order for the drug in the patient's medical record (9 CCR §785.28(a)(1)-(5)).

# Chapter VII

# Ordering, Receipt, Maintenance, and Transfer of Drugs and Devices

**What you should know after reading this chapter:**

1.  Who may order drugs for a pharmacy? By whom, and where, must the drugs be received?

2.  What record must the recipient keep of its order for a drug? Its receipt of a drug?

3.  What must a pharmacy do to provide security for its drugs?

4.  Under what conditions may a pharmacy transfer or furnish drugs to a wholesaler, another pharmacy, or a prescriber?

5.  When, how, and to whom must a pharmacy report drug theft or loss?

6.  What is an "excessive sale" of controlled substances?

7.  May a pharmacy obtain drug samples? What may a pharmacy do with drug samples?

8.  What is "secondary sourcing?"

9.  When must a pharmacy dispose of or destroy drugs? How?

10. What is the law concerning prescription drugs imported by consumers? By pharmacies?

This chapter is about drug and device purchases, maintenance, and transfers other than in connection with prescriptions. It might seem that the law governing the ordering, receipt, maintenance, and transfer of drugs and devices should be simple and straightforward, but it is not, especially in respect to controlled substances. Both federal and state drug laws have specific requirements about who may order which drugs or devices, who may provide them, and the content and form of the request (that is, written or oral). For the most part the law has not kept up with electronic data or image transmission of information, although some prescriptions now may be transmitted electronically (see Chap. IX: Prescriptions: Receipt to Labeling).

In addition, Pharmacy Law requires that all Board licensees keep records of the manufacture, sale, purchase, or disposition of dangerous drugs or devices and a current inventory (§4081(a), §1718 ("current inventory" defined); see Chap. XI: Record-Keeping). Good records are needed to meet the legal requirement that a pharmacy establish that its records and stock on hand balance, and that all its stock came from proper sources (see Chap. V: Other Board Licensees ("Wholesalers")).[1] Federal and state drug laws have very specific, detailed provisions governing drug transactions.

Federal controlled substance regulations require a biennial inventory of all controlled substances by all registrants, not just pharmacies (21 CFR §1304.11(c)). Under state law a manufacturer must record all transactions involving human prescription drugs (17 CCR§10377.5(a)). When anyone in the drug distribution chain transfers or receives drugs, their transfer or receipt must be recorded (to comply with section 4081(a)).

# Ordering the Drug or Device

**Who May Order.** Under state law, only a person licensed to handle dangerous drugs or controlled substances may obtain or possess them, except as otherwise specifically provided (H&SC §§11350, 11377; §§4059.5, 4060). Thus both sellers and buyers must be properly licensed. Anyone designated by the owner may place an order for dangerous drugs on behalf of a licensed pharmacy; the person receiving the order should know or determine that the person placing the order is authorized to do so. Only a person registered on behalf of the pharmacy (21 CFR §1305.04) or holding a power of attorney[2] from a person so registered (21 CFR §§1305.05(c), 1305.07) may order Schedule I[3] and II controlled substances on behalf of the pharmacy.

Any person, not just an attorney, may be granted power of attorney; the power of attorney form must be signed by the person who signed the most recent application for, or renewal of, the pharmacy's Drug Enforcement Administration (DEA) registration, as well as by the person being granted power of attorney. If a different person signs a subsequent renewal application for the DEA registrant, a new power of attorney form must be submitted. The DEA Pharmacist's Manual, p. 30, contains suggested language for the power of attorney form.

**Form of the Order.** The key requirement for a dangerous drug or device is that a record of any order be maintained by both supplier and recipient to allow a current, accurate, complete inventory of the items. For Schedule I and II controlled substances, an order must be made on a special, triplicate order form called a Form 222, issued by the DEA (21 CFR §1305.03).[4] These paper

---

[1] In one case, a pharmacy billed Medi-Cal for $390,000, but had records showing only $16,000 of drugs purchased for the same period. It claimed it had purchased the remainder of its stock from a person in a van who only accepted cash payments and would not provide invoices or receipts (Committee Report, K. Connell, California State Controller, *California Medical Assistance Program: Review of Selected Long Beach Pharmacies*, June 1996, p. 1). This scenario is a prime example of significant violations of record-keeping as well as many other laws.

[2] A power of attorney may be given to anyone, essentially to act as your agent for designated purposes.

[3] Federal regulations refer to orders for both Schedule I and Schedule II controlled substances. Schedule I controlled substances may be ordered by a pharmacy for use in approved research, such as a clinical drug trial, but they are not available for retail sale.

[4] It is important that the pharmacist distinguish this federal "triplicate" controlled substance order form from the California triplicate form that until 2004 was required for most Schedule II prescriptions (see Chap. IX: Prescriptions: Receipt to Labeling).

forms are obtained directly from the DEA,[5] which is working on a secure electronic alternative.[6]  The order form must be completely filled out by the ordering pharmacy, and signed and dated by the authorized person (21 CFR §1305.06).  The order may not be filled if the Form 222 is incomplete, illegible, or improperly prepared, executed, or endorsed or if it shows any alteration, erasure, or change, except for inconsequential errors (21 CFR §1305.11(a)).

The supplier keeps the first copy of the Form 222 and forwards the second copy to the DEA when the order is filled (21 CFR §1305.09(d)).  The purchaser retains the third copy (21 USC §828(c), 21 CFR §1305.09(a)), which must be kept separately from other pharmacy business records (21 CFR §1305.13(c)).  To keep an accurate inventory that meets the requirements of section 4081(a), the following information must be maintained and available for inspection: the names of the supplier and receiver; the name, form, strength, and amount of the drug supplied; and, usually, the registration or license number of both the supplier and receiver.

**Filling the Order.**  The supplier may not fill any order unless the recipient is authorized to have possession of the ordered item.  The recipient is responsible for immediately notifying the supplier of any shipping error or at least making a record of an error in order to maintain an accurate inventory.  The supplier may ship one bottle of 500 when 5 bottles of 100 were ordered, as long as the actual quantity provided does not exceed the amount initially ordered and the product supplied has the same National Drug Code number as that ordered.  If a supplier refuses an order for any reason, it must return the original (copy 1) and copy (copy 2) of the Form 222 to the purchaser with an explanation why the order was refused (21 CFR §1305.11(b)).

**Lost or Stolen 222s.**  The registrant must immediately report any lost or stolen Form 222 to the nearest DEA Diversion Field Office (21 CFR §1305.12(b)), providing the serial numbers of each lost or stolen form or, if an entire book is lost or the pharmacy cannot otherwise supply individual serial numbers, the approximate date of their issuance.  The registrant must also report if a form reported as lost or stolen is later recovered.

**Receiving the Order.**  Drugs must be received at a pharmacy by the pharmacist-in-charge or another pharmacist he or she designates (§4059.5(a)).  Hospital pharmacy drugs may be received at a central receiving location within the hospital (§4059.5(c)) and drugs may be delivered to a secured area of a retail pharmacy after hours (§4059.5(f), as discussed below and in Chapter V: Other Pharmacy Board Licensees.  Any method of receiving drugs, especially controlled substances, must be secure to prevent theft and other loss.  Controlled substances ordered using a Form 222 must be delivered to the address for the purchaser listed on the form (21 CFR §1305.09(c)).  Pharmacies should confirm that orders received are accurate, and maintain careful records of acquisition of all drugs, especially controlled substances, to fulfill their obligation to maintain an accurate drug inventory (§4081).

Strict delivery requirements are in place to foil thieves who, whether or not associated with a pharmacy, would order drugs and either pick them up from the wholesaler or arrange for their delivery to some place other than inside the pharmacy.  But such requirements have been difficult in

---

[5]  Forms 222 can be ordered at the time of initial application to the DEA and thereafter on DEA requisition forms supplied with the Forms 222 or by contacting DEA.  Each book of Forms 222 consists of seven sets of forms; a pharmacy may obtain a maximum of six books at a time unless its needs require more (21 CFR §1305.05, DEA Pharmacist's Manual, pp. 27-28).

[6]  DEA has been working on an electronic form for about five years.  A DEA official has publicly stated that regulations on this subject would be proposed early in 2005 (presentation of Patricia M. Good, Chief, Liaison and Policy Section, DEA Office of Diversion Control, annual conference of the National Association of State Controlled Substance Authorities, San Diego, CA, Oct. 21, 2004).

communities that limit commercial deliveries to off-peak hours or where traffic impedes delivery during business hours. In 2003 the Board adopted an interpretation of section 4059.5 to permit delivery of drugs to a secured area when the pharmacy is closed. This policy has now been incorporated into section 4059.5, as discussed in Chapter V: Other Pharmacy Board Licensees.

# Packaging and Labeling

A pharmacy that repackages a drug other than in filling a prescription has engaged in manufacturing under the law, as discussed in Chapter VIII: Preparation of Drugs by a Pharmacy. When a pharmacy repackages a drug within the scope of its pharmacy license, the labeling must meet federal and state drug labeling standards, just as it must when the pharmacy compounds or manufactures a drug.

A pharmacy may repackage a drug previously dispensed on prescription for a patient, or at the patient's request, without concern that it is engaging in manufacturing. It must, however, have in place policies and procedures for repackaging prescription drugs and comply with all labeling requirements (§§4033(c), 4052.7).

# Maintaining

A pharmacy must keep its drugs on the licensed premises and secure from theft or loss; ensure their continuing potency, purity, and safety; maintain their identity by not mixing them with other drugs or with other lots of the same drugs; and assure they are accurately labeled (§4116; H&SC §§111260, 111440; §1714(b),(d)).

Where controlled substances are involved, failure to assure their security may allow easy diversion of potent, valuable drugs to the street market. Even some drugs that are not controlled substances are marketable on the street; for example, there is a market for antibiotics to be diverted for sale in foreign countries and for such popular drugs as Viagra.®

California law does not expressly require that controlled substances be kept separate from non-controlled substances. Federal regulations require that Schedule II-V controlled substances be stored in a securely locked, substantially constructed cabinet, except that a pharmacy may instead disperse them among noncontrolled stock in such a manner as to obstruct the theft or diversion of the controlled substances (21 CFR §1301.75(b)). DEA provides detailed guidance for assessing what security is necessary to prevent diversion of controlled substances, given the setting, the number of people with access to the controlled substances, the level of crime in the area, the security of the building, the quantity of controlled substances maintained, and the prior history of theft or diversion on the premises. (See the DEA's "Controlled Substances Security Manual," www.deadiversion.usdoj.gov/pubs/manuals/sec/security.pdf).

Failure to properly maintain any drug may lead to a bad patient outcome if the drug has become either unsafe or ineffective. The need to assure the safety, purity, and efficacy of drugs precludes, under most circumstances,[7] allowing the return of dispensed drugs to stock and the sharing of no-longer needed drugs with others, both of which are illegal. Online "clubs" that have proliferated to promote drug-sharing are in violation of numerous federal and state laws.

---

[7] In some controlled settings FDA policy allows states to approve the return of drugs to stock for reuse (see below, "Limited Reuse of Returned Drugs").

# Transferring

"Transfer" is broad enough to encompass any provision of drugs to another party, whether by a sale or without payment, including providing drugs to another pharmacy or a prescriber and returning them to the distributor or manufacturer from whom they were originally received. Each transfer must be documented in as much detail as the initial receipt of the drugs. When a transfer involves a Schedule I or II controlled substance, the documentation must include a DEA Form 222 (21 CFR §1305.03). Even a loan of drugs, however temporary, must be documented. A transfer may be made only to a person authorized by law to receive and handle the drugs being transferred, although the drugs may be entrusted to a common carrier to transfer them from one licensee or registrant to another. The common carrier is considered a conduit, not a recipient. Every applicable law accepts common carriers handling drugs without requiring that they register, but the carriers do have to keep records (21 USC §373).

Under some circumstances, a pharmacy may be asked to supply drugs to prescribers and to such entities as pharmacies and health care facilities. The law limits those transfers to the circumstances described below.

## *To Other Pharmacies and Wholesalers*

Pharmacies through the years have sometimes engaged in wholesale sales, without needing a wholesaler license to do so. However, as of 2005, a pharmacy's authorization to supply commercially prepared drugs to another pharmacy or to a wholesaler is extremely limited. The circumstances under which a pharmacy may still engage in this practice are described in Chapter IV: Licensing Pharmacies ("Restrictions on Pharmacy Business").

## *Prescribers' Offices and Clinics*

Drugs also are needed in individual prescribers' offices and clinics, for purposes of administration to patients. Each prescriber must order his or her own stock of drugs for use in office practice, maintain it separately from the drugs of other practitioners in the same office, and dispense or administer only from his or her own stock. These rules apply even to a clinic or any group or multidisciplinary practice, except to clinics with a license from the Board, as discussed in Chapter V: Other Pharmacy Board Licensees. These limitations must be kept in mind by pharmacists asked to prepare drugs for, or transfer drugs to, a prescriber, group practice, or clinic, or to work in those settings.

A pharmacy may provide drugs to a person licensed to administer those drugs in the course of professional practice without having to register as a manufacturer (H&SC §111655(c)). A pharmacy may provide drugs to a health care provider that is authorized to purchase drugs (§4126.5(a)(6)). As also discussed in Chapter VIII: Preparation of Drugs by a Pharmacy ("Pharmacy Compounding"), a pharmacy may compound and supply to a prescriber for office use a reasonable amount of drugs (§4052(a)(1)), §1716.1).

## *Hospitals and Other Licensed Health Care Facilities*

A hospital must have its own pharmacy or, in the case of small hospitals, a permit to purchase drugs from wholesalers. Even the emergency room and ward stocks of a hospital must come from a pharmacy (see Chap. IV: Licensing Pharmacies).

A pharmacy may provide drugs to a health care provider that is authorized to purchase drugs. While the Pharmacy Law doesn't define "health care provider," various provisions in the Health and Safety Code do.  For example, section 123105 defines health care provider to include, among others, a licensed health care facility, clinic, or home health agency (H&SC §123105(a)(1)-(3)).  Included are long term care, intermediate care, and skilled nursing facilities, all of which are licensed health care facilities.

Pharmacies are often asked to provide medications to patients of  intermediate care facilities (ICFs) and long-term care facilities (LTCs).[8]  Because these are not acute care hospitals, chart orders cannot be used and controlled substance prescription forms (see Chap. IX: Prescriptions: Receipt to Labeling) are needed for Schedule II controlled substances.  In modern pharmacy practice these orders usually do not come to a pharmacy singly.  In most cases, facilities contract with pharmacies to supply the drugs for their patients; most pharmacies serving such facilities deal exclusively with one or more facilities, serving no retail patients (the "closed-door" pharmacy).  There currently is no separate license for such pharmacies.  The basic rules for receiving and filling prescriptions apply to "closed-door" as well as other retail pharmacies.

Licensed health care facilities also may need a stock of prescription items for use in an emergency.  Section 4119 specifically authorizes a pharmacy to furnish prescription drugs or devices to licensed health care facilities for storage in secured emergency pharmaceutical supplies containers in accordance with DHS regulations.  The emergency supplies must be approved by the facility's patient care policy or pharmaceutical services committee and be readily available at each nursing station (22 CCR §72377(b)).  There are strict limits on the number of doses that may be included in this supply: 24 oral dosage or suppository drugs (H&SC §1261.5); no more than six drugs, with no more than four doses each, for anti-infective, anti-diarrheal, anti-nausea, or analgesic use (22 CCR §72377(b)(1)(C)).

Skilled nursing facilities must have 24-hour prescription service available that can provide needed drugs that are not in the facility's emergency drug supply, within an hour during normal pharmacy hours and within two hours otherwise; some anti-infective and pain control drugs need only be available and administered within four hours after the order (22 CCR §72355(a)).

A pharmacy may also furnish drugs to certain licensed health care facilities through automated dispensing device systems, as discussed in Chapter IV: Licensing Pharmacies.

There are similar, but simpler, regulations for intermediate care facilities (22 CCR §§73349-73375) and ICFs for the developmentally disabled (22 CCR §§76411-76413).

## *Supplying Ambulances*

A pharmacy may receive a request to supply drugs and devices to an ambulance.  Logic dictates that ambulances must be able to obtain, maintain, and own appropriate drugs and devices, but no law addressed the subject directly until 2001.

The law now specifically provides for a pharmacy to furnish dangerous drugs or devices to an approved service provider within an emergency medical services system for storage in a secured pharmaceutical supplies container pursuant to the local emergency medical services agency's policies and procedures (§4119(b)).  The drugs or devices must be exclusively for use in conjunction with services provided in an ambulance or by other approved emergency medical services providers, and

---

[8]  Definitions of various types of health care facilities are contained in Appendix B.

within the scope of the licensed emergency medical technician's practice (§4119(b)(1),(2)). The emergency medical service provider must make a written request specifying the name and quantity of drugs and devices sought (§4119(b)(3)), and must administer, document, store, and restock the drugs and devices in accordance with the policies and procedures of the local medical services agency (§4119(b)(4),(5)). Both the emergency medical services provider and the pharmacy must keep records of each request for and furnishing of dangerous drugs and dangerous devices for three years. Controlled substances may be furnished in accordance with the California Controlled Substances Act (§4119(b)).

A hospital that is the base hospital for paramedics must have a physician medical director and a qualified physician assigned to its emergency department, to ensure a mechanism for the replacement of medical supplies and controlled substances used during treatment (22 CCR §100168(b)(6),(10),(11)). Similarly, the base hospital for an EMT-II (an emergency medical technician license category that is below that of paramedic[9]) must be supervised by a medical director; the hospital is responsible for the supply and resupply of medical equipment and drugs (22 CCR §100127(b)(7),(9),(10)).

**An emergency vehicle, staffed by a registered nurse and vocational nurses, is maintained at forest fire lines to provide a limited supply of emergency drugs to persons injured fighting fires. Is this legal? May a pharmacy stock this vehicle?**

It would be a good idea to have drugs available under such circumstances, but the emergency vehicles the law contemplates are mobile units staffed by licensed or certified emergency medical technicians (§4119(b)(2)), and not by nurses. It also contemplates an "emergency medical services system" (§4119(a)); the supplier of the emergency vehicle in the hypothetical might meet this requirement. If the emergency vehicle is not part of such a program, it is not legal under California law for the pharmacy to provide drugs for it. (If the federal or state government is supplying the vehicle, as is likely in the case of forest fires, the government will also have the means to obtain the necessary drugs without involvement of a local pharmacy.)

## Supplying Officers of Ocean Vessels

A pharmacy or wholesaler may furnish dangerous drugs to the master or first officer of an ocean vessel under a written requisition on the vessel's official stationery, signed by the first officer. The drugs are maintained on the vessel and dispensed under standardized procedures developed by a registered medical officer (a person licensed by any state as a physician). Dangerous drugs must be furnished in a sealed container either to the first officer (who has supplied proper identification) or delivered aboard the vessel. A pharmacy or wholesaler must notify the Board within 30 days of undertaking this activity (§4066).

Any controlled substance may be furnished to the ocean vessel in accordance with 21 CFR §1301.25. That section requires that a medical officer employed by the owner and operator of the vessel be registered with the DEA at the principal office of the vessel's owner or operator or elsewhere if the identifying information on the registration is maintained at the principal office (21 CFR §1301.25(b)). The controlled substances are to be acquired by and dispensed under general supervision of the medical officer (21 CFR §1301.25(a)). In the alternative, if no registered medical officer is employed, or if he or she is not accessible and controlled substances are required, the master or first officer may purchase controlled substances upon presenting in person a written requisition on

---

[9] There are three statutory categories of EMTs; the paramedic is also known as an "EMT-P" (H&SC §1797.84).

the vessel's official stationery or purchase order form containing very detailed information (21 CFR §1301.25(d)).

Any pharmacy registered with the DEA that chooses to supply ocean vessels with controlled substances first must notify the nearest DEA division office of its intent to do so by registered mail, including the date on which the activity will commence.  During any calendar year the pharmacy may not supply to ocean vessels a quantity of controlled substances that exceeds five per cent of its total volume of controlled substance dosage units dispensed (21 CFR §1301.25(f)).

The DEA regulations applicable to ocean vessels also apply to aircraft and to other entities deemed appropriate by the agency, such as emergency kits at field sites of an industrial firm (21 CFR §1301.25(a)(2),(3)).  California law, however, only extends these exceptions to ocean vessels (§4066).

## *Supplying Correctional and Other Restricted Facilities*

The law requires that emergency and basic health care services, including pharmaceutical services, must be available to correctional facility and juvenile facility inmates (15 CCR §§1200, 1202, 1400, 1403).  The role of pharmacists within such facilities and for planning and oversight purposes is discussed in Chapter VI: Scope of Practice for Pharmacists.

Regulations require that a mental health rehabilitation center must provide pharmaceutical services (9 CCR §785.00(a)) by making an arrangement for their provision by a California-licensed pharmacy (9 CCR §785.20(a)).  Drugs ordered "stat" must be available and administered within one hour during the normal business hours of a local pharmacy or hospital and within two hours outside those hours.  Anti-infectives and drugs for the treatment of severe pain, nausea, agitation, diarrhea, or other severe discomfort must be available and administered within four hours of an order; all other drugs must be available on the day of the order or the next day if therapy would not commence until then (9 CCR §785.21(a)).

# Loss and Theft

A pharmacy (or any licensed entity or person handling dangerous drugs) is always responsible for an accurate accounting for the drugs it should have on hand (§§4080, 4081(b)).  In order to maintain such an accounting, the pharmacy must keep accurate records of acquisition and disposition of dangerous drugs.  These records must include drugs lost by any means, including by theft or destruction.

From time to time, a pharmacy will lose some drugs.  Sometimes the loss will arise because drugs are ruined by adverse weather conditions, fire, or other damage to the pharmacy.  Sometimes drugs deteriorate and their disposal may be necessary.  There may be a theft or robbery.  There may be a discrepancy because of the accumulation of minor filling errors or record-keeping errors over a period of time; small discrepancies are not uncommon.  The pharmacy and pharmacist should institute changes in pharmacy operations, such as better security, as soon as inexplicable losses begin to occur.

But the key is that the pharmacy is obligated to keep accurate records.  If the pharmacy cannot match stock on hand to its records of acquisition and disposition, the pharmacy is subject to a charge of violating section 4081(a).  Not every discrepancy will lead to such charges, but a significant discrepancy, especially involving controlled substances, is likely to do so.

Therefore, the pharmacy and the responsible pharmacist (usually the pharmacist-in-charge) must watch for evidence of loss or theft.  They must have procedures in place to deal with cases of theft, diversion, or self-use by licensed employees (§4104(b)).  When they learn of loss or theft, they must document immediately and carefully the cause, nature, and, as accurately as possible, the extent of the loss and report it to the Board (§1715.6). If a significant loss of controlled substances is involved, it must be reported to the DEA (21 CFR §1301.76(b), DEA Form 106).[10] Careful contemporaneous records of loss will allow the pharmacy to explain any discrepancy to a state or federal inspector and will allay suspicion of pharmacy misconduct or failure to respond properly and promptly to the cause of the problem.

**Suppose you are a pharmacist at a retail pharmacy and discover that 1,000 penicillin tablets are missing, but you do not know why. You know the owner and several employees have relatives overseas, and they frequently speak of their concern that their relatives have no access to lifesaving drugs. If the penicillin has been diverted, you are quite certain that the motivation is humanitarian and not profit. You are not the pharmacist-in-charge. Do you have a legal obligation to report the loss to the Board? To the pharmacist-in-charge?**

There is a market for antibiotics, particularly for export. This loss could be significant as a sign of a bigger problem, even if its dollar value is relatively small. No specific statute requires an employee pharmacist to report the loss to the pharmacist-in-charge or the pharmacy owner; however, it might well be considered unprofessional conduct for a pharmacist aware of such a discrepancy not to report it to his or her employer. Also, an employer could reasonably expect a capable employee to bring this information to the employer's attention. While there is no obligation on your part to report the discrepancy to the Board, the pharmacy, as noted above, must maintain procedures to deal with theft or diversion of prescription drugs by licensed employees (§4104(b)).

**Suppose, as an employee pharmacist, but not the pharmacist-in-charge, you discover a shortage of 50 hydromorphone hydrochloride (Dilaudid®) 4 mg tablets. Your pharmacy handles about 5,000 such tablets a day. Do you have an obligation to report this finding?**

Section 4081 simply requires the keeping of accurate records. But, as noted above, regulations require that the loss of controlled substances, whether by theft, robbery, or otherwise, must be reported both to the Board (§1715.6) and, if significant, to the DEA (21 CFR §1301.76(b)). The Board's requirement refers to "loss" without specifying a quantity; a loss need not be large to trigger the requirement. Every DEA registrant, including a pharmacy, must take security measures to guard against theft and diversion of controlled substances (21 CFR §§1301.71,1301.75).

If you are neither the owner nor the pharmacist-in-charge, you may not be directly responsible for reporting controlled substances discrepancies, but you certainly have a moral and professional responsibility to do so. It is a moral responsibility because every pharmacist knows of the potential for abuse of misdirected controlled substances; it is a professional responsibility because a failure to report the discrepancy to one's superiors would place them in violation of state and federal reporting and record-keeping laws. Failure of the pharmacist to report discrepancies to the pharmacist-in-charge or the employer also could lead to loss of employment.

Every pharmacy employee is required to notify his or her employer if he or she knows of drug diversion from the pharmacy by a fellow employee (21 CFR §1301.91). This provision reflects the importance that the DEA attaches to preventing drug diversion; identifying registrants, licensees, or

---

[10] Factors in determining whether a loss is significant include: the schedule of the missing controlled substance, the abuse potential of the missing drug (generally and in the registrant's area), the quantity of the loss, whether such a loss has happened before, and whether the loss was reported to local police. If in doubt, the DEA recommends you report the loss (DEA Pharmacist's Manual, pp. 18-20). The DEA also has a pending regulation (discussed in the text, below) that would add to these factors the quantity lost in relation to the type of business, whether the loss can be associated with persons who have access to the drugs, whether there is a pattern of losses, and the results of efforts taken to resolve the losses.

unlicensed employees who may have caused diversion is considered an important aspect of diversion prevention.

Tracking losses of dangerous drugs, including controlled substances, also is self-protective. It allows a pharmacy to identify problems early, before a pattern of drug disappearance develops that cannot be explained away when an inspector or DEA agent notices. Failure to track could risk the loss of one's business or even to lead to civil liability, should the problem lead to unsafe or ineffective drugs reaching consumers.

**Suppose you are an employee pharmacist who notices an inexplicable shortage of hydromorphone hydrochloride tablets. You report the loss to the pharmacist-in-charge and nothing happens – no reporting to the Board or DEA, no changes in security or procedures. Then you report the loss to the absentee owner and again nothing happens. In fact the shortages continue to grow. What do you do?**

Unfortunately, you probably ought to begin searching for another job. Remaining employed by persons who are not concerned with compliance with the law (or perhaps actively engaged in violating it) is not a wise choice and could put your professional future at risk. Your moral and professional obligation, if not your legal obligation, is to contact the Board and/or the DEA and share your suspicions as soon as possible so that the authorities may investigate. Doing so also affords you protection against retaliatory action by your employer under California law (Lab. Code §1102.5, see Chap. XIV: Other Relevant Law), although you might not care to retain your position in a pharmacy engaging in controlled substance violations.

Drugs lost in transit and prior to receipt are the responsibility of the supplier, who must report any lost or missing controlled substances to the DEA (DEA Pharmacist's Manual, pp. 20-21). If controlled substances are simply destroyed or damaged in transit, the loss is generally not reportable to DEA, although disposal of damaged drugs or their transfer to a reverse distributor for destruction must be reported on DEA Form 41. When a pharmacy does not receive drugs it has ordered, the supplier should be notified. If the reason for non-receipt is that a Form 222, for Schedule I or II controlled substances, was never received, the pharmacist must complete a new order and prepare a statement that includes the serial number and date of the first order and verification that the controlled substances were never received (21 CFR §1305.12). A copy of that statement must be attached to the pharmacy's copies of both the original and replacement orders (DEA Pharmacist's Manual, pp. 28-29).

DEA has proposed, but not adopted, clarifying amendments to its regulations on this subject (Reports by Registrants of Theft or Significant Loss of Controlled Substances, 68 FR 40576, July 8, 2003). The proposals offer some guidance about how DEA is applying its loss and theft reporting requirements. For example, DEA states that the requirement of a report "on discovery" of the theft or loss means immediately upon discovery. DEA also recommends the loss or theft be reported to local law enforcement and regulatory agencies, although the new regulations would not require the reports.

# Excessive Sales

Because of concerns about pharmacies or other registrants, such as licensed prescribers and health care facilities, engaging in diversion of controlled substances, both federal and state law require that distributors of drugs report excessive sales (§4164, §1782, 21 CFR §1301.74(b)). These reports are detection devices intended to alert the Board or the DEA to suspicious ordering patterns. Secondarily, these reports ought to make distributors wary of selling and pharmacies or others wary of ordering unjustifiably large amounts of controlled substances. Note the reference to *unjustifiably* large amounts. Some pharmacies, prescribers, and facilities have a regular need for substantial amounts of these drugs. An obvious example is a pharmacy serving a large number of cancer patients.

The DEA provision is very open-ended. It sets no amounts and specifies no drugs; it just requires a distributor to report any sale that it believes is excessive. In contrast, the Board regulation directs the Board to specify the drugs and amounts that need to be reported, take reports as frequently as monthly (although the Board generally has asked for them quarterly), and change the drugs and amounts from time to time. The reports are used by Board inspectors to help identify licensees that may warrant investigation.

The obligation does not end with reporting. Any distributor that furnishes controlled substances for other than legitimate purposes violates its responsibility to exercise proper judgment, a responsibility similar to that imposed on pharmacists (H&SC §11153.5, §4301(e); see Chap. XII: Practice Pitfalls). In at least one case filed to enforce this responsibility (and settled without reported decision), a wholesaler paid substantial civil penalties in connection with its failure to properly report and control excessive and questionable sales.

# Drug Samples, Secondary Sourcing, and Counterfeiting

## *Drug Samples*

Concern about drug promotion and the use of samples grew in the early 1980s. Vast numbers of samples, including controlled substances, were being distributed, usually by drug company sales representatives, to convince prescribers to use their products. There were very few controls and, despite state and federal record-keeping requirements, very little tracking. Some licensees and others were removing the identifying markings from samples[11] and then selling them. Some pharmacies were among the purchasers of these samples, obviously at a lower cost than the distributor's price, to resell them in bulk or to use them to fill prescriptions. Clearly sales of samples designated "not for resale" constituted a violation of the manufacturer's intent. Because of risks to the public health and safety, both Congress and the California Legislature decided to prohibit these transactions.[12]

Under California law, a manufacturer's sales representative may not provide any complimentary sample without the written request of a prescriber, such as a physician, dentist, podiatrist, or veterinarian. Nurse practitioners, certified nurse-midwives, and physician assistants acting under standardized protocols with a physician may also sign such a request and receive drug samples to the extent identified in the protocols. The written request must contain the names and addresses of both the supplier and the requester and the name and quantity of the specific dangerous drug desired. The supplier must preserve the written request with other records of furnishing of dangerous drugs generally required of manufacturers under section 4059(b) (§4061).

The federal Prescription Drug Marketing Act of 1988 strictly limits the distribution of drug samples (21 USC §353(d)) and forbids the sale, purchase, or trade of drug samples (21 USC §353(c)(1)). The manufacturer or other authorized distributor may distribute drug samples by mail or

---

[11] The removal of the sample markings is, as discussed in Chapter VIII: Preparation of Drugs by a Pharmacy, misbranding and possibly adulteration.

[12] The prohibitions are enforced (see Bob Fernandez, *3 druggists, 2 doctors charged with illegally selling free pill samples*, PHILADELPHIA INQUIRER, Dec. 28, 2004).

common carrier to a licensed prescriber or, at the request of a licensed prescriber, to pharmacies of hospitals or other health care facilities (21 USC §353(d)(2)).[13] Because the statute only mentions hospital or other health care facility pharmacies, FDA interprets this law to forbid both the distribution of drug samples to, and receipt of drug samples by, retail pharmacies (21 CFR Parts 203, 205). FDA has stated that it will deem the presence of drug samples in a retail pharmacy to be proof of violation of the law.[14]

When a practitioner requests that samples be distributed to hospital or other health care facility pharmacies, the receipt must include the name and address of the pharmacy as well as that of the ordering practitioner (21 CFR §203.31(c)). Any drug samples so obtained by a pharmacy and then furnished to a patient must be labeled properly in accordance with both state and federal law (21 USC §§352, 353(b)(2)). The pharmacy must maintain accurate records of acquisition and disposition of drug samples, as of all other drugs (§4081).

Drug samples may be distributed to a patient by a licensed prescriber, a health care professional under the direction and supervision of a prescriber, or the pharmacy of a hospital or other health care facility that received the sample legally and when acting under the direction of a licensed prescriber (21 USC §353(d)(1)). Prescribers may donate prescription drug samples to charitable institutions such as free clinics, provided adequate records are kept and precautions taken to minimize the possibility of diversion (21 CFR §203.39).

The law requires manufacturers and distributors whose representatives distribute samples directly to practitioners and pharmacies of hospitals or other health care entities to store those samples under appropriate conditions to maintain their stability, integrity, and effectiveness, and assure they are free of contamination, deterioration, and adulteration (21 USC §353(d)(3)(B)). It also requires annual inventories of the drug samples in the possession of company representatives and records of the representatives' names and addresses and the sites where samples are kept (21 USC §353(d)(3)(C)). Inventories and records of distribution, loss, or return and of requests for samples must be kept for three years and made available to FDA on request (21 USC §353(d)(3)(C)). FDA must be notified of any significant loss or known theft of drug samples (21 USC §353(d)(3)(D)) and of any federal or state conviction of a company representative for violation of drug sample laws (21 USC §353(d)(3)(E)).

What is most important is that transactions involving drug samples must be accounted for as carefully as any other prescription drug transaction. Samples must be maintained with the same care as all other drugs. Anyone obtaining drug samples should be doing so only for legally-authorized purposes. Concern about abuse of the drug sample system persists; some policymakers have urged banning drug sampling entirely, but legislation to that effect has not made significant progress in Congress.

---

[13] A written request by a practitioner licensed to prescribe the drugs is required and must include the name, address, professional designation, and signature of the requesting practitioner, the identity and quantity of the sample requested, the name of the manufacturer, and the date of the request. The recipient of the sample also must execute a written receipt for the sample on delivery, returning the signed receipt to the manufacturer or authorized distributor (21 USC §353(d)(2)(A),(B)). Records concerning samples, including orders, may be in electronic form (21 CFR §203.60(a)).

[14] FDA has taken the position that drug starter packs, defined as prescription drug products distributed free by manufacturers or distributors for pharmacists, but intended for retail sale, are not drug samples for purposes of this law, and thus are entirely legal (21 CFR §203.38(c)). In addition, when manufacturers make arrangements to provide prescription drugs to licensed practitioners to prescribe and dispense at no cost or reduced cost to their indigent patients, those drugs will ordinarily not be considered samples. Therefore the practitioner may direct the drugs to be distributed to and dispensed by a retail pharmacy (64 FR 67720, 67744 (Dec. 3, 1999)).

## Secondary Sourcing

Some health care facilities are able to purchase drugs at special discounts, sometimes as much as 90 percent or more below the average wholesale price for other purchasers.  Drugs sold at these deep discounts are intended for particular uses, such as for hospital inpatients, members of the military, beneficiaries of the Veterans Administration, or members of Native American tribes.  An issue arose when purchasers or their agents entitled to these discounts began to purchase quantities far beyond the needs of the intended beneficiaries and resell the drugs on the open market or use them to fill other prescriptions, at significant profit.  The intended beneficiary organization is offered a fee for allowing this arrangement; the reseller profits from the resale or use in its own pharmacies of the drugs.  Competitors who have to buy their drugs at regular prices of course are at a considerable disadvantage; consequently unfair competition and antitrust laws are implicated (see Chap. XIV: Other Relevant Law).  Drugs sold for export, also at deep discounts, began to find their way back into the United States.  In addition to the competitive concerns raised above, this secondary "sourcing" of drugs raises the concern of the continuing integrity of the drugs while out of the country.  Both types of "black market" purchases and resales (involving domestically-discounted drugs and drugs for export) continue to be a significant problem.  Successful criminal prosecutions have been brought, notably in California and Florida, against wholesalers engaging in this activity.

This conduct probably was a violation of long-existing California law (B&PC §17200, concerning unfair trade or business practices).  Nevertheless, both the Congress (21 USC §381) and the California Legislature (§4380) have passed laws specifically restricting such activities.  The federal law, among other things, bars the reimportation of a prescription drug manufactured in the United States except when done by the manufacturer or as authorized by the FDA for emergency medical care (21 USC §381(d)(1),(2)).  It also is unlawful to sell or distribute, or to offer to do so, any drug purchased by a public or private hospital or other health care entity or any drug that was donated or supplied at a reduced cost to a charitable organization, except to a similar entity (21 USC §353(c)(3)).

California law prohibits resale of drugs acquired at preferentially low prices under the Nonprofit Institutions Act.  However, the law does not prohibit such resale for the acquirer's own use,[15] to another eligible entity, or on prescription to a walk-in customer if the total of such sales represents less than one percent of the drugs purchased by the seller for its own use (§4380(a)).  Violation of this section is both grounds for discipline against one's license (§4301(o)) and unfair competition under Business and Professions Code sections 17200 to 17209.

The drug sample and secondary sourcing problems underscore the need for pharmacies to know the sources of the drugs they obtain, to document those sources, and to avoid receipt and use of drugs where the source or conditions of prior maintenance are questionable.

## Counterfeit Drugs

Counterfeiting of drugs has recently been recognized as a major problem.  Some counterfeit drugs are a weaker strength of the labeled drug substituted for a greater strength; others are a substituted drug or inert substance bearing the drug's label.  Widely distributed drugs such as Lipitor® and very expensive drugs such as Procrit® are known to have been counterfeited.  FDA, which had

---

[15] Sales of drugs for one's own use include sales to inpatients, to outpatients treated at the emergency room or clinics, and to employees of the facility for their own health care needs (*Abbott Laboratories v. Portland Retail Druggists Assn.*, 425 U.S. 1, 15-17 (1976)).

been averaging five such cases per year through the 1990s, has seen a fourfold increase in counterfeiting cases in this decade.

While the three biggest drug wholesalers, which together sell 90 per cent of all pharmaceuticals sold in the United States, generally buy their drugs from manufacturers, there are more than 7,000 other wholesalers in the United States which buy and sell drugs based on short-term pricing and availability. These wholesalers profit by reselling drugs purchased from sources other than manufacturers. Even the "big three" sometimes obtain inventory (estimated at about one to three percent, or $600 million to $2 billion dollars worth of their annual business) from the secondary market – that is, not from manufacturers – to cover short-term needs. Some manufacturers are so concerned that they have announced their refusal to sell to wholesalers that buy any of their products other than from themselves or authorized resellers (Scott Hensley, *New J&J Policy Aims to Thwart Counterfeits*, WALL STREET JOURNAL, Dec. 11, 2003, p. B1; Scott Hensley, *Pfizer Acts to Halt Counterfeit Drugs, Following J&J*, WALL STREET JOURNAL, Dec. 19, 2003, p. B2). The risks and concerns involved with secondary sources and counterfeiting are the same as those under intense discussion with respect to reimportation of prescription drugs from Canada or elsewhere to save money (see below). Concerns over the reliability of certain wholesalers and the source of products purchased by pharmacies and by distributors have led to tightening of the regulation of the wholesale industry. "Pedigree" requirements under federal and state law are discussed in Chapter V: Other Pharmacy Board Licensees ("Wholesalers").

## *Authorized Discount Purchases*

As noted above, some pharmacies may legally purchase drugs at substantial discounts under several statutes providing discount programs limited to specified entities and for their own use, not for resale or for use for ineligible patients. For example, the Veterans Health Care Act of 1992 (38 USC §8126) requires manufacturers to sell to entities covered by the Act at a price which is no more than 76 percent of the regular manufacturer's price. This so-called "340B discount" (after the section number in the legislation) applies to purchases for use of Veterans Administration and military facilities, the Coast Guard, and the Public Health Service, including Indian Health Services facilities. The law and regulations encourage drop-shipping of drugs purchased by these beneficiaries to contracting pharmacies, which then maintain the drugs on their premises and dispense from this stock as orders are received from the beneficiary entity.

Allowing contracting pharmacies to be involved is critical to the program's success, because relatively few of the 11,500 covered entities nationwide have their own pharmacies. California law now allows a pharmacy and the covered entity to enter into an agreement to implement this program without either having to obtain a wholesaler license (§4126).

As also discussed above, there is a significant problem with diversion of drugs sold under these discount programs to other uses (see, e.g., Audit of the Mashantucket Pequod Tribal Nations' Use of Federal Discount Drug Programs, Office of the Inspector General, HHS, Aug. 2000, Doc. #A-0 1-99-01502 (82% of 340B stock used for ineligible patients)). A pharmacy that misdistributes 340B drugs to ineligible individuals is liable to the manufacturer for the difference between the 340B price and the non-discounted price (42 USC §256b(a)((5)(D)) and subject to discipline for unprofessional conduct (§4301(r), see Chap. XII: Practice Pitfalls).

Because of risks of diversion of 340B drugs to the secondary sourcing market, HHS and the manufacturer have the authority to perform record audits (42 USC §256b(a)(5)(C), (6)); HHS also may bar abusers of the program from further participation (Manufacturer Audit Guidelines and Dispute Resolution Process 0905-ZA-19, 61 FR 65406, 65411-65413 (Dec. 12, 1996)).

# Return and Destruction of Drugs

When a pharmacy no longer wishes to retain drugs, whether still in marketable condition or outdated, damaged, deteriorated, or of questionable integrity, or when the pharmacy is discontinuing business or is in bankruptcy, the drugs must be disposed of properly (§1708.2).  Disposing of unwanted drugs in the sewage system may violate California and federal environmental laws.

While a licensee is not specifically directed how to dispose of adulterated or misbranded drugs, the fact that both the FDA (21 USC §334(a)) and, as of 2005, the Board (§4084, see Chap. VIII: Preparation of Drugs) may seize them makes it evident that a pharmacy is not to continue to maintain or distribute them.  Several provisions of California law and regulations (§4081) make it clear that records of all disposition of drugs, including disposal and return, must be kept.  And, of course, disposal may not be to an unlicensed person or in such a way as to allow access to an unlicensed person.  Anyone in possession of dangerous drugs must dispose of them in a way that does not endanger public health or safety; if drugs are disposed of carelessly and somehow become accessible to consumers, the licensee could well be found to have distributed adulterated or misbranded drugs or to have furnished drugs illegally.

Section 4059 authorizes a pharmacy to distribute drugs to a manufacturer or wholesaler – in other words, to return them.  Formerly, prohibitions against distribution of adulterated or misbranded drugs seemed to bar the return of such drugs to a distributor.  However, the law now recognizes a category of wholesaler called the "reverse distributor," which acts as an agent for pharmacies, wholesalers, manufacturers, and other entities by receiving, inventorying, and managing the disposition of outdated or nonsaleable dangerous drugs (§§4040.5, 4043).  The DEA has, by regulation, also recognized and provided for the registration of reverse distributors (*Definition and Registration of Reverse Distributors*, 68 FR 41222-41230 (July 11, 2003)).

When controlled substances are involved, disposal by a pharmacy or other DEA registrant must be reported on DEA Form 41.  The DEA's regional office will authorize disposition either by transfer to another registrant, by delivery to the DEA, by destruction in the presence of a DEA agent or authorized person, or by other means approved by the Special Agent in Charge of the regional DEA office (21 CFR §1307.21(a),(b)).  Any registrant required to dispose of controlled substances regularly, which typically means a manufacturer, may be authorized to do so without prior approval for each disposal if certain records are kept and reports filed (21 CFR §1307.21(c)).  A pharmacy may generally obtain authority from DEA to destroy controlled substances once a year; DEA also issues blanket authorizations for destruction, on a limited basis, to registrants associated with hospitals, clinics, and similar entities that need to destroy used needles, syringes, and similar material (DEA Pharmacist's Manual, pp. 14-16).

In recent years, the DEA has discontinued receiving drugs for destruction, simply because of the time and personnel it involves.  There are registered disposal companies, and each regional DEA office maintains a list.  Currently there are six such firms nationally, one of which (EXP Pharmaceutical Waste Management in Union City) is based in California.

**A consumer comes to your pharmacy and asks you what to do with unused prescription drugs.  May you take and dispose of them?  Must you?  May the consumer dispose of them?**

This scenario may arise when a patient has died, when a patient's drug regimen has changed, when a drug has been recalled by a manufacturer, or when there has been bad publicity about a drug and the patient does not want to take it anymore.[16] Whether or not the drugs are controlled substances, there is no express prohibition against a pharmacy accepting them. Nor do they have to be drugs the pharmacy originally dispensed. But the pharmacy has no legal obligation to accept the drugs either, although the pharmacist and pharmacy ought to consider whether their disposal of the drugs for the consumer promotes personal and public safety. Once the pharmacy accepts the drugs, it must make a record as of any other drug acquisition; it also must record how it disposes of the drugs (§4081). Because such returned drugs may not be dispensed to another customer, the pharmacy must carefully segregate them from pharmacy stock until they are destroyed or otherwise disposed of.

The consumer may dispose of the drugs. The pharmacist should advise that their disposal be done with care to assure that the drugs cannot be taken by another person. Experts suggest that trash disposal is better than sewage disposal, as long as precautions are taken to assure children and animals cannot get access (such as emptying capsules and breaking tablets and returning the remains into child-proof containers). The problem of disposal of unused drugs is a major problem. For example, a study has indicated that nursing homes in the United States alone discard between $73 million and $378 million dollars' worth of drugs per year, some by incineration, some by flushing. In Australia, by 2003 consumers had returned over 760 tons of unwanted medications under a program started in 1996 (*DRUG DISPOSAL: How to dump old medicine? No easy answer*, MEDICAL LETTER ON THE CDC & FDA, Oct. 5, 2003, p. 25).

When a patient is returning drugs to the pharmacy because he or she wants to stop taking them, an additional issue arises. The pharmacist should make sure the patient understands the consequences of discontinuing drug therapy and has contacted his or her prescriber; if the patient has not and will not do so, the pharmacist might consider seeking the patient's permission to contact the prescriber on his or her behalf. Although there may be no specific legal obligation to take these steps, it might be considered unprofessional conduct to fail to do so.

**Limited Reuse of Returned Drugs.** In 1980 FDA stated as a policy that pharmacists should not return drugs to stock for reuse, even if they remain in sealed containers, citing public health concerns.[17] It endorsed state regulations specifically forbidding the practice (FDA Compliance Policy Guidelines Manual, Ch. 4, §460.300, CPG 7132.09). In 2000, in response to an inquiry by the American Medical Association, FDA issued an informal opinion clarifying that it would not object to the return of medication from nursing homes to a dispensing pharmacy for reuse, provided that the following conditions are met:

- The dispensing pharmacy is affiliated by contract with the nursing home,
- The pharmacy and pharmacist are licensed and in good standing,
- The dispensed medications did not leave the control of the nursing home after receipt from the pharmacy,
- The storage, handling, and record-keeping systems of the nursing home are adequate to document how the returned medications were handled while in the nursing home (with particular attention to storage conditions), and
- Only medication dispensed in the manufacturer's original packaging is returned.

---

[16] A significant market has sprung up on the Internet, for the pooling and sale of expensive drugs which patients were prescribed and no longer need (Alissa J. Rubin and Aaron Zitner, *Infertility Cases Spur an Illicit Drug Market; Health: Women Buy Leftover Fertility Medication From Other Patients, Often Online, But Law Enforcement is Lax*; LOS ANGELES TIMES, Sept. 10, 2000, p. A1). Notwithstanding a humanitarian purpose of making expensive drugs available at affordable prices, this practice is entirely illegal.

[17] The financial implications of prescription drug reuse are significant; some surveys estimate that 40 percent of all medication costs are for drugs that are not used.

Subsequently, in a letter, FDA said that individual states, which are directly responsible for regulation of pharmacies and health care facilities, are in a better position than FDA to make a determination on this issue for its citizens. The letter underscored the importance of processes to maintain the integrity and prevent the illegal reuse of the drugs, but gave the states the authority to make the final decision. Note that FDA has never changed its compliance guideline on this subject, cited above; the guideline remains on FDA's website, but the letters are neither referenced nor posted there.

At the present time, according to the California Department of Health Services, long-term care and similar facilities may return sealed drugs other than controlled substances to the pharmacy for destruction, but there is no provision allowing their return to stock. Unwanted drugs can no longer simply be thrown out by these institutions (22 CCR §72371); they must be disposed of as medical waste. Drugs must be destroyed in the presence of a pharmacist or a nurse; Schedule II, III, and IV drugs must be destroyed in the presence of a pharmacist and a registered nurse employed by the facility (22 CCR §72371(c)).

When drugs can be returned to stock, questions are likely to arise about the responsibility of the pharmacy and the health care facility to those who have paid for them. It seems reasonable that a person who has been billed for dispensed drugs that have been returned for resale should expect, and receive, a credit for their return. Medicaid statutes and regulations are silent on this issue.

# Import and Export

Most import and export of prescription drugs involves wholesalers and manufacturers, not pharmacies. However, there has been an exponential increase in recent years in the importation of drugs for personal medical use through the Internet, by mail, and across land borders, particularly between Canada or Mexico and the United States. In 2003 about 12 million prescriptions, in five million shipments, valued at $700 million, crossed the border from Canada alone; a similar quantity of prescriptions came from other countries (Ricardo Alonso-Zaldivar, *Bush Administration Suggests Limited Drug Imports; Supporters of allowing cheaper prescriptions into the U.S. see the proposal as too little. GOP lawmakers are among those angered*, LOS ANGELES TIMES, Dec. 22, 2004, p. A22; Rick Weiss, *Two Reports Fault Drug Importation; Government Studies Cite as Concerns Cost of Setting up Program, Safety*, WASHINGTON POST, Dec. 22, 2004, p. A25). Some Canadian pharmacies have actively sought business in the United States, including by setting up storefronts in various states to solicit customers. Some states and cities have assisted their citizens' search for sources of drug imports by providing information on websites, and some have tried to start programs to purchase Canadian drugs for their own health care systems, sometimes seeking waivers from the federal government, which have not been granted (see www.fda.gov/opacom/gonot.html; Julie Appleby, *More cities, states opt for Canadian drugs*, USA TODAY, Dec. 23, 2003, p. 3B).

Contrary to assertions made in various publications or on the Internet, importing a prescription drug from a foreign country is generally illegal. The first United States law restricting importation was enacted over 150 years ago, in 1848. The federal government has prosecuted major violators of restrictions on importation (*People v. Haas*, 171 F.3d 259 (5th Cir. 1999)), and FDA does at least some monitoring of prescription drugs sent from other countries to United States residents. Under its "compassionate use" policy, however, the FDA has long allowed the import for personal use of small amounts of drugs not approved in the United States; importation of FDA-approved drugs from overseas simply because they are less expensive does not come within this policy. An FDA Traveler's Alert explains that to qualify for the "compassionate use" exception, the drug must be for a serious condition for which no satisfactory treatment is available in the United States. The drug may not be commercialized or promoted to United States residents by its foreign distributors (presumably this includes promotion on the Internet), and must not present unreasonable risk. The patient must affirm in writing that the drug is for his or her own use, generally obtain no more than a three-month supply, and provide either the name and address of the American physician responsible for the patient's treatment with the product or evidence the product is for continuation of treatment begun outside the United States. Even if the traveler is in compliance with these guidelines, the FDA still has the discretion to seize the drugs or refuse their entry, because the importation remains illegal.[18]

In June 2004, DEA reiterated guidance it had published three years earlier to the effect that federal law and DEA regulations prohibit the importation of controlled substances except by persons with a DEA import permit (21 USC §§952, 957). A pharmacy or a patient that obtains controlled substances from outside the United States, even to fill legitimate prescriptions, is acting in violation of law (*Importing Controlled Substances From Canada and Other Foreign Countries*, DEA, 69 FR 38920 (June 29, 2004)).

Like FDA, DEA has also long had in place a "personal medical use" exemption (21 USC § 956, 21 CFR §1301.26), which allows United States residents who travel abroad and visitors to the United States to carry in controlled substances for their legitimate personal medical use. The controlled substances must have been lawfully obtained by an individual for personal medical use or for administration to an animal. They must be carried in the original container in which they were dispensed, and declared to Customs. The patient must provide the name of the drug and its schedule or, if the drug's name is not on the label, the name and address of the dispensing pharmacy or practitioner, and, if there is one, the prescription number (21 CFR §1301.26(a),(b)). The importation for personal medical use must also be of drugs for which the patient has a valid prescription in accordance with state law (21 USC §956(a)(2)).

DEA used to allow residents traveling abroad to import up to 50 dosage units of any controlled substance for which they had a legitimate medical use. Congress amended the law in 1998, citing diversion concerns, and restricted to 50 total dosage units the amount of controlled substances a United States resident could bring over an international land border (21 USC §956(a)). By regulation, DEA further limited this personal use importation by restricting all travelers to a maximum of 50 total dosage units of all controlled substances, by whatever means or point of entry they return to the United States (*Exemption From Import/Export Requirements for Personal Medical Use*, 69 FR 55343 (Sept. 14, 2004)(amending 21 CFR §1301.26)).

Federal postal regulations governing importation of controlled substances for personal use define personal use as where there is no evidence of intent to distribute or to facilitate the manufacture, compounding, or processing, delivery, importing, or exporting of the controlled substance. The regulations presume the possession is for personal use when there are no indicia of illicit drug trafficking or distribution, listing a variety of factors used to make that determination (39 CFR §233.8(a)(5)(i)(A)).

Canadian law limits its pharmacies to filling prescriptions issued by Canadian prescribers. Some Canadian pharmacies have entered into relationships with Canadian practitioners, who rewrite prescriptions issued by a patient's physician in the United States. Canadian medical authorities have raised questions about the propriety of such practices because the physicians have not examined the patients (Chris Sorensen, *Internet drugstore brews cross-border controversy*, TORONTO STAR, Oct. 18, 2002, p. F02). Mexican authorities have started to enforce similar laws, arresting and imprisoning some American citizens caught with prescription drugs dispensed in Mexico for which they did not have a prescription issued by a Mexican physician (Marjie Lundstrom, *Embracing freedom; San*

---

[18] FDA maintains a list of drugs that, even under this exception, may not be imported into the United States, in person or by Internet order. The import alert includes such drugs with safety concerns as Accutane®, Lotronex®, and Thalomid® (see www.fda.gov/oc/buyonline/consumeralert120902.html).

*Diego woman learns about Mexican drug law the hard way*, SACRAMENTO BEE, Dec. 11, 2004, p. A1).

Tension over the issue of importation, especially from Canada, has continued to rise along with the frequency with which the prohibition has been flouted; drug imports were even an issue in the 2004 presidential election campaign. FDA has taken action against Canadian pharmacies operating storefronts seeking business in the United States (Frank Green, *Judge OKs shutdown of Canada drug shops*, SAN DIEGO UNION-TRIBUNE, Nov. 7, 2003, p. C-1), and has warned employer-sponsored health plans about the illegality of drug importation (letter from William K. Hubbard, FDA Associate Commissioner for Policy and Planning, to Robert P. Lombard, Esq., dated Feb. 12, 2003, www.fda.gov/ora/import/kullman.htm). In addition, FDA has threatened legal action against state and local governments importing drugs or aiding and abetting their import (see letters from FDA to various state and local officials at www.fda.gov/importeddrugs/). In California, the Legislature passed various measures in 2004 aimed at encouraging and supporting importation; Governor Schwarzenegger vetoed the laws, but signed the resolutions urging Congressional action. At least one state has sued the federal government, arguing that it has a right to run an importation program.

Laws authorizing reimportation were passed by Congress in 2000 and 2001, and signed by Presidents Clinton and Bush, respectively. Both contained a proviso that reimportation not become law unless the Secretary of Health and Human Services issued a finding that it would both be safe to allow reimportation and result in significant cost savings to consumers. In 2000 and again in 2001, HHS Secretaries refused to issue such a finding.

At the end of 2004, an HHS Task Force on Drug Importation issued a report confirming the high volume of illegal drug importation, but calling into question the purity and safety of drugs produced and distributed outside of the FDA inspectional system. The report stated that FDA could not oversee individual consumer imports of drugs, but in theory could oversee bulk imports from a single country, Canada. It added that the cost of instituting such a system, which would involve additional middlemen (presumably wholesalers), would drop cost savings to one to two percent. A report from the Department of Commerce also issued in December 2004 concluded that while brand-name prescription drugs are considerably cheaper outside than within the United States, as a result there is less innovation in this field overseas (Rick Weiss, WASHINGTON POST, cited above). Prescription drug prices are subject to price controls in some countries; others use the market power of their national health care programs to bargain for lower prices.[19]

Both reports were met with skepticism by politicians and others, on both the cost savings and safety concerns. On the cost side, skeptics point to the profitability of the pharmaceutical industry (Marcia Angell, THE TRUTH ABOUT THE DRUG COMPANIES: HOW THEY DECEIVE US AND WHAT TO DO ABOUT IT, Random House, 2004); others cite moral concerns that profits are held in higher regard than American access to health and life-saving drugs (Peter Rost, *Medicines Without Borders*, NEW YORK TIMES, Oct. 30, 2005, p. A19).

Some safety information came from a 2003 FDA study of drugs imported for individuals. It found numerous safety-related problems, including the shipment of drugs not approved by FDA, drugs with inadequate labeling or inappropriate packaging, drugs withdrawn from the U.S. market for safety reasons, and controlled substances of concern, among other problems (*FDA/U.S. Customs Import Blitz Exams Reveal Hundreds of Potentially Dangerous Imported Drug Shipments*, FDA NEWS, Sept. 29, 2003, www.fda.gov/bbs/topics/NEWS /2003/ NEW00948.html). FDA and the Customs Service also found that drugs purportedly coming from a Canadian pharmacy were purchased from all over the

---

[19] The statute setting up the Medicare prescription drug benefit program expressly forbade such bargaining by the government for prescription drugs (see Chap. X: Dispensing and Beyond ("Prescription Pricing")).

world, shipped to The Bahamas, and repackaged there for delivery to United States residents (Christopher Rowland, *Drugs from anywhere, As importation networks spread, concerns for consumer safety grow,* BOSTON GLOBE, Dec. 16, 2004, p.A1).  Skeptics demand examples of individual consumers harmed by imported drugs, claiming there is no such evidence, and making a comparison to recent reports of significant harm from FDA-approved drugs that have had to be removed from the market for safety reasons or are under a cloud (Rick Weiss, WASHINGTON POST, cited above). Pharmacy regulators and pharmacy associations have expressed concern about the broader health care implications of prescription drug importation (see, e.g., the position paper of the National Association of Boards of Pharmacy, at www.nabp.net/ (click on "What's New," "Archives")).

As the debate goes on, California pharmacists, particularly those in proximity to the Mexican border, are likely to receive inquiries about importation policies.  Pharmacists of course may not participate in illegal importation of drugs, and importation remains illegal under both California and federal drug laws, except as described above.

**Exports.**  A pharmacy is most likely to encounter export issues in connection with a patient request to ship a prescription to him or her at an address outside of the United States.  While FDA has procedures for certifying exports, these appear to contemplate commercial shipments, not individual shipments (FDA Compliance Policy Guide 7150.01).[20]  Controlled substances may not be exported unless the shipper has registered with DEA as an exporter and has obtained a permit or submitted necessary declarations (Pharmacist's Manual, p. 50).  A significant consideration is whether the receiving country has laws regulating the entry of pharmaceuticals that the shipment might violate.

The pharmacist asked to send drugs out of the country to a patient must refuse if they are controlled substances.  Even for other drugs, the pharmacist must exercise caution to be certain the drugs will actually go to, and be used by, the patient who ordered them, and not diverted for resale or even for humanitarian reasons.  The request of a patient who is traveling for an extended period and wants to be sure to have reliable supplies of maintenance medication at each location he or she plans to visit would seem to be a legitimate one.  When in doubt a pharmacist could suggest that the patient travel with a prescription from his or her American practitioner and present it in the other country or obtain a prescription from a local practitioner in the country he or she will visit.

---

[20] A pharmacy that engages in commercial exports of prescription drugs would be wholesaling and require a license as a wholesaler.

**What you should think about after reading this chapter:**

1.  What should you know about a supplier from whom you are planning to order drugs for the first time?

2.  What should you consider (or find out) about a supplier not previously known to you who solicits business from you?

3.  Why is accurate record-keeping so important?  Why is security so important?

4.  How must you dispose of returned, outdated, or deteriorated drugs?

5.  Under what circumstances may a pharmacy receive drug samples?  To what uses may they be put?

6.  To whom may a pharmacy furnish drugs purchased at discount for limited purposes, such as under the 340B program?

7.  What role can or should a pharmacy play in importing or exporting drugs?

# Chapter VIII

# Preparation of Drugs by a Pharmacy

---

**What you should know after reading this chapter:**

1. What is pharmacy compounding?  What is manufacturing?

2. When must a pharmacy register as a manufacturer?

3. When may a pharmacy compound medication for a prescriber?

4. What are some examples of misbranding?

5. What is adulteration?

6. May you be found in violation of federal prohibitions on adulteration and misbranding if there is no proof of your intent to violate them?

7. To what extent may government control drug advertising?

---

## History

Throughout history, humans have tried various natural substances or combinations of substances, potions, or extracts to restore health or to otherwise affect the human body.  Every community on every continent developed remedies from available plants and materials; there is evidence that opium has been known and used for at least 3,000 years.

In more recent times, the apothecary or druggist controlled the process of making or compounding and providing medicinal substances.  Druggists compounded most, if not all, medications they dispensed, and generally selected the appropriate remedies for their customers.  But in the 19th and early 20th centuries, as physicians became recognized as the primary providers of medical treatment, they succeeded (with the cooperation of legislators) in driving other practitioners providing patient care either out of business or into very restricted practices.  For example, homeopaths, naturopaths, and others were outlawed in many states, including California[1];

---

[1] In California, a person may not practice or attempt to practice, or advertise or hold him or herself out as practicing, any system or mode of treating the sick or afflicted, or diagnose, treat, operate for, or prescribe for any ailment, blemish, deformity, disease, disfigurement, disorder, injury, or other physical or mental condition of any person without a valid, unrevoked, and unsuspended license from the Medical Board of California or without being authorized to perform such act under a license obtained under some other provision of law.  Violation is a misdemeanor (B&PC §2052).

Under Business and Professions Code section 2052, anything that could remotely be considered medical practice is limited to physicians (including osteopathic physicians licensed by the Osteopathic Medical Board), except as otherwise specifically provided by law.  The courts have called the definition of medical practice in California law "so all-embracing that there is no need for construction in order to bring any particular set of facts within its terms.  Every person of common

chiropractors and osteopaths, outlawed in California in the early part of this century, were reinstated by 1922 initiative acts of the people. Physicians also succeeded in strictly limiting the practices of dentists and chiropodists (now known as podiatrists).

As physicians became dominant, the authority of the people we now call pharmacists decreased. Instead of selecting how, when, and with which drugs a person was to be treated, the pharmacist had to wait for the physician's decision to prescribe. Increasing concern over the lack of quality assurance in the preparation of various concoctions and about the qualifications of those calling themselves physicians, druggists, healers, and the like led to widespread state licensing requirements. A general movement toward state restrictions on professional practice has led to widespread professional and occupational licensure, affecting as many as a hundred health and nonhealth-related professions and occupations in some or all states. Concern about the quality and consistency of drug products, justified by injury and death from dangerous preparations, led to the passage of federal and state laws governing how such products could be made. Examples include the Food and Drugs Act of 1906, forerunner of the Federal Food, Drug, and Cosmetic Act still operative today, and the Sherman Food and Drug Law in California. These laws further restricted pharmacy compounding.

Inevitably, all these forces led to the standardization of common medications and to the centralization of the business of developing, testing, and preparing medications. As companies became more efficient and consistent in the preparation of medications, it became impractical for most pharmacies to prepare their own versions of widely-used drugs. Certainly pharmacies could not perform the controlled scientific and clinical studies necessary to develop new medications and have them approved for marketing.

Eventually, the pharmacist did relatively little compounding of medications, except for special preparations requested by the physician and – ever and ever less so – invented by the pharmacist. Today, while many pharmacies do a substantial amount of preparation of drugs, as opposed to simply repackaging and dispensing manufactured drug products, a pharmacy may only do so without having a federal or state manufacturer's license if this practice fits within an "exception" to the manufacturing laws.

# Preparing From Stock

The reality of modern pharmacy is that most prescriptions are prepared from stock bottles or by simply admixing already-prepared components. The prepared drug or the admixed drug is counted or measured and placed in a container, after which the container is labeled with pertinent drug information, including the drug's brand name or the generic name and name of the manufacturer. The average pharmacy does very little actual compounding – creating a new drug product. Some more-specialized pharmacies do substantial amounts of compounding, and some do only, or virtually only, compounding, of specialized drugs. These compounded drugs are products requested by one or more prescribers or developed by the pharmacy which, because of their instability or the need to vary their formula for different patients, do not readily lend themselves to preparation on a large scale.

---

knowledge knows what 'treating the sick or afflicted' means" (*Howson v. Board of Medical Examiners*, 128 Cal. App. 35, 37 (1st Dist. 1932)).

In recent years other health care practitioners have fought for recognition or for increased authority. Naturopaths were recognized in California by a law effective in 2004 (until 2009, unless the Legislature takes further action) (Naturopathic Doctors Act, B&PC §§3610-3685). A description of the prescription authority of various medical practitioners is in Chapter IX: The Prescription Process: From Receipt to Labeling.

# Pharmacy Compounding

Virtually all drug preparation once involved compounding by druggists or apothecaries, and there were few or no companies engaged in what we call manufacturing. Today, by law, all drug making is manufacturing. Manufacturing is defined by California law as preparing, compounding, propagating, processing, or fabricating any drug or device and includes repackaging, although it does not include repackaging by a retailer taking stock from a bulk container and putting it into a smaller container for an individual patient (H&SC §109970). But a significant number of prescriptions, on the order of 30 million per year, are actually made up from medications compounded by pharmacies.

## *Federal Law*

The major issue in respect to compounding is whether the compounding done by a pharmacy is outside the scope of its pharmacy license. If the pharmacy's compounding is deemed to be outside the scope of its pharmacy license, the pharmacy must obtain a manufacturer's license from both state and federal governments and comply with laws concerning good manufacturing practices, misbranding, and new drug approval (21 USC §§353a, 360(g)(1); H&SC §111655). Until 1997, both federal and California law were vague in defining the line between compounding and manufacturing. Then a provision was included in the federal Food and Drug Modernization Act of 1997 (FDAMA) that defined with much greater specificity the contours of the pharmacy compounding exception. However, in *Thompson v. Western States Medical Center*, 535 U.S. 357, 376-377 (2002), a closely-divided United States Supreme Court held that the law's provisions violated a compounding pharmacy's right of commercial free speech. The lower court had determined that the advertising restrictions were so closely tied to the rest of the compounding provisions that the entire statutory section had to be overturned, and the Supreme Court did not review that conclusion. As a result, the federal statute is entirely invalid, and federal law is once again vague in respect to compounding.

In response to the Court's decision, the FDA promulgated guidelines (Compliance Policy Guides Manual, §460.200, May 2002) on pharmacy compounding. Unlike regulations, guidelines are not themselves enforceable; you cannot be charged with their violation, but rather must be charged with a violation of the underlying statute. They provide guidance as to the factors the FDA will consider when considering whether a pharmacy's compounding has become unlicensed manufacturing.

In the guidelines, FDA recognizes that compounding contemporaneous with receiving a prescription is part of traditional pharmacy compounding. It sets forth the following factors as indications of when the pharmacy is going beyond the limits of compounding:

- Compounding in anticipation of receiving prescriptions, except for very limited quantities in relation to the amounts of drugs compounded after receiving valid prescriptions;
- Compounding drugs withdrawn or removed from the market for safety reasons;
- Compounding drugs from bulk active ingredients that are not components of FDA-approved drugs (for other than sanctioned investigational purposes);
- Receiving, storing, or using drug substances without written assurance from the supplier that each lot has been made in a FDA-approved facility;
- Receiving, storing, or using drug components not guaranteed or otherwise determined to meet official compendia requirements;
- Using commercial scale manufacturing or testing equipment for compounding;
- Compounding for third parties who resell to individual patients or offering compounded products at wholesale to other state-licensed persons or commercial entities for resale;

- Compounding products that are commercially available or which are essentially copies of commercially available, FDA-approved products, except where necessary to make a drug variant available in a small quantity to meet the documented medical need of a patient; and
- Failure to operate in conformity with applicable state law regulating the practice of pharmacy.

The entire compliance guideline is available on FDA's website, at www.fda.gov/ora/compliance_ref/cpg/cpgdrg/cpg460-200.html.

FDA's continuing concern appears to be supported by a survey it conducted of 12 retail compounding pharmacies. More than a third of the tested samples failed to contain the amounts stated on the labels; more than half had a potency of less than 70 per cent of the labeled value. The survey results are posted at www.fda.gov/cder/pharmcomp/survey.htm. California enacted a sterile injectable compounding law several years ago because of a widely-reported death from a product compounded by a pharmacy (see Chap. IV: Licensing Pharmacies). Both state and federal regulators are concerned with the risks associated with the creation of drugs, whether in manufacturing plants or at pharmacies.

## *California Compounding Policy*

The Board has always recognized drugs compounded on prescription for an individual patient. In 1995, before passage of FDAMA, the Pharmacy Board adopted guidelines for distinguishing between legal pharmacy compounding and manufacturing. Although the Board has not yet amended those guidelines, in response either to the adoption of the federal compounding statute or its voiding by the United States Supreme Court, at the end of 2004 a Board committee had drafted proposals for both legislation and regulations on the subject.

No current California statute defines compounding.[2] Board regulations cover the compounding of unapproved drugs for prescriber office use (§1716.1) and record-keeping requirements when compounding in quantities larger than needed for immediate dispensing (§1716.2), as discussed below. The Board also has long recognized that pharmacy compounding included repackaging, in anticipation of prescriptions, of a reasonable quantity of dangerous drugs from bulk to unit of use for dispensing and retail sale to consumers, and reconstituting of finished pharmaceuticals pursuant to approved labeling (*The Script*, Summer 1995, pp.16-17).

The Board, like the FDA, also had adopted guidelines including a set of factors its inspectors should consider that would suggest a pharmacy's compounding actually has crossed the line into manufacturing. One provision of its guidelines, concerning solicitation or advertising of specific products, is no longer a valid consideration, under the decision in the *Western States* case. The others are:

- A professional relationship does not exist among the prescriber, patient, and pharmacist who compounds and dispenses the drug product.
- The pharmacy is compounding products which are essentially generic copies of FDA-approved products which are commercially available.
- The pharmacy is receiving and using drug substances or components without obtaining and retaining appropriate evidence of source or method of preparation.
- The pharmacy is compounding drugs in anticipation of receiving prescriptions, as opposed to in response to individual prescriptions. The volume of such drugs compounded by the

---

[2] However, there is now extensive regulation of the practice of sterile injectable compounding, which is discussed in Chapter IV: Licensing Pharmacies.

pharmacy is high when compared to the volume of prescriptions actually received for such drugs.

- A significant amount of compounded drugs is distributed to patients or customers outside the pharmacy's normal trade area or across state lines.
- Drugs are compounded by one pharmacy and dispensed by another pharmacy.
- The pharmacy is not in general compliance with state or federal requirements for the production, preparation and maintenance of safe and effective drug products. (*The Script*, Summer 1995, p. 17)

While silent on compounding generally, California law has specifically recognized compounding to furnish drugs in reasonable quantity for prescriber office use (§4052(a)(1), H&SC §111655, 21 USC §360(g)). The Board's regulations define "reasonable quantity" as the amount of an unapproved drug that is sufficient for prescriber office use, consistent with the expiration date, and reasonable considering its intended use and the nature of the prescriber's practice. A "reasonable quantity" may be no greater than that which the pharmacy is able to compound in compliance with pharmaceutical standards for identity, strength, quality, and purity (§1716.1(a)). "Prescriber office use" means an amount estimated by the prescriber for application or administration in the prescriber's office or for dispensing no more than a 72-hour supply to the prescriber's patients (§1716.1(c)). The regulation does not specifically limit the total amount that may be compounded and supplied to a physician at any one time for projected office use.

The Board is considering a proposal to seek legislation that would define and recognize compounding by pharmacies for their own patients and for delivery to another pharmacy for delivery or administration. It also proposes to adopt detailed regulations to implement that law, specifying requirements to assure the integrity, quality, and strength of compounded medications. The proposal, which has not yet had an airing before the full Board, was discussed at the December 1, 2004, meeting of the Licensing Committee (see www.pharmacy.ca.gov/meetings/agendas/04_dec_lic_mat.pdf). The current legal framework remains in place until any changes are made.[3]

In most cases, if a pharmacy is preparing a drug pursuant to a specific prescription for a patient, it will be considered compounding. If a pharmacy is stockpiling the drugs that it compounds, in the hope of receiving prescriptions for that stock, it is manufacturing. The most troublesome area has always involved the compounding of a large volume of a drug for which there is an ongoing demand based on past, regular prescription orders. The question of when the pharmacy crosses the line from compounding to manufacturing has no easy answer: there is no specific volume, and no exact measure for when what the pharmacist considers compounding will become manufacturing in the eyes of the FDA or DHS. Compounding in volume to meet ongoing, predicable demand seems well within the scope of acceptable compounding under federal and state law and guidelines.

Consider the following questions assuming that current California and federal law governing compounding remain in effect.

**Suppose a pharmacy, located in a medical building in which several ophthalmologists practice, has developed, over years of working with those physicians, an eye solution which those doctors regularly prescribe for patients. The pharmacy uses components from identifiable sources. It either makes up the solution when a prescription comes in or, because it regularly**

---

[3]  Seven pharmacy groups, including NABP and the USP, have created the Pharmacy Compounding Accreditation Board to provide a seal of approval for compounding pharmacies. This board will focus first on sterile compounding. It was expected that the program would have its first pharmacies accredited early in 2005 (Carol Ukens, *Compounding pharmacies offered seal of approval*, DRUG TOPICS, Apr. 19, 2004).

**receives five to ten prescriptions for the solution per week, maintains enough solution to last one week and fill about ten prescriptions. Is this pharmacy compounding?**

There is very little doubt that it is.

**Suppose other practitioners with offices elsewhere learn about the solution and begin to issue prescriptions for it. Is it still compounding?**

Yes, filling those prescriptions would still be compounding.

**Suppose the pharmacy posts on its website information about the eye solution, as a result of which it receives inquiries and, thereafter, prescriptions from additional physicians. Is this pharmacy compounding?**

Yes, it is still compounding. It is still filling prescriptions for particular patients. The fact that it promoted the sale of its product is protected under the *Western States* decision. The Board and FDA may no longer consider advertising or promotion as a factor in determining whether a pharmacy is manufacturing rather than compounding. (Advertising of course must be truthful.)

**Suppose the pharmacy, because of the popularity of its product, begins to make substantially more solution than needed for the number of prescriptions it receives, anticipating a continuing increase in business. Is it still compounding?**

This activity appears to have stepped beyond compounding to manufacturing.

**Suppose a pharmacy is given an order from a physician to make up a drug product that is not available commercially. If it does so, is it manufacturing?**

Under current law, the pharmacy may make the product under its compounding authority, without becoming a manufacturer. But if the pharmacy makes that product without specific orders or a pattern of orders it has stepped beyond pharmacy compounding into manufacturing.

**May a pharmacy compound a medication pursuant to a prescription and mail it out of state?**

Yes, as long as it is otherwise acting in compliance with California law and the law of the other state. If it regularly compounds for sale to another state, it may have to register as a nonresident pharmacy with the other state.

**Suppose a physician resells medications compounded by a pharmacy for the physician's office use?**

If the pharmacy does not know and has no reason to suspect the drugs are being resold rather than dispensed or administered by the physician, the pharmacy is not legally responsible for what would be exceeding the scope of pharmacy compounding. If the pharmacy knows or ought to know that the drugs are not being used for the prescriber's own patients, then the pharmacy is manufacturing without a license. (In either case it is responsible for the quality of the drugs it compounds, unless problems are introduced by, for example, poor storage after the product has left the pharmacy.)

**Is a pharmacy that compounds liable for the products it compounds and sells and/or dispenses?**

Absolutely.  While case law is divided over the nature and extent of pharmacy liability for the quality and safety of products that it purchases ready-made and dispenses as directed by a prescriber, there appears little doubt that a pharmacist and pharmacy will be held liable for poor quality or unsafe products that the pharmacy compounds.

## *Required Records*

The Pharmacy Board requires certain records to be kept when a pharmacy compounds "in quantities larger than required for immediate dispensing by a prescriber or for future dispensing upon prescription" (§1716.2).[4]  The pharmacy is required to maintain records that include at least the date of preparation; the lot numbers,[5] as defined in the regulation; the expiration date of the finished product, the selection of which is regulated;[6] the signature or initials of the compounding pharmacist; the formula for the compounded product; the name of the manufacturer of the raw materials; the quantity in units of finished product or grams of raw materials; and the package size and number of units prepared (§1716.2(a)).  Of course, federal and state manufacturing laws require detailed records documenting the manufacturing process employed by the pharmacy and for the manufacturing/ compounding of any particular drugs (see, for example, 21 USC §355; 21 CFR Parts 211, 310; H&SC §§110140(b), 110155, 111550(b), 111570).

# Other Federal and State Drug Laws

In addition to laws governing review and approval of new drugs, there are very detailed state and federal drug laws concerning the making, packaging, labeling, distribution, and advertising of drugs and devices (H&SC §§109875-111915, 21 USC §§301-395).  When the interpretation of these laws is at issue, the courts construe them liberally to protect the public health.

Federal law only applies to something that is in or affects interstate commerce, that is, commerce between or among the states or a state or territory and any place outside of them (21 USC §321(b)).  In practice this is hardly a limitation at all.  Even if a drug is distributed wholly within its state of manufacture, it is in or affecting interstate commerce if any of its ingredients or components were shipped across state lines to the manufacturer (*Grand Laboratories, Inc. v. Harris*, 660 F.2d 1288 (8th Cir. 1981)).  As broad as is the reach of the Federal Food, Drug, and Cosmetic Act, federal controlled substances law reaches even further.  The Congress has declared that all transactions involving controlled substances are within its jurisdiction and subject to the federal Controlled Substances Act because it is not "feasible" to distinguish between intrastate and interstate controlled substances, and federal control of intrastate incidents of traffic in controlled substances is "essential to the effective control" of its interstate incidents (21 USC §801(5),(6)).  As discussed in Chapter II:

---

[4]  There appears to be a conundrum here.  If the pharmacy believes it should be keeping records in accordance with this regulation, it may well be admitting that it has gone beyond the scope of the practice of pharmacy into manufacturing.

[5]  These may be either the manufacturer's lot numbers or new numbers assigned by the pharmacy.  If the latter, the pharmacy must also record the manufacturer's lot numbers and expiration dates, if known, or the source and acquisition date of the components.

[6]  The expiration date cannot exceed 180 days or the shortest expiration date of any component in the finished product unless a longer date is supported by stability studies in the same type of packaging as furnished to the prescriber.  An earlier expiration date may be used if it is warranted in the pharmacist's professional judgment.

Drug Classifications, a medical marijuana case to be decided in 2005 by the United States Supreme Court challenges the broad application of the federal Controlled Substances Act to activities occurring entirely within one state (reviewing *Raich v. Ashcroft*, 352 F.3d 1222 (9th Cir. 2003)).

We focus here on laws governing labeling, misbranding, adulteration, and advertising. All are highly relevant to pharmacists and pharmacies. Products that are mislabeled, misbranded, or adulterated when received by a pharmacy become the responsibility of the pharmacy and pharmacist. And a product repackaged, reconstituted, or manufactured by the pharmacy must be handled so that it does not become misbranded, mislabeled, or adulterated within the meaning of federal and state law.

## *Misbranding*

To understand misbranding, you first must know the meaning of labeling. Keep in mind that these concepts apply primarily to the commercial sale of drugs, rather than to drugs dispensed on prescription for which the Pharmacy Law provides very specific labeling requirements (see Chap. IX: Prescriptions: Receipt to Labeling).

Under federal law, "label" means a display of written, printed, or graphic matter upon the immediate container of any article (21 USC §321(k)). California Health and Safety Code section 109955 similarly defines a label as "a display of written, printed, or graphic matter on a food, drug, device, or cosmetic or upon its immediate container."

When federal law requires any word, statement, or other information to appear on a label, you are not in compliance unless that word, statement, or other information appears on the outside container or wrapper, if any, of the article's retail package or is easily legible through the outside container or wrapper (21 USC §321(k)). The label statements must be of adequate size and legibility (21 USC §352(c)). Regulations include many specific requirements for the location of certain information, such as the date of expiration (21 CFR §201.17).

Under state law (H&SC §110380), all labels must meet the requirements of the federal Fair Packaging and Labeling Act (15 USC §§1451-1476) and all federal regulations enacted thereunder. The DHS may adopt regulations for packaging and labeling of drugs and devices that diverge from the requirements of federal regulations, as long as those regulations are not contrary to federal labeling requirements for the net quantity of contents.

Under both state and federal food and drug laws, a label must not only meet the law's detailed requirements, but also must not be misleading. A drug or device is misbranded whose labeling is "false or misleading in any particular" (21 USC §352(a)). To avoid being misleading, a drug or device in package form must have a label containing the name and place of business of the manufacturer, packer, or distributor and an accurate statement of the quantity of the contents in terms of weight, measure, or numerical count (21 USC §352(b); reasonable variations are permitted and exemptions may be established for small packages). A package is misleading where any word, statement, or other information required by or under the Federal Food, Drug, and Cosmetic Act to appear on the label is not prominently placed, conspicuous (compared to the rest of the label), and in such terms as to render it likely to be read and understood by the ordinary individual under customary conditions of purchase and use (21 USC §352(c)).

A drug is misbranded unless its label bears the established name[7] of the drug, and no other nonproprietary name (except the applicable systematic chemical name or chemical formula). If the drug is fabricated from two or more ingredients, the label also must bear the established name and quantity of each active ingredient (including the quantity, kind, and proportion of any alcohol) and the name and quantity of any of 16 chemicals and substances named in the law when contained in the drug as active or inactive ingredients (21 USC §352(e)(1)(A)). The requirement for stating the quantity of the active ingredients (other than those 16 specifically named) applies only to prescription drugs.

A prescription drug is misbranded unless the established name of the drug or ingredient is printed on the label prominently and in type at least half as large as that used on the label for any proprietary name or designation for the drug or ingredient (21 USC §352(e)(1)(B)). Exemptions as to size or location may be obtained if exact compliance is impracticable (21 USC §352(e)(1)(B)). A device also is misbranded unless similarly labeled (21 USC §352(e)(2)).

A drug or device is misbranded unless its labeling bears adequate directions for use and adequate warnings against use in those pathological conditions, or by children, where its use may be dangerous to health. Warnings against unsafe dosage, methods, duration of administration, or manner or form of application that are necessary for the protection of users also are required. Where any requirement for listing directions for use is not necessary for protection of the public health, an exemption may be established by regulation (21 USC §352(f)).

FDA regulations define adequate directions for use as directions under which a layperson can use the drug safely and effectively. The distributor is required to provide very detailed information (21 CFR §§201.5, 201.56-201.57, 201.100) which is the basis for what is known as the manufacturer's package insert. The annual privately-published *Physicians' Desk Reference* contains package insert information for virtually every prescription drug currently manufactured or sold in the United States.

A drug is also misbranded that purports to be a drug recognized in an official compendium, unless it is packaged and labeled as prescribed in the compendium (21 USC §352(g)); however, its method of packing may deviate with FDA consent. A drug liable to deteriorate (as found by the FDA) is misbranded unless it is packaged in the form and manner and with the label statement of precautions required by regulation (21 USC §352(h)). A drug also is misbranded if its container is so made, formed, or filled as to be misleading; if it is an imitation of another drug; or if it is offered for sale under the name of another drug (21 USC §352(i)). A drug that is dangerous to health when used in the dosage, manner, frequency, or duration that is prescribed, recommended, or suggested in the labeling also is misbranded (21 USC §352(j)).

Drugs or devices are misbranded if their manufacturer fails to comply with:

- color additive requirements for drug use (21 USC §352(m)),
- registration requirements,
- filing of lists of drugs and devices prepared for commercial distribution,
- reporting of introduction of devices into interstate commerce, or
- requirements for the use of the uniform system for identification of devices (21 USC §352(o)).

It is also misbranding to violate safe packaging requirements, including child-resistant packaging, or to engage in the false or misleading advertising of restricted devices (21 USC

---

[7] "Established name" means the product's name as designated by the FDA under 21 USC §358; if there is no such name, it means that name recognized in an official compendium. If there is neither a designated name nor one recognized in an official compendium, it is the common or usual name of the drug (21 USC §352(e)(3),(4)).

§352(p),(q)). Omitting required information from, or including inaccurate information in, advertising or other descriptive printed matter pertaining to a restricted device constitutes misbranding (21 USC §352(r)), as does selling a device subject to a performance standard without prescribed labeling (21 USC §352(s)) or without complying with a variety of other requirements of the device laws (21 USC §352(t)).

When a claim is made that a drug is misbranded on the grounds that its labeling is misleading, the factors that will be considered are: representations made or suggested by the statement, word, design, device, or any combination of them; the extent to which the labeling or advertising fails to reveal facts material in the light of such representations; or the extent to which it fails to reveal material facts with respect to consequences that may result from the use of the article either under the conditions of use prescribed in the labeling or advertising thereof or under such conditions of use as are customary or usual (21 USC §321(n), H&SC §110290). Failure to comply with the detailed requirements of the law concerning inclusion of certain information in advertisements and other descriptive printed matter causes a drug to be misbranded (21 USC §352(n)).

In other words, virtually any violation of any law or regulation concerning drugs or devices in interstate commerce other than violations affecting the condition of the products themselves (which are treated as adulteration) renders the offending product misbranded under federal drug law. Instead of creating a set of penalties for each possible violation, the law instead defines all these violations as misbranding, and then forbids, and sets penalties for, misbranding. Under California law the same approach applies (H&SC §110290). Merely introducing a misbranded product into interstate commerce, regardless of intent, violates federal law.

### What should a pharmacist do when he or she determines a drug is misbranded or adulterated?

If the drug is in stock and was received in that condition, the misbranded drug should be returned to the distributor, with proper records of the return. If it was adulterated when received, it should either be returned or destroyed, again with appropriate records kept. If the pharmacist believes that other pharmacies may have received drugs in the same condition, he or she should immediately contact the distributor, manufacturer, and/or FDA so appropriate action (including, if necessary, a recall) can be taken. If any misbranded or adulterated product was dispensed to patients, the pharmacist should contact patients to arrange the return and replacement of the drugs. If the nature of the adulteration or misbranding is such that it might have affected patients' health, the pharmacist should make appropriate inquiries and suggest follow-up.

If the drug became misbranded or adulterated while in the pharmacy, it should be destroyed. If it left the pharmacy and was returned by a consumer in a misbranded or adulterated state it should be destroyed, again with proper records kept.

### May a pharmacy mix different lots of the same drug in a Baker cell or in a prescription vial?

The purpose of lot numbers is to maintain the ability to track drugs throughout the distribution system so they may successfully be recalled if a problem arises. There is no express prohibition on mixing drugs from different lots; if it could not be done, pharmacies would have many "leftover" pills at the bottom of stock bottles. However, because of the importance of knowing which patient received drugs from which lot, the pharmacy would need to record both lot numbers as having been distributed to each patient when that might have been the case.

# *Adulteration*

Adulteration essentially refers to a drug or device that is unfit for use, is less fit for use than it should be, or has been altered in a way that affects either its fitness for use or its ability to meet product standards.

If a drug does not have the standards of strength, purity, or quality that it is represented to contain, the drug is adulterated (H&SC §111285). If a drug has been manufactured, processed, packed, or maintained in a way that does not meet good manufacturing practices to ensure safety, quality, purity, and consistency, it is adulterated (H&SC §111260).

A drug or device is adulterated, in the words of federal law, that consists in whole or in part of any filthy, putrid, or decomposed substance or that has been prepared, packed, or held under unsanitary conditions whereby it may have been contaminated with filth or may have been rendered injurious to health (21 USC §351). Where the methods, facilities, or controls used for a drug's manufacture, processing, packing, or holding do not conform to current good manufacturing practice, the drug is adulterated (21 CFR §210.1(b)). Any drug or device container that is composed, in whole or in part, of any poisonous or deleterious substance that may render the contents injurious to health, or that contains an unsafe or improperly used color additive, is adulterated (21 USC §351(a)(3),(4)).

If a drug is represented as a drug recognized in an official compendium and its actual strength, quality, or purity differs from the compendium standard (unless clearly labeled to that effect), the drug is adulterated (21 USC §351(b)). A drug or device not covered by a compendium standard is adulterated if its strength differs from, or its purity or quality falls below, that which it purports or is represented to possess (21 USC §351(c)).

A drug is adulterated if any substance either has been mixed or packed with it so as to reduce its quality or strength or has been substituted wholly or in part for it (21 USC §351(d)). A device is adulterated if it is, purports to be, or is represented to be a device subject to a performance standard and it does not conform with that standard (21 USC §351(e)). Additional provisions apply the adulteration definition to certain non-complying class III devices, to all banned devices, and to devices that are not in conformity with requirements for manufacture, packing, storage, installation, and investigational use (21 USC §351(f)-(i)).

Effective in 2005, a Board inspector who finds or has reasonable cause to believe that any dangerous drug or dangerous device is adulterated or counterfeit has the power to embargo it. The inspector does so by affixing a tag or other marking to the product and giving notice to its owner that it is embargoed (§4084(a)). The inspector may take a sample of the product, for which a descriptive receipt must be left (§4084(c)). It is unlawful to remove, sell, or otherwise dispose of an embargoed drug or device without Board permission; if the inspector has reasonable cause to believe the embargo will be violated, he or she may remove the embargoed product from the premises (§4085). If it is determined that the product is neither counterfeit nor adulterated, the inspector will remove the tag, and the product may then be sold (§4084(b)).

If the Board believes the embargoed product is adulterated or counterfeit, it must go to court to have the product condemned (§4086(a)). If, in a final judgment, the court finds the product to be adulterated or counterfeit, it will be destroyed at the expense of its owner and under Board supervision. In addition, the owner of the product will be responsible to pay all court costs and fees and the reasonable costs of the Board's investigation and prosecution of the matter, including costs of storage and testing (§4086(c)). Even without a court order of condemnation, the Board may destroy the embargoed product either with the written consent of its owner or if it cannot ascertain its ownership within 30 days of the embargo (§4086(c)).

In an extreme, and tragic, example of adulteration (that was also charged as misbranding), a Kansas City pharmacist was accused of diluting four cancer chemotherapy drugs (Taxol®, Gemzar®, Nupogen®, and Interferon®) before filling prescriptions, with greed as his motive. An oncologist alerted by the suspicions of a Lilly company representative contacted authorities. Affected patients sued the pharmacist and pharmacy, as well as Lilly. Criminal charges alleging tampering, adulteration, and misbranding were filed, and the pharmacist was ultimately sentenced to 30 years in prison, as well as fined $25,000 and ordered to pay $10,400,000 in restitution to his victims. Judgments against the pharmacist in civil suits by victims were enormous; a jury in one case awarded $2.2 billion. (*Courtney Receives Maximum Sentence: 30 Years*, www.thekansascitychannel.com/news/1821055/detail.html, posted Dec. 5, 2002).[8]

Just as with misbranding, adulteration has been used as a "catchall" device for enforcement of the federal drug laws. Instead of having penalties for each possible violation, products that are in violation of any of a number of laws and regulations are defined as being adulterated, and adulteration is itself forbidden. The same is true under state law.

## *False or Misleading Statements*

Advertising, in the context of false or misleading statements, means virtually any oral, written, media, or other claim or promotion of a drug or device.[9] Advertising a drug or device that is adulterated or misbranded (as well as receiving, delivering, or offering to deliver such a drug or device) is illegal (H&SC §§110398, 110400). False statements or statements that would be misleading to the public also are false advertising under federal and state law (H&SC §110390; 21 USC §§45, 1125(a)). All representations made or suggested by a statement, word, device, sound, or other combination thereof are considered in determining whether misleading labeling or advertising exists (H&SC §110290). The omission of material facts about the drug or other product in its labeling or advertising may make it misleading under the law (H&SC §110290).

---

[8]  Lilly and Bristol-Myers Squibb Co. settled more than 300 lawsuits filed against them from this same series of incidents (Jeff Swiatek, *Lilly, rival settle drug-dilution suits; Agreement avoids trials in 300 cases that alleged liability for altered doses*, INDIANAPOLIS STAR, Oct. 8, 2002, p. 1A). The judgments against pharmacist Courtney are likely to be uncollectible; his assets were seized by the federal government and his pharmacy insurer sought to avoid claims that arose not from malpractice (negligence) but from the pharmacist's intentional wrongdoing.

The reported jury award was not just to compensate the victim for his actual losses (such as medical expenses, lost income, and pain and suffering), as in a typical malpractice case, where the professional has caused harm through a lack of appropriate care. The award was swollen by punitive damages, which are intended to punish, and can only be awarded for behavior that is at least reckless; in California, a plaintiff can only recover damages "for the sake of example and by way of punishing the defendant" where "it is proven by clear and convincing evidence that the defendant has been guilty of oppression, fraud, or malice" (Civ. Code §3294). There are constitutional limits on the amount even of punitive damage awards, which need to be proportionate to the wrong committed (*State Farm Mutual Automobile Insurance Co. v. Campbell*, 538 U.S. 408, 416-418 (2003)).

Courtney's 30-year sentence was upheld on appeal (*United States v. Courtney*, 362 F.3d 497, 498 (8th Cir. 2004). Courtney unsuccessfully challenged enhancements to the sentence for, among other things, his abuse of a position of trust and use of a special skill. In a similar case, a Rhode Island physician was convicted and sentenced to 10 years in prison for diluting vaccines and conspiring with a pharmacy owner to sell free drug samples to customers of the pharmacy; the pharmacy owner was also prosecuted and convicted (Tracy Breton, *Cranston physician gets jail for diluting vaccines*, PROVIDENCE JOURNAL-BULLETIN, Sept. 15, 2004, p. A1).

[9]  Also see Business and Professions Code sections 17500 to 17509, on false or misleading advertising in general. It is a violation of section 1766 of the pharmacy regulations for a pharmacist or permit holder to violate section 17500 of the Business and Professions Code. Pharmacy licensees who commit unfair trade practices, including false or misleading advertising, also are in violation of section 651 of the Business and Professions Code (see Chapter XII: Practice Pitfalls).

For example, it is unlawful in California:

- to place or cause to be placed upon any drug or device or its package the trade name or other identifying mark or imprint of another person with the intent to deceive (H&SC §110315);
- to sell, dispense, dispose of, hold, or conceal any drug or device or its package knowing the trade name or other identifying mark has been placed on the drug or device or its package in a way that is misleading or deceptive (H&SC §110320) or knowing that it is advertised falsely (H&SC §110395);
- to advertise a drug or device that is adulterated or misbranded or to receive in commerce, deliver, or offer to deliver, such a drug or device (H&SC §§110398, 110400); and
- to advertise any drug or device as having any effect on a variety of specific health conditions, including cancer, diabetes, acquired immune deficiency syndrome (AIDS), and AIDS-related complex (H&SC §110403).

State regulatory boards for many years restricted their licensees from engaging in virtually any advertising and promotional activities, no matter how truthful. Doctors, lawyers, and many other professionals were strictly forbidden to advertise their services. In large part these restrictions arose from a conviction that advertising was undignified for professionals; surely they remained in place because of concern that advertising would cause competition, especially concerning fees.

It also was forbidden in most states (including California) for pharmacists to advertise prices, although they could advertise their pharmacies more generally. Opponents of this type of legislation argued that such laws violated the First Amendment right to free speech. At one time the United States Supreme Court considered what is called "commercial speech" (speech that is part of business transactions) not to be entitled to First Amendment protection. In an extremely important decision entitled *Virginia State Board of Pharmacy v. Virginia Citizens Consumer Council*, 425 U.S. 748, 762 (1976), the United States Supreme Court struck down a prohibition on pharmacies advertising drug prices as an unconstitutional infringement on free speech, notwithstanding that it was only "commercial" speech. Today, government restrictions on commercial speech may survive only where the government has asserted a substantial interest in restricting the speech, the regulation directly advances the asserted interest, and the restriction is not more extensive than necessary to achieve the asserted government interest (*Central Hudson Gas & Electric Corp. v. Public Service Commission*, 447 U.S. 557, 566 (1980)). The United States Supreme Court applied this test in the *Thompson v. Western States Medical Center* pharmacy compounding case, discussed above.

After the *Virginia State Board of Pharmacy* decision, many professionals began to advertise, and their right to do so was regularly upheld by judicial decisions.[10] Restrictions on untruthful or misleading advertising of course may continue. Some state regulators have continued to restrict certain forms of advertising and certain types of claims as inherently misleading, and cases continue to be litigated about such provisions, particularly in regard to advertising by attorneys and other continuing restrictions by state licensing boards.[11] But, as noted above, a state may restrict

---

[10] It is interesting to note that the Supreme Court decision in the *Virginia State Board of Pharmacy* case did not arise because pharmacists were clamoring for the right to advertise prices, and thus to compete on the basis of price. In fact there was broad support within the profession for the advertising restriction, which made it difficult for discount pharmacies to disseminate information about their low prices. The plaintiffs who filed suit to eliminate the advertising restriction were consumers who wanted pharmacies to make price information available.

[11] Under Section 651(a) of the California Business and Professions Code, it is unlawful to disseminate "any form of public communication containing a false, fraudulent, misleading, or deceptive statement, claim, or image for the purpose of or likely to induce, directly or indirectly, the rendering of professional services or furnishing of products in connection with the professional practice or business for which he or she is licensed." A "public communication" is defined to include mail, television, radio, motion pictures, newspapers, books, lists or directories, the Internet or other electronic

commercial speech that is not false, deceptive, or misleading only when it meets the significant burden of the *Central Hudson* test.

California law now specifically approves the advertising of prescription drugs or devices (§4341). The law limits the advertisement of the retail price of a prescription drug to quantities that are consistent with good medical practice and requires that the advertisement include the strength, dosage form, and the exact dates during which the advertised price will be in effect (§4121(a)).

FDA has long maintained stringent restrictions on advertising as well as labeling of prescription drugs. It is concerned with material omissions as well as with affirmatively-misleading statements. All advertising of prescription drugs used to be directed to prescribers rather than to consumers. In the 1980s drug companies began direct-to-consumer advertising of prescription drugs; the volume of such advertising continues to increase dramatically. Drug companies must make required disclosures in consumer as well as professional advertising. While they need not read aloud in broadcast advertising everything they are required to include in print advertising, nevertheless disclosure requirements continue to be the subject of considerable agency-industry tension. FDA has had to step up its enforcement activities in respect to misleading drug advertising as the amount of that advertising overall has increased.

In 1999, FDA published *Guidance for Industry – Consumer-Directed Broadcast Advertisements*, to provide information on how the agency believes required disclosures must be made in television and radio commercials (www.fda.gov/cber/gdlns/advrts.htm). FDA regulations require drug advertisers to make "adequate provision . . . for dissemination of the approved or permitted package labeling in connection with the broadcast presentation" (21 CFR §202.1(e)(1)). The guidance document describes how the FDA believes advertisers can meet the "adequate provision" requirement.

## *Penalties for Violation of Food and Drug Laws*

Both federal and state governments actively enforce the drug laws discussed above. It should be noted that it is no defense to the violation of most of these laws that the violation was inadvertent or unintended. These are examples of what are called "strict liability" laws. In order to protect the public health, no intent to engage in misconduct is required. Sometimes even knowledge of the forbidden act is not required: all that must be proven is that the violation happened and that the defendant is responsible for the instrumentality through which, or the place at which, it occurred. Because the potential consequences of any violation are so serious, the threat of strict liability is used to deter any violations.

Adulteration, misbranding, and false advertising all carry substantial civil or criminal penalties, including fines. The products involved are subject to seizure, the violator is subject to injunctions, and licensees involved may have their licensees revoked (for example, see 21 USC §§331, 333, 352(f)(1), 352(o), 353, 355(a); H&SC §§111645, 111825, 111830, 111840, 111850, 111855). The same acts also may constitute unfair business practices (see B&PC §§651, 17200-17209 and similar federal laws) and false or misleading advertising (see B&PC §§17500-17922).

While the pharmacist may prepare drugs in the ordinary course of pharmacy practice without registering with the FDA or DHS as a manufacturer, under the compounding exception, extreme care is critical. The pharmacy's facilities, equipment, supplies, and methods of preparation should be

---

communication (B&PC §651(a)). Statements are considered false, fraudulent, misleading, or deceptive that contain a misrepresentation of fact or are likely to mislead or deceive because of a failure to disclose material facts (§651(b)).

adequate to avoid adulteration. Its promotion, advertising, and labeling practices should not be misleading about the nature of the product or its identity, quality, safety, purity, or consistency, to avoid misbranding. Because violation of these standards usually is based on the fact of the violation, not requiring any bad intent or carelessness, the pharmacist's responsibility under these laws is significant.

**Suppose a pharmacy maintains penicillin VK for oral solution USP (Pen-Vee®K) in the original bulk container. It is not expired but has somehow become contaminated. The pharmacy dispenses it, and a patient becomes ill. Have the pharmacy and pharmacist engaged in mislabeling? Misbranding? Adulteration? False advertising? Is the pharmacist's lack of knowledge that there was anything wrong with the penicillin relevant? Is it significant that the pharmacy had a roof leak in the area of the bulk container and the pharmacist knew about the leak? That the pharmacist didn't check the containers in the area? Didn't fix the leak? What could the pharmacist do to anticipate problems like this in the future?**

In general, drug laws are strict liability provisions. That is, if it happened, you are responsible; it does not matter whether or not you were careful. The mere fact that the penicillin was dispensed in a contaminated condition could constitute adulteration or dispensing an adulterated product. (It also could technically constitute misbranding and mislabeling because the label implicitly represents it as the described drug when, in fact, because of contamination it is not. However, the appropriately-applied violation here is adulteration.)

But even strict liability laws are infused with some reason. In the absence of circumstances suggesting the pharmacist knew or should have known the drug was contaminated or that there was a condition or circumstance that should have led her to check for contamination, her liability either should be very limited or nonexistent. On the other hand, if the pharmacy had a roof leak in the area of the stock container and the pharmacist should have known about it, her failure to observe the damage it was causing or, if she did observe the damage, to check containers or otherwise guard against contamination, by fixing the leak or otherwise, would more likely subject her to liability under drug laws. Also, the latter state of facts could lead to a finding of negligence if the injured patient filed a civil lawsuit.

# Expiration and "Beyond-Use" Dates

A drug must be labeled, when packaged or repackaged by a manufacturer, distributor, pharmacy, or other authorized entity, with an expiration date, the date beyond which the drug is considered no longer sufficiently safe and potent for distribution or use. Manufacturers are required to determine expiration dates by appropriate stability testing, in accordance with FDA guidelines.

The expiration dates chosen by manufacturers have aroused some controversy in light of testing done by FDA on stocks of prescription drugs maintained by the military for emergency use. Because the government does not want to discard unused drugs if they remain usable, it has engaged FDA in testing that has found stability years after labeled expiration dates. Of course the government has stored its emergency supplies of drugs in conditions conducive to maintaining their stability over time.

Prescription labels must include a "beyond use" date to guide the consumer's use of drugs. For single unit or unit dose packaging of non-sterile and liquid pharmaceuticals, the beyond use date, pursuant to revised 2000 USP standards, must be one year unless stability data or the manufacturer's label indicates otherwise. For all other non-sterile dosage forms, including the multiple-unit container (the classic prescription vial), the beyond use date is either one year or the time remaining to the expiration date on the manufacturer's bottle from which the drug was dispensed, whichever is earlier (USP, 4th Supplement, USP24-NF19).

For additional information on expiration and beyond-use dates, consult "Expiration Dates – Compliance Guidelines," *The Script*, July 2001, p.1 and "Drug Expiration Dates Revisited," *The Script*, Oct. 2001, p.7.

**What you should think about after reading this chapter:**

1. Why do we have misbranding, adulteration, and false advertising laws for drugs?

2. Why are there limitations on pharmacy compounding?

3. Why do we so closely regulate how drugs are prepared?

4. What concerns might a pharmacist have about drug advertising?

5. What is the pharmacist's responsibility to protect the consumer against adulterated or misbranded drugs?

# Chapter IX

# The Prescription Process: From Receipt to Labeling

**What you should know after reading this chapter:**

1. Who may prescribe drugs? For what conditions?

2. Who may transmit a prescriber's order for drugs to a pharmacy?

3. What is a mid-level practitioner? Under what circumstances may a mid-level practitioner furnish or transmit an order for drugs or controlled substances to a pharmacy?

4. Under what circumstances may a pharmacist issue an order for prescription drugs? Why isn't it called prescribing?

5. In what forms may a pharmacy receive orders for prescription drugs? For controlled substances?

6. What information should a prescription for a dangerous drug, dangerous device, or controlled substance contain?

7. How might a pharmacist determine if a prescription is a forgery?

8. When may a drug be prescribed for a use, a dosage, or a patient for which it was not approved?

9. When may an out-of-state prescriber's order be filled? A foreign prescriber's order?

10. What is electronic monitoring of Schedule II and III prescriptions? How does a pharmacy comply?

11. Who in the pharmacy may receive a prescription?

12. Who may evaluate a new prescription? What factors should be considered?

13. What is drug substitution?

14. What kind of container may be used for a prescription?

15. What information should go on a prescription label? When a placebo is prescribed?

16. Under what circumstances would a partial fill be allowed for a controlled substance prescription?

# Prescription Defined

The vast majority of dangerous drugs are provided to a patient by way of an order from a prescriber to a pharmacy for filling by the pharmacy [1]; that is, via a prescription. Section 4040 of the Pharmacy Law defines a prescription:

(a) "Prescription" means an oral, written, or electronic transmission[2] order that is both of the following:

(1) Given individually for the person or persons for whom ordered that includes all of the following:

(A) The name or names and address of the patient or patients.

(B) The name and quantity of the drug or device prescribed and the directions for use.

(C) The date of issue.

(D) Either rubber stamped, typed, or printed by hand or typeset, the name, address, and telephone number of the prescriber, his or her license classification, and his or her federal registry number, if a controlled substance is prescribed.

(E) A legible, clear notice of the condition for which the drug is being prescribed, if requested by the patient or patients.

(F) If in writing, signed by the prescriber issuing the order, or the certified nurse-midwife, nurse practitioner, or physician assistant who issues a drug order pursuant to Section 2746.51, 2836.1, or 3502.1, respectively, or the pharmacist who issues a drug order pursuant to either subparagraph (D) of paragraph (4) of, or clause (iv) of subparagraph (A) of paragraph (5) of, subdivision (a) of Section 4052.

(2) Issued by a physician, dentist, optometrist, podiatrist, or veterinarian, or, if a drug order is issued pursuant to Section 2746.51, 2836.1, or 3502.1, by a certified nurse-midwife, nurse practitioner, or physician assistant licensed in this state, or pursuant to either subparagraph (D) of paragraph (4) of, or clause (iv) of subparagraph (A) of

---

[1]  Dangerous drugs are also administered or dispensed directly to patients by prescribers (see Chap. VII: Ordering Drugs); dangerous devices are often supplied by other entities, such as home medical-device retailers. A prescription is not required for over-the-counter products sold in their original packaging and labeled in accordance with federal and state law (§4057(a), see Chap. II: Drugs).

[2]  Under California law an electronic order can either be a fax or an electronic data transmission (such as an e-mail). In some cases a prescriber may transmit an order by electronic data transmission that is received by the pharmacy in fax form. That is, the prescriber may prepare the order on a computer and send it via a modem to the pharmacy's fax machine. By law this is considered an electronic data transmission. A "fax" or "facsimile," as used in the statutes and regulations, refers to the sending of a facsimile of a hard-copy (written) prescription (see, for example, 21 CFR §1306.21(c)). The distinction is important because, under federal controlled substances regulations, an electronic data transmission, even if received by a fax machine, is not a fax. However, despite the language of its own regulation, the DEA has, in a letter response to a private inquiry, stated that an electronic data order can be honored in lieu of a fax if it follows the requirements for an oral order, as discussed below.

paragraph (5) of, subdivision (a) of section 4052 by a pharmacist licensed in this state. (See also H&SC §§11027, 110010; 21 USC §829; 21 CFR §§1306.04-1306.06.)[3]

The requirements of section 4040 apply to all prescribed drugs, even to over-the-counter drugs ordered by a prescriber for a patient.  Whenever a pharmacy receives a prescription, regardless of what is prescribed, all prescription requirements (including, for example, consultation) apply.

**May a prescription issued to Jane Jones and her husband be dispensed?  To Jane Jones and her family: "dispense enough for 5 persons?"**

No, in both cases.  A prescription may be issued for more than one person, but only if it includes the name and address of each.  It appears from the language of section 4040(a)(1)(A), referring to "name or names" but "address" in the singular, that a prescription for multiple persons must be for persons who have the same address.  In addition, the "Jane Jones and her family" prescription does not appear to specify quantity, because "enough for five persons" is not a specific quantity.  However, a pharmacist may obtain and add the information missing from these prescriptions, and then legally dispense them (§1761(a), discussed below; see Chap, XII, Practice Pitfalls).

Keep in mind that the slight variances between California and federal controlled substance schedules (see Chap. II: Drugs) may affect the form in which certain prescriptions must be received, filled, and labeled.  Remember that state and federal drug laws governing preparation, packaging, and labeling of drugs must be followed.  If federal and state law are in conflict with each other, in general the more restrictive of the two controls.

# Who May Issue the Order?

As listed in section 4040(a)(2), quoted above, a physician, dentist, optometrist, podiatrist, or veterinarian may issue a drug order.  In addition, under the authority of specific statutes, a physician assistant, nurse practitioner, certified nurse-midwife, or, as of 2005, a pharmacist may issue a drug order.  The prescriber must, with exceptions discussed below, be properly licensed in California to issue a drug order (§4039).  While not specifically mentioned in section 4040, as of 2004 some licensed naturopaths may issue drug orders (see discussion below).

Federal law provides that no one may handle or prescribe controlled substances without registering with the Drug Enforcement Administration (21 CFR §1301.11).[4]  Only practitioners registered with the DEA and licensed in the jurisdiction in which the prescription is issued may prescribe controlled substances (21 CFR §1306.03(a)).  A practitioner acting for or employed by a hospital or other institution may use its DEA registration number and the internal code number the institution must assign to each practitioner (DEA Pharmacist's Manual, p. 33) and the institutional controlled substance prescription form, as discussed below.  Physicians in the military, Public Health Service, or Bureau of Prisons prescribing in the scope of their employment need not register with DEA and may use their service identification number (21 CFR §1301.23).[5]  California law only authorizes

---

[3]  The prescriber's address, telephone number, license classification, and, if a controlled substance is involved, DEA registration number, need not be on the prescription, if that information is readily retrievable in the pharmacy (§4040(b)).

[4]  The registrations of most practitioners, including pharmacies, cover all controlled substances, but registration may be restricted, by practitioner choice or DEA action, to a particular class of controlled substances or, for example, to only nonnarcotics within a class.

[5]  DEA is now issuing numbers to military physicians to expedite the filling of their prescriptions at community pharmacies, whose computers do not recognize service identification numbers.

physicians, dentists, podiatrists, and veterinarians to issue a controlled substance prescription (H&SC §11150), although ancillary personnel may order for a physician using either the physician's prescriptions or their own, as discussed below.

In various settings – usually in licensed facilities, sometimes under the supervision of a licensed prescriber, and almost always under some form of protocol – some nurses, physician assistants, licensed naturopaths, and pharmacists effectively prescribe.[6] Some have very limited authority; some have fairly broad discretion. Because of concern among physicians about expanding who actually may do what is called "prescribing," or otherwise engage in activities considered to be the practice of medicine except under physician control, various euphemisms have been used to describe what a nurse, physician assistant, licensed naturopath, or pharmacist does, to avoid calling it prescribing. Typically it is referred to as transmitting or ordering or sometimes as furnishing.[7] The result is complex and confusing, accomplishing indirectly what should be accomplished directly.

For example, each time the Legislature has amended laws to allow certain categories of nurses to furnish or order drugs and devices, it has provided that the "drug order issued pursuant to this section shall be treated in the same manner as a prescription of the supervising physician" (B&PC §§2746.51(e)(1), 2836.1(i)(1)), and that "all references to 'prescription' in [the Business and Professions Code] and the Health and Safety Code shall include drug orders issued by" these nurses (B&PC §§2746.51(e)(2), 2836.1(i)(2)). Acknowledging what these mid-level practitioners do, without calling it "prescribing," the Legislature has added their "orders" to various provisions of the Pharmacy Law defining who may order a dangerous drug or dangerous device and whose name goes on the prescription label. Therefore, section 4040(a)(1)(F) refers to written orders from prescribers, and also from nurse-midwives, nurse practitioners, physician assistants, and pharmacists, with all of the latter limited to those working under statutes expanding their scope of practice and requiring supervision and protocols. Both the prescriber's name and the name of the mid-level practitioner must be on the prescription label (§4076(a)(4)), except only the prescriber's name is required on individual unit dose containers for a specific patient in a health care facility (§4076(c)).

The key question for the pharmacist is whether the person issuing a drug order has the authority to give or transmit it, and is acting within the scope of whatever authority he or she has. Whether that person is considered to be prescribing, ordering, transmitting, or even furnishing is relatively unimportant.[8] The Pharmacy Law clearly provides, in section 4174, that a pharmacist may

---

[6] DEA will register mid-level practitioners whose states clearly authorize them to prescribe, dispense, and administer controlled substances in one or more schedules. Thus as states authorize additional categories of health care practitioners to handle controlled substances, DEA will deem them eligible for registration. DEA specifically cautions pharmacists that they are responsible for assuring that each mid-level practitioner is prescribing within the parameters established by the state for his or her license category (DEA Pharmacist's Manual, p. 36).

[7] The terms "dispense," "furnish," "transmit," "prescribe," and "order" sometimes are used in a very confusing manner in pharmacy laws and regulations and in the laws and regulations governing the practice of physicians, dentists, podiatrists, optometrists, physician assistants, and nurses. The Board attempted to clarify the term "dispense" in section 4024; see discussion in Chapter III: Licensing Pharmacists and Other Individuals.

[8] The underlying reason for the complex law about who may send an order to a pharmacy for dangerous drugs, dangerous devices, or both, and in what circumstances, is the ongoing battle over who should have what authority over the delivery of health care. Physicians, and the organizations that represent them, have been very grudging about how much authority to cede to nurses, physician assistants, and others. For example, in 2004, dentists sought the authority to perform oral and maxillary surgery. Legislation granting that authority passed the Legislature over the vehement objections of the medical profession, but was vetoed by the Governor (SB 1336).

Nurses, chiropractors, naturopaths, and others constantly are attempting to expand their authority to match what they believe their education and training justify. Health care systems and third-party payors are concerned about overall costs and profit margins, and the government is concerned about cost, availability, and affordability of health care. These players want to rely on preventive medicine, primary caregivers instead of specialists, and the lowest level of health care

dispense drugs and devices based upon "drug orders" received from various mid-level practitioners functioning under statutes giving them authority to issue such orders, as discussed below (see also Chap. VI: Scope of Practice).

It is the dispensing pharmacist's legal obligation to determine whether a person is entitled to issue an order, including for a particular drug or for a particular condition (DEA Pharmacist's Manual, p. 24). Prescribing authority starts with and is broadest for physicians (holders of either the M.D. or D.O., doctor of osteopathy, degree, ̲ ̲ ̲ ̲ ̲ ̲ ̲ ̲ ̲ ̲ ̲ pharmacist must take steps to assure that the person transmitting an oral ̲ ̲ ̲ ̲ ̲ ̲ ̲ ̲ ̲ ̲ ̲ ̲ ̲ ̲ ̲ ̲ ̲ ̲ ̲ ̲ ̲ ̲ nd must record the name of the person who transmi ̲ ̲ ̲ ̲ ̲ ̲ ̲ ̲ ̲ ̲ ̲ ̲ ̲ ̲ ̲ ̲ ̲ ̲ ̲ ̲ ̲ ̲ ̲

> *Can a psych MD prescribe amiodarone? What to do?*
> *— RPh should call MD to make sure that is correct.*

## *Physicians*

A physician has the genera ̲ ̲ ̲ ̲ ̲ ̲ ̲ ̲ ̲ ̲ ̲ ̲ ̲ ̲ vice for virtually any purpose intended to affect the ̲ ̲ ̲ ̲ ̲ ̲ ̲ ̲ ̲ ̲ ̲ ̲ ̲ ̲ ysician must have a medical indication for prescribing ̲ ̲ ̲ ̲ ̲ ̲ ̲ ̲ ̲ ̲ ̲ ̲ h prior examination (B&PC §2242(a)).[9] ̲ ̲ ̲ ̲ ̲ ̲ ̲ ̲ ̲ ̲ ̲ ̲ ̲ ̲ ise practices outside his or her professional trai ̲ ̲ ̲ ̲ ̲ ̲ ̲ ̲ ̲ ̲ ̲ r negligence (called malpractice) or disciplinary action ̲ ̲ ̲ ̲ ̲ ̲ ̲ ̲ ̲ ̲ conduct (B&PC §2234). The pharmacist ̲ ̲ ̲ ̲ ̲ ̲ ̲ ̲ ̲ ̲ ̲ ̲ outside his or her practice area may have a duty, esp ̲ ̲ ̲ ̲ ̲ ̲ ̲ ̲ ̲ ̲ , to contact the prescriber (see Chap. XII: Practice Pitf ̲ ̲ ̲ ̲ ̲ ̲ ̲ ̲ ̲ harmacist should not fill a prescription that he or she believes ̲ ̲ ̲ ̲ ̲ ̲ ̲ ̲ e within the scope of the prescriber's practice. The pharmacist shoulu ̲ ̲ ̲ ̲ ̲ ̲ ̲ ̲ udgment and, as to controlled substances, corresponding responsibility, as discussed in Chapter XII: Practice Pitfalls.

## *Other Medical Professionals*

The authority of other medical professionals to prescribe is more limited than that of physicians. A dentist may prescribe for any purpose connected to dentistry (B&PC §§1600-1808). This restriction probably does not limit dentists to prescribing for conditions directly involving the jaws, teeth, gums, and surrounding area of the body. Dentists may probably prescribe any treatment method intended to aid in controlling, curing, or healing any dental problem. Veterinarians,[10]

---

personnel qualified to perform a particular health care function. Consumers and consumer groups want available, affordable, adequate care, but not at the cost of proper care. These ongoing conflicts, and the shifting priorities of legislators who dictate who is licensed or authorized to do what, lead to the limited and vaguely-defined expansions of authority for nurses, physician assistants, pharmacists, chiropractors, physical therapists, and others. Often the result is a complicated situation for pharmacists trying both to follow the law and to maintain relationships with practitioners and customers.

[9] A physician may write a prescription for a colleague's patient when he or she is covering patients for that physician; sometimes physicians prescribe for persons who are not their patients for public health reasons (such as exposure to infectious agents).

[10] A veterinarian's written prescription must include the name, address, telephone number, signature, and, if a controlled substance is prescribed, DEA number of the prescriber; the name and address of the animal's owner or owner's agent; the species of animal; the name, quantity, and directions for use of the drug; any cautionary statements (including, if applicable, expiration date and withdrawal time); date of issue; number of refills; and, if requested by the animal's owner, the condition for which the drug is prescribed (16 CCR §2032.2). The veterinarian must have a practitioner-client relationship with any animal and its owner or owner's agent for which he or she prescribes (16 CCR §2032.1(a)).

To issue a prescription, the veterinarian must have examined the animal, herd, or flock; have sufficient knowledge to make a diagnosis; have assumed responsibility for making clinical judgments as to the animal's health and need for treatment; have discussed a course of treatment with the owner or owner's agent; and be readily available or have made arrangements

podiatrists, and optometrists[11] similarly have limited authority related to their scope of practice. The claimed justification for any prescription must be legitimate; when a prescription seems questionable, given the prescriber's license, background, or usual area of practice, the pharmacist must evaluate it carefully. The limited nature of the authority of dentists, podiatrists, optometrists, and veterinarians underscores the pharmacist's responsibility not only to determine the authority of the prescriber, but also that he or she is acting within the scope of his or her profession.

No recent California case has addressed the "scope of practice" issue for non-physicians. The Supreme Court of Nebraska, in 1998, refused to uphold disciplinary charges against a dentist charged by the licensing board with exceeding his scope of practice. He was ordering blood and urine analyses to prescribe an enzyme to help digestion; he testified he did so only to treat problems that had manifested themselves in the oral cavity. The court decided that the regulatory agency had failed to present adequate evidence that the dentist had departed from the practice of dentistry or invaded the province of medicine (*Miller v. Horton*, 574 N.W. 2d 112 (Neb. 1998)). It seems likely that a similar approach, focusing on the practitioner's area of expertise, and evaluating whether the actions engaged in are related to that area, would be used in California in regard to prescribing of drugs and devices by dentists, podiatrists, and other health professionals.[12]

## *Nurses*

**Nurse Practitioners.** Registered nurses do not have the authority to prescribe (B&PC §2725), but may dispense to a patient upon an order by a physician within a licensed clinic (B&PC §§2725.1, 4173). Nurse practitioners (who are registered nurses with additional training) may furnish or order dangerous drugs and devices, including controlled substances, under the supervision of a physician and according to an established protocol (B&PC §2836.1, H&SC §11026(a)).[13] The nurse practitioner may only furnish or order those controlled substances specified in the protocol; when Schedule II or III controlled substances are to be furnished or ordered, the protocol must be patient-specific and approved by the treating or supervising physician. A pharmacist who is uncertain about the authority of the nurse practitioner to issue the order may request a copy of the protocol relating to controlled substances (B&PC §2836.1(f)). The order, signed by the nurse practitioner, is to be treated in the same manner as a prescription of the supervising physician (B&PC §2836.1). Both the prescriber's name and the name of the nurse practitioner must be on the label (§4076(a)(4)), except only the prescriber's name is required if the prescription is for a patient in a health care facility.

---

for follow-up evaluation in case of adverse reactions or failure of the regimen (16 CCR §2032.1(b)). A prescription must be for a duration not inconsistent either with the animal's medical condition or the drug prescribed; in no case may it be for more than one year after the date of the veterinarian's last examination of the animal (16 CCR §2032.1(c)).

[11] Optometrists who are certified to use therapeutic pharmaceutical agents now may prescribe and dispense (B&PC §§3041-3041.3); however, they may dispense only without charge (B&PC §3041(h)). Only optometrists meeting requirements adopted by the State Board of Optometry may be certified to use therapeutic pharmaceutical agents (16 CCR §§1567-1570). A certified optometrist may use appropriate topical agents, some oral antibiotics, and other agents (B&PC §3041, 16 CCR §1569(a)(3)), but may not treat children under one year of age with therapeutic pharmaceutical agents (16 CCR §1569(c)). Optometrists may now obtain dangerous drugs, including prescription controlled substances, at wholesale or retail, and order drug samples.

[12] California courts have traditionally taken a restrictive approach to the scope of authority of dentists and other health practitioners, in large part because of the sweeping language of Business and Professions Code section 2052, which makes it a misdemeanor to practice any "system or mode of treating the sick" without a physician's or surgeon's license (see Chap. VIII: Preparation of Drugs, n.1).

[13] Until 2004, a nurse practitioner could not issue an order for a Schedule II controlled substance in his or her own name. Now that the Legislature has granted that authority, nurse practitioners will be able to get DEA registrations that include ordering Schedule II drugs. A nurse practitioner whose protocol authorizes him or her to issue Schedule II orders must take a continuing education course about Schedule II drugs (Stats. 2003, ch. 748 (AB1196), amending B&PC §2836.1).

A nurse practitioner functioning pursuant to section 2836.1 may now dispense controlled substances (B&PC §2725.1) and sign for the delivery or receipt of complimentary samples of dangerous drugs or devices requested in writing by the supervising physician (§4061). Neither a nurse practitioner nor a certified nurse-midwife may order his or her own stock of dangerous drugs or dangerous devices (§4060). A nurse practitioner may also hand a properly-labeled prescription drug to a patient of the supervising physician, when the drug was dispensed on physician order and prepackaged either by the physician, a manufacturer, or a pharmacist (§4170(a)(8)).

**Certified Nurse-Midwives.** A certified[14] nurse-midwife (like a nurse practitioner, a registered nurse with additional training) may also furnish or order dangerous drugs and devices, including controlled substances, incidental to providing family planning services, routine health care or perinatal care, or care to essentially healthy persons within designated facilities or clinics (B&PC §2746.51(a)(1)). The nurse-midwife's scope of practice includes furnishing or ordering controlled substances. The nurse-midwife may furnish or order drugs only in accordance with standardized procedures or protocols under physician supervision (B&PC §2746.51(a)(2),(3)). The furnishing nurse-midwife must obtain a registration number for this purpose from the Board of Registered Nursing; the list of certified nurse-midwives must be available to the Pharmacy Board ((B&PC §2746.51(b)(1)).

The authority for nurse-midwives is very similar to that for nurse-practitioners. However, it appears that the nurse-midwife's authority to prescribe any drugs, not just controlled substances, is expected to be limited by the governing protocol (B&PC §2746.51(a)(2)(B)). For Schedule III controlled substances, the protocol must be patient-specific and approved by the treating or supervising physician (B&PC §2746.51(a)(3)), and the pharmacist has the right to request a copy of the protocol when uncertain of the nurse-midwife's authority (B&PC §2746.51(b)(3)). Like the nurse-practitioner, the nurse-midwife functioning under section 2746.51 may now dispense controlled substances (B&PC §2725.1), sign for samples requested by the physician (§4061), and hand physician-dispensed prescription drugs to patients (§4170(a)(8)). Since 2003, nurse-midwives in solo practice have been able to furnish drugs, although they must do so under protocol with a supervising physician. If a Schedule III controlled substance is involved, the protocol must be patient-specific (B&PC §§2746.5-2746.51).

The authority to furnish drugs under protocol effectively means that the nurse practitioner or nurse-midwife may, when acting within the parameters of the protocol, order drugs for dispensing by a pharmacy without the patient being seen by a physician and without physician approval for the specific order (although Schedule II and III controlled substances require a "patient-specific protocol"). Each order prepared under a protocol by a nurse-midwife should contain the name and certification number of the nurse-midwife (B&PC §2746.51(b)(1)).

Nurse practitioners, nurse-midwives, optometrists, pharmacists, and physician assistants, operating under protocols and supervision under the authority of scope of practice statutes, are all recognized as practitioners for purposes of the California Controlled Substances Act (H&SC §11026(a)). That recognition allows them to become registered with DEA; the law requires them to obtain DEA numbers in order to furnish drug orders for controlled substances. None of these mid-level practitioners, even working under protocols and supervision, may order his or her own stock of dangerous drugs or devices (§4060). Presumably qualified, licensed naturopaths will be able to obtain DEA registrations although not yet specified in the above definition.

---

[14] The Board of Registered Nursing certifies nurse-midwives (B&PC §2746).

**How can a pharmacist determine if a nurse practitioner or nurse-midwife has the authority to issue a particular order?**

Because of the pharmacist's professional obligation to ensure the identity and authority of the person issuing an order, the pharmacist may ask questions necessary to determine the scope of authority of the nurse practitioner or nurse-midwife. As noted above, the law specifically authorizes the pharmacist who is uncertain about the authority of the nurse practitioner or nurse-midwife to request a copy of the protocol, at least relating to controlled substances. When the pharmacist needs more information than is on the face of the drug order to fulfill his or her responsibility to be certain of the authority of the person ordering drugs, it seems reasonable to insist on receiving that information. Without it, the prescription order is fatally uncertain (§1761(a)) and should not be dispensed.

## *Physician Assistants*

A physician assistant also may order dangerous drugs or devices in the name of a physician and may transmit the physician's order to a pharmacy for dispensing (B&PC §3502.1(a)). These actions must be in accordance with a written formulary and protocols and under physician supervision (B&PC §3502.1). A physician assistant must have advance approval by the supervising physician for the particular patient to administer, provide, or issue a drug order for a controlled substance (B&PC §3502.1(c)(2)). As is true with respect to specialized nurses, if the order is within the protocol, the patient need not be seen by a physician and the physician need not approve the specific order (16 CCR §1399.541). The prescription should include the name and license number of the supervising physician and the physician assistant.

In any setting a physician assistant may transmit, orally or in writing on the patient's record, a prescription from his or her supervising physician. The prescription may be based either on a patient-specific order from the physician or a written protocol which specifies all criteria for use of the specific drug or device (16 CCR §1399.541(h)). A physician assistant cannot transmit any prescription for a drug not specified in the protocol or any controlled substance without a patient-specific order from a supervising physician (16 CCR §1399.541(h)). The supervising physician must, within seven days, review, countersign, and date the medical record of any patient for whom a Schedule II controlled substance drug order has been issued (B&PC §3502.1(e)). Physician assistants, like nurse practitioners and nurse-midwives, may sign for samples ordered by their supervising physician (§4061(a)) and hand properly-labeled physician-dispensed prescription drugs to a patient of their supervisor (§4170(a)(8)), but may not order their own stock of dangerous drugs or dangerous devices (§4060). As with specialized nurses' orders, the pharmacist must be careful to confirm the authority of a physician assistant transmitting a prescription for or in the name of a prescriber.

A physician assistant's drug order, like those from nurse practitioners and nurse-midwives, discussed above, is to be treated the same as a prescription or order from the supervising physician (B&PC §3502.1(b)(1)). The physician assistant's authority includes controlled substances, but for their use a physician assistant needs the advance approval of the supervising physician for the particular patient (B&PC §3502.1(c)(2)). One glitch in the law is its failure to authorize physician assistants to use their supervising physicians' controlled substance prescription forms. BNE initially decided that physician assistants should use their supervising physician's triplicates, with the physician assistant's name, DEA number, and signature appearing on the prescription; later it decided to issue triplicates to the physician assistants themselves. Presumably it will take the same approach with respect to the new controlled substance prescription forms. As noted above, physician assistants are "practitioners" for purposes of the California Controlled Substances Act, and must register with DEA as mid-level practitioners to furnish drug orders for controlled substances (B&PC §3502.1(f)).

**Suppose you receive a prescription order from a physician assistant for a patient living in a congregate senior housing facility that provides health care services. May you fill it? You are unfamiliar with the type of facility, and you do not know what role the physician, in whose name the physician assistant transmitted the order, played in issuing the prescription.**

A physician assistant employee of a congregate senior housing facility may be authorized to transmit a physician's prescription (§4072) and may be authorized to issue the drug order for the patient, if working under the supervision of a physician.[15] If the prescription is a transmission under section 4072, the pharmacist must "take appropriate steps to determine that the person who transmits the prescription is authorized to do so and shall record the name of [that] person." If the physician assistant is issuing the drug order under Business and Professions Code section 3502.1, it is valid only when the physician assistant has proper delegated authority, under an appropriate protocol. Whenever a pharmacist has any question about the prescription (§1761(a)), especially if there is any doubt or suspicion about an order for a controlled substance (H&SC §11153), it is critical to seek the information to assure the validity of the order. A pharmacist's request for information may be resented, even resisted; however, it is the pharmacist's responsibility to know who is transmitting the order and under what authority. If a problem occurs later with such an order, and the prescriber denies any knowledge of it or says it was outside the authority of the physician assistant, the pharmacist may be the one in trouble.

## Naturopaths

"Naturopathy" is defined as "a noninvasive system of health practice that employs natural health modalities, substances, and education to promote health" (B&PC §3613(e)). Naturopathic practitioners were driven out of legal existence in many states in the early 20th century when allopathic physicians began to dominate and largely control the delivery of health care. Until 2004 the practice of naturopathy was not legal in California, although there were naturopaths working in California. Two categories of naturopath have now been recognized. One is "licensed" naturopaths, who must meet certain requirements and obtain a California license. If they have the proper training and are working under the supervision of a licensed physician, licensed naturopaths may issue orders for prescription drugs to the same extent and under the same circumstances as nurse practitioners, except that they may not use or prescribe Schedule II controlled substances (B&PC §§3640, 3640.5). Naturopathic practitioners without licenses are also recognized, but they have no authority to issue orders for prescription drugs. As long as they neither claim nor suggest they are licensed by the state, and have the education or training they claim to have, they may practice naturopathy and call themselves naturopaths (§3645).

## Pharmacists

As discussed in Chapter VI: Scope of Practice for Pharmacists, pharmacists have some authority to initiate or adjust patients' drug regimens in certain settings (§4052(a)(4)(D)), (a)(5)(A)), although it is not considered or called prescribing. They also have some authority to administer drugs as ordered by a physician or, after appropriate training and as ordered by a prescriber, to administer

---

[15] A pharmacist, nurse, psychiatric technician, or other healing arts licentiate who is employed by or is a consultant to a SNF, ICF, or other health care facility may transmit an oral or electronic order, except for a Schedule II, from a person authorized to issue an order pursuant to section 4040. The pharmacy must take appropriate steps to confirm the authorization of the person sending the order, and record that person's name (§4072(a)).

drugs by injection, initiate or adjust drug regimens, or furnish drugs under protocol in certain health care settings.[16]

Pharmacists who are authorized under state law to order controlled substances may apply to DEA for their own registration number as mid-level practitioners. Otherwise they are required to issue the prescription order in the name of their supervising physician. Pharmacists are now recognized under the California Controlled Substances Act (H&SC §11026(a)). As of 2005, a pharmacist authorized to issue an order to initiate or adjust controlled substance therapy under section 4052 is required to register with DEA (§4052(c)).

## *Physical Therapists and Chiropractors*

The pharmacy has no authority to furnish dangerous drugs to such practitioners as physical therapists and chiropractors unless they are legally entitled to prescribe or use the dangerous drugs or devices. A chiropractor may not prescribe, dispense, or administer dangerous drugs but may prescribe devices (§4040(e)) and has limited authority to use modalities related to chiropractic adjustment. A physical therapist does not have the authority to prescribe or dispense dangerous drugs or devices (§4059(g)), but may apply topical medications (B&PC §2620.3). Physical therapists certified under Business and Professions Code section 2620.5 to do tissue penetration may use certain devices in their practice (§4059(f)). A pharmacy, manufacturer, wholesaler, or home medical device retailer may furnish or dispense a dangerous device to a physical therapist as long as appropriate records are kept (§4059(b),(f)-(g)).

## *Federal Employees*

Federal law requires health care practitioners in federal facilities to be licensed and in good standing in at least one state, but it need not be the state in which they are practicing. Prescribers employed by the United States military, Public Health Service, Veterans Administration, Indian Health Service, or Bureau of Prisons may prescribe, dispense, or administer drugs in the facilities in which they are employed. In addition, they may prescribe, dispense, or administer, but not procure or purchase, controlled substances within the scope of their professional duties at their place of employment. When practicing for their federal employer they do not need a California license and are not subject to California drug or controlled substance laws. Outside these employment settings, when they prescribe for dispensing from a California pharmacy, these federal employees ordinarily need a license issued by a California board.[17]

---

[16] The authority of a pharmacist to furnish emergency contraception to a consumer when following standardized procedures approved by the Pharmacy and Medical Boards, even without a protocol with a physician (see Chap. VI: Scope of Practice), certainly seems to amount to prescribing. But in keeping with physicians guarding against who may "prescribe," the emergency contraception law specifically states, "Nothing in this clause shall be construed to expand the authority of a pharmacist to prescribe any prescription medication" (§4052(a)(8)(A)(ii)).

[17] Arguably these prescriptions could be handled by a California pharmacy as prescriptions from out-of-state prescribers (as each prescriber is licensed in some state). However, the prescriptions would not likely arise from the prescriber's practice within another state. Federal employee prescribers who are practicing outside their employment within California are very likely obliged to obtain a California license to do so.

## *Out-of-State Prescribers*

**Suppose a patient brings in a prescription for theophylline issued by her New Jersey physician. She is visiting in California for three months. May you fill the prescription?**

Yes. A practitioner licensed by a state other than California may issue a prescription to be filled in California (§4005(b), §1717(d)). The pharmacist should interview the patient to verify the prescription's authenticity, to be sure the prescriber is authorized to issue the order (that is, properly licensed in his or her state of practice. The order should contain all the information expected of a California prescriber, and must be evaluated properly, especially if it is for a controlled substance. This authority extends to Schedule III-V controlled substances, but not to Schedule IIs (H&SC §11164.1). Nothing in the law requires out-of-state prescriptions for controlled substances to be written on the new California prescription forms. Controlled substance prescriptions by out-of-state prescribers for delivery to patients in another state must meet the requirements for such prescriptions in the state where the drug was prescribed (H&SC §11164.1(a)(1)).[18]  *mail-order*

Requests to fill prescriptions from out-of-state prescribers usually come from visitors who carry them in case they need to replenish their supply of prescription drugs or who have their hometown physicians authorize new prescriptions by telephone or fax. If the same person returns more than once with a request, or the pharmacy receives similar requests from other patients of the same out-of-state prescriber after the first such request is filled, and especially if the drugs involved have any "recreational" use, the validity of the prescriptions ought to be questioned. Such cross-border prescriptions may be common, and unexceptional, near state lines.

**May a pharmacist in California fill a prescription from a physician in Puerto Rico who is not licensed in California?**

California law defines "state" to include the District of Columbia and United States territories (B&PC §21), and federal law also defines "state" to include the District of Columbia and United States territories and possessions (4 USC §110(d)). Thus prescribers from the Commonwealth of Puerto Rico, the Commonwealth of the Northern Mariana Islands, the Trust Territory of Pacific Islands, the Virgin Islands, Guam, and American Samoa, as well as the District of Columbia, would be out-of-state prescribers for purposes of sections 4005(b) and 1717(d).

## *Foreign Prescribers*

A more troublesome problem is foreign prescribers and patients. No provision in California law or regulation allows a pharmacist to furnish a drug or device ordered by a prescriber from another country. Obviously, it is far more difficult to know whether a prescription from another country was properly written by a licensed professional, or whether that professional's scope of practice includes prescribing, than it is when the prescriber is from another state. Emergency situations should be handled on a case-by-case basis. However, unless there is a true emergency in which the patient would be at significant risk without immediate access to medication, the person should be referred to a licensed practitioner or appropriate medical facility. The law is no different for veterinary prescriptions.

---

[18] Schedule II and III controlled substances dispensed pursuant to this section would still have to be reported to the CURES system (see below).

# For Whom May a Prescription Be Issued?

The prescription may be issued for anyone, including oneself, a spouse, or a family member, except that prescribers may not administer, furnish, or prescribe controlled substances to or for themselves (H&SC §11170). The prescriber must have a medical indication for prescribing a dangerous drug and have conducted a good faith prior examination (B&PC §2242(a)). Controlled substance prescriptions must be issued in the usual course of the prescriber's professional practice to a patient under the prescriber's treatment for a condition other than addiction and for a legitimate medical purpose (21 CFR §1306.04(a), H&SC §11153(a)).

Often Americans with family members overseas are concerned about their access to needed drugs, and may seek to purchase drugs for shipment overseas. Because a prescriber must have examined the patient and have a medical indication for prescriptions for dangerous drugs, prescriptions by physicians here for purported "patients" overseas must be viewed skeptically. A pharmacy may not distribute drugs except on order of a licensed practitioner, and generally has no authority to send drugs or devices out of the country, even if the intent is to do a humanitarian act. The pharmacy may not send drugs overseas on prescription of a foreign prescriber because, as noted above, the foreign physician is not a legal prescriber in California.

**Suppose a pharmacy receives prescriptions from a California physician for residents of a foreign country. The prescription orders are based on actual examinations: some done when the physician visited the foreign country and examined the patient, others based on conversations by telephone or e-mail, and others through an Internet-based questionnaire. Are these prescriptions legal? What obligation does the pharmacist have to determine whether the prescription is legal in the country to which the filled order is to be sent?**

The physician is authorized to transmit an order to the pharmacy, since he or she is licensed in California, but there is an issue whether he or she is legally authorized – under our law and the law of that foreign country – to prescribe for the foreign patient. (The question whether the physician, if he or she examined the patient overseas, could legally practice medicine in the foreign country would depend on the law of that country; in most countries, the answer would likely be no.) At a minimum, the prescription is so irregular (§1761(a)) that the pharmacist should exercise great caution, especially if the drug is one for which there is a large overseas market. The pharmacist should contact the prescriber to confirm its validity, particularly to inquire about the basis for prescribing for someone in a foreign country and the reason the prescription is not being filled in that country. The pharmacist should confirm that any intermediary bringing in the prescription or picking up the filled prescription, or both, has a legitimate relationship with a real patient. And the pharmacist should be sure that is legal to send the drug overseas, not only under state and federal law, but also under the laws of the country to which it will be sent.

**Suppose a California prescriber issues a prescription for a California resident who is working in or on an extended visit to a foreign country. May a California pharmacist legally fill the prescription?**

Nothing in California law specifically addresses, or limits, filling a prescription issued by a California practitioner for a California resident who happens to be out of the country. A key question is whether sending the drugs to the patient overseas would violate federal law or the law of the country into which the drugs were being shipped; see discussion of "Imports and Exports/Exports" in Chapter VII: Ordering, Receipt, Maintenance and Transfer of Drugs and Devices. The pharmacist should be able to rely on the prescriber's judgment in issuing the order, but should consider whether the order, under the circumstances, amounts to a significant irregularity under section 1761(a).

# Off-Label Uses and Unapproved Drugs

Prescribers may order drugs for conditions for which the drug has not been approved by the FDA. Frequently drugs approved for one use are found to be useful in additional conditions, and often they are recognized as effective therapy for those conditions in advance of their manufacturer doing the controlled studies necessary to obtain FDA approval of the labeling changes reflecting those new uses. This use of approved drugs is called "off-label" use, and it is recognized by FDA and the courts (*Washington Legal Foundation v. Henney*, 202 F.3d 331 (D.C. Cir. 2000); see Chap. II: Drugs). The decision whether or not to use a drug for "off-label" use is deemed to be a matter within the practice of medicine, regulated by the states. California has supported appropriate off-label use by adopting statutes prohibiting health plans from denying coverage for unapproved uses of approved drugs (see H&SC §1367.21). But as the off-label use of some prescription drugs has increased, so have the implications for patient care and safety (see, e.g., Chris Adams and Alison Young, three-part series, www.realcities.com/mld/krwashington/news/special_packages/riskyrx/, for the Knight-Ridder news chain.

A physician may also direct the pharmacy to compound, pursuant to prescription, a drug that is not approved for marketing, as long as the components themselves meet food and drug standards (see Chap. VI: Scope of Practice). The physician is allowed to order anything that, in his or her medical judgment, is appropriate for the patient; if the physician is not acting appropriately within the standard of care expected, he or she may have to answer to the Medical Board or, if harm is done, in the courts. Often physicians order compounded medications to meet unique needs of an individual patient (such as unusual sensitivity to inactive ingredients in available pharmaceuticals). Because the physician's order is for an individual patient, the matter is considered within the practice of medicine and the drug laws are not seen to be implicated.

# Who May Transmit the Order and In What Form?

**Who may transmit the order.** The actual prescription drug order may be transmitted either by the prescriber or his or her authorized agent (§§4071-4072; H&SC §11164(b)(3); 21 CFR §§1301.22, 1306.03(b)).[19] The pharmacist must not fill the prescription if he or she knows the agent actually did not have the authority to transmit the order (*Randle v. California State Board of Pharmacy*, 240 Cal. App. 2d 254, 259 (1st Dist. 1966)).[20] The order may be oral, written, or electronic, except as discussed below for controlled substance prescriptions.

---

[19] More than a decade ago, the law was broadened to allow a prescriber's agent (who may or may not be an employee), rather than just a prescriber's employee, to transmit a prescription. In a health care facility, a pharmacist, registered nurse, licensed vocational nurse, licensed psychiatric technician, or other authorized healing arts licentiate who is an employee or serves as a consultant may transmit orally or electronically a prescription ordered by an authorized provider (§4072(a)). Whatever the source of the prescription, the pharmacy must record the name of the transmitter of the order (§4071, 4072(a)).

It is also legal for a pharmacy to pick up prescriptions from a prescriber's office or home, from an office or residence designated by the patient, or from a hospital, medical office, clinic, or institution where the patient receives treatment (§1717(e)).

[20] It is a crime chargeable as either a misdemeanor or a felony to sign another person's name, or that of a fictitious person, or in any way to falsely make, forge, utter, publish, pass, or attempt to pass as genuine any prescription for any drug (§4324(a)). This prohibition is broad enough to apply to fraud in connection with telephoned and electronically transmitted prescriptions, as well as to written prescriptions.

**Must an agent sign or place his or her name on the order he or she transmits? Or provide his or her name with an oral order?**

Sections 4071 and 4072 require the furnisher of a prescription to make a reasonable effort to determine that the person who transmits a prescription for the prescriber is authorized to do so and requires that the furnisher record the name of the agent. Thus, the agent clearly must provide his or her name to the pharmacy receiving the order to be recorded, although it need not be on the prescription itself.

A prescriber, a prescriber's agent (who holds a healing arts license under the Business and Professions Code), or a pharmacist may electronically enter a prescription or order directly into a pharmacy's or hospital's computer, including from outside the hospital or pharmacy, with the permission of that pharmacy or hospital (§4071.1). This authority does not yet extend to controlled substance prescriptions. DEA has been struggling with approval of secure electronic transmission of controlled substance prescription orders for at least five years, and gave notice in both 2001 and 2003 of its intent to promulgate a rule to allow it. DEA now expects to propose such a rule early in 2005.[21] Because of existing California law, when approved under federal law, a pharmacy or hospital will need to obtain approval for electronic entry of controlled substance prescriptions from the Board and the California Department of Justice (H&SC §11164.5(a)).

In addition, an order received in electronic transmission form now need not be reduced to writing or a hard copy if the pharmacy can, for three years from the last furnishing pursuant to the prescription, immediately upon request by the Board produce a hard copy with all the information required by section 4040, as well as the name of the dispensing pharmacist (§4070(b); H&SC §11164.5(b)). If only recorded and stored electronically, no change, obliteration, destruction, or disposal of the information, for the period the record is required by law to be retained, may be made once the prescription has been dispensed; if an error is thereafter identified, a correcting addition may be made only by a pharmacist or with his or her approval. The addition must show the date of entry, the identity of the person making it and of the approving pharmacist, and, of course, what the addition is (§4070(c), H&SC §11164.5(c)).

**Form of the order.** Except for the required use of the new controlled substance prescription form, the prescriber need not write a prescription on any particular form. Even a handwritten note on an envelope, if it contains all required information, is legal (but so odd as to give the pharmacist pause). An unusual form of prescription surely is sufficiently irregular to warrant a call to the prescriber (§1761(a)), unless the prescriber is known to the pharmacist and this is the prescriber's customary practice. (And if it is, perhaps the pharmacist should question the prescriber's judgment.) A telephoned order left as a recorded message is a proper oral order if the pharmacist, reviewing the order, recognizes the voice of the transmitter and has no reason to suspect the order is not authentic.

The use of preprinted, check-off prescription forms (with a number of drugs listed in specified strengths and amounts and a check-off box next to each) is legal in California, and there is no longer any limit to how many dangerous drugs may be ordered from one prescription blank. However, the prescriber must indicate on the blank the number of prescription drugs he or she has prescribed, if more than one. Controlled substances may not be dispensed pursuant to such forms (§1717.3).

A prescription, whether oral, written, or electronic, must contain the name and address of the patient; the name and quantity of the drug or device prescribed; the directions for use; date of issue; the name, address, telephone number, and license classification of the prescriber; and, if a controlled

---

[21] The DEA has posted its anticipated standards for electronic prescriptions for controlled substances on its website, at www.deadiversion.usdoj.gov/ecomm/e_rx/e_standard.htm.

substance is prescribed, the prescriber's federal registry number (§4040(a)). If the prescription was written, it must be signed by the prescriber (§4040(a)(1)(F)); if the prescription is for a controlled substance, both the signature and date must be in the handwriting of the prescriber, as discussed below.[22] An electronically-transmitted prescription also must include the identity of the intended recipient (§1717.4(c)). Both the transmitter and the recipient of prescriptions, whether in electronic or other forms, must ensure the security, integrity, and confidentiality of the prescription information (§1717.4(h)). A drug, including a controlled substance, also may be dispensed based on an entry in a patient chart (a "chart order") for an inpatient of a hospital (§4019, §1717(c), H&SC §11159), as discussed in Chapter IV: Licensing Pharmacies.

California law allows prescriptions for Schedule III-V controlled substance to be written, oral, or electronic (either fax or data transmission, H&SC §11164(c)). California law generally does not authorize oral or electronic transmission of prescriptions for Schedule II drugs (H&SC §11164), as discussed below. Federal regulations allow faxing of controlled substance prescriptions under certain conditions, but not electronic data transmission (21 CFR §1306.11). Because of that federal restriction, it would appear that a Schedule III, IV, or V prescription may not be sent by data transmission, despite California law. Federal regulations referring to faxes clearly mean an image transmission of the original signed prescription, not an electronically-generated order received by the pharmacy in fax form (21 CFR §1306.21(a)), even one with an electronically-generated "signature." As noted above, DEA has not adopted regulations on secure electronic transmission of prescriptions. However, in a private letter from DEA that has been widely circulated, DEA stated that "current DEA regulations allow for Schedule III, IV or V controlled substance prescriptions that are electronically created and transmitted, either directly to a computer or via a facsimile machine, to be treated as oral prescriptions" (Letter from Patricia M. Good, Chief, Liaison and Policy, Office of Diversion Control, DEA, to Clifford E. Berman, AllScripts Healthcare Solutions, Sept. 28, 2001). The validity of such orders must be ensured prior to dispensing.

DEA's letter is obviously inconsistent with its own regulations, although it is consistent with the intent of the federal "E-Sign" law (see Chap XI: Record-Keeping) to allow electronic signatures and records where written records would once have been required. DEA's failure to change its regulations in a timely fashion, particularly to bring its official policies in line with its privately-given advice, puts some in the industry at a competitive disadvantage; DEA did not post this letter, and its apparently-changed policy, on its website. The Pharmacy Board has developed an electronic order compliance guideline, which was published in *The Script* in March 2003 (www.pharmacy.ca.gov/publications/03_march_script.pdf, p. 12). It requires the pharmacy to ensure the authenticity, integrity, non-repudiation, and confidentiality of all electronically-transmitted prescriptions.

Federal regulations authorize the faxing of any Schedule II prescription as long as the original, written prescription is presented to the pharmacy before the drugs actually are dispensed (21 CFR §1306.11(a)). California authority for the use of faxed orders for Schedule II controlled substances is discussed below.

**Date of Issue.** A prescription must bear its date of issue (§4040(a)(1)(C)); both postdating and antedating controlled substance prescriptions are specifically prohibited under California and federal law (H&SC§11172, 21 CFR §1306.05(a)). A prescription for a dangerous drug does not expire, although a prescription not filled for a significant time after it was written (and how long a time is "significant" will vary depending upon the nature of the drug) surely should be considered "irregular" and require validation by the prescriber (§1761(a)). A prescription for a controlled

---

[22] The signature on a written prescription for a controlled substance must be in ink (H&SC §11164(a)(1)), but section 4040 does not specify that the signature on a written prescription be in ink.

substance may now be filled up to six months from the date of issue. Until 2004, there was no time limit for filling Schedule III-V prescriptions, but Schedule II prescriptions were valid for only 14 days.

In 2003, DEA, by private letter, stated that a physician may prepare multiple prescriptions on the same day for the same Schedule II controlled substance with instructions to fill them on different dates (Letter of Patricia M. Good, Chief, Liaison and Policy Section, Office of Diversion Control, DEA, to Howard A. Heit, M.D., Jan. 31, 2003). This advice was widely-circulated, including in the 2004 update to the prior edition of this text, and was included in Frequently-Asked Questions posted in August 2004 on DEA's website. DEA summarily withdrew from this advice in an interim policy statement published on November 16, 2004 (69 FR 67170), stating that it "is tantamount to writing a prescription authorizing refills of a schedule II controlled substance," in conflict with one of the fundamental purposes of federal controlled substances law (see Chap. X: Dispensing and Beyond).[23] This episode underscores the difficulties inherent in an agency "changing" the law through informal, unpublished advice.

# The Controlled Substance Prescription Form

## *The Triplicate System*

For over 60 years California required a special, state-issued triplicate prescription form for certain prescriptions. Initially the requirement pertained to any order for a narcotic. Once California's Controlled Substances Act passed, the requirement was limited to Schedule II narcotics; later it was expanded to encompass all Schedule II controlled substances. The system imposed greater requirements than federal law; unnecessarily, many argued. It was also argued that it effectively dissuaded practitioners from prescribing Schedule II controlled substances, especially for pain management. Objections were particularly vehement in recent years, when the purpose of the triplicate – to create databases from which to find abuse by prescribers, dispensers, and patients – was not being met, because the Department of Justice was not able to keep up with the work of entering data from the triplicate prescription forms. The triplicate prescription requirement has now been repealed, effective January 1, 2005, and replaced by a new controlled substance prescription form.

California is one of more than a dozen states that now or soon will require tamper-resistant prescription blanks for controlled substances. The change to such blanks, which some states are requiring for all prescriptions, has been deemed to be successful in reducing fraud and diversion (Fred Gebhart, *More states adopting tamper-resistant Rx pads*, Drug Topics, Nov. 22, 2004).

## *Transition to the New Form*

2004 was a transition year, but December 31, 2004, was the last day a triplicate prescription form could be honored (filled). Between July 1 and December 31, 2004, prescribers could use either a triplicate or a controlled substance prescription form. Initially July 1, 2004, was set as the date after which no more triplicate forms could be ordered or distributed, but the date was extended to November 1 because of difficulties in approving printers for the new forms. Because of ongoing problems with the printing and distribution of the new controlled substance prescription forms, prescribers who cannot obtain forms, and the pharmacists filling their controlled substances prescriptions, are being instructed to follow the procedures for emergency controlled substance

---

[23] It is unclear whether DEA also means to prohibit a prescriber from issuing a single order for a Schedule II controlled substance, dated properly, but marked "not to be filled before [a later date]." Since such an order would not be a refill and since a controlled substance prescription may be filled up to six months from the date of issue, this would seem to be legal. However, there would be very limited instances in which a prescriber would likely feel the need to write such an order.

prescriptions (H&SC §11167, see below).  The prescriber should indicate the oral, fax, or written order is being issued under the "11167 exemption."  The usual emergency order requires that the proper controlled substance prescription form follow within seven days, but it cannot under these circumstances.  Pharmacies are to satisfy themselves that the prescriber's claim not to have been able to obtain the required forms is legitimate (Letter from the executive officers of the Pharmacy and Medical Boards dated Dec. 20, 2004, www.pharmacy.ca.gov/publications/memo_11167.pdf).  If the filled order was not based on a written, signed prescription, the pharmacy should obtain a follow-up written order signed by the prescriber to comply with federal regulations, as discussed below.  If the circumstances under which the prescriber uses the method approved by the Medical and Pharmacy Boards do not constitute an emergency under federal law, the pharmacist would be well advised to require a written, signed prescription at the time of dispensing, rather than rely on a fax or oral order.

## *The New Form*

The new controlled substance prescription forms must meet very detailed requirements, both with respect to information they must include and to their security.  They are intended to be forgery and tamper resistant.  Only Board-approved printing companies may make the forms; a list of approved companies is on the Board's website.

Information requirements for the new forms include:

- The name, category of licensure, license number, and DEA registration number of the prescriber must be preprinted;
- There must be a check box for the prescriber to indicate "no substitutions";
- Each batch of prescriptions must have a lot number, with each form within each batch sequentially numbered, beginning with "1";
- There must be six quantity boxes on the form (1-24, 25-49, 50-74, 75-100, 101-150, and 151 and over), with a space to designate the units referenced when the drug is not in tablet or capsule form;[24]
- Either a statement printed on the bottom of the blank that the prescription is void if more than one controlled substance is written thereon or a space for the prescriber to specify the number of drugs prescribed on the blank and a statement on the bottom that the prescription is void if the number of drugs prescribed on the blank is not noted; and
- A description on each form of its security features (H&SC §11162.1).

Security requirements for the new forms include:

- Latent, repetitive "void" pattern printed across the entire front so that if it is scanned or photocopied, "void" appears;
- Watermark on back side of blank reading "California Security Prescription";
- Chemical void protection to prevent alteration by chemical washing;
- A feature printed in thermo-chromic ink; and
- An area of opaque writing that disappears if the prescription is lightened (H&SC §11162.1).

All the information that must be preprinted on the forms must be on the forms as purchased from the printer: the prescriber cannot have partially-printed forms to which he or she would then add some of the required information (Senate Bill 151 Questions and Answers, revised Nov. 04, 2004,

---

[24] The prescriber must mark the range of units within which the prescription falls, in addition to listing the actual dosage number ordered.

www.pharmacy.ca.gov/consumers/prescribe_dispense.htm#sb151 (hereafter "SB 151 Q&A, 11/4/04")).

The new forms may be issued in the names of multiple prescribers (such as in a group or clinic practice) provided all the required information for each prescriber is preprinted on the form and the form indicates, such as through a check-off box, which prescriber is issuing the particular form (More SB151 Questions and Answers, Sept. 24, www.pharmacy.ca.gov/consumers/prescribe_dispense.htm #moresb151 (hereafter "More SB 151 Q&A, 9/24/04"). A prescriber with multiple offices may also obtain controlled substance prescription forms with multiple addresses, as long as there is some means to indicate from which office the prescription is issued (SB 151 Q&A, 11/4/04).

A licensed health care facility (see App. B) may designate a prescriber to order controlled substance prescription forms to be used when treating patients in that facility. These forms would be preprinted with the name, address, category of licensure, state license number, and DEA number of the designated prescriber and the name, address, category of licensure, and license number of the licensed health care facility. The designated prescriber is responsible for distributing the forms to prescribers within the facility, and for maintaining a record of the name, category of licensure, state and DEA license numbers, and quantity of forms issued to each prescriber. The facility must maintain these records for three years. The forms will not be valid without the name, category of licensure, and state and DEA license numbers of the actual prescriber on them (H&SC §11162.1(c)). The Board recommends that the designated prescriber record the batch or lot numbers of the forms he or she distributes (SB 151 Q&A, 11/4/04).

## Using the New Form

Unlike the triplicate form, which was only required for Schedule II orders, the new controlled substance prescription form must be used any time a written order for any controlled substance is presented. Oral or faxed orders are still permitted for Schedule III, IV, and V prescriptions, but whenever those are in written form they must be on the new form.

Prescribers may use the new forms for non-controlled substances, for prescribing more than one controlled substance (including from different schedules), and for prescribing controlled substances and other prescription drugs. To use the forms for more than one drug, the prescriber must use the version that contains a space for the prescriber to specify the number of drugs prescribed on the blank (and a statement at the bottom that the "Prescription is void if the number of drugs prescribed is not noted") (H&SC §11162.1(a)(8)). When more than one drug is prescribed on a single form, the quantity check-off boxes must be marked for each prescription. In other words, two controlled substances, one for 60 doses and one for 100 doses, would require a check in both the 50-74 and the 75-100 boxes. The Board instructs that if both amounts are in the same range (for example, for 50-74), the prescriber should put two marks by that box (More SB 151 Q&A, 9/24/04).

The exceptions for Schedule II prescriptions for emergencies, the terminally ill, and hospice and SNF patients remain, are discussed below and in Chapter X: Dispensing and Beyond.

As was true with triplicates, the pharmacist is specifically allowed to fill in the patient's address on the form, if not specified by the prescriber (or to maintain this information in a readily retrievable form in the pharmacy) (H&SC §11164(a)(2)). Perhaps by oversight, the new law does not carry over a provision in the previous law that allowed the pharmacist to "fill a prescription for a controlled substance classified in Schedule II [the only type for which the triplicate was required] containing an error or errors, if the pharmacist notifies the prescriber of the error or errors and prescriber approves any correction." The prescriber was then required to present a corrected prescription to the pharmacist within seven days (H&SC §11164(a), inoperative July 1, 2004). Even though the current law is entirely silent on the correction of errors by pharmacists, the Board has taken the position that such authority still exists. It bases this position on the fact that the new law only requires the prescriber's signature and date to be handwritten; therefore the rest of the prescription information can be filled in by the prescriber's agent (H&SC §11164(a)). "Therefore," the Board continues, "the pharmacist [presumably acting as the prescriber's agent] can make changes to any other information on the prescription as long as the pharmacist verifies the change with the prescriber first" (More SB 151 Q&A, 9/24/04).

This interpretation is troublesome in light of the fact that the Legislature left out the authority of the pharmacist to correct errors in revising the law. In addition, the pharmacist's "correction" authority had been "checked" by the requirement of the corrected prescription, providing mutual assurance to pharmacist and prescriber of accuracy and a means for pharmacy inspectors to assure that pharmacist-made corrections were in fact approved by the prescriber. Would the Legislature, obviously concerned enough about the security of all controlled substance prescriptions to require the new forms, want the pharmacy to make corrections the accuracy and veracity of which cannot be checked in pharmacy records? Furthermore, the Board's position, which looks at the pharmacist as the prescriber's agent, would allow the pharmacist not only to correct errors but also to fill in missing information (when the law specifically allows the pharmacist to add only the patient's address) (H&SC §11164(a)(2)).

**A patient from California presents a prescription from an out-of-state prescriber for a Schedule II drug. May you fill it?**

No, the law makes no provision for Schedule II prescriptions from out-of-state prescribers. If the prescription is for a Schedule III, IV, or V, it may be filled if the prescription is oral or written and the pharmacist interviews the patient to authenticate the prescription (H&SC §11164.1, §4005(b), §1717(d)). The pharmacist should exercise his or her professional judgment in filling the prescription and may be wise to verify the prescription with the prescriber, as well as to ascertain the authority of the prescriber to issue the order under the laws of the state in which he or she is located.

**A prescription for a controlled substance from an out-of-state prescriber is presented to a California pharmacy for delivery out of state. Can you fill it?**

Such prescriptions may be filled if they comply with the law of the state where they were issued (H&SC §11164.1(a)(1)). The pharmacist should exercise care in filling the order and, if it is for a Schedule II or III, it must be reported to CURES (see below).

## Exceptions for Schedule II Prescriptions See abood's handout

There are some exceptions to the requirement that the new controlled substance form be used for Schedule II prescriptions. Such exceptions are unnecessary for Schedule III-V prescriptions, because those may be issued based on an oral, faxed, or electronic data transmission order.

**Chart Orders.** As discussed in Chapter IV: Licensing Pharmacies, an entry on a hospital chart allows a pharmacist to fill an order for a controlled substance for an inpatient; the usual controlled substance prescription form is required for discharge medications. When the order is for a controlled substance, the order must be signed by the prescriber, although the law does not specify whether the order must be signed by the prescriber before the prescription may be dispensed. The order must also include the drug, the quantity ordered, the quantity actually administered, and the date of the order (H&SC §11159).

**May an order in a clinic for a Schedule II controlled substance be filled based on a chart order entry? An order for a III, IV, or V?** *No for II. III –V see Below*

An order for controlled substances furnished to a patient of a clinic is generally subject to the usual requirements for the form of a controlled substances order. However, if the order is for a Schedule III, IV, or V controlled substance furnished to a patient in a clinic (as opposed to being dispensed for outpatient use), and the clinic has a clinic permit issued by the Board, the order is exempt from the form requirements of Health and Safety Code section 11164, if it is in writing in the patient's record, signed by the prescriber, dated, with the name and quantity of the controlled substance ordered and the amount actually furnished. The record must be maintained for seven years (H&SC §11159.1). There is no such exception for orders for Schedule II controlled substances for clinics licensed by the Board.

**SNF, ICF, and Hospice Patients.** Section 11167.5 of the Health and Safety Code provides that a prescription for a Schedule II controlled substance for use by a patient in a licensed skilled nursing facility, intermediate care facility, or home health agency providing hospice care may be dispensed upon an oral or electronic order.[25] The pharmacy must develop a form to use in such cases and fill it out before dispensing. The pharmacy must have the original of this form signed by the person receiving the drugs for the facility, and retain it for the pharmacy's records. The facility that submits the order must forward a copy of any signed telephone order, chart order, or related documentation substantiating the order to the pharmacist.

*Not Po meds*

Under federal regulations, a narcotic Schedule II controlled substance may be dispensed by a pharmacy based on a fax order for direct administration to a patient by parenteral, intravenous, intramuscular, subcutaneous, or intraspinal infusion (21 CFR §1306.11(e)). Any Schedule II controlled substance may be similarly dispensed for a resident of a long-term care facility (21 CFR §1306.11(f)) and for a patient enrolled in a Medicare-certified or state-licensed hospice (21 CFR §1306.11(g)). In these cases the fax becomes the original prescription for record-keeping purposes. Any other Schedule II controlled substance order also may be transmitted by fax, but the original written, signed prescription must be received by the pharmacy before dispensing (21 CFR §1306.11(a)).

Reconciling the somewhat inconsistent provisions of federal and state law, a narcotic Schedule II controlled substance for direct administration by infusion to a patient at home in a hospice setting or in a skilled nursing or intermediate care facility may be dispensed by a pharmacy based on a faxed order. Any Schedule II controlled substance may be dispensed for a resident of a long-term care facility based on a fax order. In either case, the pharmacy must prepare a controlled substances order form of its own devising, including all the information required by federal and state law, prior to dispensing. Regardless of the form of the order, Schedule II prescriptions must be reported to CURES (see below).

**Emergencies.** California law authorizes the dispensing of Schedule II prescriptions orally, electronically, or using an ordinary written prescription in an emergency (H&SC §11167). For purposes of this section an "emergency" is a situation where "failure to issue a prescription may result in loss of life or intense suffering." The order must contain all the information required by Health and

---

[25] California law allows electronic data transmission of these Schedule II prescriptions, but federal law does not, so it remains illegal. Federal law allows faxing of any Schedule II prescription in that situation as long as the original written, signed prescription is received prior to dispensing, but California law does not. That practice, too, is therefore illegal; it appears, however, that BNE is not concerned if the pharmacy begins with a fax for a Schedule II drug, as long as the proper prescription form is received before dispensing. Also, a fax is legal for a Schedule II under the circumstances covered by sections 11159.2 and 11167.5 of the Health and Safety Code and in emergencies pursuant to Health and Safety Code section 11167, as described below.

*[handwritten margin note top: emergency: State: Oral/fax –okay but reduce. Notify BNE in writing if written Rx not received w/in 7 days]*

Safety Code section 11164(a). Before filling the order, the pharmacist must reduce an oral or electronic data transmission order to hard copy form; if a written order is used, it must be signed and dated by the prescriber in ink (H&SC §11167(b)). The prescriber has until the seventh day following the date of issue to provide or mail the required controlled substance prescription form to the pharmacy; a postmark on a mailed order showing the seventh day is sufficient (H&SC §11167(c)). If the pharmacy does not receive the form in a timely fashion, BNE must be notified in writing within 144 hours (H&SC §11167(d)). The pharmacy must make and retain a written record of the prescription, including the date and method of notifying BNE. Nothing in section 11167 limits the emergency fill to the amount necessary for the duration of the emergency. *[handwritten: State does not specify amt.]*

Federal regulations also provide for the filling of Schedule II prescriptions in an emergency. DEA considers an emergency to be when immediate administration is necessary for proper treatment, no alternative treatment (including a drug not in Schedule II) is available, and it is "not possible" for the prescriber to provide a written prescription at the time (Pharmacist's Manual, p. 44). In such an emergency an oral order may substitute for the required signed written order, as long as a written, signed prescription, marked "Authorization for Emergency Dispensing," is provided within seven days (21 CFR §1306.11(d)(4)). If the pharmacist does not know the prescriber, he or she must make a reasonable effort to determine that an oral order came from a valid practitioner by verifying the practitioner's telephone number with the number listed in the directory and by making other good faith efforts to ensure proper identity (Pharmacist's Manual, pp. 44-45). DEA's emergency regulations specify an oral order may substitute for the signed written prescription, but DEA states in the Pharmacist's Manual (p. 44) that a fax may also be used. *[handwritten margin: Fed must have]*

If the prescriber fails to provide the follow-up written order, the pharmacy must notify the nearest DEA Diversion Field Office. If the pharmacy fails to do so, its authority to have filled the prescription will be void; in other words, the dispensing will be treated as though it had never been authorized (21 CFR §1306.11(d)(4)). The emergency order may only be filled in an amount adequate to treat the patient during the emergency period (21 CFR §1306.11(d)(1)). *[handwritten: Federal (DEA) = adequate amt to treat during ER.]*

Reconciling the conflicting federal and state provisions, if an oral or fax order is the basis for the emergency prescription, only an amount sufficient for the emergency period may be dispensed, in accordance with the federal restriction. This federal restriction on amount does not apply when an ordinary signed written prescription is used, because that is all federal law in any case requires for Schedule IIs – even though the pharmacist must rely on emergency authority because of the lack of the California controlled substance prescription form. Even though California would accept any type of electronic order – that is, a data transmission as well as a fax – under these circumstances, a data transmission order would not be legal because federal law does not allow it. As noted above, the federal regulations also do not recognize faxes, but DEA's acceptance of them in the Pharmacist's Manual means that they are acceptable.

A pharmacy that repeatedly receives and accepts "emergency" oral and fax orders for Schedule II drugs is likely to draw the attention of BNE and the Board of Pharmacy, especially when it cannot produce the covering controlled substance prescription forms from the prescribers. When the pharmacy is charged with failure to follow the law or for drug shortages, it will not be able to defend itself by blaming the prescribers or even by saying "everyone" is doing it. However, there is certain to be some latitude, as well as some confusion, during the beginning of 2005, while practitioners order and obtain the new controlled substance prescription forms.

**Terminally Ill Patients.** The exception to the triplicate requirement for Schedule II prescriptions that was created for certain terminally ill patients survives as an exception to the use of the new controlled substances order form (H&SC §11159.2). For purposes of this exception, a patient is terminally ill if, in the reasonable medical judgment of the prescriber, he or she is suffering from an incurable, irreversible illness, is expected to die within one year, and is being treated primarily for control of pain, symptom management, or both, rather than for cure of the illness (H&SC §11159.2(c)). Under these circumstances the prescription need only contain the information required by Health and Safety Code section 11164(a) and the words "11159.2 exemption" certifying the patient's terminal illness. An ordinary written and signed prescription is allowed in place of the otherwise-mandated form, as it was allowed to substitute in these circumstances for the triplicate.

The prescription must include the notation "11159.2 exemption" to indicate why no controlled substance prescription form is required (H&SC §11159.2(a)(2)). However, the pharmacist may fill the prescription although that certification contains a technical error (for example, if the section number is incorrect), if the pharmacist has personal knowledge of the patient's terminal illness and returns the prescription to the prescriber for "correction" (that is, correct inclusion of the phrase) within 72 hours (H&SC §11159.2 (b)).[26]

The notation "11159.2 exemption" is not required to be in the prescriber's handwriting. The very existence of the required notation was a compromise. Regulators wanted to protect against abuse of this exemption by practitioners fraudulently using it to circumvent the requirement of a triplicate form. Practitioners were concerned about handing patients prescriptions marked "terminally ill," given that some patients or their family members may not have been told of the patient's condition or that the condition was terminal.

The obvious problem with a "11159.2 exemption" notation is that the patient is likely to ask what it means. The problem for the pharmacist is that he or she will either have to explain, defeating the concerns that led to the compromise language, or put off the patient by referring him or her back to the prescriber for an explanation. The burdens this exception imposes on pharmacists were a matter of concern to the Pharmacy Board, which opposed the legislation in part for that reason. However, the legislation was urgently pressed by patient groups, the state medical association, and hospice physicians. Two issues of the Board's newsletter, *The Script*, dated January and April 1999, devoted significant attention to the receipt and filling of these prescriptions; these issues may be read on the Board's website (www.pharmacy.ca.gov/publications/publications.htm).

**A pharmacy receives a prescription for MSContin® on an ordinary prescription blank, marked "1159.2." May the pharmacy correct the error and fill it?**

Only if the pharmacist has personal knowledge that the patient is terminally ill and has the prescriber send a corrected copy of the prescription. The pharmacist's knowledge of the patient's illness must precede the receipt of the prescription. That is, the pharmacist cannot interview the patient or prescriber after receiving the prescription containing the error, determine the patient is terminally ill, and then fill the order.

**A pharmacy receives a prescription for MSContin® for a terminally ill patient on an ordinary prescription blank, and it is marked "11159.2 exception." Only the signature is in the prescriber's own handwriting. May the prescription be filled?**

No. Although the triplicate form only required that the prescriber's signature be in his or her handwriting, both the signature and the date on any controlled substance prescription form must be in the handwriting of the prescriber. If this were for a Schedule III, IV, or V prescription, the pharmacist could simply contact the prescriber and effectively convert the prescription to an oral order, and fill it.

---

[26] This authority is available only when the 11159.2 certification must be corrected, not if it has been omitted. In that case, the prescription cannot be filled without being returned to the prescriber for completion.

**A prescriber has been issuing prescriptions under section 11159.2 for a patient who is still alive after one year.  The pharmacy continues to receive Schedule II prescriptions on ordinary prescription blanks, bearing the "11159.2" notation, for this patient.  May they be filled?**

The "one year" limitation in section 11159.2 was an attempt to prevent practitioners from evading the special form requirements for all of their seriously ill patients who need Schedule II drugs and might, at some point, be expected to die.  The fact that a physician legitimately believed a patient was unlikely to survive for a year, but the patient fortunately did so, does not mean the physician's judgment was wrong.  If the patient's prognosis for survival remains a year or less, the physician may continue to issue, and the pharmacy to fill, "11159.2" prescriptions for the patient.  If a pharmacy is receiving such orders well after one year has passed, especially for large amounts of drugs, or for multiple patients, the pharmacist should contact the prescriber.  The pharmacist should seek to determine whether the prescriber is trying to evade the controlled substance prescription form requirement, or whether he or she simply has some patients who are living longer than expected (see Chap. XII: Practice Pitfalls).

**A physician calls in an order for a Schedule II drug to a long-term care facility, and a nurse at the facility then prepares and faxes an order to you.  May you fill it?**

No. This order appears to be legal under California law, which allows dispensing of a Schedule II drug to a patient in a long-term care facility on the basis of either an oral or an electronic order, and does not seem to preclude accepting the fax created by the physician's agent.  Federal regulations, however, allow the transmission by facsimile of a Schedule II prescription only as a limited exception to the requirement of an "original written, signed prescription" (21 CFR §1306.11(a),(f)).  They refer to the faxing of the physician's actual written and signed prescription, not of a prescription written by the physician's agent.  As has previously been noted in this text, when federal and state requirements are in conflict concerning controlled substances, the more restrictive provision must be followed.  In other words, the initiating order faxed for a resident of a long-term care facility must be one actually (not electronically) signed by the prescriber.

**Suppose the pharmacy receives a controlled substance prescription form for a Schedule II that is missing information.  What can the pharmacist do?  What if the form has been filled out using two different inks?** No. Professional Judgement

If the pharmacy receives a controlled substance prescription form that is missing information, the pharmacist may not complete it, except for a missing patient address (H&SC §11164(a)).  The prescription must not be filled and must either be returned to the prescriber or the prescriber must issue a new, properly-completed prescription.  Although this may seem a great nuisance, the law is clear on this point.[27]

If the pharmacy receives such a prescription that has two different inks, the pharmacist should at least be concerned.  When the prescriber had to fill out triplicates entirely in handwriting, two inks on the form were a significant warning sign.  Now that the prescriber only needs to sign and date controlled substance prescriptions, the fact of two different inks is a lesser concern.  However, if the pharmacist believes the change in inks suggests an irregularity (§1761(a)), he or she should contact the prescriber.  If the prescriber confirms that he or she authorized the entire prescription, the pharmacist generally may fill it.  If the circumstances suggest that the prescription might not be for a legitimate

---

[27] If the order were for a Schedule III, IV or V controlled substance, the pharmacist could call the prescriber or his or her agent, convert the prescription to an oral order, obtain the missing information, and fill the prescription.  Under the Board's logic with respect to errors, the pharmacist would be able to call the prescriber and, acting as the prescriber's agent, complete the omissions.  Such authority seems well beyond what ought to be assumed from silence in the law.

medical purpose, the pharmacist should not fill it. For example, if one ink appears to be written over another entry, and to effect a change in the original writing, the pharmacist probably should be so suspicious that he or she should not fill the prescription.

**The pharmacy receives a controlled substance prescription form for morphin sulfate. May the prescription be filled? What about a prescription for morphine sulfate 1000mgs.? May it be filled?** *Yes. RPh can correct spelling errors & strength of drug*

As noted above, the authority in Health and Safety Code section 11164 for a pharmacist to correct errors after contacting the prescriber has been repealed. However, the Board has concluded that the pharmacist, acting as the prescriber's agent, could, as with any other erroneous prescription (§1761(a)), obtain the information and correct even a Schedule II prescription. That would allow the pharmacist to correct the spelling of the drug in the first prescription, and obtain the correct strength of the drug in the second. While efficient, one must at least wonder whether the Legislature intended its repeal of the pharmacist's authority to correct errors in Health & Safety Code section 11164 to result in greater, rather than diminished, authority for the pharmacist in this regard.

## Controlled Substance Crimes

The controlled substance prescription form system is strictly controlled, as was the triplicate system. While it is not a crime to possess, without authorization, a controlled substance prescription form, as it was to possess a triplicate (former H&SC §11161(a)), counterfeiting a controlled substance prescription form or knowingly possessing three or more counterfeit forms can be prosecuted as a felony, as was true with triplicates (H&SC §11162.5(a)). No person may obtain or attempt to obtain controlled substances or a prescription for them by fraud, deceit, misrepresentation, or subterfuge, or by concealment of a material fact (H&SC §11173(a)). No person may make a false statement in any prescription, order, report, or record required by the Controlled Substances Act (H&SC §11173(b)). And no person may knowingly fill a mutilated, altered, or forged prescription for a controlled substance (H&SC §11166).

## Electronic Monitoring (CURES)

The triplicate system was intended to allow closer and more comprehensive monitoring and regulation of Schedule II prescriptions than of other prescriptions. Because it was ineffective for tracking purposes and inefficient for (and disliked by) practitioners and patients, California began moving toward an electronic monitoring system for Schedule II controlled substance prescriptions, called CURES (Controlled Substance Utilization Review and Evaluation System), in 1998. CURES began as a pilot project, but has now been made permanent and been extended to Schedule III prescriptions.

The relevant provisions of Board regulations setting up CURES have now been incorporated into Health and Safety Code section 11165, and the Board is in the process of repealing its regulations (§1715.5). Subdivision (d) of section 11165 provides that each pharmacy must submit, in a frequency and format specified by the California Department of Justice, the following information for each Schedule II or III prescription it dispenses:

- The full name, address, gender, and date of birth of the patient;
- The prescriber's license category and license and DEA numbers;
- For any prescriber using the DEA registration number of a government-exempt facility, his or her medical license number;
- The pharmacy's license and DEA numbers and the prescription number assigned;

- The NDC (National Drug Code) number of the controlled substance;
- The quantity dispensed;
- The ICD-9, or diagnosis code, if available; and
- The date of issue and date of dispensing of the prescription.

The data in the electronic monitoring system is available to the Bureau of Narcotic Enforcement and state licensing boards, including the Board of Pharmacy. Electronic monitoring is proving to be more accurate, comprehensive, and effective than the triplicate system, while also being less of a burden to patients and practitioners. More than 20 states now have electronic monitoring either to replace or supplement other forms of control over Schedule II drugs.[28] Some of those states are monitoring all controlled substances prescriptions within their electronic systems. Although states are moving to the use of secure privately-printed prescription forms for all controlled substances or all drugs, only a few retain state-issued prescription form requirements for Schedule II or other controlled substances. No state now uses a triplicate prescription form.

The CURES system was made accessible to prescribers and pharmacists in 2003. Upon written request for information, the California Department of Justice may provide information from the system about specific patients.[29] The Department may also, on its own initiative, provide such information to practitioners and pharmacies to deter the improper use of Schedule II or III controlled substances (ch. 345, stats. 2002, AB2655).

# Receipt of the Prescription

A written prescription, whether for a dangerous drug or controlled substance, may be received in a pharmacy by a nonpharmacist, but only a pharmacist may receive an oral prescription because the pharmacist has to transcribe the order (§1717(c), 21 CFR §1306.03(b)). Presumably a prescription received by fax or electronic transmission will be treated like a written prescription for these purposes, because the information is received by the pharmacy exactly as transmitted by the prescriber.

An oral prescription must be received by a pharmacist, not by a technician or other ancillary personnel, to preclude transmission errors caused by incorrectly hearing, understanding, or writing down information, including technical terminology. Oral prescriptions (including those left on a voice mail system) must be reduced promptly to writing, initialed, and noted by the pharmacist as being oral prescriptions before they are filled (§1717(c)). Oral or electronically-transmitted controlled substance prescriptions must also be reduced to writing (H&SC §11164(b)). The pharmacist need not include the address, telephone number, license classification, or, where needed, the DEA registration number of the prescriber or the address of the patient on these prescriptions if this information is readily retrievable in the pharmacy (§4040(b), H&SC §11164(b)(2)). The pharmacy receiving prescriptions electronically either must receive them in paper form or have the capacity to retrieve them on paper from its computer memory (§1717.4(e)).

As noted above, under certain circumstances a prescription may be electronically transmitted directly into a pharmacy or hospital computer, including from outside the hospital or pharmacy, by the prescriber, his or her agent, or a pharmacist. Prescription orders may be received electronically by an interim storage device, an electronic file from which the prescription may be retrieved by an

---

[28] Federal proposals to mandate or provide grant funds to support such systems in all states have not passed.

[29] The request needs to be made on a Patient Activity Report (PAR) form, which may be obtained, along with instructions for its submission, at www.ag.ca.gov/bne/content/trips.htm. The requesting prescriber or pharmacist must seek this information only for proper purposes, such as evaluation and treatment of a patient under his or her care, and must treat the information as confidential medical information subject to California's medical privacy law (see Chap. XIV: Other Relevant Law).

authorized person. Such a device must record and maintain, in addition to the other required information, the date of entry and/or receipt of the order, the date of transmission from the storage device, and the identity of the recipient of the transmission. The storage device must be maintained to ensure against unauthorized access and use of prescription information (§1717.4(d)). Electronic equipment for transmitting prescriptions or electronic transmittal technology cannot be supplied or used to circumvent any California laws or regulations governing pharmacy or controlled substances (§1717.4(g)).

**You receive a prescription with an advertisement, a picture of a drug, or a drug company logo or name on it. May you fill it?**

Yes. Nothing in Pharmacy Law specifically bars a drug company or other entity from printing prescription pads for practitioners that contain pictures, advertisements, or logos. However, the more unusual, or odd, the prescription pad, the more likely it is that a pharmacist might question the prescription.

# Evaluation of the Prescription

Only a pharmacist may evaluate a prescription (§1793.1(c)). Although a nonpharmacist, such as a technician, may be the first person to handle a written or fax prescription, a pharmacist still must review it to ensure that it is complete, comprehensible, not on its face erroneous, and has been written or transmitted by a person authorized to do so, and to do any other evaluation or interpretation necessary to begin the dispensing process. The pharmacist's review and evaluation provide an important safety check. The pharmacist might note an inappropriate or questionable dose or instructions, for example, that a nonpharmacist is not competent to assess. In those circumstances the pharmacist is expected to check with the prescriber to determine if there was a transcription error, a prescribing error, or intentional justifiable prescribing despite being beyond the usual bounds of the use of the medication. Remember: a pharmacist must not fill any prescription that contains any significant error, omission, irregularity, uncertainty, ambiguity, or alteration without checking with the prescriber for the information necessary to validate the prescription (§1761(a)).

When a prescription is for a controlled substance, the pharmacist's responsibility is even greater and defined with much more specificity by law. The pharmacist must be sure the prescription is for a proper medical purpose (21 CFR §1306.04(a), H&SC §11153, §1761(b)). Although the primary obligation to make sure a prescription is valid belongs to the prescriber, the pharmacist has what is called a "corresponding responsibility" to watch for illegitimate controlled substance prescriptions. This subject is discussed in greater detail in Chapter XII: Practice Pitfalls.

The pharmacist must refuse to fill any controlled substance prescription *even after checking with the prescriber* if the pharmacist knows or has objective reason to know the prescription is not legitimate (§1761(b), see Chap. XII: Practice Pitfalls). What this means is if the pharmacist actually knows the prescription is invalid or, from all the information in the pharmacist's possession or readily available, a reasonable pharmacist would know the prescription is invalid, the pharmacist should not fill it. This sometimes requires a very difficult analysis in which the pharmacist must exercise his or her professional training and judgment, both to avoid dispensing a medication to someone who does not need and may abuse it and to avoid depriving a patient of needed medication. It is one of the most important responsibilities of the pharmacist, necessitated by the reality that a few practitioners and a minority of people presenting prescriptions are involved in drug abuse or diversion of drugs for sale.

While only a pharmacist or intern can evaluate a prescription or verify its substantive contents, a pharmacy employee may, at the instruction of a pharmacist, contact a prescriber or his or her staff to verify non-clinical information such as the prescriber's fax or telephone number.

# Forgeries

**Dealing With a Possible Forgery.**  Any prescription, whether written, oral, or electronic, could be a forgery; that is, it could have been created, uttered, or passed without authority (§4324). There are some techniques the pharmacist can use to avoid filling forged prescriptions.

If the prescription is written, look for misspellings or errors, such as in the patient's name, common pharmaceutical words or abbreviations, or even in the prescriber's name.  Look for handwriting discrepancies from prior prescriptions from the same prescriber, and for amounts, strengths, or directions that make little or no sense.  Scrutinize controlled substance prescriptions especially carefully; prescriptions for other drugs are not as likely to be forged, although there is a market, domestically and overseas, for some common or expensive dangerous drugs.  When you find an inconsistency or irregularity, you might want to reject the prescription outright or at least contact the prescriber.

When you need to contact the prescriber about an irregular prescription, check the prescriber's telephone number in the telephone directory, a professional association list, or on the licensing board's website, because forgers often print telephone numbers on prescription blanks and then answer calls to assure pharmacists that their prescriptions are legitimate.

**How does a pharmacist know if a prescriber is legitimately registered with DEA?**

Forgers may use stolen prescription blanks, or they may print their own.[30]  When forgers create their own prescription forms, they may simply copy the information, including the prescriber's DEA number, from a legitimate prescriber's prescription.  But sometimes they make up the information, including the DEA number.  Sometimes a pharmacist can determine that the DEA number is not valid.  DEA uses a formula to create its numbers that can be applied to the number on the blank; if the DEA number does not fit the formula, it is invalid.

Prior to October 1, 1985, each prescriber's DEA number began with the letter "A."  After that date, DEA issued numbers beginning with the letter "B."  A mid-level practitioner's number begins with "M."  The second letter in the registration is the first letter of the registrant's last name; the seven-digit number that follows the two letters is computer-generated (DEA Pharmacist's Manual, p. 33).  If the letters are legitimate, and the numbers meet the test discussed below, that is a strong indication that the number is legitimate.  (That is no protection, of course, against a forger using copied information, or stolen prescription blanks.)  In case of uncertainty about the legitimacy and currency of the prescriber's registration, contact the DEA (see App. C: Other State and Federal Agencies).

To apply the DEA number formula, add the first, third, and fifth digits of the seven-digit DEA number.  Then add the second, fourth, and sixth digits and multiply that sum by two.  Then add the results of the two calculations.  If the last digit in this final calculation does not match the last digit in the DEA number, the DEA number is invalid.

---

[30]  The new controlled substance prescription forms are intended to make forgery difficult, but they cannot make it impossible.  A pharmacist should become familiar with the security features of the new forms, and then scrutinize forms received, particularly from unknown prescribers, to make sure they appear legitimate.

For example, take the DEA number AB2456941.

- First, add 2+5+9, to get 16.
- Second, add 4+6+4 to get 14, and multiply by 2 to get 28.
- Finally, add 16+28 to get 44.
- Compare the last digit of 44 (4) with the last digit of the DEA number (1). They do not match. The DEA number is invalid.

**If the last digit of this DEA number were a "4," would the DEA registration be valid?**

Not necessarily. Many people engaged in the forgery of controlled substance prescriptions are aware of this formula, and choose numbers that will not flunk this test. Also, forgers will often use a DEA number that once was valid, but is not at this time. There is no easy way to determine if a seemingly-valid DEA number is currently assigned to the prescriber whose name is on the prescription; contact with DEA is the only way to do so. If the DEA number does not fit the formula, it is invalid; if it does fit the formula, you still cannot be certain that it is valid.

**Reporting forgeries.** There is no specific legal obligation to report a forgery – that is, to contact the police to have the presenter of the forgery arrested. Depending on one's beliefs and attitudes towards drug abuse and diversion, there may be ethical considerations that suggest reporting certain forgeries is a moral obligation. An additional significant concern is personal safety. If you are sure the prescription is a forgery, it is likely that the person presenting it is involved in the illegal activity, even if he or she did not write the prescription. If the presenter is involved in diversion of drugs for sale, he or she is likely to leave your premises quickly after you refuse to fill the prescription. But if the presenter is a drug abuser or not filling the prescription would represent a substantial financial loss, he or she may be confrontational. If you intend to report the forgery, and wish to see the presenter arrested, you should make your report before you inform the presenter that you will not fill the prescription. And, of course, reporting a crime or refusing to fill the order is never worth risking your life. If you believe the "patient" is likely to confront you with a weapon, do what is necessary to get him or her to leave, including filling the order, and then call the police. Pharmacies will often have non-confrontation policies for you to follow. Pharmacies in high risk areas may even consider such security devices as silent alarms or security cameras.

**May you refuse to return the forgery to the presenter?**

Unless you are going to report the suspected forgery to the authorities, the prescription remains the property of the presenter and you probably have no legal basis to hold onto to it. At the same time, you would not want the presenter to bring the prescription from pharmacy to pharmacy until it gets filled. There appears to be no legal reason not to note on the prescription that it was received by your pharmacy and "rejected" or "not filled," or something similar, before returning it. Again, you must consider your own safety if, based on your observation and evaluation of the customer, you believe you may be at risk if you mark up or retain the prescription.

# Filling the Order

In general an order must be filled as written; a pharmacist may not deviate from the prescriber's order as received, unless the prescriber consents to the change or a substitution of a generic equivalent is authorized by law, as discussed below (§1716). The prescription must be filled in the form, strength, and amount specified in the order. The pharmacist must take care when dispensing, including when making a drug substitution, to avoid confusion among similar-sounding or similarly-spelled drug names (Dana Cassell, *JCAHO issues new look-alike, sound-alike drug list*,

DRUG TOPICS, Oct. 11, 2004; Charlie Hoppes, Carol Holquist, and Jerry Phillips, *FDA Safety Page: Generic name confusion*, DRUG TOPICS, Oct 6, 2003).

**Time limits.** Except for the six month limit for controlled substance prescriptions, discussed above, there is no specific limit on how long after the date of issue a prescription may be initially dispensed by a pharmacy. Obviously the pharmacist must consider how old the prescription is as well as other circumstances, including the purpose of the drug. For example, a prescription for a medication that has been prescribed previously for the patient, but is taken only as needed, may be of little concern if presented for filling a month or two, or even more, after the date of issue. In contrast, if a prescription for an ailment, injury, or condition that would ordinarily lead the patient to fill it right away is not presented until a month or two after its issuance, the pharmacist might wish to call the prescriber to confirm that he or she still wants the patient to take the drug. The longer the delay from issuance to presentation, regardless of the type of drug, the more the pharmacist should hesitate before dispensing it, at least without checking with the prescriber (see §1761(a)).

**Dosage limits.** Pharmacists are frequently told there is a federal or California limit on how many doses of a drug, particularly a controlled substance, may be ordered in any individual prescription. *There are no such limits under federal drug laws or California pharmacy law.*[31] There may be dosage limits imposed by pharmacy chains, insurers, or such government programs as Medicare or Medi-Cal, because of their economic concerns   But the lack of a dosage limit in pharmacy law does not mean the pharmacist should not question prescriptions of large amounts or amounts which, according to the directions for use, would last many months. There can be good reasons for prescriptions intended to last many months (for example, to supply patients with a chronic condition and a stable regimen or those traveling for an extended period) or for a very large number of dosages (for pain patients, for example, with a severe chronic condition). But the longer the time period the order would supply or the larger the amount, the more closely the pharmacist should look at the order. The pharmacist should contact the prescriber if the order seems irregular or otherwise questionable (§1761(a)), and exercise the pharmacist's corresponding responsibility where a controlled substance is involved (§1761(b), see Chap. XII: Practice Pitfalls).

**Partial filling.** Partial filling involves not filling the entire amount called for by a prescription at the time the order is presented. Partial filling may occur for a variety of reasons. The pharmacy may not have enough stock on hand to fill the entire order. There may be provider or insurer issues, or other restrictions against filling the entire amount called for in the prescription. The pharmacy may have a concern about filling the entire amount without checking with the prescriber, and the prescriber may not be available immediately. Or the patient may request that he or she not receive the entire amount at one time (perhaps because of the cost). Nothing in the Pharmacy Law bars such partial filling of a prescription for a dangerous drug. The pharmacy would, of course, need to note how much was dispensed, and when, to meet its record-keeping requirements (and each pharmacist who dispensed a part of the order should record his or her initials).

Under federal law, partial filling of a prescription for a Schedule II controlled substance is permitted if the pharmacist cannot supply the entire amount called for in either a written or emergency oral prescription. The pharmacist must note this action on the face of the order and notify the prescriber. The pharmacist may not dispense the remainder more than 72 hours after the initial partial filling (21 CFR §1306.13(a)). California's regulation on partial filling of Schedule II prescriptions is silent on the issue of the pharmacy's inability to supply the whole amount (§1745), but an amendment proposed by the Board in November 2004, implementing a statutory change, would align the rule with federal law (Proposed Regulations, www.pharmacy.ca.gov/laws_regs/regulations.htm).

---

[31] There are a few states that impose dosage limits as to some drugs, but California does not.

Both federal and state regulations permit partial filling of Schedule II prescriptions when the order is for a diagnosed and documented terminal illness or for a patient who is in a long-term care facility (21 CFR §1306.13(b), §1745). The prescription must be presented for initial filling within 14 days of its issuance, and the balance of the prescribed drugs must be dispensed within 30 days of the issuance of the prescription (§1745(c)(3)).[32] The type of patient, the date and amount of each partial fill, and the identity of the dispensing pharmacist must be recorded on the back of the original prescription and maintained in readily retrievable form. If the status of the patient is not recorded, the prescription will be deemed to have been filled illegally. As with all Schedule II prescriptions, the pharmacy will have to comply with CURES reporting.

*[handwritten margin note: CA State Federal allows up to 60 days]*

California law is also silent with respect to partial filling of any Schedule III, IV, or V prescription. Federal regulations specifically permit partial filling of these prescriptions if the subsequent partial fills are recorded in the same manner as refills, if the total quantity dispensed does not exceed the amount on the face of the original prescription, and if all such dispensing occurs within six months of the date of issue of the original prescription (21 CFR §1306.23). The pharmacist's corresponding responsibility to evaluate a prescription (see Chap. XII: Practice Pitfalls) applies to partial, as well as complete, filling of a prescription.

**Substitution.** A pharmacist may not deviate from the prescriber's order as received, except upon consent of the prescriber or in order to make a permitted drug substitution (§1716). There are now two types of permitted drug substitution.

Unless the prescriber has specified that there be no substitution, the pharmacist may substitute any drug if it is both of the same generic drug type with the same active chemical ingredients, strength, quantity, and dosage, and is less expensive than the prescribed drug (§4073). In other words, the pharmacist's authority to substitute a cheaper, equivalent generic drug is presumed. The fact of the substitution of a cost-saving drug product must be communicated to the patient, and the name of the dispensed drug product indicated on the prescription label, except where the prescriber orders otherwise (§4073(e)). When the pharmacist substitutes, the prescriber is not liable for the pharmacist's drug selection (§4073(c)).

Generic substitution, which for many years was outlawed, affords patients (and their health insurance companies) an opportunity for significant cost savings. Public policy favors substitution to contain health care costs. Manufacturers of name brand drug products often challenge the equivalency of generic substitutes and continue to seek ways to restrict when pharmacists may substitute.[33] As discussed in Chapter II: Drug Classifications, they will also strive to extend their patents (and, thus, exclusivity) as long as possible.

---

[32] Federal regulations allow 60 days for completion of the filling of the order (21 CFR §1306.13(b)), but the more restrictive California provision controls. The proposed amendment to the Board's regulation described above would allow the prescription to be presented up to 60 days after its issuance and would conform to federal regulations by allowing up to 60 days from issuance to complete the filling.

[33] In the absence of legal restrictions on substitution, manufacturers strive to protect the market share of their brand name drugs. In an extreme example of a manufacturer attempting to protect market share, Boots Pharmaceuticals, then-manufacturer of Synthroid®, refused to allow researchers at the University of California, San Francisco, to publish the results of their investigation of whether generic levothyroxine was clinically equivalent to Boots' drug. The contract by which Boots had sponsored the research required consent before publication of the study results (Ralph King, Jr., *Bitter Pill: How a Drug Firm Paid for University Study, Then Undermined It; Research on Thyroid Tablets Found Cheap Ones Were Just as Good as Sponsor's; Article Pulled at Last Minute*, WALL STREET JOURNAL, Apr. 25, 1996, p. A1). Ultimately the company relented, and the research finding that there was no clinical difference between the generic and branded versions of the drugs was published in the Journal of the American Medical Association in April 1997 (Lawrence K. Altman, *Drug Firm, Relenting, Allows Unflattering Study to Appear*, NEW YORK TIMES, Apr. 16, 1997, p. A1). This incident led to a $98 million settlement of 53 class action lawsuits filed by patients in the United States alleging deceptive practices by the company; similar suits have been filed in recent years with respect to similar situations.

Pharmacists also have the authority to make another kind of substitution. They may now "select a different form of medication with the same active chemical ingredients of equivalent strength and duration of therapy as the prescribed drug product when the change will improve the ability of the patient to comply with the prescribed drug therapy" (§4052.5(a)). Thus the pharmacist may substitute a capsule for a tablet, or a flavored liquid for an unflavored one. Substitution may not be made between long-acting and short-acting forms of a medication with the same chemical ingredients, or between one drug product and two or more with the same chemical ingredients (§4052.5(f)). As with generic substitution, the selection may not be made by the pharmacist if the prescriber indicates, orally or in handwriting, "Do not substitute," or words of similar meaning. The prescriber may also check a "do not substitute" box on the prescription if he or she personally initials the box (§4052.5(b)). The pharmacist making a substitution under this authority must communicate the use of the different form of the drug to the patient and indicate the name of the dispensed drug product on the prescription label, unless the prescriber orders otherwise (§4052.5(e)).

In exercising discretion in this fashion, the pharmacist assumes the same responsibility as would be incurred in filling the prescription with the prescribed form of medication. The prescriber is subject to no liability for the pharmacist's act or omission under this authority (§4052.5(c)). This type of substitution may be made with respect to prescriptions for patients covered by federal and state medical assistance programs (§4052.5(d)).

In another development related to substitution, manufacturers have offered incentives to pharmacists (or prescribers) to use their product – not an equivalent substitute, but a different product – for a particular condition. The manufacturers want the pharmacist or the pharmacy (sometimes through its central office) to call the prescriber, or even the patient, and suggest that this manufacturer's product be used.[34] Even when the manufacturer owns the pharmacy, or the manufacturer and the pharmacy are under common ownership, offering an incentive for the pharmacy to take such action appears to be an illegal referral or rebate under Business and Professions Code sections 650 to 657 (see Chap. XII: Practice Pitfalls and Chap. XIV: Other Relevant Law). This conclusion would appear to apply to the same offer by a third-party payor owned by the manufacturer or that owns the pharmacy. There are also privacy issues involved in obtaining and using personal health information to induce a patient to switch drugs (see Chap. XIV: Other Relevant Law ("Protecting the Patient's Right to Privacy")).

What remains to be clarified is the situation where a third-party payor is owned by a manufacturer and limits covered drugs for particular conditions to those that "happen" to be made and marketed by that manufacturer. If a pharmacist changes the prescribed drug, or asks the prescriber to change the prescribed drug, under those circumstances, it seems to be unprofessional conduct, because the pharmacist is making the choice of drug for a reason other than the best interest of the patient. In addition, calls to suggest changes in a patient's prescription might well involve a breach of confidentiality, through improper disclosure of patient information, disclosure to an inappropriate person, or misuse of information for purposes beyond the scope of the authority under which that information was obtained (Civ. Code §56.10(c)).

**May a pharmacist substitute a brand name drug when a generic is prescribed, at the request of the patient?** Yes.

When a prescription is written giving the generic name of a drug, the pharmacist is required to select one manufacturer or another's version of that drug. Even after generic competition exists for the original brand of a drug, the original tends to remain more expensive. If the patient wants the brand name version, that is what the pharmacist should dispense, with an explanation that it is more

---

[34] "Substitution" of a different product is not legally substitution at all, but requires the issuance of a new prescription.

expensive (and sometimes not covered under insurance plans). The pharmacist must, of course, keep a record of the particular brand dispensed and might be wise to document why the more expensive, brand name drug was dispensed.

**Placebos.** Pharmacists may receive requests by a prescriber to fill a prescription for a particular drug with a placebo, or to label a container as if it contained something other than its actual contents. Physicians occasionally have important medical reasons to order a placebo for a patient. For example, a physician may believe that a patient's symptoms are psychosomatic and so prescribe a placebo to relieve the patient's anxiety about not receiving treatment for the imagined condition. Or a patient may be psychologically addicted to a drug, such as an anti-anxiety drug or sleeping pill, the continued use of which would do the patient harm; the physician may wish to terminate or gradually decrease the dose of the drug without the patient realizing he or she is no longer receiving it. Or the physician for other reasons may wish to give a drug different from the one the patient believes he or she is receiving. And, of course, in a controlled clinical experiment the contents and labels of the drugs given to the group receiving the test drug and those serving as controls must be identical.

Section 4078(a) prohibits dispensing a prescription container with, or placing on a prescription, a "false or misleading" label; however, "false" labels are legal when directed by the prescriber as a necessary part of a clinical or investigational drug program or project approved by the FDA or when, in the professional opinion of the prescriber, such a label is appropriate for the proper treatment of the patient (§4078(b)). The furnisher of the placebo drug must make, and retain for three years, a record stating how the label differs from the actual contents and documenting the prescriber's order to "falsely" label the prescription. The prescriber must also make and retain a record of his or her order to so label the prescription.

**What should the pharmacist say when he or she is required to provide consultation, or the patient requests consultation, about a prescription that has been falsely labeled at the prescriber's direction?**

This is a conundrum beyond the conundrum of the placebo label itself. If the pharmacist provides consultation based on the drug the patient *believes* he or she is getting, the consultation is false; if the pharmacist provides consultation based on the drug the patient actually *is* getting, the prescriber's intent is defeated. Discretion suggests that in such a case the pharmacist should "duck" by providing the minimally-necessary consultation – directions for use and storage, the importance of compliance with directions, precautions and relevant warnings (§1707.2(c)) – and suggesting the patient contact the prescriber if he or she has any further questions.

**What price should the pharmacist charge for a placebo prescription?**

Pricing presents yet another problem. If the pharmacist charges for the labeled contents, rather than for the actual contents (the placebo would generally be much less expensive), he or she is committing fraud, either on a third party payor or on the patient. But if the pharmacist fails to charge for what is labeled, particularly when the patient has previously purchased this medication and is being weaned from it, it may well undermine the purpose of prescribing the placebo. This is likely to be a problem only with respect to treatment use of a placebo; in clinical trials the trial sponsor is probably paying for the drugs. If to charge the "true" price of the placebo would jeopardize the patient's treatment, the pharmacist should charge the price for the drug the patient believes he or she has received. If so, the pharmacist should document the reason for that charge, as protection from a later allegation of fraud. If there is a third-party payor involved, the pharmacist should ask for its advice on how to make it appear that the price was at the level of the real drug, while arranging to collect only the price of the placebo.

# Preparation of the Prescription

In general, the drug to be dispensed must be selected carefully and accurately from unexpired stock that meets quality standards (including proper storage and maintenance) and is packaged and labeled properly. The pharmacist, intern, technician, or technician trainee who removes drugs or drug components from stock (and no one else may do so) must handle them so as to preserve their identity and purity until the time of dispensing. Failure to do so may lead to an adulterated or misbranded product, the dispensing of which is both a violation of specific statutes and regulations and unprofessional conduct.

Only a pharmacist, or an intern, technician, or technician trainee acting under a pharmacist's supervision, may prepare the drug in the form in which it will be dispensed. As indicated in Chapter IV: Licensing Pharmacies, some prescription drugs must be prepared and dispensed in compliance with special rules. Radiopharmaceuticals, parenteral drugs, injectable sterile drugs, and dialysis supplies all fall into that category.

# Prescription Containers

A prescription container must be new and conform with standards established in the official compendia. However, a pharmacist may dispense and refill a prescription for nonliquid products in a clean, multiple-drug patient medication package or patient medi-pak if:

- it is reused only for the same patient,
- no more than a one-month's supply is dispensed at a time, and
- each patient medi-pak has an auxiliary label reading, "Store in a cool, dry place" (§1717(a)).

Under the provisions of the federal Poison Prevention Packaging Act of 1970 (15 USC §§1471-1476), a child-resistant container must be used for all prescription drugs in oral dosage forms (15 USC §§1471(2)(B), 1472; 16 CFR §§1700.1(b)(3), 1701.1), unless the prescriber specifically directs otherwise or the patient specifically requests that a child-resistant container not be used (15 USC §1473, 16 CFR §1701.1(d)). The required child-resistant packaging means packaging designed or constructed to be significantly difficult for a child under the age of five to open or to obtain a toxic or harmful amount of the substance from within a reasonable time. Normal adults should be able to use the container properly without difficulty (15 USC §1471(4), 16 CFR §1700.1(b)(4)).[35]

A manufacturer may distribute drugs to pharmacies in ordinary packaging unless the drugs are intended to be distributed to the ultimate consumer in that packaging (16 CFR §1701.1(b)). Prescriptions may be dispensed in unit dose packaging for patients in skilled nursing, intermediate care, or other health care facilities (§4076(b)).

# The Prescription Label

The label on the prescription container must include either the trade or generic name of the drug and the manufacturer's name, except where the prescriber orders otherwise. Commonly used

---

[35] Special child-resistant packaging also is required for a number of nonprescription drugs (such as aspirin), particularly in oral dosage forms (16 CFR §1700.14(a)). The manufacturer or distributor may offer one size of the product in nonconforming packaging for the benefit of the elderly or handicapped, as long as the product also is offered in conforming packages and the nonconforming packaging is conspicuously labeled, "This package for households without young children" (15 USC §1473(a)(2)) or, if the package is too small for such a label, "Package Not Child-Resistant" (16 CFR §1700.5(b)). California has parallel provisions (H&SC §§108675-108700, 108750-108755).

abbreviations are acceptable and preparations containing two or more active ingredients may be identified by the manufacturer's trade name, the commonly used name, or the principal active ingredients (§4076(a)).

The label must include adequate directions for use of the drug, the name of the patient, the name of the prescriber, the date of issue, the name and address of the furnisher and a prescription number or other means of identifying the prescription, the strength and quantity of the drug, and the expiration date of the effectiveness of the drug if the manufacturer is required to place that information on the original label (§4076(a), H&SC §111480). The condition for which the drug is prescribed must be included if the patient requests it and it is indicated on the prescription (§4076(a)(10)). The label also must contain any required warnings (§4074(a)-(b)).

If a pharmacy technician participates in the preparation of a prescription, the pharmacist must indicate he or she has verified the prescription before it is dispensed to the patient by initialing the prescription container label (§1793.7(a); the pharmacist need not initial the label for prescriptions for hospital inpatients or inmates of correctional facilities).[36]

Effective in 2006, prescription drug labels for outpatients will have to include a physical description of the medication, including color, shape and any identification code that appears on the drug. There are exemptions for drugs dispensed by veterinarians, for all new drugs for their first 120 days on the market (and 90 days where the national reference file for such drugs has no description available), and for medications for which no commercially available data base contains a physical description (§4076(a)(11)). If the Board adopts regulations covering this subject before January 1, 2006, these requirements will not go into effect (§4076(a)(11)(D)), but it has not issued any proposal at this time.[37]

If the prescription is for a patient of a skilled nursing facility, intermediate care facility, or other health care facility that uses a unit dose medication system, the labeling requirements of section 4076 are considered satisfied if the unit dose medication system contains the required information or if the information otherwise is readily retrievable at the time of the administration of the drug. Prescription devices are exempt from the labeling requirements of section 4076 when provided to patients in skilled nursing facilities or intermediate care facilities (§4077(c)).

The label on Schedule II, III, and IV controlled substance prescriptions must contain a caution that it is illegal to transfer the drug to any person other than the person for whom it was prescribed (21 CFR §§290.5, 290.6 (Spanish language transfer caution)). It is also illegal to transfer all other dangerous drugs to a person other than the one for whom it was prescribed, but regulators apparently deemed such transfers not to require the same warning on the label.

**A pharmacy offers to prepare prescriptions for specialized drugs for a pharmacy that receives such orders but is not equipped or does not wish to prepare them. May the pharmacies agree to such an arrangement? Which pharmacy's name goes on the prescription label?**

*Yes. dispensing pharmacy ± preparing pharmacy*

[36] A proposed regulation pending in December 2004 would allow a pharmacist to comply with the initialing requirement through an electronic entry in a computer system by secure means, provided that the computer will not allow alteration of the information and that the record can be retrieved immediately in the pharmacy (proposed §1712).

[37] The purpose of requiring identification information on the prescription label is to reduce medication errors. For the same purpose, FDA is requiring bar codes on drug and blood products for inpatient use (*Bar Code Label Requirement for Human Drug Products and Biological Products* (69 FR 9120 (Feb. 26, 2004)). Experiments with bar code technology in institutional settings have produced dramatically-reduced rates of medication errors, saving lives as well as money (Howard Wolinsky, *Bar codes, chips joined to stem surgical errors*, CHICAGO SUN-TIMES, Nov. 23, 2004, p. 57; Victoria Colliver, *Hospital of the future; High-tech system helps improve quality of care,* SAN FRANCISCO CHRONICLE, Feb. 23, 2004. It is likely that this technology will be widely-adopted, even mandated, including in the retail setting.

Such an arrangement seems comparable to the concept of "refill" and central fill pharmacies (see Chap. IV: Licensing Pharmacies). It would appear to be logical to allow a pharmacy to arrange for a better-equipped, or more experienced, pharmacy to prepare a specialized order, without transferring the prescription, so the patient can both obtain the specialized medication and retain his or her choice of pharmacies. There appears to be no legal barrier to such an arrangement. The preparing pharmacy is acting as an agent for the pharmacy that actually dispenses the prescription to the patient, which will be legally responsible for its agent's work. At least the name and address of the pharmacy dispensing to the patient must be on the label; the other pharmacy's name and address may be on the label as well. The patient should be provided written information with the prescription that describes which pharmacy to contact with questions or in case of emergency.

# Before Dispensing

A prescription that has been packaged and labeled is not yet ready for dispensing. As Chapter X: The Prescription Process: Dispensing and Beyond outlines, the pharmacist must engage in additional evaluation, checking, and patient education activities. Patient profiles are addressed in Chapter X, but the pharmacist may well have consulted the profile in the original evaluation of the prescription – and may do so again prior to dispensing. Patient consultation must be provided where mandated or sought. And at least at the end of the process (and perhaps at multiple points in the process), the pharmacist must check the accuracy of the work of ancillary personnel, including interns, technicians, technician trainees, and clerk-typists who have participated in the prescription-filling process.

---

**What you should think about after reading this chapter:**

1. What kind of information might you wish to obtain about a new patient? About a prescriber who is not familiar to you?

2. Suppose a prescription is not complete. How do you obtain the needed information? What if the prescriber is unavailable or uncooperative?

3. Why do we restrict the circumstances when nonphysicians may prescribe, furnish, or transmit an order for drugs?

4. Why do we have close state monitoring of Schedule II and III prescriptions?

5. What are the benefits and risks of drug substitution for the patient? For the pharmacy?

6. What legal, professional, or practical difficulties may dispensing a placebo pose for a pharmacist?

---

# The Prescription Process: Dispensing and Beyond

**What you should know after reading this chapter:**

1. To whom and where may a filled prescription be delivered?

2. What information should be in a patient profile?  How does the pharmacy obtain that information?

3. When is patient consultation required in California?  What information is required to be provided to the patient?  What other information should the pharmacist provide?

4. With whom may a pharmacist share information about patients?  For what purposes?

5. Who may physically dispense a prescription?

6. Under what circumstances may a pharmacist refill a prescription?

7. When may a pharmacist provide drugs for a patient in an emergency?

8. When and how may a prescription be transferred?

9. When may prescription data be maintained in a common electronic file?

10. What restrictions, if any, are there on the price a pharmacy may charge for a prescription?

## Before Dispensing

Between the time a prescription arrives in the pharmacy and the completed order is prepared for dispensing, it has likely been handled not only by a pharmacist, but by one or more ancillary personnel in the pharmacy, such as interns, technicians, technician trainees, and clerk-typists.  These non-pharmacist employees play significant roles in the preparation of prescription orders, but their work is subject to the supervision of the pharmacist.  Even if the pharmacist has engaged in close supervision of these employees, and trusts the accuracy of their work, the pharmacist must do a final check to assure that the order is accurately prepared.  And even if a pharmacist has personally handled each step in the prescription-filling process (an increasingly rare situation), prudence dictates that the pharmacist check the final prescription to protect against his or her own errors.  That check should comprise comparing the prescription against the container, the label, and the contents.

This final check and written verification is required by law if a technician or technician trainee has been involved in preparation of the prescription (§4115.5(b)(3) (technician trainee), §1793.7(b) (technician), see Chap. III: Licensing Pharmacists).  While the Pharmacy Law does not expressly require such a final check on each prescription that an intern prepared or helped to prepare, the fact that the supervising pharmacist is absolutely responsible for the accuracy of prescriptions prepared by an intern suggests the wisdom of this procedure.

Even after this physical check, the pharmacist has responsibilities with respect to review and, if necessary, updating of the patient profile and the provision of consultation, as discussed below.

# Patient Profiles

A pharmacy is required to keep patient profiles (or patient medication records) for all current patients. The profile, which may be maintained either manually or electronically as long as the information is readily retrievable during the pharmacy's normal operating hours, must include the patient's name, address, telephone number, birth date or age, and gender. As to each prescription dispensed, it must include the details of the prescription, identification of the prescriber including the DEA number if relevant, the date of dispensing or refill, and the prescription number and any other information required by section 1717 (§1707.1).

Section 1717(b) requires the profile to include the brand name of the drug dispensed (generic name if it is generic), the distributor's name, the name or initials of the dispensing pharmacist (and the supervising pharmacist's initials if the prescription was filled by an intern), and quantity and initials for any refill. The profile also must contain relevant patient drug history and information related to drug use (including allergies) or other information communicated by the patient or that the pharmacist deems appropriate.[1] The record must be retained for one year after the date the last prescription was filled, except when the pharmacist reasonably believes the patient will not continue to obtain prescription medications at that pharmacy (§1707.1). The most important requirement is that the pharmacist must review a patient's drug therapy and patient profile before each prescription drug is dispensed (§1707.3). Federal regulations, which apply to prescriptions for Medicaid (called Medi-Cal in California), impose the same requirements for patient profiles (42 CFR §456.705(d)).

Increasingly, pharmacies depend on computer software to alert personnel to problems that might be posed by a patient's new prescription, either because of a patient's known medical conditions or the potential for adverse medication interactions. While an effective computer program is a useful aid, the Board's regulations require that the pharmacist review the patient's drug therapy and patient profile and determine its import for any prescription being filled. The pharmacist must actually review the patient's profile information. In the case of an adverse medication interaction, the pharmacist cannot escape responsibility by asserting reliance on the computer to "red flag" any possible problems. It is also the pharmacist's clear responsibility to make reasonable efforts to obtain and update, as warranted, adequate, useful information to place in the profile; otherwise the requirement is of limited public health value. Patient profiles, like all patient information in the pharmacy, are subject to privacy rights and confidentiality protections, discussed below.

# Patient Consultation

Because of the importance of patients receiving information about medications, the requirement of mandatory patient consultation is taken quite seriously by the California Board (§1707.2). California was a leader in requiring consultation, which is now a condition for the state's

---

[1] Increasingly pharmacies are asking patients for information on their use of OTC drugs and herbals, to include on their profiles, because of heightened awareness about their interaction with prescription drugs (*Why Your Pharmacist Wants to Know About Your Herbs*, THE WASHINGTON POST, May 1, 2001, p. T06).

participation in the Medicaid program (42 CFR §456.705(c)).  This requirement recognizes the special competence of pharmacists to provide drug information and the paucity of medication information often provided by prescribers.[2]

Of course, California pharmacists have been required for years to use professional judgment when dispensing drugs and devices to provide patients with appropriate information or warnings and cautions (§4074, discussed below), and to answer patient questions and ask needed questions of patients.  In most states, in the absence of a specific requirement, the pharmacist has not been required to do more than describe the drug and directions for use and relevant precautions and warnings.[3]  In California, as in an increasing number of states, consultation is now mandatory:

- when the patient or patient's agent requests it (§1707.2(a)(1));
- when the pharmacist, in his or her professional judgment, believes it is warranted (§1707.2(a)(2)); and
- whenever the prescription is for outpatient use, is a drug not previously dispensed to the patient or one with a new dosage form or strength or new directions for use, and the patient or patient's agent is present when the prescription is dispensed (§1707.2(b)).

An increasing number of pharmacies are providing written material describing the drug and its major possible consequences as a regular supplement to patient consultation.  Written material is valuable to patients, but it is not a legal substitute for required oral, face-to-face consultation.[4]

Consultation is not required for an inpatient of a health care facility licensed under section 1250 of the Health and Safety Code (see App. B: Definitions of Various Health Facilities) or for

---

[2]  Computer technology may reverse the declining role of physicians in providing medication information.  Drug manufacturers and wireless pocket device makers have been collaborating in efforts to convince prescribers to use the devices to access drug product databases, including interaction information, online.  In 2001, the three largest pharmacy benefit manufacturers created an electronic exchange through which physicians could use electronic prescribing technology to link to pharmacies, PBMs, and patient health plans (see www.rxhub.net).  Improved use of patient-specific information and the provision of more information to patients are two pieces of a bigger package of benefits (particularly improved accuracy in prescription transmission) that are considered likely from electronic prescribing (see, e.g., *Electronic Prescribing: Towards Maximum Value and Rapid Adoption,* eHealth Initiative, April 2004 (posted at www.ehealthinitiative.org/initiatives/erx/).

[3]  The courts in most states have not held pharmacists liable for negligence (malpractice) for failure to provide consultation as to the proper use and storage of drugs, but as the pharmacy profession has taken on the responsibility to provide information, or had it imposed by law, the responsibility to do so accurately is certain to follow.  Now that consultation is mandatory in California, the California courts are considerably more likely than in the past to hold pharmacists liable if their failure to properly fulfill the consultation requirement causes or contributes to patient harm (see, e.g., Lauren Fleischer, *Note: From Pill-Counting to Patient Care: Pharmacists' Standard of Care in Negligence Law,* 68 FORDHAM L. REV. 165 (1999)).

[4]  Requiring written patient information for prescription drugs has been an issue on the federal level for many years.  In the 1980s FDA adopted, and then withdrew, regulations mandating patient package inserts for prescription drugs.  FDA proposed regulations in 1995 setting performance standards defining acceptable levels of information distribution and quality for prescription drug products.  Congress passed a law in 1996 mandating that the private sector be given the opportunity to meet distribution and quality goals for useful patient information.  Currently the goal is for 95 percent of prescriptions to be accompanied by useful patient information by 2006 (*Status of Useful Written Prescription Information for Patients; Public Meeting,* 65 FR 7022 (Feb. 11, 2000)).  In a study conducted in 2001, FDA found the average "usefulness" of the information disseminated was only about 50% (*Current Status of Useful Written Prescription Drug Information for Consumers: Public Meeting,* 68 FR 33724 (June 5, 2003)).  FDA does have authority to mandate patient labeling for a particular drug when it determines that such labeling could prevent serious adverse effects, or the drug has serious risks relative to benefits of which patients should be made aware, or when the drug is important to health and patient adherence to directions for use is crucial to the drug's effectiveness (21 CFR §208.1(c)).

inmates of correctional or juvenile facilities, except upon the patient's discharge (§1707.2(b)(3)). When a patient is discharged from a health care facility licensed under section 1250, consultation by a pharmacist is not required for discharge medication as long as the same type of information is provided to the patient by a registered nurse or a physician (§4074(d), §1707.2(b)(3)).

When consultation is provided, it must include at least directions for use and storage, the importance of compliance with directions, and precautions and relevant warnings, including common severe side or adverse effects or interactions that may be encountered (§1707.2(c)). When the pharmacist deems it warranted, oral consultation also shall include:

- the name and description of the medication;
- the route of administration, dosage form, dosage, and duration of drug therapy;
- any special directions for use and storage;
- precautions for preparation and administration by the patient, including techniques for self-monitoring drug therapy;
- prescription refill information;
- therapeutic contraindications, avoidance of common severe side or adverse effects or known interactions, including serious potential interactions with known nonprescription medications . . . and the action required if such side or adverse effects or interactions or therapeutic contraindications are present or occur; and
- action to be taken in the event of a missed dose (§1707.2(d)).

Section 4074(a) requires oral or written notice from the pharmacist to the patient of harmful effects of a prescribed drug that poses a substantial risk when taken in combination with alcohol or if the drug impairs the ability to drive a motor vehicle. By regulation the Board has determined that the following classes of drugs may impair a person's ability to drive a motor vehicle or operate machinery when taken alone or in combination with alcohol:

- muscle relaxants;
- analgesics with central nervous system depressant effects;
- antipsychotic drugs including phenothiazines;
- antidepressants;
- antihistamines, motion sickness agents, antipruritics, antinauseants, anticonvulsants, and antihypertensive agents with CNS depressant effects;
- all Schedule II, III, IV, and V depressant or narcotic controlled substances as set forth in Health and Safety Code at sections 11055-11058, prescribed in doses which could have an adverse effect on a person's ability to operate a motor vehicle; and
- anticholinergic agents and other drugs which may impair vision (§1744(a)).

Know

The Board also has listed drugs that may have harmful effects when taken in combination with alcohol, although they may or may not affect the person's ability to operate a motor vehicle. They are:

- disulfiram and other drugs (for example, chlorpropamide, metronidazole) which may cause a disulfiram-like reaction,
- monoamine oxidase inhibitors, and
- nitrates (§1744(b)).

The consultation requirement of section 4074 does not apply to drugs furnished to patients in conjunction with treatment or emergency services provided in a health care facility, provided that the facility has a written policy to ensure each patient receives information regarding each medication given on discharge (§4074(c),(d)). only RN, prescriber, and RPh can do counseling

Concern has been raised recently that prescribers and pharmacists are failing to provide adequate consultation to patients about so-called "black box" drugs. About 450 approved drugs have such a high risk of significant side effects that FDA has required them to include this information in a black-boxed warning. Failure to exercise special care in providing consultation for these drugs is almost certainly a violation of the consultation regulation. Evidence demonstrates that the warnings, by themselves, do not adequately inform consumers (Fred Gebhart, *Black box warnings: How well do they work?* DRUG TOPICS, Apr. 19, 2004).

**When a drug carries a black box warning, what impact should it have on the patient consultation? What if there are additional FDA requirements for dispensing the drug?**

If a drug carries a black box warning, the pharmacist should be aware of the issue covered by the warning and address it with the patient during consultation. (Certainly the prescriber should have addressed the issue, but he or she might not have done so, or the patient might not adequately have understood the information.) If there are additional FDA requirements for prescribing and dispensing the drug (such as the signed consent form and medication guide required for isotretinoin (Accutane®) and under consideration for antidepressants when prescribed for children), the pharmacist must be familiar with those requirements and the pharmacy's role in implementing them. The pharmacist should be particularly alert to the understanding of the patient (and, if the patient is a minor, the patient's parent or guardian) about the issues that have given rise to these additional requirements.

The pharmacy profession has registered concern that it does not get paid for the service of providing consultation. Nothing in the law either prevents or requires such fees. The consultation that is required by law in dispensing prescriptions is part of the cost of filling prescriptions; price competition, and reimbursement limits by third-party payors, obviously limit what pharmacies are able to charge.

Only pharmacists who work in nursing homes have commonly been paid for the service of consulting. However, about 500 pharmacists nationwide counsel patients for a fee, generally styling themselves as "independent pharmacy consultants." Most of those consultants only earn part of their living from this service (Elizabeth Agnvall, *The Druggist Is In; A New Type of Pharmacist Seeks to Help People Manage Complex Drug Regimens. The Catch: Someone Has to Pay*, WASHINGTON POST, Dec. 14, 2004, p. F01). Pharmacy consultants may play a role in the new Medicare prescription benefit, which will require insurers that provide Medicare drug plans to offer a medication consulting service for patients whose conditions and drug needs meet certain thresholds. Insurers favor meeting the requirement by making a pharmacist available at a toll-free number to answer questions; retail pharmacies would prefer to provide this consultation (Marc Levy, *Drugstores test adding on-site consultations*, CONTRA COSTA TIMES, Oct. 3, 2004, p.4).

Nonresident pharmacies (see Chap. IV: Licensing Pharmacies) must maintain a toll-free telephone service to facilitate communication between patients in California and a pharmacist at the pharmacy with access to the patient's records. The toll-free number must be disclosed on a label affixed to each prescription container delivered in California (§4112(f)). Whenever a pharmacy, whether in-state or nonresident, delivers or ships a prescription to the patient, it must ensure that the patient receives written notice of his or her right to request consultation and the telephone number to call to receive consultation from a pharmacist who has ready access to the patient's records (§4112(g), §1707.2(b)(2)).

As also noted in Chapter IV: Licensing Pharmacies, the Board has been authorized to pass additional consultation regulations governing mail-order pharmacies, as long as they are the same for both in-state and nonresident pharmacies and do not unnecessarily delay medication reaching the patient (§4112(g)).  When the Board proposed strengthened consultation requirements for mailed or shipped prescriptions, strong opposition from the affected pharmacies blocked their adoption.

While the Board's consultation regulation does not specify that the pharmacist must be the one who offers the opportunity for consultation to a patient, the Board takes the position that where section 1707.2 requires that the pharmacist provide consultation, the purpose of the requirement is defeated if the patient is or may be dissuaded from consultation by the actions of a nonlicensee, such as a technician or a clerk (§§1707.2, 1793.1(b)).

**Suppose a patient is picking up several new prescriptions.  You offer consultation, mentioning that there are important cautions in regard to these particular medications.  The patient refuses.  What should you do?**

A patient has the right to refuse consultation.  When consultation is offered and refused, the pharmacist is not required to document in writing the patient's refusal to receive the consultation.  However, it would be wise for the pharmacist to make such a notation as protection against a later claim of injury from the drug caused by a failure to provide consultation, particularly if the pharmacist believes there was a specific need for the patient to receive information about the drug.  The pharmacist should consider it his or her ethical obligation to educate the patient about the importance of receiving consultation and should encourage the patient to take the time to hear about the drug.

**Suppose the patient picking up a new prescription, to whom you offer consultation, clearly does not understand English.  Do you have an obligation to provide consultation in another language?**

It obviously is beyond the expectation of the law that a pharmacist must be able to communicate other than in English.  However, if the pharmacy advertises its services other than in English (in foreign language newspapers or even by signs indicating that another language is spoken in the pharmacy), thus suggesting its services are accessible to those who are more fluent in or understand only that language, it should be prepared to make consultation available in that language.[5] If a nonpharmacist must translate, the patient must agree to that person's access to private prescription or other medical information that might be revealed during consultation.  If the pharmacy provides written information to patients, it should consider its responsibility to have this information available as well in the languages to whose speakers the pharmacy promotes its services.

# Who May Dispense?

The term "dispense" is used in several different ways in the law (see Chap. IV: Licensing Pharmacies).  It is used to refer to the prescriber giving his or her patient medication for home use (§4024(b)).  It is used to refer to the steps in the dispensing process (receiving the prescription, reading and interpreting the prescription, selecting or preparing the drug, placing the finished product in the container to be furnished to the patient, labeling the prescription, giving the prescription to the patient, and, possibly, consulting with the patient).  It also is used to mean the act of the pharmacist providing

---

[5]  The California Supreme Court has held that because state and federal law require drug warnings only in English, a manufacturer was not liable for harm from failing to label a nonprescription drug, baby aspirin, with a warning concerning Reye's syndrome, other than in English (*Ramirez v. Plough*, 6 Cal. 4th 539 (1993)).  The Court was concerned, among other things, with uniformity nationwide and the vast number of languages spoken in the United States.  The situation of an individual pharmacy that encourages trade from customers by signs or advertisements indicating they can receive assistance in their native language is easily distinguishable.

the drug to the patient pursuant to a prescription (§4024(a)).  It also refers to a physician or other authorized prescriber who dispenses to a patient from his or her office or clinic (§4024(b)).[6]

Section 4051(a) states that only a pharmacist may dispense a dangerous drug or controlled substance.  Whether for a walk-in patient or patient's agent or a patient in an acute care hospital, whether the prescription is mailed or shipped, the pharmacist must do the dispensing.  This means that the pharmacist *must* check the final package, including both the contents and the label, against the original order, to make sure the contents, packaging, and labeling are all correct and in conformity with federal and state law.  It does not mean an intern, technician, or technician trainee is barred from undertaking steps of the dispensing process under appropriate supervision.

No nonpharmacist, and thus no technician, may dispense; an intern pharmacist, acting under the supervision of a pharmacist, may dispense (§1727(e)).  So, regardless of who receives the initial order, or in what form, or who takes down the stock bottle or the components and prepares the individual order and the label, the pharmacist, or an intern supervised by the pharmacist, must make the initial evaluation of the prescription and check the final product.  Of course the pharmacist also must oversee the functions performed by any technician or by any clerk typing labels.

# To Whom May the Prescription Be Delivered? 1717(e)

The prescription may be dispensed to the patient, or to the patient's authorized agent or representative (including an employee of a facility where the customer is a patient or a resident).[7]  There is no requirement that a prescription be delivered to an adult.  A minor certainly may pick up his or her own prescriptions; the minor's parents may not be aware that their child is receiving the treatment (for example, contraception or medicine for a sexually-transmitted disease).  A minor who is authorized to do so may also pick up a prescription for someone else.

As of 2004, when a Medi-Cal provider dispenses or furnishes prescription drugs or devices to a beneficiary it must maintain a record of the signature of the person who receives the drug or device.  If the drug or device is picked up or delivered to someone other than the beneficiary, the provider must also maintain a record on which the name of the beneficiary is printed, along with the recipient's relationship to the beneficiary, the date the prescription was signed for, and a prescription number or a description of the item or items dispensed (Welf. & Inst. Code §14043.341).  This provision is intended to help limit Medi-Cal fraud.

Effective consultation could be an issue if a person's prescription is picked up by a minor or by someone who appears unable either to fully understand the consultation or its purpose or to communicate information fully or accurately.  The same difficulty arises when a prescription is picked up (for himself or herself or for another person) by someone who is not proficient in English.  In these situations, written information would be particularly useful.

Previously the Board prohibited what it called "depoting": the leaving of filled prescriptions at a prescriber's office or elsewhere for the patient to pick up.  Board regulations now allow delivery of

---

[6]  A physician, dentist, podiatrist, optometrist, or veterinarian may dispense dangerous drugs, in accordance with sections 4170 to 4175 (see Chap. IV: Licensing Pharmacies).  A pharmacy may provide drugs to the prescriber for his or her office use without a prescription (see Chap. VIII: Preparation of Drugs).

[7]  When a prescription for a controlled substance has been transmitted to a pharmacy by an oral or electronic order, the pharmacy may not furnish the filled order to any person unknown to the pharmacy unless that person satisfactorily establishes his or her identity (§4075).

filled prescriptions to a hospital, institution, medical office, or clinic at which the patient receives health care, even if the patient is not present at the time the prescription is delivered (§1717(e)). "Depoting" remains illegal unless the person for whom the drugs were prescribed receives treatment at the location where the filled prescriptions were left for pickup. So if the wife is a clinic patient and her husband is not, her prescriptions, but not his, could legally be left at the clinic. And the ban on depoting applies to all settings other than those specified in the regulation.

**A patient brings in prescriptions for herself, her husband, and both of her minor children. She can't wait for you to fill them, and asks if you can deliver them to the office listed on her prescription, in this case her doctor's office. After she leaves, you notice that the prescriptions for her husband and children are written by doctors who are not at the office where she wants the prescriptions left. Can you still leave them all there for her to pick up later?**

Under section 1717(e) this would constitute illegal depoting. The Board can waive the depoting restrictions upon formal request. While obviously a request would not make sense for a single occasion, if many of your patients receive their health care at, for example, a maternal and child health clinic, and often bring prescriptions for other adults in their families with their own, a waiver request to allow prescriptions to be left for them at this clinic might make sense.

**Suppose a man comes to the pharmacy counter and asks to pick up a prescription for Thomas Smith. The prescription, for a Schedule III controlled substance, had been faxed to the pharmacy. You find the filled prescription, offer consultation (which is refused), take payment, and give the man the prescription. Have you violated any law?**

Because this is a prescription for a controlled substance, you have violated section 4075 unless you know the man to be Thomas Smith or know Thomas Smith and know his connection with the man who picked up the prescription. You must obtain adequate proof of identity to dispense the prescription. Identification containing a photograph, such as a driver's license in the name Thomas Smith, with a picture that matches the person offering it, would certainly suffice.

By law, Need to ask for ID when it's oral / data transmission

**What if the man produces a license that shows him to be Edward Jones, and he states that he is Thomas Smith's brother-in-law. Is that enough?**

The evident purpose of section 4075 is to prevent unauthorized persons from receiving controlled substances. You will need to use your professional judgment to determine what additional inquiry, if any, is appropriate here.

Prescriptions may be mailed, shipped, or delivered. Publication 52 of the United States Postal Service (available at www.usps.com/cpim/ftp/pubs/pub52.htm), entitled "Hazardous, Restricted, and Perishable Mail," details postal service requirements for mailing dangerous drugs, including controlled substances, in section 48. Registered practitioners or dispensers (including pharmacies) may mail dangerous drugs other than controlled substances to their ultimate user. Pharmacists or practitioners who dispense controlled substances may mail them, but only to patients under their care. Mailing of controlled substances other than prescriptions is limited to situations where both the mailer and addressee are registered with DEA or exempt from such registration (such as military, civil defense, or law enforcement personnel performing official duties). Publication 52 details the packing and labeling requirements for mailing controlled substances.

In addition to meeting general packaging requirements, controlled substances must be placed in an inner packaging marked and sealed in accordance with applicable provisions of the Controlled Substances Act. The inner packaging must be securely held within a plain outer wrapper or packaging and no markings of any kind that indicate the nature of the contents may appear on the outside of the package. Other medicines must be mailed in a plain outer wrapper or packaging with no outside markings to indicate the nature of the contents. Private shippers, such as United Parcel Service and Federal Express, have their own rules; it is likely all shippers require that the sender remain responsible for ensuring compliance with all government regulations concerning the shipped goods. When controlled substances are involved, the shipment must also be in compliance with all DEA regulations.[8]

# Refills

Most prescriptions, for both dangerous drugs and controlled substances, may be refilled with prescriber authorization (§4063; H&SC §11200; 21 CFR §1306.22(a)).[9] A prescription for a Schedule II controlled substance may not be refilled (H&SC §11200(c), 21 CFR §1306.12).

There is no specific limit on the number of refills for a dangerous drug or the period of time during which the prescription may be refilled.[10] A prescription may be refilled on the basis of authorization for refills in the original order or by receiving subsequent oral refill authorization (§4063). A prescriber may authorize refills "as needed" of dangerous drugs, but not for controlled substances (§4063).[11] The pharmacist refilling the prescription must record the date, the name or initials of the dispensing pharmacist, and the quantity dispensed (§1717(b)). Even when the pharmacist may legally refill the prescription without contacting the prescriber, the pharmacist always should exercise professional judgment concerning the patient and his or her drug regimen. When the pharmacist's assessment suggests any question about the necessity or propriety of ongoing drug therapy, it is the pharmacist's duty to contact the prescriber before refilling the prescription. The amount of time since the issuance of the prescription, the amount of time since it was last filled, and the need for patient evaluation and/or clinical tests for appropriate use of the medication over a period of time are all factors that might suggest the prescriber should be contacted.

A prescription for a Schedule III or IV controlled substance may be refilled only up to five times over no longer than a six-month period from the date of issue and in an amount, all refills taken together, not exceeding a 120-day supply (H&SC §11200, 21 CFR 1306.22). Federal regulations require that the date of each Schedule III or IV refill be noted on the back of the prescription or in another appropriate record (21 CFR §1306.22(a)). No individual refill for a III or IV may exceed the

---

[8]  There are federal requirements for the export of prescription drugs (see Chap. VII: Ordering Drugs ("Import and Export")).

[9]  Certain pharmacies, including nonresident pharmacies, may dispense replacement contact lenses (§4124). The dispenser must register with both the Pharmacy and Medical Boards. Dispensing is strictly limited to contact lenses that need no fitting or adjustment, and they must be dispensed as packaged and sealed by the manufacturer. They must be dispensed under a prescription with an express expiration date no later than one year from the date of the prescriber's last examination of the patient; the prescription must specify it is for contact lenses and the lens brand name, type, and tint, including all necessary specifications. The pharmacy may make no substitutions and must provide specified oral and written advice and warnings.

[10]  Many chain pharmacies, third party payors, and others who direct or influence pharmacy policy may require that a new prescription be obtained when six months or a year have passed since the original fill, but that is not mandated by any law.

[11]  Interestingly, California's Food, Drug, and Cosmetic Law states that a prescription for a prescription drug or device can only be refilled as indicated on the prescription (H&SC §111470), which is obviously in conflict with Section 4063. As a practical matter, the Pharmacy Law always has controlled on this point, but does it legally? Probably it does. The Food, Drug, and Cosmetic Law regulates drugs generally while the Pharmacy Law more specifically regulates dangerous (prescription) drugs and devices. The more specific law usually controls when two state laws appear to be inconsistent.

amount of the original order (21 CFR §1306.22(a)(l)-(4)).  An automated data system may be used for storage and retrieval of refill information if the database includes all necessary information, provides for on-line retrieval, and is checked for accuracy (21 CFR §1306.22(b)).

**Emergency Refills.**  If no refills have been authorized, and the pharmacist makes every reasonable effort to contact the prescriber about a refill and cannot do so, and, in the pharmacist's professional judgment, failure to refill the prescription might interrupt the patient's ongoing care and have a significant adverse effect on the patient's well-being, the prescription may be refilled _= the entire amt. is_ (§4064(a)).  The pharmacist must make an appropriate record, including the basis for the decision to _okay._ proceed under this section (§4064(d)).  The patient must be informed that the pharmacist refilled the prescription pursuant to section 4064 (§4064(b)), and the prescriber must be informed within a reasonable time (§4064(c)).  The prescriber incurs no liability for the pharmacist's decision to refill  _Federal law:_ (§4064(e)).  For Schedule III, IV, and V prescriptions under these circumstances, the pharmacist may _+ emergency_ only provide a refill in a "reasonable" amount until the prescriber can be contacted (H&SC §11201). _refill is allowed_ The patient's possession of the drugs without a prescription (as there is truly no prescription for refills _if there's an_ dispensed under these circumstances) is considered an exception to the prohibition of section 4060 for _immediate need_ possessing controlled substances without a prescription.[12] _OR intense suff_

Suppose a patient asks for a refill of a prescription, and you notice the prescription was issued five years ago.  May you dispense the refill?  Should you?  Suppose the drug is levothyroxine sodium (Synthroid®)?  Suppose the drug is cimetidine (Tagamet®) 400mg?

There is no legal prohibition against refilling a prescription for a dangerous drug (other than a controlled substance) even if it was issued several years before.  On the other hand, as discussed above, a pharmacist always has the responsibility to exercise his or her professional judgment as to whether it is appropriate to fill or refill any prescription.  The longer the patient has gone without seeing the prescriber  or the longer it has been since the pharmacist has contacted the prescriber, the more important it is that the pharmacist think before simply continuing to refill the prescription without question.  This is true even for chronic or permanent drug regimens.  Remember, a pharmacist must provide consultation whenever it is warranted, not just for new prescriptions (§1707.2(a)(2)), and the pharmacist may be held liable when failure to exercise professional judgment results in patient harm.

Suppose a patient asks for a refill of a prescription that called for 30 aspirin with codeine phosphate (APC®) tablets #4, to be taken 1-2, q.i.d.  There is no refill authorized on the prescription.  You call the prescriber, who authorizes you to refill it for 45 doses.  May you do so?

If the amount of the drug dispensed is increased, or the drug, its form, its strength, or the directions for use are changed in any significant respect, this is not a refill and a new prescription is required.   However, although you may not refill the prescription, you may fill it, since prescriptions for all drugs except those in Schedule II may be ordered orally.  You simply would have to treat it as a new prescription, follow the rules for oral orders, and issue a new prescription number.

A prescription is written for "#30, 1 b.i.d., refill 5xs, #100 each?"  For how much may the prescription be refilled?

---

[12] The authority of pharmacists, pharmacies, and the Board to meet prescription needs in declared public emergencies is discussed below.

Of primary concern is that this prescription contains an irregularity (§1761(a)), because a refill usually is not for an amount larger than the original fill.  The pharmacist should, upon receipt, contact the prescriber to clarify his or her intent as to both the initial fill amount and the refill amount.  If the prescription is for a Schedule III or IV controlled substance, it is subject not only to the restriction of a 120-day supply for all refills combined, but also to the prohibition against refills for Schedule IIIs or IVs exceeding the amount of the initial fill (discussed above).  Since the prescription is for two a day, a 120-day supply would amount to 240 doses.  However, since the refill could not exceed the original amount, 30 doses, refills would be limited to 30 doses each, and the five refills (assuming all were requested within 180 days of the issuance of the prescription) would be limited to 150 doses total (5x30), or a 75-day supply.  This result underscores the importance of contacting the prescriber about this prescription.

**A patient presents a prescription for #30 Ativan®, with authorization for four refills, on a weekend.  The patient is a cash patient and wants all 150 doses, the initial 30 and the four refills, at once.  Should the pharmacist fulfill the request?**

Absolutely not.  The prescription is written for #30 initially, with *refills*.  The prescriber clearly intended the patient to obtain 30 initially and to return for refills as indicated or needed, consistent with the directions for use.  If the prescriber had intended the patient to obtain 150 doses at once, he or she would have written the prescription that way.

# Transfer of a Prescription

Any prescription, except for a Schedule II controlled substance, may be transferred to another pharmacy at the patient's request, for refilling.[13]  Both the receiving and transferring pharmacies must document the transfer carefully, including the date of the transfer, all the information required for the original prescription, the number of refills remaining on the original prescription, and the identity of both the transferring and receiving pharmacies (§1717(f)).  The pharmacy to which a prescription for a controlled substance is transferred may not dispense it unless the patient is known or is able to properly establish his or her identity (§4075).  Federal regulations allow only one transfer if a prescription is for a Schedule III, IV, or V controlled substance, unless the transfer is between pharmacies that electronically share a real-time on-line electronic database.

Such transfers are subject to the following requirements:

- the transfer must be communicated directly between two licensed pharmacists;
- the transferring pharmacist must write "VOID" on the face of the invalidated prescription, record on its reverse the name, address, and DEA number of the transferee pharmacy and the name of the receiving pharmacist, and record the date of the transfer and his or her own name;
- the transferee pharmacist must write the word "transfer" on the face of the transferred prescription, provide all required information on the prescription including the date of the original prescription, the original number of authorized refills, the date of original dispensing, the number of valid refills remaining and dates and locations of previous refills, the name of the transferring pharmacist, and the name, address, DEA number, and prescription number of

---

[13] There is no legal barrier to transferring a prescription not for controlled substances for the original fill (as might be requested if one location in a chain is out of stock of a drug, or the patient wishes to pick up the filled prescription from another location).  DEA contemplates data transfer for *refill* dispensing (Pharmacist's Manual, p. 42), but has yet to allow electronic transmission of prescriptions for any other purposes.  However, Schedule III-V prescriptions may be faxed from prescriber to pharmacy, so a fax from one pharmacy to another should be acceptable.

both the transferring pharmacy and the pharmacy where the prescription was originally filled; and

- the original and transferred prescriptions must be maintained for two years after the last refill (21 CFR §1306.25).

**May a pharmacy in Idaho transfer a prescription to a California pharmacy? May a California pharmacy transfer a prescription to an Idaho pharmacy?**

If the transfer of the prescription otherwise complies with California, Idaho, and federal law, it is legal in California.

**Suppose a customer asks a pharmacy in Los Angeles to transfer a prescription from a pharmacy in San Francisco. The San Francisco pharmacy had obtained the prescription by transfer from a pharmacy in Reno, Nevada. May the prescription now be transferred to Los Angeles?**

The second transfer may be made. If the prescription is for a controlled substance, it may only be made if the pharmacies share an electronic database as described above.

**Suppose a woman requests that your pharmacy transfer a prescription for Sarah Smith, for aspirin with codeine phosphate #4, from another pharmacy in your chain. She identifies the prescription by number and patient name. You make the transfer and she takes the prescription. You assume she must be Sarah Smith (or her agent) because she had the prescription number, as well as the patient's name. Have you violated any law?**

Because this is a prescription for a controlled substance, unless you know the woman to be Sarah Smith, or know Sarah Smith and know she has a connection with the requester, you have violated section 4075 by failing to obtain adequate proof of identity.

**Suppose the woman produces a driver's license showing that she is Barbara Jones. Is that adequate? What if she produces a license showing she is Barbara Smith and states that she is Sarah Smith's sister? Is that enough?**

The ability to transfer prescriptions heightens the risk that unauthorized persons might receive controlled substances. The person presenting a name and prescription number to obtain a transferred refill might have copied that information without authorization from someone's legitimate prescription. The presentation of an empty container does not negate the possibility of misuse, because the container could have been taken without authorization or even retrieved from garbage. If the person seeking to pick up a transferred controlled substances prescription is not the person for whom the prescription was written, you are on notice to make inquiry about that person's unavailability to pick up the prescription herself and urged to be suspicious and use caution. If the drugs dispensed on this transferred prescription are misused and injuries result, you may be liable if you failed to make adequate inquiry.

**If a patient goes outside the country on vacation and forgets to bring necessary medication or runs short, may a California pharmacy transfer his or her prescription to that country?**

Probably not. First, there is no provision for international transfers of prescriptions. Second, even if legal here, the transferring pharmacy would have to ensure such a transfer complied with federal law and the laws of the other country. For a discussion about shipping prescription medications outside the country, see Chapter VII: Ordering, Receipt, Maintenance, and Transfer of Drugs and Devices ("Import and Export").

# Common Electronic Files

Two or more pharmacies may establish and use a common electronic file to maintain required dispensing information for dangerous drugs (§1717.1(a)). For controlled substances, common electronic files may be maintained only to the extent permitted by federal law (§1717.1(b)). All such common electronic files must contain complete and accurate records of each prescription and refill dispensed (§1717.1(c)). Pharmacies maintaining common electronic files must protect against violations of the Confidentiality of Medical Information Act by developing and implementing written policies and procedures to maintain confidentiality and prevent unauthorized disclosures (§1717.1(d),((e), see below).

A pharmacy that establishes a common electronic file for prescription information must post a notice in a conspicuous place informing consumers about this shared electronic filing system, telling them the names of the pharmacies with which the file is shared and that they may refill their prescriptions at any of those locations (§1717.2(a)). That notice must also advise patients that they may notify the pharmacist-in-charge if they do not want their prescription information to be placed in the common electronic file (§1717.2(b)). Consumers who object to the sharing of their prescription information must be asked to sign a form to that effect. A copy is given to the consumer and the original is maintained by the pharmacy for three years after the date of the last prescription transaction for that consumer.

# Patient Privacy

The information received by a pharmacy in a prescription, stored in a patient profile, or contained in other types of patient records, is extremely private. The pharmacist is obliged to protect a patient's privacy and the confidentiality of the medical information in the pharmacy (Civ. Code §§56-56.35; CALIF. CONST. art. I, §1; §§1717.2, 1717.4(h), 1764). More extensive discussion of this subject is in Chapter XI: Record-Keeping and Chapter XIV: Other Law Relevant to Pharmacy. This obligation extends to conversation, including consultation, with a patient where others may overhear private information, and to maintaining records where third parties may see or access them. This obligation requires the pharmacist to exercise discretion about what he or she says to or about a patient or a patient's medical condition or information where someone other than the patient or agent (including members of the pharmacy staff who have no need for the information) may hear. In addition, the pharmacist should exercise discretion when asking the patient questions about the legitimacy of a prescription under the same circumstances. Although the legal concern is for privacy, the pharmacy ought to consider methods of obtaining information necessary to validate prescriptions that would avoid unnecessary embarrassment to patients.

The pharmacist may not share personal patient information except as authorized by law or with clear patient consent, and may only share it for a proper purpose. Protectible patient information includes all personally identifiable information that might enable someone to know that a patient is receiving medical treatment, as well as what treatment. Unless the patient is not individually identifiable, no information may be shared except when the information is needed for medical or billing purposes (Civ. Code §56.10(c)).

When a patient asks you to obtain a prescription from another pharmacy and refill it for her, you may ask that other pharmacy for the prescription, and that pharmacy may provide it. If you are in a shared system with the other pharmacy (whether or not you have common ownership), you may access the patient's other information, such as the patient profile, from the other pharmacy if the patient has been notified previously of the arrangement or if you obtain the patient's express permission. But the patient's consent should not be assumed, unless you are certain the other pharmacy gave patients notice about the information-sharing arrangement.

It is a violation of the law to share personal patient information even with the patient's spouse or adult child without the patient's permission. There are situations when you cannot share such information even with the parents of minor children, as discussed in Chapter XIV: Other Law Relevant to Pharmacy ("Protecting the Patient's Right to Privacy"). Privacy protection also requires that information obtained for one purpose not be used for another. For example, information provided to the pharmacy's corporate offices for billing cannot be used for marketing. purposes.

The federal medical privacy law (known as HIPAA; see Chap. XI: Record-Keeping and Chap. XIV: Other Relevant Law) was also intended to ensure that health care entities, including pharmacies, adequately protect personal health information. That protection requires care both in using information (as during consultation with patients) and in protecting its physical security (as when it is transmitted or stored electronically).

# Emergency Provision of Drugs

**Public Emergencies.** Under California law any drug or device, including any controlled substance, may be dispensed during a federal, state, or local emergency without a prescription. The pharmacist must keep a record of the date, name and address of the patient, and the name, strength, and quantity of the drug or device furnished; this information must be communicated to the patient's physician as soon as possible (§4062(a)). In times of general emergency of the type that might disrupt the health care system, the pharmacist is authorized to use judgment while acting in good faith.[14]

Several other provisions of California law concerning emergencies are of interest. The Legislature has declared that "maintaining the delivery of food, pharmaceuticals, or other emergency necessities . . . in light of disruptions caused by previous earthquakes and other disasters, is a paramount priority and should be considered an essential public service" (Stats. 1991, ch. 1186, §2). Government Code section 8627.5 gives the Governor the authority to issue regulations during a state of emergency that temporarily suspend any laws or regulations "imposing nonsafety related restrictions on the delivery of food products, pharmaceuticals, and other emergency necessities."

---

[14] There is some conflict between section 4062 and the prescription provisions of California's Controlled Substances Act, particularly because the latter specifically indicate when a Schedule II controlled substance may be prescribed on an ordinary prescription blank rather than on the required controlled substance form because of an emergency. Because the Controlled Substances Act's exception to the prescribing rules during certain emergencies is restricted to the form of the order only, it would be usual to interpret that provision as meaning there is no other emergency exception – certainly not one that would allow Schedule II drugs to be furnished *without* a prescription. However, the provision in the Pharmacy Law that allows dispensing during a federal, state, or local emergency without a prescription begins, "Notwithstanding . . . any other provision of law": "any other provision" would include the state Controlled Substances Act. Federal law is entirely silent about exceptions to the prescription requirements for controlled substances that might make sense in an emergency. However, as noted below, federal authorities would be unlikely to act against California licensees who act in accordance with California law to ensure the availability of prescription drugs at a time of emergency.

It is instructive to note that after the 1994 Northridge earthquake the Board of Pharmacy issued certificates honoring numerous pharmacists for their humane actions during the emergency. In an emergency, Board inspectors and sometimes pharmacist Board members travel to the affected area to ensure that pharmacies are in operation and that adequate drugs are available.

Such emergency regulations would be in writing, widely publicized, and immediately effective, and would remain in effect until rescinded by the Governor, the termination of the state of emergency, or for 60 days, whichever occurs first. Under this authority the Governor could modify in whatever way was deemed appropriate (and not unsafe) California pharmacy law and regulations, but federal laws would remain in effect. The Pharmacy Board also now has the authority to suspend any provision of the Pharmacy Law or Board regulations in such emergencies (§4062(b)), as discussed in Chapter XIII: The Board of Pharmacy and Other Agencies. The Governor, but not the Board, could modify or waive provisions of the California Uniform Controlled Substances Act in any emergency; neither, of course, may waive the provisions of federal law. However, it would be extremely unlikely for federal authorities to take action against California licensees whose actions to assure the continued supply of pharmaceuticals to the public during a declared state of emergency were in technical violation of federal law or regulations and encouraged by state authorities. Taking advantage of such an emergency situation to engage in drug diversion, in contrast, undoubtedly would lead to severe action by federal and state authorities.

**Personal Emergencies.** California pharmacy law does not authorize a pharmacist to dispense a drug or device in a personal emergency without an existing prescription, even where a patient would suffer intensely or might face serious injury or death without immediate access to medication. If the patient has a prior order by a physician who cannot be reached, the pharmacist may refill the prescription in advance of notifying the prescriber in compliance with section 4064; if the prescription is for a Schedule III, IV, or V controlled substance, a refill in a "reasonable" amount may be provided until the prescriber can be contacted (H&SC §11201), as previously noted.

**Suppose a patient visiting California is shopping in your pharmacy and doubles over with severe chest pains. He says he has been treated for angina in the past, but has been feeling fine and now does not carry any nitroglycerin tablets. On your way to call for emergency medical assistance, could you dispense one nitroglycerin tablet for him? (Are there other circumstances of true personal emergency you can hypothesize for which the law does not provide?) What should you do in such circumstances?**

Remember that you will be responsible for the consequences of the decisions that you make. Because this is a question implicating professional judgment, there is no simple answer. If it seems the patient is having an angina attack that has responded previously to nitroglycerin, and you believe that his ingestion of that medicine will not do him any harm, the dispensing of a nitroglycerin tablet in this emergency would seem to be the appropriate choice. Your decision might well depend upon the length of time it will likely take to obtain emergency medical assistance for the patient, your judgment of the likelihood that the attack is in fact angina, and the risk that failure to provide a single dose of medication might lead to greater harm than could be produced by the drug. But because California law does not authorize a pharmacist to provide even a single dose in such a situation (that is, where there is not a disaster, you do not have a prescription on file, and you cannot contact the patient's physician), this technically is illegal. You may well be liable if anything adverse happens to the patient because there is a serious question whether your license permits you to make such a decision.

**Suppose that same patient says he has also taken OxyContin® for these attacks. Could you give him a tablet or two while he waits for the ambulance?**

Because of the stringent legal restrictions on dispensing Schedule II controlled substances, the question of their emergency dispensing is specifically addressed in the law. Under federal regulations, a pharmacist may dispense Schedule II controlled substances upon oral (or, in accordance with DEA advice, faxed) order in an emergency in an amount adequate for the emergency period (see Chap. IX:

Prescriptions: Receipt to Labeling).[15]  But there is no authority under California or federal law to dispense a Schedule II, or any other, controlled substance without a prescription in a personal, as opposed to public, emergency.

**Pharmacists as Good Samaritans.**  Another provision of the Government Code, section 8659, often called a "good Samaritan" law, immunizes from liability any pharmacist, among other named health care professionals, who renders services during a state of war emergency, a state of emergency, or a local emergency "at the express or implied request of any responsible state or local official or agency."  The immunity is from liability for any injury sustained by any person by reason of the "good Samaritan's" services, regardless of the circumstances or the cause of the injuries, except that the immunity does not apply in the event of a willful act or omission by the professional.  While there is a similar provision protecting physicians who render aid at the scene of any emergency (Bus. & Prof. Code §2395) or to a participant in a high school or community college athletic event (Bus. & Prof. Code §2398), pharmacists are not covered by those protections.

**Does the good Samaritan law protect those who charge or are reimbursed for services rendered in an emergency?**

While the concept of a "good Samaritan" suggests a person acting entirely without commercial motivation, the California statute by its terms does not so limit the protection.  In many emergency situations, the notion that anyone would be able to bill and receive payment for professional services seems far-fetched.  Under some circumstances, however, professionals might well have the opportunity to present bills for payment; pharmacists might wish to have volunteered their services, but be anxious to be reimbursed for the costs of drugs dispensed in an emergency.  The idea behind the laws is to encourage the cooperation of professionals in emergency situations, when they otherwise have no legal obligation to become involved and might choose not to do so for any number of reasons.  For example, the emergency might call for the use of skills not regularly exercised in the professional's usual practice or the professional might never accept a patient in his or her regular practice who refuses to agree to arbitration of malpractice claims.

# Prescription Pricing

In general, prices charged for prescription drugs – by a manufacturer or distributor to each other or to a pharmacy, or by a pharmacy to its customers – have not been regulated at the state or federal level.  A pharmacy may charge whatever the customer will pay, or whatever the insurer or third-party payor will pay.[16]  The fact that one pharmacy is charging substantially more to fill a prescription than another is entirely a matter of competition in the marketplace, as with most other goods and services.  Historically the only situations involving money that were of concern to the Pharmacy Board involved violations of statutes that prohibit improper payments, such as kickbacks, rebates, or referrals.  These financial relationships were prohibited between actors in the health care

---

[15] Because, under federal regulations, prescriptions for Schedule III, IV, and V controlled substances may be oral or faxed, no parallel emergency provision is required to cover their dispensing in an emergency.

[16] Determining what an insurer or third-party payor will pay, and what co-payment must be charged to the patient, and then getting reimbursement from the insurer or third-party payor, are time-consuming clerical tasks for the pharmacy.  A law effective in 2002 requires certain health care service plans and disability insurers that offer prescription drug benefits and issue identification cards to their enrollees to issue a card containing uniform information necessary to process claims for prescription drug benefits.  The uniform cards must be issued to new enrollees or whenever there is a change in enrollee coverage that impacts the data content or format of cards (H&SC §1363.03, Ins. Code §10123.194).  The eventual uniformity of these documents should ease the burden of claims management at pharmacies.

system for fear they would both inflate prices and lead to prescribing and dispensing decisions based on financial considerations rather than good patient care (B&PC §§650-650.1, see Chap. XII: Practice Pitfalls). And of course outright fraud had always been a concern of licensing agencies.

Today, the price of prescription drugs is a major public policy issue, as the discussion in Chapter VII: Ordering, Receipt, Maintenance, and Transfer of Drugs and Devices of the controversy over importing drugs from Canada or other countries for personal use reflects. Rising drug costs have led a significant number of patients to stop filling prescriptions, many without telling their health care providers, according to a federally-funded study (*Prescription Drug Costs Force Many Chronically Ill People to Limit Use, Study Finds,* CALIFORNIA HEALTHLINE, Sept. 16, 2004).

**California Prescription Drug Benefit Programs.** Both the United States Congress and the California Legislature have had to confront whether, and how, to add prescription drug benefits to government health care programs and how to assure the affordability of drugs to the elderly and the disadvantaged. In California, Medi-Cal, the federal government-supported state-provided health care plan for low income people, includes prescription drugs. Medi-Cal sets the fee a pharmacy may charge, over its cost of drug acquisition, to fill a prescription for a Medi-Cal beneficiary (Medi-Cal Pharmacy Provider Manuals, www.medi-cal.ca.gov ("Publications," then "Provider Manuals")). California law requires pharmacies that participate in Medi-Cal to charge no more than the Medi-Cal-set price for all prescriptions (except compounded prescriptions and prescribed OTC drugs) to senior citizens who participate in Medicare, which has had no prescription drug coverage (§4425).[17]

DHS was required to provide a mechanism to calculate and transmit to pharmacies the price to be charged, but the Medi-Cal drug utilization review process does not apply under this program (§4425(b)). DHS must report annually to the Legislature about pharmacy participation; a major concern was that pharmacies, faced with a greatly-increased population obtaining the Medi-Cal price, would discontinue participation in the Medi-Cal program. DHS was also required to conduct a study of the adequacy of Medi-Cal pharmacy reimbursement rates (§4426). The bill enacting this program did raise reimbursement rates for Medi-Cal (and thus Medicare) prescriptions by $0.25 per prescription as of January 1, 2000, and by another $0.15 as of July 1, 2002.

A 2001 law created the Golden Bear State Pharmacy Assistance Program to provide additional prescription price relief for seniors. That program (H&SC §130404) was to involve discounts negotiated with manufacturers that would be passed on to eligible registrants; it appears that it was never implemented. The Governor vetoed four bills passed in 2004 that approached the prescription drug price problem by enabling importation, by the state or by consumers, from Canada (AB 1957, SB 1144, SB 1149, SB 1333). In the opening days of the 2005-2006 legislative session, a bill was introduced to establish the California Rx Program to authorize the Department of Health Services to negotiate drug rebate agreements with drug manufacturers (an approach like the Golden Bear program) and to require the Department of Consumer Affairs to educate Californians about low-cost drug options, in particular drug importation (SB 19). California has not been alone among governments in these actions. As of February 2004, 40 states had a variety of plans to assist low-income elderly and disabled persons to purchase prescription drugs, through several methods (state-negotiated discounts, direct subsidies, tax credits, and coordinating access to manufacturers' charitable purchase assistance programs) (National Pharmaceutical Council, *Pharmaceutical Benefits 2003, Section 6: State Pharmacy Assistance Programs,* www.npcnow.org/resources).

---

[17] The Medi-Cal rates thus determine the price a pharmacy can charge to virtually all of its customers age 65 and over. The pharmacy is also allowed to charge an additional amount set by the Department of Health Services to cover any electronic transmission charges (§4425(a)).

Some state programs have been controversial and led to challenges in court. Maine's program, intended to reduce prescription prices for its residents through state negotiation with drug manufacturers for rebates, went all the way to the United States Supreme Court. Under that program, manufacturers that refused to enter into rebate agreements would have their drugs subjected to a prior authorization requirement under Maine's Medicaid program, thus making practitioners less likely to order them. Drug makers claimed the program violated the Commerce Clause of the United States Constitution, but the United States Supreme Court disagreed (*Pharmaceutical Research and Manufacturers of America v. Walsh*, 538 U.S. 644 (2003)). Even after the *Walsh* decision, manufacturers continued to challenge similar programs from other states, so far without success (*PhRMA v. Thompson*, 362 F.3d 817 (D.C. Cir. 2004). States have also organized interstate programs for joint drug purchases, aimed at lowering each state's purchasing costs. Over continuing objections from drug manufacturers, the federal Centers for Medicare and Medicaid Services approved such programs (Cyril T. Zaneski, *Md. applying to join drug-buying pool; Interstate cooperative got federal OK last week*, BALTIMORE SUN, Apr. 25, 2004, p. 1A).

SKIP **Federal Prescription Drug Benefit Program.** Several years ago, at the federal government level, the President put forth a pharmacy discount card plan for Medicare beneficiaries after Congress was not successful in reaching agreement on a Medicare prescription drug plan. That discount card plan was enjoined by the federal courts as unauthorized by Congress, and having been adopted without appropriate rulemaking procedures (Amy Goldstein, *Judge Blocks Prescription Discount Plan*, WASHINGTON POST, Sept. 7, 2001, p. A01). Some drug companies then announced their own discount plans (Francesca Lunzer Kritz, *What's In Your Wallet?; Drug Discount Cards Offer Seniors Little Relief*, WASHINGTON POST, Nov. 20, 2001, p. F01).

Finally, in December 2003, a federal Medicare prescription drug benefit, officially part of the Medicare Prescription Drug, Improvement, and Modernization Act of 2003, was enacted (42 USC §1395w). Although the widely-discussed and debated drug benefits for Medicare beneficiaries do not take effect until 2006, a provision for drug discount cards took effect immediately. This provision, which expires when the new benefit begins in 2006, is intended to allow beneficiaries to purchase drug discount cards from private companies participating in the program. The program limits beneficiaries to a single card at any time (and the right to change cards only twice). Each discount program offers different drugs, at different prices, making it confusing to determine which program, if any, is financially beneficial to a particular person (Mary Jo Feldstein, *Retirees remain confused about Medicare changes; Private health plans struggle to understand program, too*, ST. LOUIS POST-DISPATCH, Dec. 10, 2004, p. A01). Information about this program is available at www.medicare.gov/AssistancePrograms. All of the different cards are presented to pharmacies for the discounts. The HHS rules and publications provide a variety of information, including about contracts with pharmacies for use of the cards. This information is available at the website of the Centers for Medicare & Medicaid Services, www.cms.hhs.gov; of particular interest is www.cms.hhs.gov/medlearn/drugcard.asp, the page about the new drug benefits program.

The overall value of this interim program is much debated. Without doubt its complexity has limited its usefulness.[18] A financially-beneficial pilot program for early prescription drug coverage, for which an estimated 600,000 Medicare beneficiaries were eligible, had 50,000 available slots, but fewer than 7,000 people had applied by September 2004 (*Few Medicare Beneficiaries Apply to Participate in Prescription Drug Benefit Pilot Program*, CALIFORNIA HEALTHLINE, Sept. 12, 2004).

---

[18] Obtaining accurate information about the program's benefits, even from Medicare itself, has been difficult (Robert Pear, *A Help Line for Medicare Doesn't Help 39% in Study*, NEW YORK TIMES, Dec. 12, 2004, p. A37). It also appears the discount cards may not offer a benefit to nursing home patients (Robert Pear, *New Medicare Drug Plan Is Raising Difficult Issues for Nursing Home Patients*, NEW YORK TIMES, Dec. 5, 2004, p. A38).

In addition, insurance companies, which tend to favor limited formularies and generic drugs, were battling brand-name manufacturers over which drugs should be covered by discount cards ( Robert Pear, *Medicare Rules Set Off a Battle on Drug Choices*, NEW YORK TIMES, Sept. 26, 2004, p. A1).

The drug benefit that will replace the discount cards in 2006 is very complex. Because of the premium charge and the deductibles and co-payments imposed, it may not produce a financial benefit except for Medicare participants with annual prescription drug costs of over $3,500. In addition, the legislation bars the federal government from negotiating with drug companies for price discounts. Plus, the price of the health care premium for Medicare patients has taken its largest jump in 40 years, to pay for the new benefit (James Toedtman, *Ouch!: Part B premiums are going up 17 percent next year?; What's a Medicare recipient to do?* NEWSDAY, Oct. 2, 2004, p. B06).

Skip **Financial Pressures on Pharmacy.** Private insurers offering prescription drug coverage generally contract with pharmacies, often through pharmacy benefit managers (PBMs), sometimes with specific providers, to obtain low prices in return for providing significant amounts of prescription business. Government agencies providing prescription drug benefits in government-sponsored health plans may operate in a similar fashion or offer a fixed dispensing fee on top of a maximum allowable cost for the drugs themselves. The large numbers of prescriptions involved in these plans virtually guarantee that pharmacies will agree to the offered terms. The result is that a significant percentage of prescription transactions are priced under "wholesale" contracts that afford the pharmacy a lower profit than it would earn through "retail" individual sales transactions.

Government purchasing of pharmacy services is subject to budget pressures. Because of the ongoing budget crisis, California had projected a five percent cut in January 2004 in its rate of reimbursement for health care services in the Medicaid and workers' compensation programs, with another ten percent cut possible in July 2004. However, these cuts were enjoined by a federal judge as violative of the guarantee in federal Medicaid law of quality and equal access to care (Jeffrey L. Rabin, *Cuts in Medi-Cal Payments Blocked*, LOS ANGELES TIMES, Dec. 24, 2003, p. B1). Congress also was considering cuts in reimbursement rates in late 2004 (Lawrence M. O'Rourke, *Medicaid cuts 'on the table' for 2005; GOP deficit cutters target huge health care program for the poor*, SACRAMENTO BEE, Dec. 11, 2004, p. A1).[19] As reimbursement rates decline, fewer providers are willing to provide services to Medi-Cal patients.

In addition to the restrictions on how much pharmacies may charge that are imposed by government programs and arise from a marketplace with a small number of third-party payors, pharmacies are facing increasing competition from mail-order pharmacies (including those tied to the three largest PBMs, which will play a major role in administering the Medicare drug benefit) and from Internet operations, including illegal ones. Fighting back, 14 Northern California pharmacies sued major drug manufacturers in August 2004, claiming an illegal conspiracy to inflate U.S. drug prices, while charging much lower prices to foreign customers for the same drugs (Julie Appleby, *U.S. drugmakers accused of violating antitrust law*, USA TODAY, Aug. 27, 2004, p. 1B).

---

[19] Reimbursement rate cuts were under consideration in part because an HHS Office of the Inspector General report suggested that pharmacies were being paid a very high rate of return over their cost for drugs (Lawrence M. O'Rourke, *Medicaid emerges as target for budget-cutters; The government's largest health care program, serving 53 million vulnerable Americans, is no longer seen as a sacrosanct entitlement*, STAR TRIBUNE, Dec. 12, 2004, p. 13A). An earlier report by that office found that drug companies were overcharging public hospitals and clinics (*HHS Office of Inspector General Report Finds Drug Makers Overcharge Public Hospitals, Clinics*, CALIFORNIA HEALTHLINE, June 30, 2004).

# Prescription Price Information

A pharmacist is required to provide prescription price information to a consumer upon request (§4122(b)). The obvious purpose of this section is to enable price comparison and lower drug costs. When the requester asks for more than five prescription prices and does not have a valid prescription for each of them, the pharmacist may require that the request be in writing, may refuse to respond to more than three such requests from any such person or entity within a six-month period, and may charge a reasonable fee (§4122(c)). The pharmacist must respond within a reasonable period of time, which is deemed to be ten days or the time period stated in the written request, whichever is later (§4122(c)(2)). The pharmacy also must prominently post a notice provided by the Board that informs consumers about the availability of prescription price information and the possibility of generic product selection. It also encourages patients to talk to the pharmacist, and educates them about the kind of information a patient needs (§4122(a), §1707.2(f)). The "Notice to Consumers" may be downloaded from www.pharmacy.ca.gov/licensing/site_license.htm in English, Spanish, Chinese, Vietnamese, Korean, and Russian. The pharmacy need not respond to a request for price information from a competitor or out-of-state requester, or provide controlled substance prices in response to a telephone request (§4122(e)). This section of the law also does not apply to a pharmacy located in a licensed hospital that is accessible only to hospital medical staff and personnel (§4122(d)).

### Must a pharmacy provide its Medi-Cal prices for a particular drug?

It appears that the pharmacy must provide the applicable price on request. Providing the cash price to a Medicare beneficiary entitled to pay the Medi-Cal price (plus an electronic transmission fee), would hardly serve the purpose of the prescription price information requirement. While the Medicare beneficiary would not necessarily be searching for the best price (because Medi-Cal participating pharmacies should quote similar prices, perhaps varying only with different acquisition costs), he or she may need to know the price to bring adequate funds, to determine if the prescription is affordable, or perhaps merely out of curiosity. The consumer need give no reason for making the request. The pharmacy's only obligation is to provide its own prices; it need not provide information about its competitor's prices, even if it knows what they are. If a pharmacy does indicate that one of its prices is lower than its competitors, it must take care to do so accurately, to avoid accusations of unfair competition from the competitor.

# Internet Practice and Transactions

## *Telemedicine*

Increasingly, health care services, including clinical advice, patient consultation, and prescription issuance and dispensing, are being provided electronically and across state lines, by telephone, through computer connections, by videoconferencing, and over the Internet. This practice raises many legal and public health and safety issues. By which laws are these transactions governed? Is "telepractice" legal and ethical health care? California, along with other states and the federal government, has been grappling with whether and how to regulate some or all of these activities.

California is one of a number of states to have adopted a telemedicine statute. It defines telemedicine as "the practice of health care delivery, diagnosis, consultation, treatment, transfer of medical data, and education using interactive[20] audio, video, or data communications" (B&PC

---

[20] "Interactive" means a real time or near real time two-way transfer of medical data and information (B&PC § 2290.5(a)(2)).

© 2005 William L. Marcus and Marsha N. Cohen

§2290.5(a)(1)). Although the law applies directly to physicians, podiatrists, clinical psychologists, and dentists, it will affect pharmacists who receive prescriptions written after telemedicine diagnoses.

Basically, the statute authorizes the practice of medicine in other than a face-to-face context as long as the patient has given both verbal and written informed consent (B&PC §2290.5(c)(1)). The purpose, and the hope, of the statute is to make additional medical care available to underserved rural and urban areas (Stats. 1996, ch. 864, §1).

The telemedicine statute specifically authorizes a medical practitioner to diagnose and treat a patient through electronic contact that is real-time or near real-time. California residents may receive their health care via telemedicine. However, this authority does not override the requirement in the Medical Practice Act that there be both a medical indication for any prescribing and a good faith prior examination.[21]

## *Telepharmacy*

There are many entirely legitimate pharmacy services operating electronically. If those sites merely receive and fill valid prescriptions by licensed prescribers, they are no different from mail-order pharmacies. As discussed in Chapter IV: Licensing Pharmacies, nonresident pharmacies, including those in cyberspace, must be registered to do business in California, and comply with certain requirements of California law. Operation on the Internet also does not exempt the participants from compliance with federal drug laws and regulations.

Many other online pharmacies, however, appear to be skirting the requirements of the law. A number of web sites offer to dispense prescription drugs to consumers who have not seen a physician and do not have a prescription when they log on to the site. These sites offer to obtain a prescription for the drug that the consumer wants, and either fill it, delivering the drugs by mail, or refer the consumer to a pharmacy that will fill the prescription. The typical pattern is to have the consumer fill in a questionnaire that is forwarded for review to a prescriber, who provides the prescription. The pharmacies may be located anywhere in the United States or overseas. The prescribers may also be located anywhere, and may not be in the same state or even country in which the pharmacy is located. In fact, the drugs often do not come either from within the United States or even from the country, such as Canada, where the supplying pharmacy purports to be. At least one supposedly Canadian pharmacy whose shipments were intercepted was supplying drugs from Europe that were coming through The Bahamas (CanadaRx.net of Hamilton, Ontario, set up a pharmacy operation in the Bahamas; Clifford Krauss, *Internet Drug Exporters Feel Pressure in Canada*, NEW YORK TIMES, Dec. 11, 2004, p. A1). In addition, problems have arisen concerning whether drugs were properly manufactured and maintained, and about counterfeit drugs (see, e.g., Melissa Healy, *A Web of Drugs: Online "Rogue Pharmacies" Offer Quick Access to Prescription Drugs, Many of Them Addictive and Dangerous*, LOS ANGELES TIMES, Dec. 1, 2003, p. F1; Gilbert Gaul and Mary Pat Flaherty, *U.S. Prescription Drug System Under Attack*, WASHINGTON POST (series, from Oct. 19-23, 2003, p. A01, covering the unregulated shadow market, the Internet as a pipeline for deadly drugs, dangerous doctors feeding addictions through the Internet, counterfeit drugs, and our porous borders with Mexico and

---

[21] The Medical Board and case law have consistently interpreted the required examination to mean a physical examination (Medical Board of California policy statement on Internet prescribing, www.medbd.ca.gov/buyerbeaware.htm). However, a physical examination is not required on every occasion when a prescription is issued for a patient. When a physician has examined a patient sufficiently and recently enough for a condition for which a prescription is to be issued, a new prescription or a refill can be issued following a telephone conversation with the patient. The same should be true for other electronic contacts, including over the Internet.

Canada). As has been widely reported in the popular media, prescription drug sales via the Internet are rapidly increasing, fueled largely by the promotion of so-called "lifestyle" drugs such as Viagra®.[22]

Much of this activity is in violation of state or federal law. California law expressly bars a person or entity from prescribing, dispensing, or furnishing, or causing to be prescribed, dispensed, or furnished, any dangerous drug or dangerous device to any person in California via the Internet unless there has been a good faith prior examination of the patient and a medical indication for the drug or device for that person (B&PC §§2242.1(a), 4067). Dispensers or furnishers of drugs or devices are in violation if they either know or reasonably should have known that the prescription was issued without a good faith examination (§4067). The fines or civil penalties are steep: up to $25,000 for each violation (B&PC §2241.1(b)). Licensees of California licensing boards may be disciplined for violations of the law, and violators who are not residents of California are to be referred, where applicable, to their professional licensing authority (B&PC §2242.1(e)). Although controlled substances are readily available for sale on the Internet, the DEA does not currently permit a prescription for any controlled substance received via the Internet to be filled (DEA Pharmacist's Manual, pp. 46-47).

The Board of Pharmacy sought $88,700,000 in fines against a pharmacy that it alleged had filled over 3,500 Internet prescriptions illegally (Christopher Heredia, *2 L.A. druggists draw $88.7 million fine; State board issues harsh penalty over illegal online prescriptions*, SAN FRANCISCO CHRONICLE, Wed., May 29, 2002, p. A1). The Medical Board has filed similar cases (see, e.g., Douglas E. Beeman, *Doctor facing license hearing: INTERNET: Investigators say the Colton physician had been told to stop prescribing drugs online*, THE PRESS-ENTERPRISE, Apr. 16, 2002, p.B01). The Pharmacy Board's published position on Internet dispensing noted its intent to pursue violators aggressively (*The Script*, www.pharmacy.ca.gov/publications/03_oct_script.pdf, Oct. 2003, pp. 6-7).

Various states have taken disciplinary and civil enforcement actions against licensees for improper or illegal Internet practices, and some have initiated criminal investigations. Every state takes the position that a prescriber who does not have a pre-existing relationship with the patient and does not establish one has no authority to prescribe via the Internet. Criminal investigations are being conducted in several states.

The National Association of Boards of Pharmacy has developed 17 criteria for evaluating on-line pharmacies; those that satisfy the criteria may be awarded a VIPPS (Verified Internet Pharmacy Practice Site) certificate. Those sites may display the VIPPS logo, which links to the NABP website to enable verification that the online pharmacy is actually entitled to the logo. While NABP indicated in its newsletter (Vol. 29, No. 10, Dec. 2000, p. 142) that more than 50 Internet pharmacies had been evaluated by the fall of 2000, only 13 sites were listed as approved in December 2004 (www.nabp.net/vipps/consumer/listall.asp). Like all voluntary systems, VIPPS can only evaluate those sites that choose to participate in the program.

Federal agencies, including the Federal Trade Commission, FDA, and DEA, have taken actions to monitor and control drug prescribing and dispensing activities on the Internet. FDA has posted a page on its web site to educate consumers to distinguish between legitimate online drugstores and those that sell drugs illegally. FDA has examined thousands of websites and taken regulatory

---

[22] See, for example, Carl T. Hall, *Peddling Viagra Online; You can get hot new drug, and others, on the Net – without ever seeing a doctor*, SAN FRANCISCO CHRONICLE, July 2, 1998, p. A1. Online prescription sales were expected to increase from $23 million dollars in 2000 to a billion dollars by 2002 (NABP Newsletter, Vol. 30, No. 3, Mar. 2001, p. 44, citing research by Jupiter Communications).

action against hundreds of them. However, even though FDA has obtained over 100 criminal convictions, the problem largely continues unabated (see Healy, LOS ANGELES TIMES, Dec. 1, 2003, and Gaul and Flaherty, WASHINGTON POST series, cited above). DEA has also taken action, for example suspending a Nevada pharmacy for dispensing over 1,500,000 dosage units of controlled substances in six months without proper patient evaluation (DEA News Release, Dec. 20, 2002, www.usdoj.gov/dea/pubs/pressrel/pr122002.html).

Some Internet entities try to circumvent licensing requirements by claiming they are not pharmacies, but merely serve as facilitators that connect people who want their prescriptions filled to a pharmacy. Such "facilitating" is still the practice of pharmacy and requires licensure, or registration as a nonresident pharmacy (see Chap. IV: Licensing Pharmacies).

The pooling and sharing, or resale, of unused prescription drugs among consumers, which also has been happening through the Internet, is also illegal, even if no one profits. Drugs that have been dispensed to one patient cannot be transferred to another person (or, in most cases, returned to stock; see Chap. VII: Ordering Drugs ("Return and Destruction of Drugs")). Even if the transfers were legal, engaging in or arranging for them, whether for free or for a fee, would be wholesaling, for which a license is required.

States face many difficulties enforcing laws against Internet operations located out-of-state or outside the country. Even federal cooperation makes the task only marginally easier. The General Accountability Office, noting the convenience and benefits from legitimate Internet pharmacy operations, has recommended that new federal regulation focus on disclosure of adequate, identifying information about such websites (*Internet Pharmacies, Adding Disclosure Requirements Would Aid State and Federal Oversight*, GAO, Oct. 2000, [GAO-01-69]).[23]

---

[23] GAO has issued reports on some of the troublesome aspects of Internet pharmacies, including *Internet Pharmacies: Some Pose Safety Risks for Consumers*, GAO-04-820, June 17, 2004, and *Internet Pharmacies: Hydrocodone, an Addictive Narcotic Pain Medication, Is Available Without a Prescription Through the Internet*, GAO-04-892T, June 17, 2004).

**What you should think about after reading this chapter:**

1. How much reliance should a pharmacist be able to place on medical information software to identify potential concerns?

2. Are written consultation and pharmacist availability for telephone consultation sufficient substitutes for face-to-face consultation?

3. What can, or should, a pharmacist do to improve patient compliance? Patient understanding?

4. Why are there limitations on prescription refills?

5. Should the pharmacist ever hesitate or refuse to provide an authorized refill?

6. When does an emergency justify dispensing a refill without prescriber authorization? Dispensing without a prescription?

7. How, if at all, should a pharmacy be able to help a patient who is overseas obtain a refill of a current medication?

8. What might a pharmacist do if a patient cannot afford the cost of prescribed drugs?

9. What role can the Internet safely play in the dispensing and refill process? The prescribing process?

# Chapter XI

# Record-Keeping

---

**What you should know after reading this chapter:**

1. What are acquisition and disposition records?  How long must they be kept?

2. What is a current inventory?  A biennial inventory?

3. Who is responsible for the accuracy of a pharmacy's records?

4. What information about which transactions must be recorded?

5. What records must be kept on the premises?  For how long?

6. When are electronic records and signatures permitted?

---

# Records for Dangerous Drugs and Dangerous Devices

Section 4081 of the Pharmacy Law provides:

(a) All records of manufacture and of sale, acquisition, or disposition of dangerous drugs or dangerous devices shall be at all times during business hours open to inspection by authorized officers of the law, and shall be preserved for at least three years from the date of making.  A current inventory shall be kept by every manufacturer, wholesaler, pharmacy, veterinary food-animal drug retailer, physician, dentist, podiatrist, veterinarian, laboratory, clinic, hospital, institution or establishment holding a currently valid and unrevoked . . . license . . . or exemption who maintains a stock of dangerous drugs or dangerous devices.

(b) The owner, officer, and partner of any pharmacy, wholesaler, or veterinary food-animal drug retailer shall be jointly responsible, with the pharmacist-in-charge or exemptee-in-charge,[1] for maintaining the records and inventory described in this section.

(c) The pharmacist-in-charge or exemptee-in-charge shall not be criminally responsible for acts of the owner, officer, partner, or employee that violate this section and of which the pharmacist-in-charge or exemptee-in-charge had no knowledge, or in which he or she did not knowingly participate (B&PC §4081).

---

[1]  "Designated representative-in-charge" is substituted for "exemptee-in-charge" on January 1, 2006 (Stats. 2004, ch. 857 (SB 1307).

# The Importance of Records

Pharmacy is one of the most closely regulated professions, not only because drugs have the potential to cause injury or death instead of to preserve or improve life, but also because of the potential for diversion and misuse of abusable drugs. Hundreds of federal and state cases arising from enforcement actions against pharmacists, pharmacies, and prescribers attest to the importance of accurately accounting for drugs (see Chap. XII: Practice Pitfalls).

The Board of Pharmacy, DEA, DHS, and other agencies with any authority over pharmacies and pharmacy practice take the record-keeping requirements very seriously. Any discrepancy, either an overage or a shortage, is a violation of section 4081(a). The Board has always recognized that over time very small variances are common because of minor miscalculations or miscounting. However, the advent of computerized record-keeping means there is less excuse and therefore less tolerance for inaccurate records; all one needs to do is assure accurate data entry. Recording the transactions through which one obtains or disposes of drugs, including their names and amounts, hardly requires a degree in accounting, and in fact requires far simpler computations than those every pharmacist has used in chemistry and pharmacology.

A pharmacy may be disciplined or otherwise penalized for any discrepancy, no matter how small (§4332), if the circumstances are deemed to warrant it. The greater the discrepancy or the slower a pharmacy or the pharmacist-in-charge was to recognize the discrepancy, account for it, and determine its cause, the more likely there will be enforcement action taken.

Penalties for the failure to produce records to account for drugs can be quite severe. A pharmacist or pharmacy owner risks not only loss of licensure for drug shortages, even without any proof of bad intent or negligence (that is, the licensee will be subject to "strict liability"), but also may face criminal prosecution (*United States v. Green Drugs*, 905 F.2d 694 (3d Cir. 1990); *United States v. Bycer*, 593 F.2d 549 (3d Cir. 1979)), by state or federal authorities or both. In one case that went to trial in Los Angeles, a pharmacy owner, who was also a pharmacist, was convicted of record-keeping violations and sentenced to 18 months in jail for failure to have records to account for over 500,000 doses of APC #3®. No proof was needed of where the missing controlled substances went, or why they were missing (*People v. Walker*).

# What Records Are Required?

The record-keeping requirement itself is deceptively simple: anyone – not just pharmacies – who handles dangerous drugs or devices must, at all times, have accurate records that account for the acquisition and disposition of all of those drugs and devices and must keep those records for at least three years (§4081; §1718; 21 CFR §1304.03; H&SC §§11179, 11205-11206, 11252-11253). Prescriptions filled, and all records required by section 4081, must be kept on file and open for inspection (§4333(a)).[2] If such records are maintained in electronic form, the person responsible for the premises must be able to produce a hard copy and electronic copy of all such records at all times

---

[2] Section 4081(a) requires that records of manufacture, sale, and disposition of dangerous drugs must be retained. This means the pharmacy's original record (or its copy of the original or an electronic record) must be retained. In the case of certain controlled substances, it means the federal Form 222; otherwise, it is usually the order form and/or the invoice provided on receipt. In the case of a prescription, it is either the written order, the written record of an oral order, the fax, or a computer record.

when the licensed premises are open for business (§4105(d)).[3]  Records of a discontinued business must be kept at a board-licensed facility for three years after discontinuance (§4333(a)).

The simplicity of the record-keeping requirement should not lull those responsible for records into neglecting them.  The record-keeping requirement means recording a distribution to anyone, whether pursuant to prescription, transfer to another licensee,  return to a manufacturer or wholesaler, or otherwise.  It includes recording changes in the drug form, for example, when a drug is reconstituted or combined with other drugs to make a new end product.  It includes recording, as accurately as possible, destruction of damaged, dated, or otherwise unusable drugs and any loss or theft.[4]

Record-keeping plays a critical and central role in enforcement of drug and device laws.  In addition to the obvious concern about theft and diversion, careful records of drug acquisition and disposition are critical to track drugs to the customer level or up through the distribution chain in the event of a drug safety or quality problem requiring a recall.  Sloppiness concerning this obligation will inevitably result in time-consuming, expensive, and potentially disastrous enforcement actions against licensees.  The newly-adopted requirement for drug distributors, including pharmacies, to maintain a drug's "pedigree"[5] – a trail from manufacturer to the retail level – places additional importance on the ability to maintain accurate records.

Many sections of law and regulations demand that pharmacies keep various types of records.  A lengthy, but not necessarily exhaustive, list of those records, and the chapters in this text in which they are discussed, is at the end of this chapter.

## Record-Keeping Requirement: Overview

The record-keeping requirement demands that the pharmacy maintain records of acquisition and disposition of all drugs and devices.  The pharmacy needs a separate record for each drug (in each strength and form) showing when it was obtained and from whom, as well as other information required by law (for example, its manufacturer).  As a practical matter, all information should be kept that would be necessary or helpful in keeping an accurate inventory.  This includes the receipt or purchase from any source; any transfer, whether a purchase or exchange, from any source, including other pharmacies under common ownership; and any returns to the pharmacy from any source.  Detailed records also must be kept of drugs that the pharmacy compounds for future use or for a prescriber (§1716.2).

## The Inventory

Every manufacturer, wholesaler, pharmacy, veterinary food-animal drug retailer, physician, dentist, podiatrist, veterinarian, laboratory, clinic, hospital, institution, or other establishment holding a

---

[3]  The existence of computer records does not eliminate the need to maintain a written prescription or the pharmacy's written transcription of an oral order, if such records are received or otherwise required to be made and maintained.  In addition, electronic records may need to comply with certain standards; for example, the DEA has detailed requirements for electronic records of prescription refills (21 CFR §1306.22(b)).

[4]  Loss and theft must also be reported to the Board of Pharmacy (§1715.6) and, if controlled substances are involved, to the DEA (21 CFR §1301.76(b), see Chap. VII: Ordering Drugs ("Loss and Theft")).

[5]  As of 2006, the pharmacy must obtain a pedigree for dangerous drugs it obtains and provide one for those it resells to other than retail customers (see Chap. VII: Ordering Drugs).  The pedigree is a detailed record that shows everyone – manufacturer, wholesaler or other distributor, and retailer – who handled the drug.

currently valid and unrevoked license that maintains a stock of dangerous drugs or devices must keep a current inventory of them (§4081(a)). "[E]very . . . institution, or establishment . . ." sweeps very broadly, including licensees of agencies other than the Pharmacy Board, such as all the licensed health care facilities that maintain stocks of drugs, even if only for emergency use.

"Current inventory" includes complete accountability for all dangerous drugs and devices handled by every named licensee (§1718). In *Banks v. State Board of Pharmacy*, 161 Cal. App. 3d 708, 713-715 (2d Dist. 1984), the court held that the requirement of a "complete and accurate" record of the drugs in a pharmacy was easy to understand ("[k]eeping track of one's possessions is not an esoteric skill"), and that the Board had no obligation to "provide guidelines or training in recordkeeping" to pharmacists. Not only records, but also stock, of the drugs or devices must be open to inspection by authorized officers of the law at all times during business hours (§4080). Authorized officers of the law include peace officers,[6] Board inspectors, DHS food and drug inspectors, and investigators from the Department of Consumer Affairs Division of Investigation (§4017).

The Pharmacy Law does not state how often a formal inventory should be done, but since federal law requires each registrant to take an initial and biennial inventory of controlled substances (21 USC §827, 21 CFR §1304.11) most pharmacies will need at least a biennial inventory. However, in addition, it would seem prudent for a pharmacy or other entity licensed by the Board to do an inventory at the start of business (or at the time a business's ownership is transferred) and at the time the pharmacy closes down or is transferred to another owner. A pharmacist-in-charge would be well-advised, for his or her own protection, to do a complete formal inventory when he or she becomes the pharmacist-in-charge and when he or she leaves the position. A full inventory is also advisable, and probably unavoidable, when there is any significant theft, diversion, or other loss of a drug; it might be possible to limit the inventory to the types of drugs involved in the theft or loss.

A separate inventory must be kept for each registered location and for each different activity (pharmacy, wholesaler, manufacturer) at each location (21 CFR §1304.11(a)). The federal regulations concerning the mandatory initial and biennial inventory of controlled substances require an actual count of all Schedule II controlled substances. The amounts of Schedule III, IV, and V drugs may be estimated except for open containers with more than 1,000 dosage units in them (21 CFR §1304.11). When a drug not previously scheduled becomes a controlled substance, an inventory of that drug must be taken. An inventory must also be taken of any controlled substance that is damaged, defective, or impure and awaiting disposal, being held for quality control purposes, or maintained for extemporaneous compounding (DEA Pharmacist's Manual, p. 27). Along with other required information, that inventory must include the reason why the substance is being maintained, and whether it is capable of being used in the manufacture of any controlled substance in a finished form. There are additional record-keeping requirements that pertain to certain types of transactions involving controlled substance precursors (see Chap. II: Drugs).

Inventories must include the date; the time of day (opening or closing of business); the drug name, strength, and form; the number of units or volume of each drug; and the total quantity. DEA recommends the inventory also include the name, address, and DEA registration number of the registrant and the signature of the persons responsible for taking the inventory (DEA Pharmacist's Manual, pp. 25-26). While DEA requires the various controlled substances inventories to be taken, they need not be submitted to the agency.

---

[6] "Peace officers" include investigators from the Medical Board of California and the Board of Dental Examiners. Division of Investigation investigators work on cases involving osteopathic, nursing, and veterinary licensees, among others. DHS has authority to inspect records in regard to Medi-Cal patients.

# Keeping and Producing Records

All records must be kept for at least three years, although some must be kept longer (for example, clinics licensed by the Board to maintain a joint drug stock must keep their records for seven years, as noted in Chapter V: Other Pharmacy Board Licensees).

Failure to produce records when requested by one authorized to do so is a misdemeanor (§4332).  Technically, the loss or destruction of records is a valid explanation for not producing them, but the Board is likely to discount questionable or delayed explanations.  Some such explanations received by the Board over time have been suspiciously odd (for example, accidental burning of nothing but the prescriptions, prescriptions "accidentally" blown up by firecrackers that somehow went off in the pharmacy on the Fourth of July, and filled prescription records "stolen" from a pharmacy with no sign of forced entry and no loss of drugs).  Nor is it acceptable for the pharmacist-in-charge, the pharmacist on duty, or an exemptee/designated representative to delay or refuse production of records on the basis that he or she is unable to access electronically-maintained information; he or she is required to be able to access such data (§4105(d)).

# Maintaining Records on the Premises

Because acquisition and disposition records are subject to production on request during normal business hours, they obviously must be maintained on the premises.  Section 4105(a) specifies that all acquisition and disposition records must be retained on the licensed premises in a readily retrievable form.  If original records must be temporarily removed for license-related purposes, a duplicate set must be retained (§4105(b)).  The records must be retained on the licensed premises for three years (§4105(c)).

The Board has the authority to waive, upon written request, the requirement that the records be kept on the licensed premises (§4105(e)).  In a regulation, the Board has provided that any licensed entity will be granted a waiver unless, within the last five years, it has failed to produce requested records or has falsified records covered by section 4081 (§1707(a)).  However, all prescription records must be kept on the licensed premises for one year from the date they are made (§1707(e)); all prescription records for controlled substances must be kept on the licensed premises for two years from the date they are made (§1707(f)), in accordance with the federal requirement.

An entity with a waiver must maintain the off-site storage area so that the records are secure, including from unauthorized access, and be able to produce requested records within two business days of a request by the Board or an authorized officer of the law (§1707(b)).  If the entity fails to comply with these requirements, the Board may cancel the waiver without a hearing (§1707(c)).  The entity may reapply for a waiver when it can demonstrate it will now be in compliance (§1707(d)).

Even without a waiver, any licensed entity may store required records in a storage area at the same address as the entity, or adjoining the entity, if those records are readily accessible to the pharmacist-in-charge and, upon request, to the Board or authorized officers of the law (§1707(g)(1)).  That storage area must also be secure and assure the confidentiality of any patient-related information (§1707(g)(2)).

**A Board inspector comes to the pharmacy and asks to see records of acquisition and disposition of certain dangerous drugs for the last six months.  How long does the pharmacy have to produce them?**

Unless the pharmacy has a waiver, it must produce them immediately. If the records are stored off the premises, they must be available within two business days. If the originals have been temporarily removed for a license-related reason, copies must be available. If the inspector requests the originals, they should be produced promptly, unless there is a convincing reason why their temporary removal does not allow their production quickly. Prescription records for these drugs must be on-site and immediately available, whether or not the pharmacy has a waiver, because they would be less than one year old (§1707(e),(f)).

**Is the answer different if the inspector asks to see records for acquisition and disposition of Pen VK® and methylphenidate for the preceding 18 months?**

As to Pen VK®, the same answer applies, except that, if the pharmacy has a waiver, prescription records for Pen VK® that are more than one year old may be stored off-site. Because methylphenidate is a controlled substance and the requested records are less than two years old, the prescription records for it must be maintained on the licensed premises for two years, under federal law.

## *Records of Controlled Substances*

All records of acquisition and disposition of controlled substances must be retained, including receipts and invoices, all inventory records, reports of theft, loss, or surrender of controlled substances, and Forms 222, as well as prescription records. The Forms 222 required to purchase certain controlled substances must be retained for two years and produced on request (21 USC §828(c)(1), 21 CFR §1305.13). Used or unused Forms 222 that are lost or stolen must be reported immediately to the DEA (21 CFR §1305.12(b)); unused Forms 222 must be returned to the DEA upon termination, suspension, or revocation of the holder's license (21 CFR §1305.14).

Inventories and records, including prescriptions, of Schedule I and II controlled substances must be kept separately from all other records (21 CFR §1304.04(h)(1)). Records of Schedule III, IV, and V controlled substances either must be maintained separately from all other records, including those for Schedule II controlled substances, or in such a form that the information is readily retrievable and separable from other pharmacy records. All controlled substance prescriptions may be kept together if the Schedule II prescriptions are readily distinguishable from the others. If the pharmacy keeps all of its controlled substances prescriptions together, or keeps all of its prescriptions (except Schedule IIs) together, the Schedule III, IV, and V controlled substance prescriptions are considered readily retrievable and distinguishable either by stamping them in the lower right-hand corner with a red C at least one inch high or by having an electronic recordkeeping system which permits identification by prescription number and retrieval of original prescription documents by prescriber name, patient name, drug dispensed, and date filled (DEA Pharmacist's Manual, pp. 24-25, 21 CFR §1304.04(h)(2)).

**If a controlled substance prescription form has an order for a Schedule II controlled substance and for a Schedule III or IV controlled substance, how must it be maintained?**

The form may be kept with other controlled substance prescriptions, provided it is either stamped with a red C or the pharmacy's computer system permits the Schedule II order to be identified by prescription number and the original document can be retrieved by prescriber name, patient name, drug dispensed, and date filed.

**What about a controlled substance prescription form with an order for a Schedule II controlled substance and an order for a non-controlled substance?**

Under federal law, prescriptions for Schedule II controlled substances must be kept separate from all other records (unless, as described above, they are maintained with other controlled substance prescriptions). The purpose for this federal restriction is to enable prescriptions for controlled substances to be readily located. That purpose would be served either by keeping the prescription containing a Schedule II and a non-controlled substance order with the other Schedule II prescriptions or by having a compliant computer system, as described above. The prescription-filing requirement does not need to be read to mean that, despite California law, a prescription form for a Schedule II controlled substance could not also contain an order for a non-controlled substance.

**What about a controlled substance prescription form with an order for a Schedule III, IV, or V controlled substance and an order for a non-controlled substance?**

Under federal law, prescriptions for Schedule III, IV, and V controlled substances must be kept separate from those for non-controlled drugs or kept so that the information is readily retrievable. If the pharmacy keeps a separate file for controlled substance prescriptions, this prescription should be maintained there. If the pharmacy files all of its prescriptions together, this prescription will need to be marked with the red "C." That requirement is waived if the pharmacy has an electronic system that allows the identification and retrieval of the Schedule III, IV, and V prescriptions.

A pharmacy must document the receipt of all controlled substances, including the dates of receipt and confirmation of the accuracy of the order. These records must be kept in a readily retrievable manner for DEA inspection (21 CFR §§1304.04, DEA Pharmacist's Manual, pp. 22-23). When a registration is terminated or transferred, DEA must be notified, and the certificate of registration and any unused Forms 222 (marked "void") returned.[7] DEA must be notified where any controlled substance inventories and records will be kept and how controlled substances were transferred or destroyed; these records must be available for two years after the discontinuance of business. DEA must be notified at least 14 days prior to the transfer of a registered business, and an inventory must be done on the date of transfer and copies kept both by the transferee and the transferor entities (21 CFR §1301.52, DEA Pharmacist's Manual, p. 13).

In addition to records of acquisition and disposition of controlled substances and inventories, a pharmacy must maintain its blank 222s, any power of attorney authorization to sign 222s, receipts and invoices for threshold quantities of List 1 chemicals ordered (as well as distribution records for those chemicals), any DEA Form 106 reports of loss or theft, any DEA Form 41 reports of drugs surrendered for disposal, and the DEA registration certificate (DEA Pharmacist's Manual, p. 23).[8]

Failure to keep required records subjects the registrant to criminal prosecution. Registrants are strictly liable for record-keeping violations; their lack of intent to break the law is no defense. Nor is it a defense to charges of failure to follow DEA requirements that the business has otherwise complied with reasonable commercial record-keeping practices (*United States v. Poulin*, 926 F. Supp. 246, 250 (D. Mass. 1996)).

---

[7] DEA must be notified if 222s are lost or stolen, providing the serial numbers of each form. If an entire book of forms has been lost or stolen and the pharmacy cannot provide the serial numbers, the pharmacist must report the approximate date of issuance to DEA. When the lost or stolen form involves an order that was never received, the pharmacy should complete a new order and attach a statement that includes the first order's serial number, the date of that order, and a verification that the ordered drugs were never received. The pharmacist must keep a copy of the statement with the pharmacy copies from both the initial and replacement orders (DEA Pharmacist's Manual, pp. 31-32).

[8] A DEA registrant may maintain shipping and financial records at a central location away from the location registered by the DEA if it notifies the nearest DEA Diversion Field Office and the DEA does not notify the registrant within 14 days that permission is denied (DEA Pharmacist's Manual, p. 24 ).

## *Why Are the Record-Keeping Laws So Strict?*

While all these record-keeping requirements may seem excessive, the reality is that the maintenance of accurate, up-to-date records of all dangerous drug and controlled substance transactions is the centerpiece of drug law requirements. Only if these records are kept meticulously can responsible agencies track, prevent, or prove violations of drug laws and federal and state controlled substance laws, or track the source of drugs that are or may be tainted or dangerous to prevent their further distribution or to permit recalls. Requiring detailed records, particularly of controlled substances, may dissuade people from diverting drugs, especially in large quantities, and enables regulators to hold accountable those whose drug shortages may well have been caused by purposeful diversion. In the pen-and-paper era, it was understandable that records became imperfect as a result of the accumulation of small errors. In our electronic age, the expectation of accuracy is heightened, but the burden required to be accurate is much diminished.

# Accountability of the Pharmacist

In order to assure accountability for the filling and refilling of prescriptions, each pharmacy must have written procedures that identify each individual pharmacist responsible for the filling of prescriptions and for the entry of prescription information into either a manual or an electronic database. The pharmacist must create a record of such filling in his or her handwriting or through hand-initialing an electronic record not later than the beginning of the pharmacy's next operating day. This record must be maintained for at least three years (§1717(g)).

The owner and pharmacist-in-charge are jointly responsible for the accuracy of pharmacy record-keeping (§4081(b)). The law recognizes that non-pharmacist owners occasionally may engage in illegal activity pertaining to acquisition or disposition of drugs and relieves the pharmacist from *criminal* liability for such conduct if the pharmacist had no knowledge of it or did not knowingly participate in it (§4081(c)).

Note that this immunity is solely from criminal liability; no such immunity shields the pharmacist from either civil liability or disciplinary action even if he or she knew nothing of the conduct of the owner. Such importance is attached to accountability that the pharmacist-in-charge's license is made strictly liable if the pharmacy cannot account for drugs. That is why it is deemed prudent for the pharmacist-in-charge to insist on a complete inventory the day he or she starts work and the day he or she leaves.

# Other Records

### *Patient Profiles* = released upon subpoena. Rx records = released when BoP is inspected ↘ subpoena not needed

Pharmacies must also prepare and maintain patient profiles (see Chap. X: Dispensing and Beyond). They must be maintained for at least one year after the last prescription was filled or refilled for the patient (§1707.1). Pharmacy inspectors need to have access to patient profiles to determine whether a pharmacy is maintaining them as required by Board and Medicaid regulations.

However, patient privacy rights are implicated by access to profiles. Although no published court decision has directly addressed whether patient profiles must be released to a Board inspector on demand, the prudent pharmacist should probably insist on a subpoena or patient release before complying to avoid potential liability for privacy violations (see below and Chap. XIV: Other Relevant Law). Prescription records, which are subject to inspection by Board inspectors and others without a subpoena or patient release, also obviously involve personal health information.  The reason for the distinction is that section 4081, a statute, specifically requires producing records of dangerous drug or device acquisition or disposition on demand of a pharmacy inspector, and those records include prescriptions.  Patient profiles, which contain substantially more personal, protected health information than prescriptions, are not really records of disposition.  Also, the mandate that patient profiles be created and retained was created by a Board regulation, not a statute.  Although the regulation is well within the Board's power, and the Board has the power to enforce its regulations, the Board cannot by regulation diminish the privacy rights granted by statute.

### *Miscellaneous Records*

In addition to prescription information, patient profiles, compounding records, billing records maintained for Medi-Cal, and drug acquisition and disposition records, a pharmacy is required to maintain records of many of the policies and procedures it must develop.  Even if the statute or regulation does not specify that these documents must be kept, the only way to demonstrate that the pharmacy was compliant – in fact had policies and procedures – is to maintain records.  A list of policies and procedures required to be maintained by pharmacies is found in Chapter IV: Licensing Pharmacies.

Like other businesses, a pharmacy also has obligations to other government agencies to keep business and tax records.

## Privacy, Record-Keeping, and Interlinked Prescription Data Systems

Computer use has increased the sharing of data among pharmacies and others, including health care providers, health care facilities, third party payors, billing services, and government agencies.  At least some of these groups have direct access to pharmacy data.  Every pharmacist and pharmacy using interlinked systems or allowing direct access to a pharmacy's system and the data in it must be aware of and very attentive to privacy.  The fact that certain records are required to be kept does not mean that their confidentiality need not be maintained.  Even when the records are being disposed of or destroyed, their continuing confidentiality is a critical factor.  There are both state and federal laws requiring health care providers to preserve the confidentiality of their records, and significant penalties for their violation, as discussed in Chapter XIV: Other Law Relevant to Pharmacy, as well as other covered entities, must be in compliance with federal HIPAA-mandated security regulations governing personal health information records by April 21, 2005 (HHS, *Health Insurance Reform: Security Standards*, 68 FR 8334 (2003)).

Pharmacies that maintain common electronic files must do so in accordance with Board regulations (§§1717.1-1717.2) that require giving patients notice of the common file and the opportunity to object to their own prescription information being maintained in this manner (see Chap. X: Dispensing and Beyond).  With the transmission of prescriptions to pharmacies by electronic means, there are requirements to assure the completeness of the electronically transmitted information as well as its security and confidentiality (§1717.4, see Chap. X: Dispensing and Beyond).

## Electronic Records and Signature Laws

Electronic versions of records and other documents are replacing traditional written ones at rapid speed.  The advent of technology has created pressure for electronic records and signatures to be given the same authority as their written counterparts.  In 1999, a Uniform Electronic Transactions Act

(UETA) was developed to be a model for state laws in this area. Many states have already adopted the UETA; California did so in 1999, effective in 2000. The law (Civ. Code §§1633.1-1633.17) is intended to apply to transactions where both parties have agreed to conduct business by electronic means (Civ. Code §1633.5(b)), and to assure that these transactions are legally enforceable, as they would be if they were written and signed in the traditional way. This statute does not affect other requirements of the law that mandate handwritten information or signatures, as do California's controlled substances laws.

A federal law effective in 2000 has a potentially broader reach. The Electronic Signatures in Global and National Commerce Act created a general rule that a signature, contract, or other record may not be denied legal effect solely because it is in electronic form (15 USC §7001(a)(1)). The law expressly applies to both state and federal government agencies and preempts any government requirement of written records, contracts, or signatures, except as specifically set out in the law. None of those exceptions apply to pharmacy practice.

Some commentators suggested, at least initially, that this law eliminated all state or federal requirements that certain business be conducted in writing or signed or that written records be used and maintained. If that were so, requirements of handwriting and prescriber signatures for controlled substances would vanish. The authors have found nothing to indicate the law is being interpreted to change the handwriting and signature requirements remaining in the law. However, many complex questions raised by this law await answers from the United States Department of Commerce, charged with its enforcement.

In 2003, Congress mandated movement to electronic prescribing in the Medicare prescription drug program (Medicare Prescription Drug Improvement and Modernization Act of 2003, P.L. 108-173). HHS has received the first set of recommendations from the committee working on the issue; a pilot project is anticipated in 2006, with e-prescribing anticipated to be required in 2007 (http://ncvhs.hhs.gov/040902lt2.htm).

Efforts by government and the private sector to promote the expanded use of medical technology for health information, with the hope of preventing medical errors that arise from the unavailability of information and inaccurate transmissions of orders, will inevitably move additional pharmacy data, and more prescriptions, into electronic form. At this point in the development of pharmacy law, the potential impact on pharmacy from electronic signature requirements is essentially limited to handwriting mandated on controlled substance prescription forms. Other prescriptions and pharmacy records already may be, and commonly are, created in electronic form; if created in written form, they may be maintained in electronic form.

# Required Records: The List

As noted above, the following list, while lengthy, is not necessarily complete.  It is a list of those records required to be kept by a California pharmacy that are discussed in this text, with the chapters provided for reference, and generally listed in the order in which the discussion appeared.

*Chapter III: Licensing Pharmacists and Other Individuals*

Compliance with pharmacy technician requirements
Computerized record systems

*Chapter IV: Licensing Pharmacies*

Quality assurance programs
Transfer of drugs
After-hours dispensing
Sterile injectable products compounded from one or more non-sterile ingredients
Parenteral preparations
Refills by refill pharmacies
Automated dispensing devices

*Chapter V: Other Pharmacy Board Licensees*

Hypodermic needles and syringes

*Chapter VII: Ordering, Receipt, Maintenance, and Transfer of Drugs and Devices*

Handling of dangerous drugs and dangerous devices
Ordering, supplying dangerous drugs or dangerous devices
Forms 222 for Schedule I and II controlled substances
Transfers of dangerous drugs and dangerous devices
Loss and theft
Acquisition and disposition of drug samples
Return and destruction of drugs
Furnishing dangerous drugs and devices to providers in an emergency
medical services system

*Chapter VIII: Preparation of Drugs by a Pharmacy*

Compounding for prescriber office use
Compounding in general
Adulterated or misbranded drugs

*Chapter IX: The Prescription Process: From Receipt to Labeling*

Person transmitting oral or electronic prescription
Furnishing dangerous device to physical therapist
Agent of prescriber transmitting order
Electronic transmission of prescription
Controlled substance prescription forms
Faxed controlled substance forms

**What you should think about after reading this chapter:**

1.  What information, other than that required to be kept, should a pharmacy maintain?

2.  Why might you want a waiver of the on-site records storage requirement? What records might you want to store outside the pharmacy if you receive a waiver?

3.  What responsibility does an employee pharmacist who is not the pharmacist-in-charge have concerning records?

4.  Why is so much importance placed on accurate record-keeping in the handling of drugs, devices, and controlled substances?

5.  What are the advantages and disadvantages of creating and maintaining records electronically? Are there some transactions or records that should be required to be in writing?

**What you should know after reading this chapter:**

1. What are the kinds of practice errors that might lead to disciplinary action?

2. What is corresponding responsibility?

3. What factors might a pharmacist consider when evaluating a controlled substance prescription?

4. May a pharmacist dispense controlled substances to an addict?  For what purpose?

5. Is abuse and diversion of controlled substances a significant problem?

6. What is the role of opioids in pain management?

7. To what extent is a pharmacist legally responsible for the acts of others in the pharmacy?

8. What constitutes a false document?

9. What is a kickback, rebate, or referral?

10. What is a "substantially related" crime or act?

11. When might sexual harassment be a basis for discipline?

12. How might failure to meet personal financial responsibilities affect your license?

13. To what different types of liability, aside from discipline, is a pharmacist exposed?

Pharmacists are entrusted by society with very significant responsibilities in a context of very detailed laws and regulations.  Pharmacists must know, and follow, state and federal laws and regulations governing pharmacy, including both drug and controlled substance laws.  They must know the laws governing honest business practices and participation in government programs.  And they have significant responsibility for supervising other personnel and ensuring that those personnel also follow the law.  Pharmacists must ensure that patients receive the medications legally prescribed for them.  They must use their knowledge of pharmaceuticals and clinical skills to counsel patients and work with prescribers to assure appropriate therapy.  Furthermore, because pharmacists are entrusted with drugs that are capable of harming as well as healing, they must take action to prevent theft and diversion of those drugs.

Most pharmacists handle these responsibilities capably and honorably throughout their careers, but some do not.  There are many potential pitfalls in pharmacy practice; some are obvious, while some are less so.  This chapter sets out many of those pitfalls, with the intention of alerting pharmacists before they encounter them in practice.

A pharmacy owner is generally subject to disciplinary action for the conduct of any person whom the owner chooses or employs to operate the business. If a corporation owns a pharmacy, the Board may take disciplinary action against the corporation, not only for violations that occur in the operation of the pharmacy, but also whenever there are grounds for disciplinary action against persons holding ten percent or more of the corporate stock or any officer or director of the corporation (§4302).

# Grounds for Discipline

## *In General*

The key standards in the Pharmacy Law for judging whether the conduct of a pharmacist or other licensee of the Board is a basis for discipline of a license are described in section 4301.[1] That section begins by providing that a licensee is subject to discipline if his or her license has been procured by fraud or misrepresentation or was issued by mistake,[2] or if the licensee has been guilty of unprofessional conduct. There follows an impressive list of varieties of unprofessional conduct, which are grouped for discussion here in several major categories: quality of care issues (including incompetence, gross negligence, and other practice errors), drug-related conduct (including personal misuse, violation of drug laws, drug-related convictions, and failure to properly evaluate controlled substance prescriptions), fraud and other improper business practices, and criminal convictions and discipline by other jurisdictions.

Section 4301 notes that unprofessional conduct includes everything delineated in the statute, "but is not limited to" even this lengthy list of bad acts. That list is not exclusive (*Smith v. California State Board of Pharmacy*, 37 Cal. App. 4th 229, 246 (4th Dist. 1995)): *any* improper conduct or inaction may be a basis for discipline, even if it is not specified in the Pharmacy Law as unprofessional conduct, and even if it does not clearly fall within one of the categories described in the Pharmacy Law. Establishing as unprofessional conduct something not listed in statute or regulation will generally require an expert's opinion that the conduct was unprofessional for a pharmacist.

## *Quality of Care Issues*

There are several standards for evaluating whether a licensee's conduct (or failure to act) is actionable as below the quality a patient, the public, or the profession has the right to expect. Establishing that a pharmacist falls short of the standard that he or she must meet will generally require the supporting opinion of one or more qualified expert pharmacists.

**Incompetence (§4301(b)).** Conduct that demonstrates a present lack of ability or knowledge of the level possessed or demonstrated by the ordinary professional licensee, judged by community (generally statewide) standards, constitutes incompetence. This lack of competence can be

---

[1] These standards are also applied at the time of application for licensure to determine whether the application should be granted or denied.

[2] The Board may take action against a licensee whose license was issued by mistake (§4301), whether that mistake was caused by conduct of the applicant (such as misrepresenting his or her training) or was just a bureaucratic error (such as the Board's recording a passing instead of a failing score on the licensure examination). Generally the Board must prove only that the license should not have been issued. That means discipline may be imposed on a licensee for conduct that occurred prior to licensure (*Hughes v. Board of Architectural Examiners*, 17 Cal. 4th 763, 768 (1998)) or conduct that would have warranted denial of the license (§4301(p)). It means that a mistakenly-issued license may be voided even when a significant amount of time has passed since its improper issuance.

demonstrated from the treatment of a single patient, although it usually requires a pattern: a "single, honest failing" does not establish incompetence (*Kearl v. Board of Medical Quality Assurance*, 189 Cal. App. 3d 1040, 1055 (2d Dist. 1986)). Although incompetence can be demonstrated from conduct that occurred years prior to the disciplinary action, as in *Kearl*, it usually requires evidence from more recent conduct.

**Gross Negligence (§4301(c)).** Gross negligence has been defined, for disciplinary cases, as an extreme departure from community standards for the profession, or the want of scant care. Proving a charge of gross negligence requires a failing that is more than simple negligence[3] – it requires proof of a substantial departure from community standards. Because the purpose of discipline is public protection, rather than redressing private harms, the fact of actual harm, or whether or not it was severe, is irrelevant (*Kearl v. Board of Medical Quality Assurance*, 189 Cal. App. 3d 1040, 1053 (2d Dist. 1986)). The fundamental difference between incompetence and gross negligence is that an incompetent practitioner is one who apparently is unable to meet community practice standards, while a grossly negligent practitioner may have the knowledge and ability to practice properly but fails to do so.

## *Errors and Omissions*

Five areas that can be considered on their own, but which also involve quality of care issues, are prescription errors, mishandling drugs, failure to consult, failure to communicate, and failure to supervise premises or employees under one's direction. Depending upon the facts of each case, a licensee may be charged with unprofessional conduct, gross negligence, or incompetence for any of these failures.

**Prescription Errors.** Errors in the process of reading, interpreting, and processing prescriptions happen. It is impossible to eliminate all possibility of human error. But prescription errors are a matter of serious concern to the Board because of their risks and costs.[4] Prescription errors reported to the Board are investigated, particularly if they caused personal injury, and especially if a patient death occurred.[5] Errors certainly can be minimized, probably to the vanishing point, by the careful development and use of procedures for filling and checking prescriptions before they leave the pharmacy. It is the pharmacist's professional responsibility to follow procedures that are designed to minimize the chance of errors. The quality assurance program each pharmacy must have in place (see Chap. IV: Licensing Pharmacies) is intended to enable pharmacists to assess errors that occur in the dispensing or furnishing of prescribed medications so appropriate action can be taken to avoid their recurrence (§4125).

The pharmacist is also obligated to be alert to errors or problems in the prescription, and to bring those to the attention of the prescriber. Unquestioningly filling a prescription as it is written –

---

[3] At least one appellate court has ruled that although "mere" negligence is not specified as a basis for discipline in the Pharmacy Law, while gross negligence is so specified, simple negligence can nevertheless be a ground for discipline if adequate expert testimony is presented that the negligent conduct amounts to unprofessional conduct (*Smith v. California State Board of Pharmacy*, 37 Cal. App. 4th 229, 246 (4th Dist. 1995)).

[4] The risks and costs of prescription errors throughout the medical system have become a matter of considerable national public concern. See, for example, two reports on the subject from the Institute of Medicine of the National Academy of Sciences: *Crossing the Quality Chasm: A New Health System for the 21st Century* (2001) and *To Err Is Human: Building a Safer Health System* (2000) (www.nap.edu).

[5] This comment may seem inconsistent with the statement above that whether or not there is actual harm is irrelevant. However, the reality is that when a mistake by a professional results in a patient's death, the agency involved will lean on the side of filing charges because of concern about legislative and media reactions if no action is taken.

that is, accurately filling the order – does not satisfy the standard of care of today's reasonable prudent pharmacist.

It is also the pharmacist's duty to rectify any errors that do occur. Board members and staff frequently encounter pharmacists who are in trouble not solely because of their errors, which are often forgiven, even in our litigious times, by patients who recognize that mistakes can happen, but because of their behavior after an error was called to their attention. When a mistake is called to the pharmacist's attention, admitting the error and offering to correct it immediately without cost or inconvenience to the patient are critical, for two reasons. First, if an improper medication has been dispensed, the pharmacist must act to retrieve it so it does not cause harm (or additional harm) and to replace it with the correct medication, for which there may be an immediate need. Second, the patient who finds that his or her pharmacy has taken responsibility for correction of its error may never even report the incident.[6]

**Suppose a customer telephones to say that the medication he has started to give his son is a different color than it was the last time the child had the same ailment. You learn that the medication is white; last time it was pink. Checking the prescription, you determine that the proper medication in fact is pink. Checking the shelves for medications that might have been used by mistake to fill the prescription, you isolate the white medication that probably is in the customer's bottle. What are all the things you ought to do? Should it make any difference if you are the only pharmacist on duty?**

It does not matter whether you are the only pharmacist on duty. You must first act to ensure the health of your patient. If the wrong medication threatens or can compromise the health or recovery of the patient, you have an ethical obligation to provide the proper medication, to retrieve the erroneous prescription (if the patient is willing to give it back to you), and, if the error threatens serious consequences, to so advise the patient. Even if you must incur significant expense to deliver the correct prescription (even if you must close the pharmacy to do so), you need to rectify the prescription error to prevent injury or further injury, and to get the proper medication to the patient. You have the obligation to contact the prescriber and notify him or her of the error or, at the very least, to urge the patient to do so immediately. These are not statutory or regulatory requirements, nor just a way to fend off or minimize any discipline, but simple matters of ethical professional conduct.

---

[6] Attorneys specializing in malpractice or disciplinary defense might object vigorously to the notion of admitting one's error to the "victim." However, in most cases of misfilled prescriptions, the fact of the error is obvious: the prescription calls for one drug, the bottle is filled with another (or the wrong strength or form). The patient also is less likely to pursue a lawsuit where the pharmacist has resolved the error satisfactorily, at least in the absence of significant harm, than if the patient's concerns were unresolved. The medical establishment, and its insurers, is in any case reconsidering the approach of denying any responsibility for error, in response to findings that patients do in fact often want an apology and recognition of their harm rather than a lawsuit (Rachel Zimmerman, *Medical Contrition: Doctors' New Tool To Fight Lawsuits: Saying 'I'm Sorry'; Malpractice Insurers Find Owning Up to Errors Soothes Patient Anger; 'The Risks Are Extraordinary'*, WALL STREET JOURNAL, May 18, 2004, p. A1).

Fortunately, most prescription errors are caught without significant harm occurring to the patient – most often by the pharmacist before dispensing to the patient, often by an alert patient who questions the appearance of the medication. In those cases the civil liability risk to the pharmacist is low, but the risk of disciplinary action for failure to act professionally to correct the error may be significant. Of course, where a patient alleges error but the pharmacist believes that no error has occurred, the pharmacist should not admit an error merely to mollify the patient.

A California statute makes statements, writings, or benevolent gestures expressing sympathy or the like in connection with pain, suffering, or death of a person involved in an accident inadmissible in a civil court action as an admission of liability (Evid. Code §1160(a)). "Accident," defined as any occurrence that results in injury or death which is not the result of willful action by a party (Evid. Code §1160(b)(1)), is so broadly defined that it could well apply to the misfilling of a prescription. The law distinguishes statements of fault (for example, "I'm sorry, this was my fault") from statements of sympathy (for example, "I'm sorry he died").

Making the error is alone a basis for discipline under section 1716.  Failure to take the above actions will increase the possibility of injury, and also of a lawsuit and a complaint that may lead to disciplinary action.  An uninjured patient who feels you have acted promptly, responsibly, and courteously in correcting the prescription error is far less likely to report your error to the Board, or sue, than a patient whose legitimate complaint fails to receive prompt attention.  An apology for a confirmed error is likely to be appreciated (as would be an offer to reverse the charge for the prescription).  But the key reason to proceed as suggested is fulfillment of your ethical, professional obligation.

You must follow the Board's quality assurance requirements and any more stringent requirements of your pharmacy's quality assurance program.  Where they appear inadequate to meet your professional obligations to the patient, you should do whatever else you believe the circumstances warrant.  In any event, you should retain the erroneous prescription container and its contents, if the patient has returned it to you, until you are certain the matter is resolved (both with the patient and, if you know a complaint has been filed, with the Board).  To maintain accurate records, as required by section 4081, you also would need to retain for three years a record showing the disposition and reacquisition of the drugs.  The conscientious pharmacist will make few significant errors, but occasionally will make one.  Any delay that the proper handling of an error might cause in processing other prescriptions or performing other duties in the pharmacy is no excuse for not giving the error, and the patient, full and immediate attention until the problem, or at least urgent treatment issues it raises, is resolved.

**A prescription is prepared with the wrong contents, but it is caught before it is actually handed to the patient.  What should you do with the container?  With the contents?**

If the prescription never reaches the hands of the patient, there is currently no requirement that the container must be retained, although the pharmacy's quality assurance program may require its retention to assess the error.  Because the drugs never left the pharmacy's control, they may be returned to stock.

**A pharmacist sells a customer an OTC product.  Is he or she liable for adverse reactions to that OTC product?**

A pharmacist will not ordinarily be subject to discipline for an OTC product sold in its original container.[7]  However, he or she could be subject to discipline for recommending the product carelessly (negligently) or providing false or misleading information about the product or its uses (see Chap. II: Drugs).

**Failure to Consult.**  Traditionally, pharmacists were sued for injuries caused by drugs almost exclusively when they erred in filling prescriptions.  But now that pharmacists are mandated to use their knowledge and experience with drugs to provide information to patients (see Chap. X: Dispensing and Beyond), their failure to provide accurate and complete information will be considered negligence when patient harm results.[8]  Failure to provide required consultation also is grounds for

---

[7] Under strict product liability law, a patient may sue the retail seller, such as a pharmacy, as well as the manufacturer, when alleging that an OTC product was defective and caused harm.  Even if such a lawsuit were successful, it would not subject a pharmacist to discipline without proof that the pharmacist was negligent, incompetent, or engaged in other unprofessional conduct.  (And generally the retail seller would seek to be compensated by the wholesaler or manufacturer that was the source of the defective product.)

[8] Because the pharmacist's review of the prescription at the time of consultation provides another check on the accuracy of the prescription, consultation is likely to help prevent erroneous prescriptions from leaving the pharmacy.

discipline (§4301(o)) or for a citation. Related to the failure to consult is the failure to maintain, and use, patient profiles (§§1707.1, 1707.3).

The obligation to consult means adequate and appropriate consultation, including the information expressly required by the law, both when required to be provided and whenever, in the pharmacist's professional judgment, consultation is warranted. It includes having and properly using patient profiles. If profile review and patient consultation can be done for an individual patient in a minute or so, then a minute is enough. But if proper review and use of the profile and consultation with the patient take longer, then the time must be spent. Where management creates an unworkable burden, you either persuade it to change, handle fewer prescriptions but do so properly, find another job, or complain to the Pharmacy Board. You may not violate the law or regulations, including by taking shortcuts; your hard-earned license may be on the line.

The Board is committed to strong enforcement of its consultation requirements. The Board regularly cites pharmacies and pharmacists for violation of section 1707.2, the duty to consult, under its cite and fine authority, discussed in Chapter XIII: The Board of Pharmacy and Other Agencies.

**Failure to Communicate.** The failure to communicate effectively with patients can prevent the pharmacist from fulfilling his or her professional role at the very time patients are coming to expect more communication, beyond the minimum required by the patient consultation mandate. Failures of communication – with patients, prescribers, employees, and co-workers – also may lead to unprofessional conduct in the form of avoidable errors.

The ability to communicate orally is an increasingly important skill for pharmacists who are under a mandate to perform the consultation required by state and federal laws and regulations, and to ensure the patient adequately understands the drug regimen and written warnings. In all cases the pharmacist must be able to communicate adequately in English. Because of the increased need for effective oral communications skills, the Board of Pharmacy adopted an English proficiency requirement for graduates of foreign pharmacy schools (§1719(c)), after having eliminated a previous such requirement some years earlier.

No law requires the pharmacist to be able to convey information to a patient other than in English. However, if a substantial number of a pharmacy's patients have a primary language other than English, the pharmacy's ability to provide effective service will be diminished if it has no way to communicate with those patients. (If the pharmacy advertises the availability of its services in a language other than English, or indicates that another language is spoken in the pharmacy, by signs or otherwise, it must be able to fulfill this expectation.) Effective communication may require cultural understanding as well as language skills. Pharmacists also should consider their need to communicate with people with impaired hearing or sight (see discussion of the Americans with Disabilities Act in Chapter XIV: Other Law Relevant to Pharmacy).

**Failure to Supervise.** Pharmacists must competently supervise other persons in the pharmacy, including ancillary personnel and, at times, other pharmacists. The pharmacist-in-charge is responsible for everything that happens in the pharmacy and may be held liable, both to discipline and in lawsuits by injured patients, for the acts of others that violate laws or regulations governing pharmacy or constitute unprofessional conduct, negligence, or incompetence. Personal knowledge or approval of the other's acts is not necessary for liability. The Board has taken the position that the liability of the pharmacist-in-charge is absolute: he or she is liable for every violation of law that occurs while serving in that position. In *Smith v. Board of Pharmacy,* 37 Cal. App. 4th 229, 243, 247 (4th Dist. 1995), the court, while overturning the Board's decision for other reasons, specifically upheld the Board's authority to discipline the pharmacist-in-charge for his or her own negligent failure to ensure the pharmacy's compliance with laws and regulations, in accordance with what is now section 4113. The court left open the question whether the pharmacist-in-charge could be held responsible for the acts of others where he or she was not negligent, and the Board has recognized that it should not try to hold the pharmacist-in-charge responsible in every situation. A recent statute, section 4306.6, provides that when disciplinary charges are filed against a pharmacist-in-charge for actions in which he or she did not participate and about which he or she was unaware at the time of their occurrence, the Board must consider it a mitigating factor in deciding upon discipline if the pharmacist-in-charge reported the actions to the Board when they came to his or her attention.

An individual pharmacist is responsible for acts undertaken under his or her supervision or control, including the acts of any intern or technician the pharmacist is supervising or responsible for and the acts of other pharmacists or nonpharmacists he or she is supervising.

The pharmacy owner is absolutely liable for the conduct of those who are allowed to operate the pharmacy, regardless of knowledge of the misconduct *(Arenstein v. California State Board of Pharmacy,* 265 Cal. App. 2d 179, 192 (2d Dist. 1968)). That liability may be found even where the owner, upon learning of the misconduct, terminated those who committed it. As with the pharmacist-in-charge, if the incident is isolated, the pharmacy and its owner may well not be held accountable by the Board, but they can be. In fact, if the pharmacy owner is a licensed pharmacist, his or her individual license as a pharmacist may be disciplined for the conduct committed in the pharmacy, even though the owner-pharmacist took no actual part in the misconduct *(Banks v. State Board of Pharmacy,* 161 Cal. App. 3d 708, 713 (2d Dist. 1984)).

In other words, one who, as a pharmacy owner, allows others to run his or her business or uses others to perform some of the activities in a pharmacy may be held liable not only for what he or she does, or what he or she directs be done or allows to be done, but also, regardless of knowledge, for what simply happens at a facility he or she owns.

**The pharmacy and the pharmacist-in-charge have policies and procedures in place for the operation of the pharmacy, including for handling and processing prescriptions. While the pharmacist-in-charge is off-duty, violations of law and professional standards are committed by other pharmacists and other pharmacy personnel. Is the pharmacist-in-charge liable?**

The simple answer is yes. The pharmacist-in-charge may be subject to discipline for any violation of law or regulations while he or she is the designated pharmacist-in-charge. Whether the Board will take action depends on all the circumstances, including such considerations as the existence and adequacy of the pharmacy's policies and procedures, whether the policies and procedures were communicated to all employees and were actually in use, how serious the violations were or over how long a period the violations occurred, whether the pharmacist-in-charge should have been aware of the problem, and how the pharmacist-in-charge responded when he or she learned of the problem.

**Mishandling Drugs.** Only certain people are authorized to take control of dangerous drugs, including controlled substances. When a pharmacy for any reason transfers drugs in its possession or under its control, it must ensure that the recipient also is licensed to handle those drugs. When a pharmacy closes because of bankruptcy, family illness, or any other cause, the responsibility for the drugs does not end. Upon bankruptcy, for example, lien holders may not take possession of the pharmacy's drug stock unless they are licensed to do so (although they may well have a right to the value of those drugs). It is the continuing responsibility of the pharmacist and pharmacy owner, and one that all too frequently is overlooked, to ensure that all its drugs remain in proper hands.

A serious problem concerns drugs that have been mishandled before reaching the pharmacy, and that may be adulterated or misbranded. It is the responsibility of the pharmacy and the pharmacist to be certain that they are purchasing drugs from reliable and legal sources, so that they have the best possible assurance of the drugs' integrity and safety. Because drug laws are also involved, the mere fact of unlicensed transfer, misbranding, or adulteration may be a violation of law and, under Section 4301(o), grounds for discipline (violating laws governing pharmacy), as discussed below.

## *Drug-Related Conduct*

Not surprisingly, violation of virtually any drug law can be a basis for discipline – from abuse of drugs or alcohol to a variety of drug or alcohol-related convictions to filling controlled substance prescriptions that are not for a legitimate medical purpose.

**Self-use.** Self-administration of controlled substances or the use of a dangerous drug or alcoholic beverages so as to be dangerous or injurious to oneself, to another licensee, or to the public, or to the extent that the use impairs the ability of the licensee (whether pharmacist, technician, or exemptee/designated representative) to conduct his or her licensed practice safely, is unprofessional conduct (§4301(h)). This prohibition does not mean pharmacy licensees cannot use controlled substances (if they are properly prescribed) or drink alcoholic beverages. But it does mean that they cannot use them in such a way as to cause danger to themselves or others, both in general and when they are practicing under their licenses. The use of a prescribed drug, even according to the directions for use, which leaves the pharmacist in the condition described above, might constitute a violation of this provision if the pharmacist knew or should have known that he or she would likely be impaired to an appreciable extent while working in the pharmacy.

Pharmacies are obligated to have procedures in place to take action to protect the public from any licensed employee known to be chemically, mentally, or physically impaired to the extent it affects his or her ability to practice his or her profession or occupation (§4104(a)). Similarly, pharmacies must have procedures for taking action to protect the public when a licensed employee is known to have engaged in theft, diversion, or self-use of prescription drugs belonging to the pharmacy (§4104(b)).[9]

**May a pharmacist or a pharmacy technician ever have a drink before going on duty? During a lunch break?**

The law does not expressly bar a licensee from working after having had a drink, but it does bar use of alcoholic beverages "to the extent or in a manner" that impairs the ability to conduct practice safely (§4301(h)). A licensee would have to be extraordinarily cautious in mixing any alcohol at all with work in a pharmacy. The law does provide that it is a crime, while on duty, to sell, dispense, or compound any drug while under the influence of intoxicating liquor or a narcotic or hypnotic drug (§4327). If an error is made after a licensee has consumed alcoholic beverages, it could be very difficult to demonstrate that the alcohol was not a factor that impaired the licensee's judgment or ability to practice safely. Even though there is no express prohibition, it would seem like an unwise choice for pharmacy licensees to consume any alcoholic beverages before or during working hours. Employers are likely to frown on such behavior as well (assuming they do not have an express policy against it).

**Furnishing to an Addict.** Knowingly selling, furnishing, giving away, or administering or offering to sell, furnish, give away, or administer any controlled substance to an addict or habitual user, unless otherwise authorized by law, is unprofessional conduct (§4301(i)). Although this bar is stated as an absolute, there is a difference between furnishing to an addict to support or maintain his or

---

[9] The Board is authorized to issue regulations establishing requirements for reporting such conduct or incidents to the Board (§4104(c)), but to date it has not done so.

her addiction and furnishing for legitimate treatment of other conditions. There are also circumstances, discussed below, under which a pharmacy may legally supply controlled substances for office-based treatment, or maintenance, of an addiction.

**Violation of Any Statute Regulating Controlled Substances or Dangerous Drugs.** This catch-all provision is not limited to the federal and state controlled substances acts or even to the Pharmacy Law (although it of course includes them). It also covers violation of any part of the federal and state food and drug laws that pertains to dangerous drugs. All such violations are unprofessional conduct (§4301(j)). A conviction for violating federal or state controlled substances laws or state dangerous drug law is conclusive evidence of unprofessional conduct (see §4301(*l*). Although it does not commonly occur, occasionally charges of violation of federal controlled substances law are resolved by the payment of significant fines (a "cash compromise"). Resolving a violation with a cash compromise still is unprofessional conduct under the Pharmacy Law (§4301(m)).

**Criminal Convictions Involving Drug or Alcohol Use.** The conviction of any felony or of more than one misdemeanor involving the use, consumption, or self-administration of any dangerous drug or alcoholic beverage, or combination of both, is unprofessional conduct (§4301(k)). This provision would cover driving convictions related to drug or alcohol use (driving under the influence).

# Improper Filling of Controlled Substance Prescriptions

A pharmacist presented with a prescription for a controlled substance has a very demanding obligation to review it and satisfy himself or herself that it is legitimate before the prescription may be filled (H&SC §11153(a), §4301(d), 21 CFR §1306.04(a), §1761). He or she simultaneously has the important obligation to ensure legitimate patients get needed medication. The obligation to evaluate whether a controlled substance prescription is legitimate is generally referred to as the pharmacist's "corresponding responsibility," and is set forth in state and federal law and regulation. Under California law, the clearly excessive furnishing of controlled substances in violation of section 11153(a) of the Health and Safety Code constitutes unprofessional conduct (§4301(d)). "Clearly excessive furnishing" is not defined precisely in the law, but basically means a large-scale pattern of filling illegitimate prescriptions, regardless of actual knowledge. The federal regulation, which is virtually identical to Health and Safety Code section 11153(a), provides:

> A prescription for a controlled substance to be effective must be issued for a legitimate medical purpose by an individual practitioner acting in the usual course of his professional practice. The responsibility for the proper prescribing and dispensing of controlled substances is upon the prescribing practitioner, *but a corresponding responsibility rests with the pharmacist who fills the prescription.* An order purporting to be a prescription issued not in the usual course of professional treatment or in legitimate and authorized research is not a prescription within the meaning and intent of section 309 of the Act (21 USC §829) and *the person knowingly filling such a purported prescription,* as well as the person issuing it, *shall be subject to the penalties provided for violations of the provisions of law relating to controlled substances* (21 CFR §1306.04(a) (emphasis added)).

What this means is that once the prescription reaches the pharmacy, it is not enough that the prescriber is legally authorized to prescribe and that the prescription is in the right form with all the required information. The fact that the prescriber is responsible for the initial decision to issue a prescription and is supposed to issue only legitimate prescriptions does not free the pharmacist from the responsibility to exercise his or her professional judgment as to the actual legitimacy of the prescription. As the United States Supreme Court made clear in *Jin Fuey Moy v. United States,* 254 U.S. 189, 194 (1920), not every piece of paper labeled a prescription is a prescription.

The reason this is a very important concept is that a person who knowingly violates this standard loses the protection given by his or her professional license. That is, both federal and California law make possession, possession for sale, and sale of all controlled substances illegal except as otherwise provided by law (21 USC §801, H&SC §11152). As a professional, the pharmacist is exempt from these types of charges only because he or she has the legal authority to possess, prescribe, or dispense, *but only to the extent that he or she does not abuse that authority.* Pharmacists and prescribers who have abused their legal authority to prescribe and dispense controlled substances may be and have been prosecuted for illegal sale of drugs and possession of drugs for sale, not just for the lesser crime of issuing an invalid prescription *(United States v. Moore,* 423 U.S. 122 (1975); *People v. Doss,* 4 Cal. App. 4th 1585 (2d Dist. 1992)).

In addition to his or her other evaluative responsibilities concerning all prescriptions for dangerous drugs, the pharmacist has an absolute duty to evaluate each controlled substance prescription. This obligation requires the pharmacist to consider the prescription itself, the prescriber, the patient, and other readily available or accessible information to determine whether the prescription in fact is legitimate. The pharmacist must exercise professional judgment and not simply defer to the authority of the prescriber. And, as noted above, while checking with the prescriber to confirm the legitimacy of a prescription is important, it is not absolute protection against discipline or criminal action for knowingly filling an illegitimate prescription (*United States v. Kershman,* 555 F.2d 198, 200-201 (8th Cir. 1977)).

Of course, the extent of the scrutiny needed for each controlled substance prescription will vary, depending, typically, on how well, if at all, the pharmacist knows the patient and the prescriber and whether the prescription is standard therapy for the condition for which it is prescribed and for the prescriber's practice. The less one knows about the patient or the prescriber and/or the more "unusual" the prescription itself, the more closely the pharmacist should consider the prescription, and the more likely the pharmacist should, pursuant to corresponding responsibility and section 1761 of the Board's regulations, contact the prescriber.

A violation of "corresponding responsibility" may be the basis for criminal prosecution as well as disciplinary action. The standard for criminal prosecution is "knowledge" that the prescription is illegitimate. That "knowledge" may consist of evidence either that the pharmacist had actual knowledge or that the pharmacist had every reason to know the prescription was illegitimate (in other words, hiding one's head in the sand to avoid seeing what anyone paying attention would see). Neither studied avoidance nor deliberate ignorance of known or available facts is a defense (*United States v. Kershman,* 555 F.2d 198 (8th Cir. 1977) (pharmacist criminally convicted even after "confirming" prescriptions with the prescriber)).

The standard for disciplinary action in California is clearly excessive dispensing of illegitimate prescriptions (§4301(d)) or dispensing a controlled substance prescription that the pharmacist knows or has *objective reason to know* was not issued for a legitimate medical purpose (§1761(b)). "Objective reason to know" means, in essence, that the ordinary prudent pharmacist would know, from the circumstances, that the prescription was not issued for a legitimate medical purpose.

The pharmacist's duty to determine if a prescription is valid does not mean the prescriber must be contacted every time a controlled substance prescription is received. Nor does it mean a pharmacist should, or must, refuse to fill every controlled substance prescription about which he or she has questions. For example, if the pharmacist knows the prescriber and his or her practice and prescribing tendencies, and is satisfied the prescriber and the prescription are legitimate, there may well be no need to contact the prescriber, even about a new patient, unless some other factors or suspicions make the pharmacist wary.  The proper exercise of the responsibility to determine the validity of controlled substance prescriptions unfortunately may sometimes anger the prescriber, who may not understand the pharmacist's legal and professional role in the dispensing process.  It may also anger or frustrate the patient, who resents any inquiry or delay in receiving medication.  Thus this responsibility must be exercised both carefully and with great sensitivity.

Pharmacists attempting to comply with the law may find it difficult to appreciate the enormity of the problem for which these responsibility requirements were designed.  In the single most striking example of flouting of controlled substance law in California legal history, if not nationally, a Los Angeles pharmacy dispensed controlled substances in massive amounts in illogical combinations, in consecutive strings from a single prescriber, to patients with unlikely names (like Terry Tune, Fairlane Ford, and Pearl Harbor).  More than a thousand prescriptions were written by a supposed prescriber who, it was later discovered, was not even licensed as a physician.  The pharmacy and pharmacists defended themselves by claiming each individual prescription was clear, in the proper form, and contained all the required information, so the pharmacy was not obligated to question the prescription further, despite the corresponding responsibility imposed on pharmacy by federal regulation and state law.  Furthermore, they asserted that the Board had failed to give them guidelines for evaluating which prescriptions were invalid.  When the California court of appeal upheld the revocation of the pharmacy permit and the owner's pharmacist license, it said, in language unusually strong for appellate courts:

> . . . when the control inherent in the prescription process is blatantly mocked by its obvious abuse as a means to dispense inordinate and incredible large amounts of drugs under the color and protection of law, pharmacists are called upon to obey the law and refuse to dispense . . .

> . . . society entrusts to persons in [pharmacy and medicine] the responsibility for control over a force which, when properly used, has great benefit for mankind, but when abused is a force for evil and human destruction.  It follows that society cannot tolerate the presence of individuals within these professions who abdicate their professional responsibility and permit themselves to be used as a conduit by which these controlled substances reach the illicit market and become that force of evil to which we allude.

> . . . *such prostitutors of their profession will not be heard to explain their dereliction by the juvenile-like complaint "Nobody told me it was wrong."  A true professional does not have to be told such things* (Vermont & 110th Medical Arts Pharmacy v. Board of Pharmacy, 125 Cal. App. 3d 19, 25 (2d Dist. 1981) (emphasis added)).

The Pharmacy Board had, prior to this decision, discussed amending its regulations to include a lengthy list of factors to be considered when determining the validity of a controlled substance prescription.  The Board declined to do so at that time because of heavy opposition from pharmacists. But after the profession recognized the risk of failure to adequately inquire about the validity of facially-valid prescriptions (and the fact that California had a major diversion problem involving prescribers and pharmacies), pharmacists requested that the Board adopt guidelines.  The Board revised section 1761 in 1985 to provide that a pharmacist could not fill a controlled substance prescription that he or she knew *or had objective reason to know* was not for a legitimate medical purpose.  Guidelines adopted at the same time instruct practicing pharmacists by drawing upon decisions in California and federal cases in which pharmacists were found to be in violation of their corresponding responsibility obligation.

**What factors should the pharmacist consider in deciding whether to fill a prescription?**[10]

First, the pharmacist must consider the prescriber.

- Is the prescriber known to the pharmacist and known to be reliable (or known to be of questionable judgment)?
- Does the prescribing fit the prescriber's practice or specialty? (Is the prescriber a gynecologist, but the prescription is for a man? Is the prescriber an oncologist, but the prescription is for methylphenidate (Ritalin®), for attention deficit disorder?)
- Does the prescribing fit the prescriber's past patterns?
- Does the prescriber appear to write in significantly larger quantities than others in his or her area without a reasonable explanation?
- Has the prescriber been disciplined or had criminal or other action taken against his or her license or DEA registration, especially for drug violations?[11]
- Where is the prescriber's office located in relation to the pharmacy? In relation to where the patient lives or works? If there is some distance between them, is there some reasonable explanation why the patient is traveling such distances?
- Are the physician's prescriptions appearing at the pharmacy in bunches? Do his or her patients seem to come into the pharmacy together or all within a short time?
- Are the prescriptions all for the same drugs or the same combinations of drugs or in the same strengths and amounts (leading to a suspicion that the physician is not individualizing treatment)?
- Are the prescriptions for apparently inconsistent or antagonistic combinations (such as depressants and stimulants) without a reasonable explanation? Or, again without a reasonable explanation, written in quantities or dosage forms or with directions (or some combination of the above) that significantly vary from usual or accepted medical use?
- Does the prescriber appear to prescribe noncontrolled drugs in an appropriate relationship to the number and variety of controlled substances he or she prescribes?
- Is the prescriber's telephone number legitimate? Does the prescription appear altered? Or have erasures? Appear to be a photocopy? Does the handwriting on a written prescription match past prescriptions from that doctor's office? Is it *too* legible?
- Does the prescription use odd or nonstandard abbreviations? Or read as if it were copied from a textbook?

Then, consider the patient:

- Does the patient appear, if it can be observed or determined by reference to a patient profile, to fit the drug or diagnosis?
- Does the patient exhibit the characteristics of a drug user or diverter? For example, does the patient say suspicious things or look suspiciously nervous? Does the patient say anything suspicious or inconsistent with the prescription or any given diagnosis or with legitimate use?
- Does the patient come in with a group of other patients? Does the patient pick up the prescription or does someone else pick up (and sometimes bring in) a number of

---

[10] These factors are drawn from a number of federal and state cases involving pharmacies and assessing the legitimacy of controlled substance prescriptions, from the DEA Pharmacist's Manual, and from the Board's guidelines. Also instructive is DEA's *A Pharmacist's Guide to Prescription Fraud*, www.deadiversion.usdoj.gov/pubs/brochures/pharmguide.htm (Feb. 2000).

[11] Information about prescriber discipline may be obtained from licensing boards or the DEA (see App. C: Other State and Federal Agencies).

prescriptions?  Does the patient pick up prescriptions for multiple patients for controlled substances?

- Do an increasing number of patients of one or a few doctors, who are not regular patrons, begin to come to the pharmacy with the same, or very similar, prescriptions?
- Where does the patient live or work in relation to the pharmacy?
- Does the patient appear anxious to get the drugs quickly?  To leave the pharmacy quickly?
- Does the prescribing fit any prior pattern established by the patient at the pharmacy?
- How long has the prescribing been going on?  Does the patient appear to be making any progress on the regimen?  (For example, if the prescriptions are for controlled substances for diet purposes, after a period of time is there evidence of any weight loss?)
- Are the amounts of the drugs increasing without a reasonable explanation (from the patient, the prescriber, or both)?
- Is the patient coming in at intervals inconsistent with how long previous prescriptions, according to directions for use, should last?
- Does the patient have proper, reliable identification?

And as to the drug itself:

- How common is abuse of the drug, historically and currently, especially in your area ?
- Is the drug appropriate for the diagnosis or for other conditions the patient has, or in the context of other drugs the patient is receiving or has received?
- Are the amounts, numbers and/or combinations of the drugs increasing without an obvious medical reason?
- Does the prescribing fit the manufacturer's recommendations or other, accepted medical standards or conditions for use (including recognized off-label uses)?
- Is the drug being combined with antagonistic or contraindicated drugs?

These are just some of the factors one might consider.  But it is equally important to remember that many factors that might lead one to suspect an illegitimate prescription also could have a perfectly valid explanation.  Most of these factors, if standing alone, would not necessarily establish that the prescription is invalid.  The pharmacist must consider each factor separately and in the context of all available information.  It is at least as great a violation of your professional responsibility to refuse to fill controlled substance prescriptions without adequate reason as it is to fill without thought any controlled substance prescription you receive.  You actually must *exercise* professional judgment.

**Suppose a customer has children who all get methylphenidate hydrochloride prescriptions for attention deficit disorder and who frequently get prescriptions for antibiotics. If the customer always picks up the methylphenidate hydrochloride promptly, but often fails to pick up antibiotics for several days, should that concern you?  Would you also suspect child abuse?**

The pharmacist does have obligations in regard to child abuse reporting (discussed below under Other Grounds for Discipline: Child Abuse Reporting).  These facts might suggest child neglect, and they might suggest a lack of knowledge on the part of the customer; you definitely should counsel this customer that when antibiotics are prescribed, dosing should begin at once for the health of the patient.  If you believe inadequate compliance with physician orders might put the children at risk, a call to the appropriate authorities is in order.  The speed with which the methylphenidate prescriptions are picked up should certainly arouse suspicion about their proper use as well.  Are the prescribing patterns of the physician also suspicious?  The prescriptions may be entirely proper; however, you should continue to be alert to patterns of this sort.

**Examples of Corresponding Responsibility Cases.** While a corresponding responsibility case in theory could be based upon a single prescription, the reality is that a case based on one or just a few prescriptions requires evidence (usually gathered through witnesses or undercover operators) that the pharmacist actually knew the prescription was illegitimate. Inevitably a situation will arise in which an earnest customer will convince a pharmacist of the legitimacy of his or her prescription; only after the customer has received the drugs will it appear that he or she in fact was abusing or selling them.[12]

A more typical corresponding responsibility case involves dozens to hundreds, even thousands, of such prescriptions for multiple patients over anywhere from a few months to a year or more. The most serious cases have involved hundreds of such prescriptions being filled daily over weeks, months, or even years. In the early 1980s, several small pharmacies in southern California were ordering as many as 1,200,000 aspirin with codeine phosphate #4 (APC®) tablets per year, along with massive amounts of other highly abused drugs. One such pharmacy filled over 200 prescriptions per day for just four highly-abused Schedule III and IV drugs, all in their maximum strengths. It dispensed about 60,000 such prescriptions per year and over 2,000,000 doses, just of those four drugs; in addition, it dispensed significant quantities of those drugs in lower strengths, as well as other Schedule II, III, and IV drugs.[13] Another example is the *Vermont & 110th* case discussed above.

**The Scope of Diversion and Abuse of Prescription Controlled Substances.** Why is there so much concern about this behavior? Although when we think of drug abuse we tend to think of street drugs, there is and historically has been a major problem with diversion and abuse of prescription controlled substances. Until the explosion of cocaine use in the 1980s, prescription drugs consistently caused the vast majority of emergency room visits involving drugs reported in the federal Drug Abuse Warning Network system. Even now, prescription drugs account for about half of the reported incidents. An estimated 6.3 million Americans abuse prescription drugs (using them for non-medical purposes or exceeding prescribed dosages). In addition to other social problems related to drug abuse, physical harm to abusers themselves is a significant problem (*National Survey on Drug Abuse and Health*, NIDA, Sept. 2004). The drugs most abused may vary from year to year and from region to region. For example, massive amounts of Preludin®, a weight control drug now off the market, were prescribed in the Long Beach area in the early 1980s – fully 600 times per capita the amounts prescribed in Sacramento. It sold for as much as $20-30 per dose on the street. Dilaudid® was the most abused Schedule II opioid (with the highest street price, as much as $100 a dose in some

---

[12] When facing discipline for violation of the corresponding responsibility obligation, pharmacists (or their attorneys) often ask which specific prescription was invalid. That is, at what point in the receipt of a string of apparently invalid prescriptions should the pharmacist have stopped filling them? In these cases, the Board generally obtains proof of a large, sometimes extraordinary, volume of suspect prescriptions, making it clear that the pharmacy filled so many that there cannot be a legitimate excuse. It is recognized that drug diverters and abusers are adept at fooling prescribers and pharmacies; isolated instances of the filling of prescriptions recognized only in retrospect as invalid are not the basis of serious disciplinary action.

[13] One of those pharmacies ordered nearly 600,000 doses of aspirin with codeine phosphate #4 tablets in just three months and, when audited, had none on hand and no records to show how the drugs left the pharmacy. The licenses of that pharmacy and its pharmacist owner were first enjoined and then revoked, and the owner was eventually convicted of criminal drug charges and sent to jail for over 18 months (*In the Matter of the Accusation Against Viscount Drugs, Nelson Walker et al.*). The importance of the pharmacy in the drug supply chain was so great that, when it was closed suddenly because of a court injunction, the street supply of the codeine phosphate #4 tablets dried up overnight in certain areas of another state.

The *Walker* case was prosecuted about ten years before the *Doss* case made it clear that a pharmacist who knowingly dispenses illegitimate prescriptions or who intends to use his or her stock to fill illegitimate prescriptions may be prosecuted for felony sale of drugs or possession for sale (*People v. Doss*, 4 Cal. App. 4th 1585 (2d Dist. 1992); H&SC §§11351-11352 (narcotics), §§11378-11379 (nonnarcotics)). The criminal penalties would likely have been more serious after *Doss*.

places in the U.S.) in the early to mid-1980s, while OxyContin® appears to win that dubious title in recent years, reaching prices as high as $120 per dose (Debra Rosenberg, *Kentucky's Pain*, NEWSWEEK, Sept. 20, 2004, p. 44).

The desire by abusers to obtain drugs to which access is controlled by prescription requirements drives up the street prices of those drugs, making supplying them financially tempting, including to organized rings of diverters. A number of other controlled substances have substantial street value, including codeine-based drugs, benzodiazepines, hydromorphone, amphetamines, and other hypnotics and sedatives. Until methaqualone (Quaalude®) was switched into Schedule I and made illegal to produce in the 1980s, entire clinics were set up, especially in California and Florida, where it was virtually the only drug dispensed or prescribed; at $20 to $30 per dose, its street value was enormous. As one drug becomes less popular or goes off the market, another pops up. When phencyclidine (PCP) became more closely watched and regulated, its successor drug, ketamine, was abused and had to be added to the controlled substance schedules in California. When the combination of aspirin with codeine phosphate #4 tablets and glutethimide (Doriden®), called "Dors and 4s" or "loads," became popular and led to dozens of deaths in the early 1980s, many abusers switched to diazepam (Valium®), other benzodiazepines, or even other central nervous system depressants to mix with their "4s."

Though the breach of professionalism is sad, it is no wonder a few (a very few) pharmacies were, in the early 1980s, charging patients up to $450 to fill a prescription for 60 phenmetrazine hydrochloride tablets that had cost the pharmacy less than $30 wholesale and would sell for up to $1,800 on the street. Even if the pharmacy filled only two per day, six days per week, or a total of 600 per year, the pharmacy was making over $250,000 a year from those prescriptions. And such pharmacies typically filled a considerably higher volume of these illegitimate prescriptions. The typical dishonest physician issuing an illegitimate prescription for hydromorphone 4 mg. might charge $100 to $200 for each prescription for 100 tablets. The person receiving the hydromorphone (or the person to whom it was resold for sale on the street) might well receive up to $5,000 for that one prescription (and occasionally much more). Even with a premium price paid to a pharmacy to fill the prescription without questioning it, it is easy to see there is plenty of profit for everyone involved.

Some drugs that have been formulated to eliminate their abuse potential have been cooked down by street users to isolate the desired active ingredient (or to remove the undesired ingredients). For example, pentazocine was heavily abused in the 1970s and early 1980s. Its primary manufacturer reformulated it (Talwin Nx®) but, for some years, street users just cooked it to remove the agonist. Some abusers have apparently even found ways to abuse Fentanyl® patches.

While physicians and pharmacists have been responsible for some of the diversion of OxyContin®,[14] much of the illegal supply has reached the street through numerous robberies of pharmacies in eastern states. While pharmacies have always been a target of after-hours burglary and daytime robbery to obtain controlled substances, the "Oxy" robberies were at an epidemic level. As a

---

[14] OxyContin® is a version of oxycodone that offers steady 12-hour pain relief with fewer side effects than comparable pain medications (Charley Gillespie, *Getting OxyContin Can Be an Ordeal for Those Who Need It*, LOS ANGELES TIMES, Oct. 14, 2001, p. A-26). It has been particularly popular with drug abusers in the eastern United States, and was quickly dubbed "hillbilly heroin" because of its abuse in Appalachia, It is extremely addictive when crushed and injected, instead of swallowed. The typical pharmacy might charge $2 for a 10 mg. pill, and under $3 for a 20 mg. pill; the street price is as much as $120 for one 80 mg. tablet (Debra Rosenberg, *Kentucky's Pain*, NEWSWEEK, Sept. 20, 2004, p. 44). More than 100 deaths have been attributed to OxyContin® abuse, although there is considerable debate whether the OxyContin® or the victims' simultaneous use of other drugs and alcohol was responsible. While OxyContin® abuse was most widespread on the eastern seaboard and in Appalachia, it was not confined there. The problem has caused considerable expense in the law enforcement, drug abuse prevention, and health care systems (Debra Rosenberg, *Kentucky's Pain*, NEWSWEEK, Sept. 20, 2004, p. 44).

result, pharmacies became fearful of stocking the drug and physicians hesitant to prescribe it, notwithstanding its significant benefits to pain patients (Leslie Miller, *"Hillbilly Heroin" Heads to the City*, LOS ANGELES TIMES, July 8, 2001, p. A-17). Some states have limited its availability under the Medicaid program, and Virginia police have distributed fingerprint kits to pharmacies to use on patients seeking the drug. Ironically, California was probably spared a significant OxyContin® problem because heroin is cheap and plentiful here, unlike in the rural areas where this problem first developed (Elizabeth Mehren, *Hooks of "Hillbilly Heroin": Abuse of prescription painkiller OxyContin ravages poor areas in the East*, LOS ANGELES TIMES, Oct. 4, 2001, p. A-1). Many lawsuits have been filed against the manufacturer of OxyContin® by individuals and by state government agencies. While the vast majority have been dismissed, at least one, in which West Virginia claimed Purdue Pharma inappropriately marketed its drug to state residents, resulted in a $10 million dollar settlement, with the money going to drug abuse and education programs (Landon Thomas, Jr., *Maker of OxyContin Reaches Settlement With West Virginia*, NEW YORK TIMES, Nov. 6, 2004, p. C2). The negative publicity and legal complications have led Purdue Pharma, manufacturer of OxyContin®, to cooperate with law enforcement officials to stem abuse and monitor prescribing and dispensing. The company has also attempted to create a form of the drug that would not be so susceptible to abuse (see www.pharma.com/pressroom/news/20032506.htm, *RxPatrol Initiative Launched to Prevent Pharmacy Theft*).

Unfortunately, over the years different areas of California have been centers for drug diversion. A small number of very aggressive pharmacies, clinics, and prescribers have been responsible for a large amount of diversion. In addition, there have been organized efforts to obtain valuable controlled substances from honest or careless prescribers and pharmacies by using "professional patients" to con them. This activity has not increased in the last decade or so, and may even have decreased to some extent. Vigorous enforcement activities, resulting in disciplinary actions by the licensing boards as well as criminal prosecutions against the most egregious violators, surely account for some of the decrease. Chance – such as the OxyContin® epidemic being centered elsewhere – probably also has played a role. But diversion remains a major problem to which a small number of practitioners, some intentionally or knowingly and others carelessly or naively, contributes.[15]

## *Meeting Patients' Needs for Controlled Substances: Pain Management*

While a pharmacist whose conduct amounts to diversion is no different from a street pusher (see *United States v. Badia,* 490 F. 2d 296, 298-99 (1st Cir. 1973), involving a physician), a pharmacist has *at least* as strong an obligation to ensure that patients in need receive medication as to turn away those who have no legitimate medical need. This dual obligation is what makes the entire concept of corresponding responsibility so difficult for the ethical practicing pharmacist. But the pharmacist is a professional with the education, training, and intelligence to make these judgments; a pharmacist who exercises his or her judgment rarely will dispense a prescription that is not valid and will just as rarely refuse to fill a prescription that is valid. The area of medical practice that is most heavily impacted by concerns in regard to controlled substances is pain management. When evaluating controlled substance prescriptions, pharmacists must consider not only the possibility of diversion or abuse, but also the consequences of denying a patient needed medication.

---

[15] The DEA has traditionally categorized practitioners who issue illegitimate prescriptions as falling into one or more of the following categories: dated (their knowledge of proper use of drugs is not current), duped (taken advantage of by "patients"), disabled (impaired – physically, mentally, or by substance abuse), or simply dishonest.

**History.** Knowledge about pain and its management is changing rapidly: new approaches to treatment and new modalities, including new classes of nonnarcotic analgesics, are under investigation or already in use. It now is generally recognized that substantial amounts of narcotics, sometimes in combination with each other and sometimes in combination with nonnarcotic controlled substances or non-drug modalities, are appropriate for the ongoing management of pain in terminal patients and cancer patients. Use in acute pain and surgical and postsurgical pain is also more broadly approved. Historically, because of a combination of fear of addiction, poor knowledge about pain, and lack of knowledge about opioids, there has been great resistance to the use, especially ongoing use, of opioids for patients outside a hospital setting. When the prescriber, the pharmacist, or the patient lacks adequate, accurate knowledge, or has unwarranted fears, of effective pain medications, patients do not receive adequate care (David Joranson and Aaron M. Gilson, *Pharmacists' Knowledge of and Attitudes Toward Opioid Pain Medications in Relation to Federal and State Policies,* 41 JOURNAL OF THE AMERICAN PHARMACEUTICAL ASSOCIATION 213 (Mar./Apr. 2001) (www.medsch.wisc.edu/ painpolicy/publicat/01japhak/index.htm)).

**California Developments.** While still a subject of some debate, the chronic use even of substantial amounts of narcotics and other controlled substances for nonterminal, intractable pain has been gaining acceptance over the last 15 years. California is one of at least 17 states with an Intractable Pain Treatment Act (IPTA, B&PC §2241.5); about 45 states have laws, statements, or guidelines on pain management. California's Medical Board adopted pain management guidelines in 1994, and the Pharmacy[16] and Nursing Boards adopted pain guidelines shortly thereafter. The Medical Board guidelines, titled *Guidelines for Prescribing Controlled Substances for Pain,* were updated in 2003 and are available at www.medbd.ca.gov/Guidelines.htm. The guidelines promote pain management and are intended to provide licensees a sense of what conduct is deemed to constitute proper pain management. The current Medical Board guidelines, for example, recognize that addicts in need of pain relief require special attention, but "a patient in pain who is also chemically dependent should not be deprived of appropriate pain relief." A new law creates an interdisciplinary panel combining law enforcement and medical concerns and expertise to establish standards for criminal cases where pain management is an issue (Pen. Code §11161.5). While illegitimate prescribing and other violations of controlled substances laws remain actionable, the IPTA, along with legislation known as the Pain Patient's Bill of Rights (H&SC §§124960-124961), promotes the appropriate use of controlled substances in the treatment of intractable pain where the prescriber has tried and considered alternatives and found, and documented the finding, that they did not relieve the pain.[17]

Policy statements in the model Controlled Substances Act, on which many state acts are based, and by the DEA encourage the use of controlled substances where needed by patients. The DEA has tried to focus attention on patient need for controlled substances, even while prosecuting abusers. It has issued, jointly with 21 pain management and professional associations, *Promoting Pain Relief and Preventing Abuse of Pain Medicine: A Critical Balancing Act,* www.medsch.wisc.edu/ painpolicy/Consensus2.pdf.[18] The DEA Pharmacist's Manual restates that controlled substances,

---

[16] The Pharmacy Board devoted the first issue of its *Health Notes* magazine to pain management. It is currently producing an updated *Health Notes* on pain management, which will be available on the Board's website.

[17] The Pain Patients' Bill of Rights gives patients in chronic and severe intractable pain the right to refuse pain management therapies that would require invasive techniques and still receive opiates, where consistent with IPTA, as well as the right to receive information about pain management specialists from physicians who do not wish to prescribe opiates to manage the pain.

[18] An FDA advisory committee, in 2003, rejected proposals to restrict the use of OxyContin® to patients in severe pain, finding modified release opioids appropriate for use in moderate pain (www.fda.gov/ohrms/dockets/ac/03/minutes/ 3978M1.pdf, pp. 3-4). The National Association of Attorneys General has also weighed in on the importance of proper

particularly narcotic analgesics, may be used to treat patients with a terminal illness or intractable pain (p. 55). This position also is consistent with international drug treaties.

A recent spate of California legislation addresses the availability of controlled substances for, and the need to assess, pain.[19] As noted in Chapter VI: Scope of Practice for Pharmacists, pain must now be assessed in any California licensed health facility at the same time traditional vital signs are taken (H&SC §1254.7); similar requirements are now part of JCAHO standards for accreditation (JCAHO Standards for Various Health Facilities, 2000).

The failure to provide adequate pain relief to patients in need has many personal, social, and economic consequences. A person in pain has a poorer quality of life and is less able than other people to participate in or enjoy everyday activities, work, and family. Undertreated pain also leads to additional and lengthy hospitalizations and slower-than-expected recovery. From the legal perspective, pharmacists and prescribers are at risk of discipline or malpractice [20] for failure to provide adequate pain treatment. Oregon was the first state to discipline a physician for inadequate use of opioids, and California has now done so as well. A California family prevailed at trial in a lawsuit charging a physician with elder abuse and reckless negligence because of his failure to give their elderly father adequate pain medication when he was dying of cancer. The California Medical Board's investigation led to no disciplinary action in that case (Matthew Yi, *Doctor found reckless for not relieving pain*, SAN FRANCISCO CHRONICLE, June 14, 2001, p. A1).[21]

The very real problems of prescription drug abuse, particularly in light of the media attention to OxyContin® abuse, make it difficult for prescribers and pharmacists to focus on the medical needs of patients for whom these drugs have proven beneficial. High-profile prosecutions for murder or manslaughter against prescribers and pharmacists also dissuade practitioners from prescribing to pain

---

treatment that involves opioids (*Improving End-of-Life Care: The Role of Attorneys General*, www.naag.org/publications/naag/end_of_life/pdf/report-end_of_life.pdf, 2003). In mid-2004, DEA and pain management organizations and advocates finalized a set of frequently asked questions intended to ease practitioner fears and clarify standards for investigators and prosecutors (*Prescription Pain Medication: Frequently Asked Questions and Answers for Health Care Professionals, and Law Enforcement Personnel*, see link at http://headaches.about.com/od/medsarticlesandinfo/a/dea_meds_faq.htm). DEA summarily withdrew its support from this document in October 2004; its website says, "The document contained misstatements" (www.deadiversion.usdoj.gov/faq/pain_meds_faqs.htm).

[19] Schedule II prescriptions for terminally ill patients are excepted from the controlled substance prescription form requirement, as they were from the triplicate (H&SC §11159.2, see Chap. IX: Prescriptions: From Receipt to Labeling). A law addressing clearly excessive prescribing and administering of drugs and other treatments was amended to clarify that use of controlled substances in compliance with the Intractable Pain Treatment Act was legal and would not subject the prescriber to discipline (B&PC §725). Health plans that provide prescription drug benefits must now cover appropriately-prescribed pain medications for terminally ill patients (H&SC §1367.215(a)). Also in this recent flurry of legislation are the creation of the multidisciplinary panel to create standards for criminal prosecutions involving pain management (Pen. Code §11161.5) and the Pain Patient's Bill of Rights (H&SC §§124960-124961), discussed above.

[20] There are a number of legal bases for lawsuits based on inadequate pain management (see Barry R. Furrow, *Pain Management and Provider Liability*, 29 JOURNAL OF LAW, MEDICINE & ETHICS 28 (2001)).

[21] The California case was later settled (*Lawyer says doctor paid for negligence*, SAN FRANCISCO CHRONICLE, June 20, 2002, p. A18). The facts of this case also inspired the passage of legislation in 2001 that requires most current physicians to complete, by December 31, 2006, one 12-hour continuing education course on pain management and the treatment of terminally ill and dying patients, and newly-licensed physicians to do so within four years of initial licensure (B&PC §2190.5). That law also mandated the Medical Board to develop standards for review of complaints regarding under- and over-treatment of patients' pain (B&PC §2241.6) and to report annually to the Legislature about disciplinary actions involving controlled substances, including their inadequate use (B&PC §2313 (Stats. 2001, ch. 518 (AB 487); Tyche Hendricks, *Pain management classes for doctors*, SAN FRANCISCO CHRONICLE, Oct. 30, 2001, p. A15).

patients, particularly those with complex problems or needs.[22]  Patients who would be helped by OxyContin® now find significant barriers to their access to it, with physicians unwilling to prescribe it, pharmacists afraid to stock it, and even Medicaid restricting access to it.

**Drug Abusers in Pain.**  Sometimes the person in need of controlled substances for medical reasons happens to be an addict.[23]  California law on furnishing controlled substances to addicts is somewhat confusing.  Section 4301(i) provides that, except as otherwise authorized by law, knowingly selling, furnishing, giving, or administering or offering to sell, furnish, give away, or administer a Schedule I or II controlled substance to an addict or habitual user is unprofessional conduct.  Health and Safety Code section 11156 states that, except as provided by California's controlled substances law, no person may prescribe for, administer, or dispense a controlled substance to an addict or habitual user.  Although these sections would seem to forbid dispensing a controlled substance to an addict, the "except as otherwise authorized" phrase suggests there is authorization to do so elsewhere in the law.

The Health and Safety Code, in sections 11215 to 11222, provides for the treatment of addicts for their addiction, treatment that often requires the provision of controlled substances.  These sections specify the amounts and types of drugs that may be prescribed to an addict, and the settings in which they may be prescribed (see also 21 CFR §1306.07).

Elsewhere the law seems to suggest that prescribers are authorized to use controlled substances for any patient suffering from a disease, ailment, injury, or infirmity attendant on old age – but not for addiction to a controlled substance – when they believe in good faith that the patient's condition requires that treatment (H&SC §11210).  So it appears that the law does not restrict treatment of any patient, including an addict, with controlled substances, for conditions except for the addiction itself.  Health and Safety Code section 11217, which provides that a prescriber may use controlled substances in the emergency treatment of an addict or where a patient's addiction is complicated by incurable disease, serious accident or injury, *or* the infirmities of old age, seems to

---

[22] Dr. Frank Fisher in Anderson, California was first charged with murder and felony fraud as the result of several deaths that appeared to involve overdoses.  A judge dismissed the charges; the prosecutors followed with misdemeanor fraud charges, but a jury acquitted.  Fisher was California's largest prescriber of OxyContin® under Medi-Cal.  (See, concerning Fisher's story and other physicians' concerns about prescribing narcotics, Maia Szalavitz, *Dr. Feelscared: drug warriors put the fear of prosecution in physicians who dare to treat pain*, REASON , Aug. 1, 2004, p. 32; J. Scott Orr, *DEA may tighten access to pain drug; Hydrocodone abuse is at alarming levels*, TIMES-PICAYUNE, Mar. 31, 2004, p. 1).  Some practitioners have been convicted in criminal prosecutions related to the prescribing of OxyContin®.  Most recently, a prominent Virginia physician, Dr. William Hurwitz, was convicted of 50 felony counts, including trafficking (Jerry Markon, *Mistrial in Pain Doctor's Last 3 Charges; Conviction Stands on 50 Counts in Va. Drug Trafficking Case*, WASHINGTON POST, Dec. 17, 2004, p. B02, and Jerry Markon, *Pain Doctor Convicted of Drug Charges; Va. Man Faces Possible Life Term on Trafficking Counts*, WASHINGTON POST, Dec. 16, 2004, p. A01).

[23] An addict is defined differently for different purposes.  The federal Controlled Substances Act defines an addict as an individual who uses any narcotic drug so as to endanger public morals, health, safety, or welfare, or who is so far addicted to the use of narcotic drugs as to have lost the power of self-control with reference to the addiction (21 USC §802(l)).  There does not appear to be a definition of addict in current California statutes.  One definition adopted in 1939 was repealed in 1957 (former H&SC §11009); the California Supreme Court has even remarked on the changing content of the definition of addict in the law (*People v. O'Neal*, 62 Cal. 2d 748, 751 (1965)).  The California courts still are having trouble reconciling historic definitions with current medical knowledge.

The pain management community defines addiction as compulsive, aberrational drug-seeking behavior despite adverse personal, family, financial, or other consequences.  While physical dependence and tolerance can both be present in addiction, both are common physiological responses to substantial and/or ongoing regimens of narcotics and other drugs even when there is no addiction.  In fact, many studies indicate addiction is rare in patients receiving narcotics for medical treatment where there is no history of substance abuse (see, for example, Russell K. Portenoy, M.D., *Opioid Therapy for Chronic Nonmalignant Pain: A Review of the Critical Issues*, 11 JOURNAL OF PAIN AND SYMPTOM MANAGEMENT 203, 210 (Apr. 1996)).

underscore this conclusion. Health and Safety Code section 11153(a) appears to define as illegitimate a controlled substance prescription to maintain an addict's customary use, but says nothing to suggest that controlled substance prescriptions for an addict's medical needs are not legal. The Medical Board underscores this in the 2003 version of its pain management guidelines, noted above. DEA recognizes the legality of treating chemically-dependent patients with opioids for their other medical conditions (Pharmacist's Manual, p. 54).

**You receive a prescription for a pregnant woman for a drug to which you know she is addicted. You contact the prescriber, who acknowledges the addiction. You ask whether the drug is to treat the patient's pain, and the physician says that it is not; the purpose of the prescription is to maintain the addiction because of possible adverse consequences to the fetus if the patient does not maintain the addiction, is forced to the streets to obtain her drugs, or is weaned from the addiction during the pregnancy. May you fill the prescription?**

Health and Safety Code section 11156, which provides that one may not prescribe controlled substances to an addict, seems to make this prescription illegal. But is this prescription really for the pregnant woman, or to prevent harm to the fetus (and medically indicated for that purpose)? Although prior to filling the prescription the pharmacist must do a thorough evaluation, ask the right questions, and make a careful record, it would appear that the prescription is appropriate. Looked at carefully, the prescription is not to "feed" or maintain an addiction, but to ensure the well-being of the fetus. This answer assumes that there is some medical basis for the physician's concern and conclusion.

The interpretation that controlled substances may be prescribed for an addict is consistent with guidelines promulgated by the Medical and Pharmacy Boards. Both Boards have recognized that, just as with any other patient, it is acceptable medical practice to treat an addict for a condition other than addiction itself with needed controlled substances, although with more careful initial and ongoing evaluation. These guidelines were adopted notwithstanding that the Medical Practice Act itself allows the use of controlled substances in the treatment of an addict only where there is both an emergency and the patient's addiction is complicated by incurable disease, serious accident or injury, or infirmities of old age (B&PC §2241(a)).

**Office treatment of addicts.** Drug treatment of addicts has been strictly controlled by federal and California law. In the past any drugs given to maintain, rather than wean, addicts could have been administered or dispensed only by specially-licensed narcotic treatment programs. Use of drugs in an office setting to wean addicts was strictly limited to non-narcotics. However, under a law passed in 2000, DEA and FDA in 2002 authorized the use of two formulations of buprenorphine, Subutex® and Suboxone®, for community-based treatment of addicts. Under the program participating physicians will be allowed to issue prescriptions for filling at pharmacies.

The prescribing of these drugs is limited to physicians with special training who are treating a limited number of patients with them. Detailed information to determine whether a prescriber is authorized to order these drugs, special confidentiality requirements for addiction treatment patients, and cautions and contraindications important for competent patient consultation is available at www.buprenorphine.samhsa.gov.[24]

---

[24] Additional information is at www.fda.gov/cder/drug/infopage/subutex_suboxone/default.htm, including links to documents directed to patients, prescribers, and pharmacists. The Board covered this subject in *Physician Office-Based Opioid Addiction Treatment, The Script*, Oct. 2003, p. 14 (www.pharmacy.ca.gov/publications/03_oct_script.pdf). Oddly, the current edition of the DEA Pharmacist's Manual, posted in April 2004, does not mention office-based treatment and the role of pharmacy in filling prescriptions for such treatment in its brief discussion of narcotic treatment programs (pp. 54-55).

**Assisted Suicide and Pain Management.**  Persons in severe pain may consider suicide. Whatever one might think of his behavior, it is interesting to note that a number of the assisted suicide cases attended by Dr. Jack Kevorkian reportedly involved people in substantial, unrelieved pain. Concern about intractable pain has been a major factor in the close votes on assisted suicide ballot initiatives, including California's Proposition 161, which failed to pass in 1992.  Surveys in Oregon show an increased prescribing of morphine for patients in ongoing, severe pain since the enactment of an assisted suicide ballot measure, called The Death with Dignity Act.[25]

Opposition to assisted suicide laws among the general public is largely based on ethical and religious reasons and concern about the potential for abuse of such laws.  Opposition within the medical community is often based on the belief that, before legalizing assisted suicide, society should pay considerably more attention to assuring the universal availability of relief from pain and other discomforts of terminal illness; some physicians also believe assisting someone to die violates the Hippocratic Oath.

Federal legislation has been proposed, but has not passed, to ban assisted suicide by prohibiting the use of controlled substances for this purpose and subjecting the prescriber to revocation of his or her DEA registration, criminal prosecution, or both for violation.  United States Attorney General John Ashcroft sought a similar result by enforcement action in 2001, when he instructed DEA to revoke the DEA registrations of physicians who prescribe controlled substances for the purpose of assisted suicide.  This action contradicted the position stated by the previous attorney general (William Booth, *Judge Blocks Sanctions Over Assisted Suicide; DEA Told Not to Go After Oregon Doctors*, WASHINGTON POST, Nov. 9, 2001, p. A02).  DEA officials have consistently argued that prescribing controlled substances for purposes of assisted suicide, even if legal in the state where the prescription is written, is a violation of the Controlled Substances Act.  The federal courts, however, sided with Oregon, holding the so-called Ashcroft Directive unlawful and unenforceable because it "violates the plain language of the [Controlled Substances Act], contravenes Congress' express legislative intent, and oversteps the bounds of the Attorney General's statutory authority" (*State of Oregon v. Ashcroft*, 368 F.3d 1118, 1120 (9th Cir. 2004)).  The Justice Department has asked

---

[25] Morphine use doubled nationwide between 1995 and 1997. Oregon, which ranked 11th among the states in morphine use before passage of its assisted suicide law, jumped to among the top three states afterward (Alissa J. Rubin, *National Perspective; Congress; Fight Ensues to Block Undoing of Doctor-Assisted Suicide Law; Some Fear Bill Would Stop Oregon Physicians from Prescribing Pain-Control Drugs*, LOS ANGELES TIMES, Sept. 15, 1998, p. A5).

The legal history of assisted suicide is complex. Dr. Jack Kevorkian's personal and public assistance at suicides led to multiple criminal trials. At first there was significant positive response to his work, but it largely evaporated because his later patients seemed not as carefully chosen as his earlier ones, and not so clearly in need of assistance to die. Ultimately Kevorkian was convicted and jailed; his medical licenses have been revoked. Physicians in Washington and New York challenged their states' prohibitions against assisting suicide in court, claiming that they were unconstitutional. The United States Supreme Court ultimately disagreed, upholding the right of the states to prohibit assistance in dying (*Washington v. Glucksberg*, 521 U.S. 702 (1997); *Vacco v. Quill*, 521 U.S. 793 (1997)).

The states may, however, choose to allow assisted suicide. Oregon did so by initiative in 1994. The legislation's effective date was delayed for several years by legal challenges, which ultimately failed. Oregon's voters reaffirmed its Death with Dignity Act at the ballot box by a 60-40 vote in November 1997, and the law has been in effect since then. The measure includes detailed rules about the form and number of requests the patient must make to multiple physicians to obtain a prescription for a lethal dose of medication. The role and obligation of the pharmacist in respect to the furnishing of those lethal doses have barely been addressed.

While the number of Oregonians who have sought and used physician-assisted suicide has increased each year since the legislation passed, the numbers remain small. In 2003, 42 physicians wrote 67 prescriptions for lethal doses of medication. Of those 67 recipients, 39 ingested the medication and died. During 2003, 18 others died from their illnesses, and ten were alive at the end of the year. Three patients who had received the medication in earlier years ingested it and died in 2003 (*Sixth Annual Report on Oregon's Death with Dignity Act*, Mar. 10, 2004, Oregon Department of Human Services, www.ohd.hr.state.or.us/chs/pas/ar-index.cfm).

the United States Supreme Court to review the decision (David G. Savage, *Ashcroft Wants Oregon Suicide Law Blocked; The attorney general urges the Supreme Court to let federal agents go after doctors in the state who help patients end their lives,* LOS ANGELES TIMES, Nov. 10, 2004, p. A20).

The use of drugs, including controlled substances, for purposes beyond their labeled uses is well-accepted as "off-label" use, and long recognized as governed by state licensing authorities (see Chap. II: Drugs). The prescribing of controlled substances to assist suicide is specifically authorized by Oregon law. Interestingly, no challenge has ever been brought by DEA against physicians who prescribe lethal doses of controlled substances to implement capital punishment, also authorized by the laws of a number of states.

## *Fraud, Deceit, and Corruption*

Fraud, in all its many manifestations, is unprofessional conduct. The law provides that it is unprofessional conduct to commit "any act involving moral turpitude, dishonesty, fraud, deceit, or corruption, whether the act is committed in the course of relations as a licensee or otherwise," and whether or not the act is a crime (§4301(f)). This provision is quite sweeping. "Moral turpitude" is an open-ended term, essentially referring to misconduct so offensive as to indicate the offender is morally deficient.[26] Other similar kinds of conduct, also considered unprofessional conduct in the law, are described below.

**Procurement of a license by fraud or mistake (§4301).** This and related provisions in the Business and Professions Code, and in Board regulations, make any cheating on or in connection with an examination or application (either your own or someone else's) unprofessional conduct. Allowing someone to substitute for you, or substituting for someone else, on an examination, violation of examination rules or security, or misuse of examination information, questions, or answers are all bases for discipline or license denial (B&PC §§123, 583-584; §§1721, 1723.1). It is a misdemeanor knowingly to buy or receive a fraudulent, forged, or counterfeit license (B&PC §119(g)); fraudulent, for this law, includes containing a misrepresentation.

**False documents.** It is unprofessional conduct to knowingly make or sign any certificate or other document that falsely represents the existence or nonexistence of a state of facts (§4301(g)). This prohibition applies not only to declarations, affidavits, or other documents signed under penalty of perjury, but also to any other signed document. Signing the document knowing it falsely represents the facts is the violation; the fact that one's intent was not criminal and may have been well-intentioned is no defense, although it may mitigate the level of discipline.

Mere signing and submitting a false claim to Medi-Cal is a violation, even without proof of intent to defraud (unlawfully profit from) Medi-Cal (*Fort v. Board of Medical Quality Assurance*, 136 Cal. App. 3d 12, 22 (1st Dist. 1982); *Brown v. State Department of Health*, 86 Cal. App.3d 548, 554-556 (3d Dist. 1978)). In *Fort* the physician falsely certified he performed individual psychotherapy when the therapy provided was group therapy conducted by nonphysicians. At the time, Fort knew Medi-Cal only covered individual physician psychotherapy. It was no defense to the charge of signing a false document that he turned all the funds received back into providing psychotherapy for Medi-Cal patients.

---

[26] "Gross immorality," which is also unprofessional conduct (§4301(a)), is, like moral turpitude, an open-ended term. What is deemed immoral varies over time depending on societal attitudes. These charges are generally reserved for conduct that is particularly outrageous.

Submission of false claims to Medi-Cal is forbidden by Welfare and Institutions Code section 14107. Medi-Cal rules require as a condition of reimbursement that the pharmacy has both dispensed the medication and billed for it in accordance with all applicable laws and regulations. If a patient's address is not in the pharmacy's records, as required, Medi-Cal inspectors will deem that patient's prescriptions improperly dispensed, and will not pay the pharmacy for them. Sloppy record-keeping practices have cost pharmacies dearly in Medi-Cal reimbursements over the years. Pharmacies that truly have engaged in fraud, filing claims for prescriptions not filled, or filled with less expensive medications than claimed, have been subject to significant civil penalties, criminal prosecution, and disciplinary actions against their licenses, and have been required to reimburse the government for Med-Cal payments they have received.

**Insurance Fraud.** Any health care professional who knowingly presents a false or fraudulent claim for payment under a contract of insurance is engaging in unprofessional conduct. It also is unprofessional conduct to knowingly prepare, make, or subscribe any writing with the intent to use it in support of a fraudulent claim (B&PC §810(a)). It also is grounds for discipline to violate various sections of the Insurance Code on fraud (for example, section 1871.4 on fraud in worker's compensation claims) (B&PC §810(b)). Criminal law also broadly forbids insurance fraud (Pen. Code §550).

## *Improper Business Practices*

A number of business practices that are expressly forbidden by law may result in disciplinary action against pharmacy licensees. In some cases the following practices might be deemed corrupt, fraudulent, or otherwise actionable unprofessional conduct. Probably as importantly, the conduct subjects the licensee to civil actions for which there are substantial civil penalties.

**Kickbacks, rebates, and referrals**[27] forbidden by the Business and Professions Code may also be the basis for a charge of unprofessional conduct. Obviously, great financial benefit can accrue to a health care provider if others in the health care system will steer business to it. The conduct is not inherently fraudulent, but concerns about fraud are at the core of such provisions. The risks to patients are both economic (because such steering would diminish free and open competition and artificially raise prices) and health-related (because the referral might not benefit the patient's health, and financial motives might override the health care provider's or practitioner's primary obligation to the well-being of the patient). Government has thus forbidden certain financial relationships among health care providers. The Business and Professions Code contains a number of provisions regulating kickbacks, rebates, and referrals, including self-referrals to or from entities in which the licensee has an ownership interest. Federal law makes it a felony, punishable by up to five years in prison and a $25,000 fine, to knowingly and willfully solicit or receive any remuneration as a kickback, bribe, or rebate for the referral of patients who are covered by the federal Medicaid (Medi-Cal in California) program (42 USC § 1320a-7b(b)).[28]

---

[27] Terms such as kickback, rebate, and referral refer to any compensation, in cash, in property, in indirect payment (such as a discount on goods), or other benefit, in exchange for getting or referring health care business. The law uses a variety of terms to describe the violative behavior to make clear the intended breadth of the prohibitions and to minimize the ability of persons engaged in such practices to find a legal loophole in the law.

[28] Violations can occur in indirect ways. For example, many common pharmaceutical marketing practices could violate federal fraud and abuse laws, such as offering incentive payments or other tangible benefits to physicians, health plans, or pharmaceutical benefits managers to encourage or reward prescribing or purchase of particular drugs or to shift a patient from one drug to another (Robert Pear, *Drug Industry Is Told to Stop Gifts to Doctors*, NEW YORK TIMES, Oct. 1, 2002, p. A1). Federal regulators have warned against such practices, and the pharmaceutical industry has been fighting restrictions, such as on gifts to physicians (Robert Pear, *Drug Makers Battle a U.S. Plan to Curb Rewards for Doctors*, NEW YORK TIMES, Dec. 26, 2002, p. A1). The Inspector General of HHS issued a lengthy opinion about the relationship between a

Section 650 of the Business and Professions Code provides that (except as to agencies licensed to make referrals to various health care facilities) the offer, delivery, receipt, or acceptance by any person licensed under Division 2 of the Business and Professions Code (which includes Board licensees) of any rebate, refund, commission, preference, patronage dividend, discount, or other consideration, whether in money form or otherwise, as compensation or inducement for referring patients, clients, or customers to any person, irrespective of any membership, proprietary interest, or co-ownership in or with any person to whom these patients, clients, or customers are referred, is unlawful.[29]

In simpler terms, no licensee may take or offer anything for referring a patient, client, or customer to any other person, even if the licensee making the referral has no interest in the person or entity to which the referral is made. That means a physician may choose to refer patients to a particular pharmacy (because it is owned by his friend, because the pharmacist gives excellent advice, because it is nearby), but may not accept any money or gift in exchange for his referrals. The conduct forbidden by section 650 includes the rendering by a pharmacist or pharmacy of consultant pharmaceutical services to a licensed health care facility for no cost, nominal cost, or below reasonable cost, if that pharmacist or pharmacy obtains patients, clients, or customers and/or their prescription orders from that licensed facility (§1765).[30]

Payment or receipt of payment for services other than the referral of patients, even if based on a percentage of gross revenue or similar type of contractual arrangement, is not unlawful if the financial value received is commensurate with the value of the services furnished or the fair rental value of any premises or equipment leased or provided by the recipient to the payor. In other words, if the payment is not a "cover" for what are in effect referral fees, it does not violate section 650. That means a pharmacist may rent space in a building owned by physicians who might refer a lot of patients to the pharmacy. If the rental is based upon a percentage of pharmacy revenue the physician building owners obviously would stand to gain from the success of the pharmacy. Under section 650 the percentage lease agreement would be valid if the actual rental received represents the fair rental value of the space rented. One test is, considering the prime location in a medical building, would nonphysician owners charge the same rent?

Under section 650 it also is not unlawful (with some statutory exceptions) for a licensee to refer a person to a laboratory, pharmacy, clinic, or health care facility in which the licensee has a proprietary interest or co-ownership as long as the licensee's return on the investment or co-ownership is based solely upon the amount of his or her capital investment or proportional ownership and not on the number or value of any patients referred. However, a licensee who makes any such referral without valid medical need is in violation of this law.

---

chronic disease management business that would provide an Internet-based clinical compliance program for patients and the health plans and employers that would enroll their members. While the opinion appears to approve the plan, it also warns that it could potentially generate illegal remuneration under the anti-kickback statute, depending upon the intent of the parties (Advisory Opinion No. 02-12, www.oig.hhs.gov/fraud/docs/advisoryopinions/2002/ao0212.pdf).

[29] Neither California nor federal law prohibits the distribution of coupons or vouchers to patients for free or reduced price prescriptions, as long as this distribution is otherwise according to law.

[30] HHS has also issued an opinion expressing the view that giving something of value to a Medicare or Medicaid beneficiary to influence his or her selection of provider of goods or services (for example, a particular hospital) is illegal. Gifts valued at up to $10, and no more than $50 aggregate per year, would not be considered illegal. However, a provider could waive or reduce patient co-payments without running afoul of the law, and could fund independent entities that provide services to financially needy beneficiaries, subject to some restrictions. Penalties for illegal gifts are up to $10,000 per violation. (HHS, Office of the Inspector General, *Publication of OIG Special Advisory Bulletin on Offering Gifts and Other Inducements to Beneficiaries*, 67 FR 55855 (Aug. 30, 2002)).

As discussed in the section on Substitution in Chapter IX: The Prescription Process: From Receipt to Labeling, incentives offered by manufacturers to pharmacists to switch patients to their products from others appear to violate the intent of section 650. Developments in this area are likely as practices that skirt the edge of the law increase.

A first violation of Section 650 is chargeable as either a felony or a misdemeanor (at the option of the prosecutor), a fine of up to $50,000, or both; a second or subsequent offense is a felony.

Section 650.1 of the Business and Professions Code is intended to prevent circumvention of the restrictions on pharmacy ownership in section 4111(a). Persons or corporations not allowed to own pharmacies may not enter into any rental, lease, or service arrangements for furnishing or supply of pharmaceutical services and products that are based upon a percentage of sales or charges, or any measure of hospital or pharmacy revenue or cost.

Under section 654.2 it is unlawful for a licensee to charge, bill, or otherwise solicit payment from a patient on behalf of, or refer a patient to, an organization in which the licensee, or the licensee's immediate family, has a significant beneficial interest unless the licensee first provides written disclosure of the interest and advises the patient that he or she may choose any organization to obtain the services. These disclosure requirements do not apply either where the significant beneficial interest is limited to ownership of a building where space is leased at the prevailing rate under a straight lease agreement or when the licensee's interest is in ownership of publicly-traded stocks (B&PC §654.2(e)). Nor do the disclosure requirements apply where the licensee is providing or arranging for health care services under a prepaid capitated contract with the DHS (B&PC §654.2(f)(3)). The prohibitions of section 654.2 are in addition to other restrictions in sections 650 to 657 (B&PC §654.2(f)(2)).

There are many other complex and sometimes convoluted statutory provisions concerning this subject, both in the Business and Professions Code and the Health and Safety Code (not to mention federal law). What is most important for pharmacists or pharmacy owners to understand is that:

- any payments made or received, or benefits given or received (including future business gain), when accepting or making referrals may be illegal when the payments are not for services, material, or equipment;
- there must be a valid medical need for, or patient benefit from, all referrals;
- where a pharmacist or pharmacy owner, or a member of his or her family, has a financial interest in a provider to whom he or she makes a referral, disclosure is required and the patient must be told that he or she is free to go elsewhere; and
- whenever even the slightest question arises about the legality of a business arrangement involving other entities or persons in the health care system, seek competent legal advice: the price of a violation can be very high.

**Unfair competition** is also a basis for unprofessional conduct charges. Unfair competition means unlawful, unfair, or fraudulent business practices, including false or misleading advertising or statements (B&PC §§17200, 17500). The unfair competition laws aim to protect consumers from fraudulent and other injurious business practices and by assuring that honest practitioners and businesses can thrive. The prohibitions can be applied very broadly to protect the public and competitors from harm (*People v. Servantes*, 86 Cal. App. 4th 1081 (2001)).

In the context of holders of various professional and occupational licenses, these statutes reach behavior that might not violate other anti-fraud statutes, but which is deemed unfair to consumers and competitors. The focus of such laws is controlling or punishing conduct through which someone, by broadly violating laws and standards to which legitimate practitioners or businesses are subject, unfairly competes with other, similar practitioners or businesses. Unfair methods of competition, unchecked, often result in poor quality services and products, reduced selection, and higher prices. "Unlawful" practices include all practices forbidden by either civil or criminal statutes, regulations, local law or ordinances, or case law (*People v. McKale*, 25 Cal. 3d 626, 633 (1979)).

Section 651(a) of the Business and Professions Code makes it unlawful for certain licensees (including Pharmacy Board licensees) to disseminate or cause to be disseminated any form of public communication containing a false, fraudulent, misleading, or deceptive statement or claim. An "intent" to deceive or defraud is not required. The prohibited communications include those made for the purpose of or likely to induce consumers, directly or indirectly, to use services or purchase products in connection with the licensee's professional practice or business. "Public communication" includes, but is not limited to, television, radio, motion pictures, newspapers, books, or lists or directories of healing arts practitioners.

A false, fraudulent, misleading, or deceptive statement or claim includes a statement or claim that:

- contains a misrepresentation of fact,
- is likely to mislead or deceive because of a failure to disclose material facts,
- is intended or is likely to create false or unjustified expectations of favorable results,
- relates to fees other than a standard consultation fee or a range of fees for specific types of services without fully and specifically disclosing all variables and other material factors, or
- contains other representations or implications that in reasonable probability will cause an ordinarily prudent person to misunderstand or be deceived (B&PC §651(b)).

Any advertisement of price must be exact, without using words or phrases such as "as low as," "and up," or "lowest prices." Comparative advertisements referring to services or costs of services must be based on verifiable data that the advertiser is prepared to produce. Price advertising (including statements about discounts, premiums, or gifts) must not be fraudulent, deceitful, or misleading. The advertised price for any product must include charges for any related professional services, unless their omission is indicated specifically and clearly (B&PC §651(c)).

Licensees are forbidden to compensate in any way any representative of the press, radio, television, or other communication medium in anticipation of, or in return for, professional publicity unless the publicity reveals the fact of such compensation (B&PC §651(d)). Nor may a licensee use any professional card, professional announcement card, office sign, letterhead, telephone directory listing, medical list, medical directory listing, or similar professional notice or device if it includes a statement or claim that is false, fraudulent, misleading, or deceptive as defined in section 651(b) (B&PC §651(e)).

Acts of unfair competition may be enjoined (B&PC §17203) and a civil penalty of $2,500 may be sought for each individual violation (B&PC §17206; $2,500 extra per violation may be sought where senior citizens or the disabled are the victims (B&PC §17206.1)). These actions may be brought by the Attorney General or a city or district attorney (B&PC §17204). The scope of these provisions is very broad. An entity can even be forced to substantiate claims that it has made or cease and desist from asserting those claims (B&PC §17508(b),(c)).

**Illegal Resale of Drugs Purchased for Patients of Covered Entities.** Subsection (r) of Section 4301 makes it grounds for discipline to sell, trade, transfer, or furnish drugs obtained at preferential prices under government-regulated programs (42 USC §256b, see Chap. VII: Ordering Drugs ("Secondary Sourcing")) to a person the licensee knows or reasonably should have known is not a patient of an entity entitled to benefit. In other words, secondary sourcing of drugs purchased under the 340b discount program to a person or entity not entitled to receive them is grounds for discipline.

# Other Grounds for Discipline

In addition to the broad categories of quality of care, drug-related conduct, and improper business practice charges, there are additional kinds of conduct deemed unprofessional under the Pharmacy Law.

## *Criminal Convictions*

It is unprofessional conduct to be convicted of any crime substantially related to the qualifications, functions, or duties of a licensee (§4301(*l*), B&PC §490). A conviction means a plea or verdict of guilty or a conviction following a plea of *nolo contendere* (no contest). "Substantially related" is not specifically defined either in the law or in court cases. It is fair to say it does not mean "integrally connected" to the license, but rather that it has some logical, identifiable connection to one or more aspects of the licensed practice involved. To determine whether there is a substantial relationship, the Board may inquire into the circumstances of the crime (§4301(*l*)).

It is not difficult to find a substantial relationship between most felony convictions and a board-issued license. It is particularly easy to see that any felony conviction involving drugs is "substantially related" for a Board licensee. But a felony drug conviction's connection to, for example, a barber's license might not be so clear, and many misdemeanor convictions might well not be "substantially related" for a Pharmacy Board licensee. Determining whether a conviction is substantially related requires consideration of the qualifications, functions, and duties of the licensee in question and the specific facts of the case. Licensing boards frequently err on the side of filing charges based upon criminal convictions, leaving it to the accused parties to make the case at a hearing that the conviction is not substantially related to their license.

**Workers' Compensation and Medi-Cal Fraud.** As of 2004, various professional licensing boards, including the Pharmacy Board, are required to file a disciplinary action against any licensee who is convicted of felony workers' compensation, Medi-Cal, or Denti-Cal fraud. When the boards receive proof of the conviction, they are to suspend the licensee automatically. Outright revocation is mandated if a licensee is prosecuted and convicted of a felony in at least two separate prosecutions, unless the licensee can establish sufficient mitigating circumstances (B&PC §810(c)).

**Discipline by Another Jurisdiction.** The revocation, suspension, or other discipline by another state of a license to practice pharmacy, to operate a pharmacy, or to do any other act for which a license is required by the Pharmacy Law is unprofessional conduct (§4301(n)). A related provision, section 4301.5, provides for automatic suspension of a pharmacist's license if his or her license or authority to practice in any other state or by an agency of the federal government is suspended or revoked. The suspension is for the duration of the other jurisdiction's suspension or revocation, although the Board has the discretion to decline to impose the suspension. Disciplinary action by an agency of the federal government or by another country also can lead to discipline of a California license (B&PC §141(a)). These provisions, coupled with the discipline reporting system maintained by the National Practitioner Data Bank, mean that a pharmacist disciplined in another jurisdiction should assume the discipline will be reported to the Board and likely be the basis for a California disciplinary action.

# *Violation of Laws Governing Pharmacy*

Violating or attempting to violate, directly or indirectly, a law governing pharmacy or assisting in, abetting, or conspiring to violate any such law is also unprofessional conduct (§4301(o)). This is an extremely broad proscription, because it covers not only all federal and state drug and controlled substance laws but also laws concerning government medical assistance programs and even laws enforced by the Nuclear Regulatory Commission concerning radiopharmaceuticals.

It is not possible to catalog all the laws and regulations governing or affecting pharmacy, violations of which could lead to disciplinary charges. Following are some of the more relevant ones, all of which are criminal:

- Unauthorized printing or reproduction of any prescription blank (§4325);
- Representing oneself falsely as a physician or other lawful prescriber, or as the agent of such a person, in a telephone or electronic communication with a pharmacist in order to obtain any drug (§4323);
- Signing the name of another, or of a fictitious person, or falsely making, altering, forging, uttering, publishing, passing, or attempting to pass as genuine, any prescription for any drugs (§4324(a));
- Possession of any drugs obtained by a forged prescription (§4324(b)); and
- Making false representations on your own or another's behalf to become licensed as a pharmacist, or falsely holding yourself out to be a pharmacist (§4322).

Although these violations are most likely to be committed by nonpharmacists, sometimes a dishonest pharmacist or other licensee may violate them directly or by aiding and abetting their violation.

It is also a violation of the law to knowingly or willfully use a minor as an agent to violate any of the dangerous drugs provisions of the Pharmacy Law (§ 4336(a)). This section does not apply "to a pharmacist furnishing such drugs pursuant to a prescription" (§ 4336(b)); it is likely that the Legislature had in mind punishing adults who might use juveniles, for example, to pick up controlled substance prescriptions, to minimize their own risk, when the prescriptions are invalid. However, pharmacists possibly could be charged under this section if they know or ought to know the prescriptions are invalid and a minor is involved in their diversion, because the courts have noted that the protections of the law only apply to valid prescriptions, not to any piece of paper that styles itself a prescription *(United States v. Moore*, 423 U.S. 122 (1975); *People v. Doss*, 4 Cal. App. 4th 1585 (2d Dist. 1992)).

If a licensee violates any of these laws, and is not charged with a crime, he or she still is subject to disciplinary action on the basis of the same facts. If a licensee is charged with a crime, and is acquitted, disciplinary action can still be taken on the basis of the same facts. This is not "double jeopardy"; the standards for the government prevailing in administrative and criminal cases are very different. The purpose of the disciplinary case is public protection, not punishment. If a licensee is charged with a crime and convicted, disciplinary action can be taken on the basis of the same facts and on the basis of the conviction itself; under those circumstances it will be easy for the Board to prevail.

## *Miscellaneous Grounds for Discipline*

Additional grounds for discipline may be based on violations of laws outside the Pharmacy Law.

**Discrimination.** A little-known provision of the Business and Professions Code makes it a ground for disciplinary action if a licensee of a board refuses to perform the licensed activity, incites refusal to perform the activity, or discriminates or restricts the performance of any licensed activity because of the race, color, sex, religion, ancestry, disability, marital status, or national origin of the person seeking services. Such discrimination ought not be tolerated (for good business reasons as well as moral reasons), and it is a ground for license revocation (B&PC §125.6).

Note that the antidiscrimination provision includes prohibition of discrimination on the basis of "disability." For these purposes a disability means a physical or mental impairment that substantially limits one or more of the major life activities of the individual, a record of such impairment, or being regarded as having such an impairment. Section 125.6 does not apply to discrimination in employment, but other legal provisions protect many classes of people from such discrimination (and apply to pharmacies as well as to other businesses). It also does not apply to the presence of architectural barriers to an individual with physical disabilities when the building conforms to applicable state or local building codes. Nor does this antidiscrimination section permit an individual to participate in, or benefit from, the licensed activity where that individual poses a direct threat to the health or safety of others.

Section 125.6 is largely consistent with state and federal civil rights legislation, constitutional provisions, and the Americans with Disabilities Act (ADA, 42 USC §§12101-12213). The ADA bars discrimination based on disability and requires that reasonable accommodation be offered to a disabled person if requested. Because the ADA is relatively new, and its language allows for a lot of balancing of interests between the disabled seeking access and persons who must provide access, the precise accommodations that may be required are not clear.

The ADA applies to disabled persons seeking accommodations both as pharmacy employees (see Chap. XIV: Other Relevant Law) and as pharmacy customers. A pharmacy is likely to have a higher percentage of disabled patrons among its customers than patrons of other types of retail stores. Reasonable accommodations are not limited merely to access, such as a wheelchair or walker-accessible entrance and exit and aisles. Pharmacy management in particular might wish to consider what accommodations to customers might be offered in advance of individual requests: for example, assistance by a clerk in reaching high-shelf items for persons who use wheelchairs or in identifying shelf items for the visually impaired, leaving telephone messages as well as using label stickers for patients who are visually impaired, and communicating for purposes of consultation with hearing-impaired persons by writing down comments.

**Sexual Misconduct.** Sexual misconduct by health care professionals is a growing concern. Although most pharmacies do not offer private settings as conducive to sexual misconduct as, for example, a doctor's office, pharmacy nevertheless is included in the umbrella of protection provided by Business and Professions Code section 726. That section makes it grounds for discipline to engage in any act of sexual abuse, misconduct, or relations with a patient, client, or customer. It is violated not just by sexual conduct that the licensee claims is a part of treatment (as some licensees have claimed), but by any sexual conduct that occurs because a licensee abuses his or her professional relationship to take advantage of a patient's trust and seduce the patient (*Green v. Board of Dental Examiners,* 47 Cal. App. 4th 786 (2d Dist. 1996)). Section 726 does not, however, generally apply to consensual sexual relationships. In *Gromis v. Medical Board of California,* 8 Cal. App. 4th 589 (1st Dist. 1992), the court overturned discipline of a physician, finding the relationship consensual. In *Green,* the dentist claimed that the sex was consensual, but both the trial and the appellate court found otherwise because the dentist was using an osteopathic treatment (craniosacral therapy, for temporal mandibular joint conditions) that was both unusual and intimate for dentistry, and used soft lights, music, and flattery to seduce the two patients.

What a "current" patient is depends on the type of professional relationship. For a pharmacist, a current patient or customer probably would be anyone who has his or her prescriptions filled at the pharmacy with any regularity, even if there has been no prescription or refill for some period of time. So if a pharmacist is enamored with someone met at the prescription counter, he or she had best be sure that the patient clearly and voluntarily severs the relationship with the pharmacy before developing a relationship with the pharmacist.[31]

**A pharmacist starts a sexual relationship with a former patient. The relationship ends and the patient later comes to the pharmacy for professional services. May the pharmacist provide them?**

Because there was no sexual relationship during any period in which professional services were being provided, there appears to be no violation of section 726. But, as a practical matter and in the exercise of his or her professional judgment as to what is appropriate, the pharmacist may want to consider carefully whether he or she should resume providing professional services to the patient. Among other things, if the patient later becomes dissatisfied for any reason, the pharmacist may suddenly find that his or her recollection of the circumstances of the relationship, including how and when the relationship started and stopped, particularly in relation to the provision of professional services, is significantly different from what the patient asserts.

**Records of Cash Payments to Employees.** Another little-known provision of the Business and Professions Code, section 140, allows the Board to take disciplinary action against any licensee for failure to record and preserve for at least three years any and all cash transactions involved in the payment of employee wages by the licensee or for failure to provide such records to the Board on request. When a charge under this section is sustained, the Board is entitled to actual investigative costs not to exceed $2,500.

**Child Abuse Reporting.** Pharmacists are not as likely as other health professionals to come into possession of facts that suggest that a child is being abused physically or psychologically. However, a pharmacist may be alerted to the possibility of such abuse through information gained in the course of pharmacy practice. If so, it is important to recognize that public policy strongly favors the reporting of such suspicions by health professionals. Privacy rights of patients are superseded by the mandated reporting.

Federal law (42 USC §13031) requires that pharmacists, among other health care professionals, who are employed on federal land or in federally-operated (or contracted) facilities, report suspected child abuse. These facilities are required to maintain a standard form for written reports, which are not to substitute for immediate oral reporting when the situation so requires. The law provides immunity from liability for persons making such reports in good faith. A parallel state law, the Child Abuse and Reporting Act, Penal Code sections 11164 to 11174.3, is very broad and requires all persons licensed as health professionals pursuant to Division 2 of the Business and Professions Code, including pharmacists, to report (Pen. Code §11165.7(a)(21)). A child abuse report is required when the health practitioner knows of or observes a child whom the practitioner knows or reasonably suspects has been the victim of sexual, physical, or emotional abuse (Pen. Code §11166(a)). Reports must be made immediately to the local child protective agency. Licensing boards are required to provide their licensees with notice of their obligations under this law (Pen. Code §11166.5(b),(c)).

---

[31] Sexual harassment of fellow employees or staff, although not covered by section 726, may well constitute general unprofessional conduct (§4301) because of its impact on the trust, cooperation, and efficiency essential to effective and safe delivery of pharmacy services to the public.

Reports made pursuant to this law are generally confidential and exempt from disclosure (Pen. Code §11167.5(a)). Health professionals who make a report are immune from civil and criminal liability for doing so, even if they acquired their knowledge or suspicion outside of their professional capacity (Pen. Code §11172(a)). In addition, if a groundless suit is brought against a reporting practitioner, he or she may be able to recoup attorney's fees, up to $50,000, from the state (Pen. Code §11172(c)).

**Compliance with Child Support Orders.** The Pharmacy Board may suspend a pharmacist's license under the provisions of Welfare and Institutions Code section 11350.6 for failure to comply with a child support order or judgment (B&PC §490.5). Noncompliance is reported by district attorneys to the state Department of Social Services, which in turn sends a list to each professional and occupational licensing board. The Board is forbidden to renew the license until the licensee has paid the back support or judgment or has made arrangements to do so; the law provides for the issuance of a 150-day temporary license to allow arrangements for payment to be made.

**Defaulting on Educational Loans.** The Pharmacy Board and other licensing boards have the authority to cite and fine or discipline licensed health care practitioners who are in default on federal HHS educational loans. In deciding whether to take action on this basis, the Board may consider the population being served by the licensee as well as the practitioner's overall economic status (B&PC §685).

## Board Discipline as Grounds for Other Agency Action

Just as discipline by another state or federal agency is grounds for discipline by the Board, discipline by the Board is often grounds for action by other states or by federal agencies. For example, DEA can deny, revoke, or suspend a registrant for, among other grounds, having had his or her state license or registration suspended, revoked, or denied (21 U.S.C. §824(a)(3)). At one time a licensee disciplined in one state could simply pick up and move to another state without fear of his or her record following, but today information on such discipline is readily available to licensing agencies (see Chap. XIII: Board of Pharmacy ("Monitoring Systems")). As of 2005, various boards, including the Pharmacy Board, must report to the Department of Health Services the name and license number of any person who, because of discipline, voluntary surrender, or changing to inactive status, is not entitled to practice (B&PC §683). The express purpose is to prevent Medi-Cal reimbursement to health professionals no longer entitled to receive it.

# Special Concerns for Employee Pharmacists

In the past, pharmacists frequently owned their own pharmacies or were employed by other pharmacists. Today, most pharmacists are employees of non-pharmacists, whether individuals or corporations. Most employers will be seeking to remain competitive, so there often will be pressure on employee pharmacists to do more, faster, and with fewer resources. Pharmacists may be asked to take responsibility for and supervise nonpharmacist employees over whom they have little or no hiring, disciplinary, or firing authority. Employee pharmacists must be especially cautious not to engage in unprofessional conduct because of pressure from above, fear of job loss, or the desire to succeed in a competitive environment.

The pharmacy will generally be held responsible for misconduct of its employees (*Arenstein v. California State Board of Pharmacy*, 265 Cal. App. 2d 179 (2d Dist. 1968)), even if the pharmacy did not participate in or know of the misconduct (*Banks v. Board of Pharmacy*, 161 Cal. App. 3d 708 (2d

Dist. 1984)).[32] The individual pharmacist's license is very much at stake as well. A pharmacist cannot use an employer's directives or pressure as an excuse for violating laws or regulations or allowing them to be violated by those he or she supervises. Each pharmacist must keep in mind, it is *my* license that is at risk if laws or regulations are violated.

**Suppose you are the only pharmacist at a pharmacy owned by someone else, and the owner directs you to use a technician who is not licensed. What is your responsibility? Suppose you find out the pharmacy's licensed technician is drinking on the job, and the owner refuses to let you discipline or fire the technician. What can you do? What must you do?**

You must refuse to use an unlicensed technician to perform a technician's duties, even at the risk of losing your job. If you use a licensed pharmacy technician whom you know or ought to know is impaired or otherwise unreliable, the public may be endangered. You and the pharmacy may be liable for harm to patients caused by the technician, and your license also will be at risk.

**Suppose you are the pharmacist-in-charge and you have a technician working under your supervision who you feel is incompetent or just plain careless. Suppose the owner will not let you terminate the technician. What do you do? Suppose you are an employee pharmacist supervising that same technician and the pharmacist-in-charge will not do anything about your complaints. What do you do?**

If you allow a technician whose work you believe is unacceptable to continue performing pharmacy tasks under your direct or general supervision, you may be held liable for any injury that results, and you may be subject to discipline by the Board. You should attempt to correct the situation; if you cannot, you may be faced with the choice of either leaving the position or facing civil and disciplinary liability.

**Suppose you come in one morning and find the nonpharmacist owner in the pharmacy area. You warn her that her action is illegal, but she does it again. What do you do? What must you do? Suppose a subsequent audit by the Pharmacy Board discovers drug shortages; who is responsible?**

There are no easy answers to these hypothetical problems. You are responsible for the violations of law and mistakes of practice committed by others under your supervision and in the pharmacy where you are the pharmacist-in-charge. Pharmacists not in a management role in these situations also have at least an ethical obligation to protect the public. With professional licensure comes an obligation to uphold the law. You are responsible for the safety, security, and purity of the drugs. If there are shortages, your license is at stake. If drugs become unsafe (or prescriptions are misfilled) because of the owner's conduct, you also will be responsible. If you cannot stop the conduct, you might just have to quit. To do nothing risks harm to the public and ultimately sanctions against your license.

You may reasonably believe that your job is at risk if you contact a pharmacy inspector about the violations at your pharmacy. California law does protect employees who disclose information regarding their employer's violation of law to a government agency against retaliatory action by the employer (Lab. Code §1102.5). Even with that protection, it will not be easy or pleasant to uphold

---

[32] Effective regulation would not be possible if an owner could escape responsibility by blaming an employee or independent contractor for legal violations. "[A] licensee that is liable for its employees will be more likely to exert constant effort to control [their] conduct . . . than a licensee that is responsible only for having the proper management policies and procedures in place to control employee conduct . . ." (*California Assn. of Health Facilities v. Dept. of Health Services*, 16 Cal. 4th 284, 295-296, 303 (1997)).

your personal commitment to legal and ethical practice in the face of the type of dilemma suggested by these hypothetical cases. These situations are all too real for some pharmacists; it is not always easy to tell when a problem is significant enough to force the decision to take action to protect the public safety (and your license) at the risk of continued secure employment. It is important to consider how you would handle such a problem. In some cases, you may have no choice but to quit.

**Suppose you are an employee pharmacist and are receiving prescriptions for dextroamphetamine sulfate (Dexedrine®) for weight control that you think are questionable. Your store owner, who also is the pharmacist-in-charge, tells you to keep filling them or find another job. You fill them, but you are convinced they are not legitimate prescriptions. What do you do?**

As noted above, there is employment protection in California for an employee who contacts government officials concerning violations of the law at his or her workplace (Lab. Code §1102.5). The employee is not protected merely by informing a supervisor or owner. In this hypothetical situation, both because you may be liable for filling the prescriptions and in order to be covered by the Labor Code section, you are well advised to contact the Pharmacy Board and/or the DEA. A pharmacist's expressions of disapproval of pharmacy policies solely to management also will not protect him or her from being charged with responsibility for the violations (see *Smith v. California State Board of Pharmacy*, 37 Cal. App. 4th 229 (4th Dist. 1995)).

Employee pharmacists have sought the assistance of the Pharmacy Board in the area of working conditions, expressing concern of potential harm to the public, as well as their own risk of charges of unprofessional conduct, from these conditions. California's Department of Labor is the agency charged with dealing with working conditions. The Board, in contrast, has no clear authority to limit working hours or conditions or to set limits on the number of prescriptions a pharmacist can be required to dispense, or supervise the dispensing of, per hour or per shift. The Board does have the authority to control the number of non-pharmacist personnel who may be supervised by any single pharmacist (see Chap. III: Licensing Pharmacists and Chap. IV: Licensing Pharmacies). Legal and regulatory changes in recent years have secured the right of pharmacists to hours limitations and assurance of breaks and meal time (Lab. Code §1186, §1714.1).

**Suppose you are an employee pharmacist. The expectations of management concerning your productivity are quite clear; you believe that the only way to meet these expectations is to avoid patient consultation as much as possible. Management disagrees; memos to all pharmacy managers make it clear that all requirements of the law, including consultation, must be met. Your pharmacist-in-charge has asked for more staffing, but it has been refused. When you ask what you are to do, the pharmacist-in-charge says, "Do the best you can." From your observation of her behavior, that means that when a patient insists on consultation, it should be as brief and basic as possible. What should you do?**

The obligation to consult means adequate and appropriate consultation, as discussed above ("Failure to Consult"). Even when faced with an unmanageable workload, you cannot shortchange your patients without risking your own license. If you cannot persuade management to provide appropriate resources for the number of prescriptions at the pharmacy, you may wish to complain to the Pharmacy Board and perhaps seek another job. The Board is committed to strong enforcement of its consultation requirements. It has cited, and continues to cite, pharmacies and pharmacists for violation of section 1707.2 pursuant to its cite and fine authority (see Chap. XIII: Board of Pharmacy).

Ordinarily an employee pharmacist who is not supervising other pharmacists and who is not the pharmacist-in-charge will not be held responsible for the conduct of other pharmacists; however, he or she can be, depending on the circumstances. For example, a fellow pharmacist might well be held to account for the conduct of another pharmacist when he or she knows of some conduct, or omission, by that pharmacist that poses a public health, safety, or welfare threat or endangers a patient or the public, and takes no action.

# Categories of Liability

Pharmacy licensees face a number of types of liability in addition to discipline. Liability risks fall into at least four major categories.

## *Regulatory Liability*

The most immediate concern, and the one most likely to arise, is the risk of various regulatory actions or sanctions. The Pharmacy Board, after investigation and the provision of due process, may impose disciplinary sanctions of various types, from informal sanctions, to citations and fines, to suspension or even revocation of licenses on one or more of the grounds discussed above. The Board of Pharmacy's enforcement process is briefly discussed in Chapter XIII: The Board of Pharmacy and Other Agencies. A person with a pending application may have it denied on the grounds of the types of conduct catalogued in this chapter. DEA may seek revocation of the DEA registration any licensee holds. The Department of Health Services may seek to remove a pharmacy from participation in the Medi-Cal program and may seek recoupment of overpayments received. The Food and Drug Section of DHS or the Board may seize adulterated or misbranded drugs.

## *Criminal Liability*

Although such actions are reserved for the most egregious cases, licensees may be charged with crimes for their alleged illegal activity.[33] If criminal charges are brought, the Board and other regulatory agencies may take disciplinary action based on the same facts and may also take action based on a criminal conviction, as discussed above.

Some criminal laws require proof the defendant specifically intended to violate the law for there to be a crime. More typically, a crime simply requires proof the defendant intended to do the prohibited act, whether or not he or she knew the act violated the law. We all are presumed to know the law; ignorance of the law, it is said, is no defense. So, if the act itself was volitional – done of the pharmacist's free will, even if he or she didn't expressly intend to violate the law and didn't know he or she was violating the law – there may be criminal liability.

In some cases the mere fact that the law was not followed is a crime. Not only does the defendant's lack of intent to violate the law not matter, but also it does not matter that the defendant did not intend to do the prohibited act. These cases typically involve acts considered to be so potentially dangerous to public health, safety, or welfare that the Legislature has decided that every violation should be subject to punishment. The more highly regulated a field is, the more likely it is that a number of the laws governing the field will authorize criminal prosecution even for entirely unintentional violations.

---

[33] For example, note the pharmacy owner prosecuted for drug shortages (discussed above) and the Kansas City pharmacist sentenced to 30 years in prison for adulterating cancer chemotherapy drugs (see Chap. VIII: Preparation of Drugs). Also consider the felony elder abuse and grand theft charges brought against a pharmacist for luring pharmacy customers into a fraudulent investment scheme. He was sentenced to a year in jail and 10 years' probation, and his assets were seized to pay restitution of the $400,000 he obtained from his acts (*Pharmacist Sentenced for Bilking Elderly Customers; The Thousand Oaks man gets a year in jail for taking $400,000 for an investment scheme, His home is seized*, LOS ANGELES TIMES, Oct. 29, 2004, p. B3).

Violations of law may only be punished as crimes if the statute makes the violation a crime. Some statutory schemes make a violation of any of the law's provisions a crime. The knowing violation of any provision of the Pharmacy Law is a criminal misdemeanor, except where a section of the law provides a specific, different penalty (§4321(a)). For example, violation of some sections of the Pharmacy Law may be charged as a felony (see §4324, forgery of a prescription). When it cannot be established that the violator of the Pharmacy Law knew the act was a violation of law, only an infraction can be charged (§4321(b)). An infraction technically is a crime, but it is punishable only by a small fine.

While lack of intent or even the care with which one acted may not relieve a pharmacist of liability for the violation of law, nevertheless evidence that explains how and why the violation occurred and of rehabilitation (what the person has done to avoid a recurrence) will be useful in persuading a prosecutor to drop charges, file lesser charges, or accept a plea bargain. It also will be useful in attempting to persuade the jury not to convict, or to convict on lesser charges, and the judge to impose the lowest possible penalty.

## *Asset Forfeiture*

In some types of cases in which criminal prosecution may also be brought, the government may use asset forfeiture laws to seek out assets used to commit or facilitate the commission of a crime. While rarely employed against licensed professionals, these laws do apply to major drug law violations, generally those involving illegal possession, possession for sale, or sale of controlled substances. If asset forfeiture is sought, the government may take anything used in, or to "facilitate," the drug deal. "Facilitate" is, intentionally, a very broad word. It means that if you dispense illegitimate prescriptions in your pharmacy, using pharmacy equipment, and use your car to pick up the illegitimate prescriptions or to deliver the filled prescriptions, the government may be able to seize the pharmacy, the equipment in the pharmacy, possibly the stock in the pharmacy (certainly the stock of the drugs involved), and the car. If the circumstances support it, even the place (such as a clinic or a nursing home) where you picked up the prescriptions or where you delivered the drugs also may be subject to forfeiture. Computers, cellular phones, and other equipment used to arrange the transaction also may be subject to forfeiture.

Both the California and federal governments have the authority to seize assets used in drug trafficking (H&SC §11470; 21 USC §§853 (criminal forfeiture), 881 (civil forfeiture)). A criminal conviction is not always a necessary prerequisite for a successful forfeiture action. An asset forfeiture action may also be filed and pursued in an independent civil proceeding. These laws have been used successfully against health care practitioners who abused the prescribing and dispensing process. Asset forfeiture quite obviously has the potential for great financial loss on the part of the accused.

The leading case as to professionals is *United States v. Schifferli*, 895 F. 2d 987 (4th Cir. 1990), in which a dentist's entire office was forfeited because he wrote illegitimate prescriptions there.[34] The court said that it was enough to sustain forfeiture that he only wrote a few "bad" prescriptions, even if the illegitimate prescriptions were only a small percentage of all the prescriptions he wrote in his office. In 1999, a federal appellate court upheld the forfeiture of a physician's license to practice medicine because he wrote and sold numerous illegitimate prescriptions for controlled

---

[34] There is a limit to the extent of the forfeiture. In *United States v. Bajakajian*, 524 U.S. 321 (1998), the defendant violated federal law by failing to report over $357,000 in currency he was removing from the United States: a statute required that transactions involving more than $10,000 be reported. The Supreme Court, in a 5-4 decision, found that the forfeiture of the entire $357,000 was grossly disproportionate to the gravity of the offense and therefore unconstitutional as an "excessive fine" in violation of the Eighth Amendment.

substances. The court pointed out that a license to practice medicine was property subject to forfeiture within the meaning of the federal asset forfeiture law (*United States v. Dicter*, 198 F.3d 1284 (11th Cir. 1999)).

## *Civil Liability*

Civil liability refers to liability for violations of the private rights of others, such as for injury you have caused to the party pursuing the action. In pharmacy practice, both errors and conduct that constitutes unprofessional conduct might lead to injured parties seeking compensation for their harms by suing you. These types of lawsuits are called "torts" suits; when a professional is involved, suits concerning negligence are generally referred to as malpractice. Injured parties may seek compensation for their physical injury and property damage, as well as their emotional distress.

A pharmacist will be judged negligent if he or she failed to act as the ordinary prudent pharmacist would have acted under similar circumstances. In the practice of pharmacy, this may come up when someone is injured in or around a pharmacy because, for example, the premises were carelessly maintained, but the most common conduct for which such a claim is made is in connection with the dispensing of drugs. It can be for anything from providing the wrong drug or directions for use to failing to consult (or to consult adequately). And such a suit is always a possibility when there is any significant injury to a patient in connection with the use of dispensed drugs.[35]

The person making the claim must establish, usually through the opinion of a qualified expert pharmacist, that he or she was someone to whom the pharmacist (and/or pharmacy) owed a duty to be careful, that the pharmacist failed to meet that duty by acting as the ordinary, prudent pharmacist would have done in the same circumstances, that the patient suffered some injury and loss, and that the injury was caused by the pharmacist's failing. Proving that the pharmacist or pharmacy was negligent (that is, can be held liable) is harder than claiming it; anyone can file a lawsuit for practically anything. It is up to the defendant to seek to have baseless lawsuits tossed out of court as early as possible or, if that doesn't succeed, to prevail at hearing or trial.

## *Miscellaneous Liability Risks*

In case the risks of regulatory and criminal action, asset forfeiture and malpractice suits, are not sufficient to bolster your moral aversion to violating the law, government has additional tools for punishment of drug law violators. Where billings to state or federal programs are involved, actions for recoupment of payments are possible. Tax law violations (either criminal or civil charges) may be brought as well for failure to report or under-reporting income. The state may seek to recover unpaid sales taxes where the evidence could support the conclusion that the pharmacy was receiving more money for prescriptions or drugs sold or missing than was reported to tax authorities. There often are substantial financial penalties attached to both criminal and civil tax cases. If you use the mail or the telephone to aid in a fraudulent transaction, you are subject to federal criminal charges for mail or wire fraud. There also are money-laundering statutes and special conspiracy statutes that may be applied in cases involving illicit drug activities. There are even abatement statutes that can be used to shut down, in some cases forfeit, structures where illegal drug activity is permitted to occur (H&SC §11570). Despite the intimidating weight of all these potential bases for disciplinary or other liability, the fact is that the ethical pharmacist will never face the criminal or other serious charges described in this

---

[35] The most common reason for such lawsuits is surely improperly-filled prescriptions. In a 2004 case, for example, a pharmacist dispensed double the prescribed dose of thyroid medication. The patient, who had a leg amputated as a result, was awarded $1,000,000 by the jury which found the pharmacy chain liable (*$1 Million Verdict for Wrong Dose*, RX IPSA LOQUITUR (American Society for Pharmacy Law), July/August 2004, p. 3).

chapter. Nor is the prudent pharmacist very likely ever to run afoul of the incompetence, corresponding responsibility, gross negligence, or general unprofessional conduct standards that are catalogued here.

---

**What you should think about after reading this chapter:**

1. Why is the term "unprofessional conduct" so broad?

2. What kinds of things might one do to minimize practice errors? To respond to errors when they happen?

3. What information might affect your decision whether or not to fill a controlled substance prescription?

4. May a pharmacist ever steer a patient to a company in which he or she has an financial interest?

5. What kind of crimes should be considered grounds for discipline of a pharmacist? Crimes of violence? Tax evasion? Driving under the influence of alcohol? Possession of a small quantity of marijuana?

6. What obligation does a pharmacist have to ensure that a patient's pain is managed adequately?

7. When might an employee pharmacist need to consider quitting a pharmacy position in order to protect his or her license?

---

# Chapter XIII

# The Board of Pharmacy and Other Agencies

**What you should know after reading this chapter:**

1. What are the qualifications to be a member of the Board of Pharmacy? How are Board members appointed?

2. What are the qualifications to be the Executive Officer of the Board of Pharmacy? How is the Executive Officer appointed?

3. What right do you have to notice of Board meetings? To participate in Board meetings?

4. What is the function of the Board's central complaint unit?

5. What recourse, if any, do you have if you do not like a regulation adopted by the Board?

6. What records and documents can you get from the Board? How?

7. What records and information may the Board maintain about you? How can you find out what is in those records?

## The Board of Pharmacy

The State of California requires licensure for many professions, occupations, and businesses, and others are licensed or registered at the local level. State government accomplishes this licensing of millions of people and businesses through executive branch (or administrative) agencies that are under the control, direct or indirect, of the Governor. The Legislature passes statutes establishing the licensing scheme and the nature and extent of the agency's powers and responsibilities. Often legislative provisions are quite broad in scope; each agency, within the limits set out in its statutes, enforces the laws through decisions made on a case-by-case basis and through the establishment and enforcement of rules and regulations further defining, refining, and limiting its authority. While many today question the number, size, and scope of authority of administrative agencies, keep in mind that only legislatures have the authority to create, or terminate, the programs that agencies are required to implement.[1] If a program is a necessary and valuable part of government, it requires an implementation and enforcement mechanism; agencies to which authority over legislative programs is entrusted provide that mechanism.

---

[1] When Governor Schwarzenegger took office, he requested a review of the agencies of California government. The California Performance Review Commission has prepared a 2,500 page report, available at www.report.cpr.ca.gov. Among its recommendations are to move the healing arts licensure boards, including the Pharmacy Board, to a new California Department of Health and Human Services. It is likely that legislation, and perhaps a ballot proposition, to enact at least some of the report's recommendations will be introduced in 2005.

The Board of Pharmacy, established in 1891, is one of the oldest administrative licensing agencies in California. The Board is responsible for the initial interpretation and enforcement of California Pharmacy Law and those portions of the state Controlled Substances Act that pertain to prescription controlled substances (§§4001(a), 4011). Since 1971, the Board has been part of the California Department of Consumer Affairs, an umbrella agency that includes most of the state's professional and occupational licensing boards and bureaus. The Department of Consumer Affairs is, in turn, part of the State and Consumer Services Agency, one of six state cabinet-level agencies.

The Board controls its own day-to-day affairs, but its budgets and regulations must be approved by the Department. Budgets also must be approved by the Legislature and the Governor; regulations also must be approved by the Office of Administrative Law. The Department has input and often approval power or control over other major decisions. The Board licenses some 30,000 pharmacists, 3,500 intern pharmacists, 27,500 pharmacy technicians, nearly 6,000 pharmacies, and over 400 wholesalers (*The Script*, April 2001, pp. 1, 9).

Public protection, a statute proclaims, is to be Board's "highest priority," considered "paramount" when in conflict with other interests sought to be promoted (§4001.1). Thus, in adopting regulations, protecting the public is to be a consideration above that of protecting the profession; in disciplinary cases, concern for public protection is to outweigh the interests of the licensee.

## *Structure of the Board*

**Board Membership.** The Board consists of thirteen members, including six public (or nonpharmacist) members. At least five of the seven pharmacist appointees to the Board must be pharmacists who are actively engaged in the practice of pharmacy. At least one pharmacist member must come from each of the following practice settings: an acute care hospital, an independent community pharmacy (a pharmacy whose owner owns no more than four pharmacies in California), a chain community pharmacy (chain of 75 or more stores in California under the same ownership), and a long-term health care or skilled nursing facility. One of the pharmacist appointees must be a member of a labor union that represents pharmacists (§4001).

The President of the Senate and the Speaker of the Assembly each appoint one public member, and the Governor appoints four. All members are appointed for a four-year term, and no member may serve more than two consecutive terms. A member who is not immediately replaced at the end of a term may remain on the Board until he or she is replaced, or for one year, whichever comes first (§4001(d)).

The Board annually selects its own officers and appoints an executive officer, its chief staff member, who may be a member of the Board, but has not been in at least three decades (§§4002(a), 4003(a)).[2] The Board has had only three executive officers in the last 20 years, all of them nonpharmacists. The Board's public members participate fully in all issues that come before the Board; several public members have served as Board president.

The Board's president appoints committee members (usually in consultation with other Board members), sets (with the executive officer) Board meeting agendas, presides over the Board meetings, issues correspondence in the name of the Board (as does the executive officer), and appears for and speaks on behalf of the Board before the Legislature, before other bodies, or at other functions. The executive officer or other staff members, at his or her direction, also appear for and speak on behalf of

---

[2] The executive officer serves at the Board's pleasure and so may be replaced at any time, virtually without cause. There is no limit to the term of years an executive officer may serve.

the Board. The Board President may authorize other Board members to make such appearances. The President signs those documents required by law to be signed by the Board, as well as those that Board policy dictates are to be signed by the Board.

**Board Meetings.** The Board acts primarily at regular meetings of its full membership. Currently it meets four times each year, typically for two days each meeting, in Sacramento or another major California city. In recent years it has held half its meetings in Sacramento, and alternated between northern and southern California for its other meetings. Notice of meetings, including the agenda, is made available in advance to the public; discussion and action at meetings are limited to items on the agenda. Anyone interested may attend, comment on any agenda item, or suggest future agenda items; the Board may control the length of comments. Virtually all of the Board's deliberations are in public (see discussion of public meetings law below). The Board maintains a mailing list of persons who wish to receive notice of meetings and other documents produced by the Board. There are fees to receive some items; meeting notices are provided free of charge. The Board posts meeting notices, agendas, and minutes at www.pharmacy.ca.gov/about/meetings.htm.

**Strategic Plan.** The Board uses a master plan, called a strategic plan, to guide its activities. The plan, which is regularly reviewed and updated as necessary, sets out the Board's goals, priorities, and timelines for accomplishing specific tasks. The Board uses the strategic plan both to test its own accomplishments and to help prioritize issues that the Board and its committees must handle. A copy of the Strategic Plan, most recently revised in April 2004, is available from the Board and posted on its website (www.pharmacy.ca.gov/publications/strategicplan_2003.pdf). In the plan, the Board states that its mission is to protect and promote "the health and safety of Californians by pursuing the highest quality of pharmacist's care through education, communication, licensing, legislation, regulation, and enforcement" (*Strategic Plan*, p. 4).

In its current plan, the Board identifies 10 areas of focus:

- Cost of medical/pharmaceutical care
- Aging population
- Pharmacists' ability to provide care
- Changing demographics of California patients
- Laws governing pharmacists
- Legislative issues for pharmacies
- Electronic prescribing/automation
- Internet issues
- Disaster planning and response
- Qualified staff
  (*Strategic Plan*, pp. 9-11).

**Board Committees.** The Board generally acts through committees, both standing committees that continue from year to year and committees formed to deal with issues as the need arises. The goals of the Board's standing committees are as follows:

- **Communication and Public Education.** "Encouraging the public to discuss their medications with their pharmacist and emphasizing the importance of patients complying with their prescription treatment regimens; and helping pharmacists to become better informed on subjects of importance to the public."
- **Licensing.** "Ensure the professional qualifications of those entering the practice of pharmacy, as well as those continuing to practice, meet minimum requirements for education, experience, and knowledge, and ensuring that facilities licensed by the board meet minimum standards."

- **Enforcement.** "Protecting the public by preventing violations, and effectively enforcing federal and state pharmacy laws when violations occur."
- **Legislation and Regulation.** "Pursuing legislation that ensures better patient care and providing effective regulation of the individuals and firms who handle, dispense, furnish, ship and store prescription drugs and devices in California."
- **Organizational Development.** "Conducting strategic planning, budget management and staff development activities to ensure the efficient achievement of the board's mission and goals." (See Committee Quarterly Reports at www.pharmacy.ca.gov/about/meetings.htm#enforce.)

An example of a committee formed to deal with a specific issue is the Task Force on Pharmaceutical Benefit Managers Regulation, formed to explore whether regulation of PBMs should be pursued.

## *Authority of the Board*

The Board is authorized to enforce the Pharmacy Law (§§4000-4427)[3] and to adopt any regulation that is reasonably necessary to carry out its purposes, including by giving additional detail to the law (§4005, see Chap. I: Law). The Board has the authority to use a variety of remedies to enforce the Pharmacy Law, most notably by bringing disciplinary actions against licensees for misconduct; its other remedies include asking the courts to enjoin violations of the law (§4339). The Board may, and does, delegate significant authority to its executive officer to conduct the Board's business, particularly in regard to the disciplinary process (§4003(a), §1703).

As of 2004, the Board has the authority to waive the application of any provision of the Pharmacy Law or of its own regulations during a declared federal, state, or local emergency if the "waiver will aid in the protection of public health or the provision of patient care" (§4062(b)). The Governor has the authority, in an emergency, to temporarily suspend any laws or regulations that impose nonsafety related restrictions on the delivery of pharmaceuticals (GC §8627.5). It appears that determining whether (and which) safety-related laws and regulations should be suspended during the emergency would be in the hands of the Board. Dealing with pharmaceutical care overall during an emergency would require cooperation between the Board and the Governor, because only the Governor could suspend the (nonsafety related) controlled substances provisions of the Health and Safety Code (see Chap. X: Dispensing and Beyond ("Emergency Provision of Drugs")).

The Board is authorized to hire inspectors to inspect places where drugs are compounded, dispensed, or sold (see below), to make certain arrests, and otherwise to investigate violations of the Pharmacy Law or other laws and regulations over which the Board has authority (§4008).

In common with other state agencies, the Board has broad authority to subpoena witnesses and records for investigatory purposes to enable it to meet its important public protection function (see GC §§11180-11191; *Arnett v. Dal Cielo,* 14 Cal. 4th 4, 8 (1996)). These powers are especially broad in the case of closely regulated professions such as pharmacy (*People v. Doss,* 4 Cal. App. 4th 1585, 1598 (2d Dist. 1992)).

---

[3] The Board also has authority to enforce the California Hazardous Substances Act (H&SC §§108100-108515) as it applies to pharmacies, pharmacists, and others subject to the Board's jurisdiction. The California Hazardous Substances Act substitutes for the more traditional regulation of poisons, which was a significant matter when products were packaged in bulk and distributed at the retail level rather than packaged by manufacturers for consumer sale.

## *Continuity of the Board*

California is one of many states that has decided to re-examine the effectiveness of professional and occupational licensing boards every few years, and decide whether each should continue to exist.  This process has come to be known as "sunset" review.  While it is extremely unlikely that the Board of Pharmacy, or any other health professional board, will be eliminated any time in the foreseeable future, nevertheless the Board must, every few years, justify its continued existence to the Legislature.  It must demonstrate that it is complying with the requirements, intent, and purpose of its governing statutes, and meeting the needs of the public and those it licenses.

The Board's most recent sunset review report to the Legislature was published in September 2002 (www.pharmacy.ca.gov/publications/sunset02.pdf).  Thereafter the statutes establishing the Board and enabling it to appoint an executive officer were extended; they will become inoperative as of July 1, 2008, and on January 1, 2009, the Board will lose all authority to operate, unless the statutes are again extended (§4003(e)).  As 2008 nears, the Board will again need to prepare an assessment of its operations and respond to extensive questions by the sunset review committee of the Legislature.

## *Staff*

Most of the Board's day-to-day work is done by its executive, investigative, and support staff in Sacramento or, in the case of inspectors, in the field.[4]  The staff implements statutes, regulations, and policies and procedures in accordance with the direction of the Board.  Staff members handle inquiries from licensees, and inquiries and complaints from the public, distribute forms and publications, and create systems and materials for communicating information to licensees and the public.  The Board's central complaint unit tracks all public complaints and other cases at the Board from receipt and assignment until closure.  Staff members process license and examination applications, handle renewal and continuing education paperwork, and track investigations and formal and informal disciplinary actions.

The Board's website, at www.pharmacy.ca.gov, cited frequently in this text, contains a substantial amount of information, including requirements for licensure, various forms, minutes of Board meetings, details of regulations under consideration by the Board and legislative positions taken by the Board, and educational materials such as *The Script*, the Board's general newsletter, and *Health Notes*, its periodic publication on health topics of particular interest to pharmacy.

The Board does not have its own legal staff.[5]  The Licensing Section of the Office of the Attorney General provides legal representation to the Board, as it does for most boards and bureaus in the Department of Consumer Affairs.  A liaison deputy attorney general advises the Board on pending or possible litigation and interpretation of Board and other statutes and regulations, staffs Board committees, and is available to represent the Board in communications with individuals, other agencies, and the Legislature.  The Licensing Section's most important function for the Board is to file and prosecute disciplinary actions and handle citations against licensees and applicants, both at the

---

[4]  The Board no longer maintains field offices that are open to the public.  With modern communications technology, inspectors working in the field can keep in touch with the Sacramento office and other field staff using laptop computers, pagers, cellular phones, and voice mail.

[5]  California state agencies are represented by the Attorney General's office unless the Legislature otherwise authorizes or the Attorney General permits another arrangement.  The Board has sought to represent itself, but it has not received permission to do so from the Attorney General.

administrative and court levels (see below). The deputies in the section also represent the Board when it is sued.

A staff attorney for the Department of Consumer Affairs acts as counsel for the Board on matters of general application, such as regulation adoption and public meetings and records laws, and assures consistency in policies with other boards within the Department.

The Board uses several tools to assure consistency in implementation of the law. It maintains and regularly updates a comprehensive manual for its inspectors. It also regularly conducts workshops for inspectors on general inspection and investigation issues, as well as particular issues of recent interest.

## *The Executive Officer*

The executive officer may, but need not, be a Board member, a pharmacist, or both. The executive officer is hired by the Board through a competitive process, and serves at its discretion. He or she is responsible for managing the day-to-day affairs of the Board, including overall administration and the hiring of all support staff, including the assistant executive officer and inspectors.

The executive officer often attends conferences or other meetings on behalf of the Board, and speaks or acts on its behalf. The Board has specifically delegated to the executive officer the authority to file accusations, to process disciplinary cases (subject to the Board's final decisionmaking power), and to issue summary suspensions under section 4311 (§1703). The executive officer decides whether or not to pursue investigations, to sign and file accusations, and to negotiate case settlements, subject to subsequent Board approval. The executive officer, usually working with the president, sets Board meeting dates and Board agendas; with committee chairs, he or she sets the dates and agendas of those meetings. The executive officer is responsible for the supervision of all the Board's responsibilities.

## *Access to Board Meetings and Records*

After many years during which government operated without encouraging or enabling public oversight, public policy took a significant shift several decades ago. The result, on both federal and state government levels, was the passage of statutes granting broad access by the public to government meetings and to records created and maintained by the government. California's provisions are among the broadest. The Open Meeting Act declares that the business of public agencies should be conducted in public so that the public can remain informed (GC §11120). The Public Records Act describes access to information regarding the conduct of the people's business as a fundamental right of every Californian (GC §6250). Under both public meeting and public records law, the presumption is that the public has access. Access may only be denied when the agency can substantiate that its right to meet behind closed doors or protect a record from disclosure is covered by an exception in the statutes granting that right. The exceptions most commonly involve privacy rights of employees or others, ongoing investigations or litigation, and licensure exams. Denials of the right to access may be challenged in court, in proceedings in which the agency may have to pay the challenger's attorneys' fees if it loses.

**Public Meetings.** Meetings of the Board and its committees must be in public (GC §11121(b),(d)). There must be adequate notice to the public of these meetings, including an agenda that briefly discusses each item to be discussed or acted upon (GC §11125(b)), at least 10 days prior to the meeting (GC §11125(a)). Notice is given by appropriate publication and personally to those on the Board's mailing list. Meetings must be open to the public, and there must be an opportunity for public comment on every agenda item before the Board takes action on it (GC §11125.7), unless the subject may legally be discussed in a closed session and the agenda gave notice of a closed session (GC §11126.3). The law strictly limits the types of matters that may be discussed in closed sessions; these include pending litigation, decisions in disciplinary actions, examination preparation and grading, and certain personnel matters. The law provides for special or emergency meetings for a very limited number of reasons, including the need to discuss pending litigation or legislation where immediate action is needed (GC §11125.4).

Formal agendas are not needed for committee meetings, but these meetings are limited to the types of business described in the meeting notice (GC §11125(c)). All public meetings may be held by teleconference as long as the proceedings are audible to the public at the site where the meeting is noticed and the notice identifies each of the teleconference locations (GC §11123(b)). The public may make a video or audio recording of any public meeting as long as it is done in a non-disruptive manner (GC §11124.1(a)). The public may also view or hear any tape or film record the Board has made of its meetings prior to their destruction; agencies commonly keep these records only until the subsequent meeting when their minutes are approved.

**May the Board discuss an item on its agenda prior to the time indicated on the agenda for that item to be considered?**

The Board usually includes in its meeting notices the statement that the date, as well as the time, of its anticipated consideration of each agenda item is subject to change at the meeting; this practice is permitted. Sometimes meetings proceed more quickly than anticipated; the Board often takes up a matter early when it is running ahead of schedule or has a need to shift another matter. However, it rarely switches to a different day any matter it suspects will draw significant public input. When notified in advance by those who plan to attend part of a meeting, for a particular item, it tries to accommodate their planned time of attendance.

**Public Records.** Most Board records are public records, in accordance with the statutory presumption that all documents or items in possession of or generated by government agencies are public records (GC §6253(a)). Fees to obtain records may be charged; however, records requested and not exempt from disclosure must be provided at a cost not to exceed the actual, direct cost of their copying (GC §6253(b)). The Board must generally respond to the request within ten days, providing a specific ground set out in statute for any records it decides to withhold (GC §6253(c)). Under certain circumstances it may have an additional 14 days to respond to requests. Some of the types of records the Board may (and sometimes must) exempt from disclosure include:

- Most records of active investigations (GC §6254(f)),
- Personal, medical, or similar records where disclosure would be an unwarranted invasion of privacy (GC §6254(c)),
- Preliminary drafts, notes, or memoranda not ordinarily retained by the agency as part of its permanent records (GC §6254(a)),
- Records pertaining to pending litigation (GC §6254(b)),
- Test questions and other material used to create or administer a licensing examination (GC §6254(g)),
- Records privileged or prohibited from disclosure by other state laws or by federal law (GC §6254(k)),
- Records that reveal the agency's deliberative processes (GC §6254(p)), and
- Personal financial data the Board required in connection with an application for licensure (GC §6254(n)).

A detailed list of exemptions is in the Government Code (§§6276.02-6276.48). The Department of Consumer Affairs is required to have written guidelines for public record requests, post them in its offices, and provide copies to the public (GC §6253.4(a)).  If you believe records have been improperly withheld, you may file suit to obtain an order that the agency release the records.  The Board will have the burden of establishing that the records requested are in fact exempt from disclosure (GC §6255(a)).  Court costs and reasonable attorneys' fees may be awarded to a victorious plaintiff; if the lawsuit, however, was clearly frivolous, the plaintiff can be ordered to pay the agency's costs and attorneys' fees (GC §§6258, 6259(d)).

The Board is required to maintain certain types of records.  It must maintain a central information file on all its licensees that includes, among other information, certain criminal convictions and judgments and settlements in excess of $3,000 in malpractice cases (B&PC §800).

**Confidentiality of Personal Information Held by Board.**  The "flip side" of public records is the concern that confidential personal information in the hands of government agencies will be made public.  The Board obviously maintains considerable information about licensees, such as their license history and status, including records of disciplinary proceedings.  There may even be financial information requested by the Board as part of an application process.

Some of these items are public records that must be disclosed upon request.  For example, citations or accusations, as well as final disciplinary decisions, are public records, as are a summary of the license history and status of licensees and their address of record.  (Because a licensee's address of record is public, and available on the Internet, licensees are well advised to use a business rather than home address for this purpose.)

The Information Practices Act of 1977 (IPA) (Civ. Code §1798-1798.78) protects the confidentiality of personal information obtained or maintained by government agencies. The IPA was passed, along with California's express constitutional right of privacy, in the wake of the Watergate scandal, to protect the privacy of individuals by subjecting the maintenance and use of personal information by government to strict limits (Civ. Code §1798.1(c)).  The law requires that each agency establish safeguards to ensure the security and confidentiality of its records, and maintain only that personal information which is "relevant and necessary" to accomplish its legitimate functions (Civ. Code §§1798.14, 1798.21).  This law is complex and contains significant exceptions.

It is important to know that, as with credit reporting laws, an individual has the right to know if an agency retains personal information about him or her (Civ. Code §1798.32), has the right to inspect those records (Civ. Code §1798.34(a)), and to recommend an amendment to the record to correct errors in it (Civ. Code §1798.35).  If the agency refuses to make the change, the individual may provide a statement of reasonable length for the file setting forth the disagreement with that portion of the records (Civ. Code §1798.36).  There are exceptions to the right to see one's own file; for example, records of a pending criminal investigation may be withheld (Civ. Code §1798.40(b)).  The requester must generally receive written notice of the agency's finding that the information is not subject to disclosure (Civ. Code §1798.41(a)).  There is a right to sue for violations of rights given by the IPA (Civ. Code §1798.45).

Privacy rights associated with California's Confidentiality of Medical Information Act and federal HIPAA regulations regarding personal health information are discussed in Chapter XIV: Other Law Relevant to Pharmacy.

## *Obtaining Information from the Board*

**Board Publications.**  The Board communicates with its licensees and the public through a number of publications.  The Board publishes a newsletter called *The Script* several times a year; the issues since October 1998 are archived on the Board's website and indexed in the March 2004 edition (pp. 17-19) (www.pharmacy.ca.gov/publications/publications.htm). *The Script* includes discussions of new laws and regulations and developments and issues relevant to pharmacy licensees. It provides answers to important questions about legal and practice issues and short summaries of disciplinary decisions issued by the Board. The Board's special reports called *Health Notes* (found on the same web page as *The Script*) have focused on a variety of subjects. The first, in 1996, was on pain management; as noted in Chapter XII: Practice Pitfalls, a revision is underway. Others have covered women's health, alternative medicine, quality assurance, care of children and adults with developmental disabilities, anticoagulant therapy, and drug therapy considerations in older adults.

Issues of *The Script* and of *Health Notes* may be of special interest to applicants for licensure as a pharmacist. Although the CPJE (see Chap. III: Licensing Pharmacists) is called a "jurisprudence" examination, it appears to include some topics that are primarily clinical, rather than legal, in nature. The applicants' handbook (www.pharmacy.ca.gov/publications/phy_handbook.pdf) specifically recommends review of these publications as well as California pharmacy law and regulations. For that reason, references to *Health Notes* and *The Script* are included in Appendix A, which primarily references the pages in this text to the elements in the CPJE content outline.

The Board also publishes booklets and pamphlets on various aspects or functions of the Board, directed variously to licensees, applicants, and members of the public (with some of the latter translated into Spanish). Applications and related documents, such as instructions, are almost all available on the Board's website.

**Communications with the Board.** Any person may contact the Board in writing, by fax, by phone, through e-mail, or in person. Certain requests for documents or records are required to be made in writing, including requests for declaratory decisions about the applicability to specific circumstances of a statute or regulation (see Chap. I: Law). The Board has no specific time in which it must respond, except in the case of public records requests. The Board's website, www.pharmacy.ca.gov, is a valuable tool in the Board's communications with the public.

**May a person obtain license information by telephone?**

Yes, the Board will respond to telephonic requests for information.

## *The Application Review Process*

When an application for a license is received by the Board, it is reviewed by staff for completeness and for compliance with substantive criteria set forth in statute and regulations. Criminal background checks are performed on individual applicants and on the key personnel of corporate applicants. Assuming no information is produced that requires further investigation, the applicant is permitted to take the appropriate examination and, if he or she passes, is licensed. If there is no examination, the applicant is licensed forthwith. If the application is for a permit for premises, the applicant must certify that the premises comply with section 1714. Board inspectors no longer routinely inspect premises prior to the issuance of permits. However, they do generally inspect new licensees within a few months of licensure and will cite the licensee or recommend the filing of formal disciplinary charges if, upon inspection, it is determined that the certification of compliance with section 1714 was false.

The Board has established timelines for processing applications: 30 days to notify an applicant that an application is incomplete or deficient and what is needed to correct the deficiency, and 30 to 60 days to notify the applicant of a decision after the complete application is filed (§1706.1). Any application for a premises or a technician license must be completed within 60 days of notice of deficiencies in the file or the application may be deemed abandoned (§1706.2).

The Board's actual processing times have yet to meet these established expectations, for several reasons. First, staffing problems, including shortages of inspectors and office staff, have made it difficult to reduce processing times. Second, the Board often needs to request additional information from applicants, which adds to processing time. Overall, the Board is obligated by law to investigate applicants for licensure thoroughly (§4207), a mandate that conflicts with the mandate to process applications quickly.

## *The Investigative and Inspection Process*

The Board, through its inspectors, is authorized to inspect all "pharmacies, wholesalers, dispensaries, stores, or places where drugs or devices are compounded, prepared, furnished, dispensed, or stored" (§4008(a)).[6] Board inspectors have traditionally been required to be licensed pharmacists; a law change effective in 2004 allows the Board to hire nonpharmacists (§4008). In addition to their inspectional powers, inspectors may arrest, without warrant, any person they reasonably believe has, in their presence, violated Pharmacy Law or the state Controlled Substances Act. When the inspector reasonably believes the violation is a felony, the inspector may arrest without a warrant for a violation not committed in his or her presence (§4008(c)).

Inspectors conduct routine inspections of new licensees and periodically of all licensees. In addition, they conduct inspections in response to complaints or information suggesting violations of the law. Inspectors routinely file inspection reports to establish that an inspection was conducted and to note any areas, usually minor and correctable, of concern. The pharmacist in charge or owner, if present, will be asked to sign the report; otherwise, the on-duty pharmacist will be asked to sign. If the inspection finds violations more significant than those merely noted on an inspection report, but not worthy of formal action, the inspector may prepare a warning notice to document them. When a warning notice is issued, a follow-up visit will occur to determine whether those violations have been corrected.

For more serious violations still not necessitating referral to the Board for more formal action, since 2004 the inspector has had the option to issue a written order of correction (§4083). The person to whom the order is issued may appeal it by requesting an informal conference before the Board's executive officer. This process is less formal than other Board proceedings, described below. While the executive officer's decision is appealable to the courts, it will only be reversed if the court finds a prejudicial abuse of discretion, a difficult standard to meet. The licensee who is the subject of a final written order of correction must comply and submit a written corrective action plan documenting compliance (§4083(c)(2)). Orders of correction are not considered disclosable public records unless the licensee appeals to the courts or receives a citation or letter of admonishment, or a disciplinary proceeding is instituted concerning the facts of the violation (4083(g)).

When the inspector believe the violations justify greater action than a written order of correction, he or she may recommend to the Board that an admonishment letter or a citation be issued, disciplinary charges filed, or, in the most serious cases, referral made to a local, state, or federal prosecutor for the filing of criminal charges. Each of these procedures is discussed below.

---

[6]  This authority extends even to clinics that do not have a drug permit from the Board and to individual prescriber offices. However, in order to ensure patient confidentiality, the authority is limited to examining stock of dangerous drugs and dangerous devices and the records of their acquisition and disposition (§4008(b)).

# *Actions Available Against Licensees*

The Board may take, or recommend, a variety of actions against licensees or others, such as applicants for licensure and those who handle prescription drugs and devices without licensure.

**Admonishment letters.** An admonishment letter is similar to an order of correction, but issued by the Executive officer or his or her designate. As with a written order of correction, the person to whom this order is issued may appeal by requesting an informal office conference, and the rules governing that conference and any appeal from it are the same as for the order of correction, including the limited scope of the court's review. Unless the court finds a prejudicial abuse of discretion on the part of the Board it must uphold the order (§4315(c)(1)(E)). As with a final order of correction, the licensee must comply and submit a written corrective action plan (§4315(c)(2)); failure to comply can result in discipline.

**Citations and fines.** The Board has statutory authority (B&PC §125.9) to cite any licensee or nonlicensee for a violation of any provision of the Pharmacy Law or of the Board's regulations (§4314). The Board also has the authority to issue citations for violations of California's Confidentiality of Medical Information Act, for certain Internet dispensing violations, and for defaulting on a federal HHS education loan. Citations are issued by the Executive Officer and may include a fine, an order of abatement, or both (§1775(a)). The Board's regulations for implementing its citation and fine authority are in sections 1775-1775.4.

The person or entity cited may appeal the citation, and may choose to have an informal office conference or a hearing governed by the Administrative Procedure Act, discussed below. If not satisfied after the informal conference, an APA hearing may still be requested. The Board has the burden to demonstrate the charges it has made in the citation by a preponderance of evidence. The cited person or entity may appeal any adverse final order to the courts. However, once a citation is final, compliance is required. The Board may go to court to enforce any fine that is part of the citation. It may seek either civil or criminal action for failure to comply with any order of abatement that is part of the final order; an order of abatement requires that someone take action, such as bringing a facility into compliance or no longer violating the Pharmacy Law.

Fines under this authority may be quite significant in size,[7] and once they are set in a final order, they must be paid before a license can be renewed. The licensee who fails to comply with a final order is subject to discipline, in which the facts of the citation violation may not be contested. All that is relevant at that point is whether the citation was properly issued, is final, and has not been complied with, and what discipline is appropriate (§§1775.1(d), 1775.3).

---

[7]  For most violations, the Executive Officer has the authority to impose fines of up to $5,000 per violation (§1775.1, B&PC 125.9). The fine for defaulting on an HHS education loan cannot exceed $2,500 (§1775.1(c)). Fines for violation of the sterile injectable drug products law and regulations cannot exceed $2,500 per occurrence (4127.4). Fines of up to $25,000 per violation may be imposed for unlawful prescribing or dispensing via the Internet (B&PC §2242.1, §4067(b)).

A fine of up to $2,500 may be imposed *per violation* for negligent disclosure of information in violation of the Confidentiality of Medical Information Act, regardless of whether a consumer has suffered damage as a result (Civ. Code §56.36(c)(1)). Fines escalate for knowing and willful violations. Knowing and willful obtaining, disclosing, or use of confidential medical information by a health care professional can lead to a fine of $2,500 for a first violation, but a maximum of $25,000 for a third or subsequent violation (Civ. Code §56.36(c)(2)(B)). Knowing and willful violation for financial gain by a health care professional is subject to a fine of up to $5,000 for a first violation, ranging up to *$250,000* per violation for a third or subsequent offense (Civ. Code §56.36(c)(3)(B)). A health care provider (including pharmacies and pharmacists) who negligently disposes, abandons, or destroys medical records may be fined up to $2,500 per violation; this is deemed the equivalent of disclosure of information (Civ. Code §56.101).

**Disciplinary action.** The Board can file formal disciplinary actions against an applicant or licensee for more serious violations or to address repeat violators or a pattern of violations.[8] It is important to understand what the formal disciplinary process is – and is not. It is not a criminal or quasi-criminal process. As the courts have noted in distinguishing professional discipline from criminal cases, the main purpose of a professional disciplinary proceeding, and any "penalty" imposed in it, is to protect the public from dishonest or otherwise unfit practitioners, rather than to punish the licensee (*Hughes* v. *Board of Architectural Examiners*, 17 Cal. 4th 763, 786-787 (1998)).

Because the disciplinary process is not criminal in nature, the constitutional and statutory protections applicable to criminal proceedings do not apply. But some constitutional rights do apply, particularly the right to due process of law, which guarantees, among other things, appropriate notice and the opportunity to be heard on the charges. Various statutory protections govern the hearing process, providing rights within the disciplinary context and the right to court review of that process. In California, the bulk of the statutory rights governing the disciplinary process are found in the California Administrative Procedure Act (APA), codified in the California Government Code.

An administrative adjudication "bill of rights" includes the right to written notice of charges and an opportunity to be heard, including: the opportunity to present and rebut evidence (GC §11425.10(a)(1)); a copy of the governing procedure (GC §11425.10(a)(2)); a hearing open to public observation (GC §11425.10(a)(3)); the separation of the adjudicative function from the investigative, prosecutorial, and advocacy functions within the agency (GC §11425.10(a)(4)); a presiding officer subject to disqualification for bias, prejudice, or interest (that is, for not being impartial, GC §11425.10(a)(5)); a written decision, based on the record and including a statement of facts and the legal basis for the decision (GC §11425.10(a)(6)); the use of decisions in prior cases as precedent only if the agency has designated and indexed the decisions as such (GC §11425.10(a)(7)); the restriction of ex parte communications (GC §11425.10(a)(8)); and the availability (in certain agencies) of language assistance (GC §11425.10(a)(9)). Other sections of the APA provide more detail about, and certain limitations upon, the above rights.[9]

The formal disciplinary process begins with a pleading, called an "accusation," prepared by a deputy attorney general from the Licensing Section of the Office of the Attorney General and based on an investigation report and other materials provided by the Board. The accusation must contain sufficient facts so that the licensee knows what incidents are alleged as the basis for action and so that he or she can effectively defend against the charges (see *Goldsmith v. State Board of Pharmacy,* 191 Cal. App.2d 866, 872-874 (2d Dist. 1961)). The accusation will inform its recipient that a notice of defense must be filed within 15 days, to avoid a default decision (GC §11505(a)).

In appropriate cases, the Board has the authority to seek an order barring a licensee from using the license, or limiting its use, pending hearing of the charges. The Board may either seek an administrative or interim suspension order from the Office of Administrative Hearings (B&PC §494)

---

[8] The Board has the legal authority to file a formal disciplinary action even when a violation is minor, but like all enforcement agencies it must exercise discretion about when to take which types of action because it does not have unlimited staff or funding. Its less formal enforcement tools, such as the letter of admonishment and citations and fines, are intended to enable the Board to maximize the efficiency of its enforcement budget while encouraging compliance by licensees and others without the greater burdens and risks of the formal disciplinary process.

[9] With the consent of the parties, mediation and arbitration are available alternatives to the formal hearing process. In limited circumstances, such as where the underlying facts are not in dispute (and only legal issues remain) or where minimal damages or potential disciplinary sanctions are involved, the law provides for an informal hearing, with simpler procedures (GC §11445.10). To date the Pharmacy Board has not employed either arbitration or the informal hearing process.

or a restraining order from the superior court (B&PC §125.7).[10] In either case, if such an order is imposed the licensee has the right to a disciplinary hearing on a priority basis (typically within 45 days of the issuance of the order).[11]

Very detailed and specific rights govern these proceedings (as well as the formal citation appeal hearings discussed above). They may be found in the APA (GC §§11400-11529), available at the website of the Office of Administrative Hearings (www.oah.dgs.ca.gov/Laws/default.htm). Additional information is also available in such publications as CALIFORNIA ADMINISTRATIVE HEARING PRACTICES, published by California Continuing Education of the Bar (2d ed., 1997). While some people or entities faced with formal disciplinary proceedings represent themselves, the assistance of an attorney should certainly be considered.

In addition to the bill of rights described above, the subject of an accusation may request a hearing, request (discover) relevant information and evidence in possession of the Board, and appeal the final decision to the courts. As with a citation, the Board has the burden of going forward with evidence, so the accused does not need to defend himself or herself until seeing the Board's evidence. Unlike in criminal prosecutions, the accused cannot refuse to testify. The accused may contest the facts, produce evidence to show the violations were less serious than they might appear (mitigation), or produce evidence or argue that the accused's actions since the violations justify no penalty or a less serious penalty than might otherwise be deemed appropriate (rehabilitation). The accused also can raise substantive or procedural defenses.

If the case involves a pharmacist, the Board must prove its charges by clear and convincing evidence to a reasonable certainty (*Ettinger v. Board of Medical Quality Assurance*, 135 Cal. App. 3d 853, 856 (2d Dist. 1982)). In cases involving licenses for which there are no professional qualifications, such as a pharmacy or wholesaler, the Board must only prove its charges by a preponderance of the evidence (*San Benito Foods v. Veneman*, 50 Cal. App. 4th 1889, 1891 (6th Dist.

---

[10] The Board can seek a restraining order and injunctive relief against non-licensees who violate the Pharmacy Law, for example those who are practicing pharmacy without a license.

[11] The Board has the authority and the responsibility to take immediate action against licensees convicted of certain crimes. The Board must automatically suspend a licensee who has been incarcerated after a felony conviction, for the length of that incarceration (§4311(a)). It need not make any determination of fact or law to take this action. The Board must summarily suspend any licensee for a felony conviction committed in the course of a business or practice for which the Board issues a license, or committed in a manner that a client, customer, or patient of the licensee was a victim, and involving either specific intent to deceive, defraud, steal, or make a false statement or the illegal sale or possession for sale of or trafficking in any controlled substance (§4311(b)). To summarily suspend a licensee under this provision, the Board must first make the determination there has been a conviction that requires the suspension, because not all felony convictions are covered by the statute.

The Board also must issue an interim suspension order against any license holder convicted of a felony substantially related to the qualifications, functions, or duties of the licensee (§4311(c)). This order also requires a fact determination by the Board, that the felony conviction is so related.

The licensee is entitled to notice of, and a hearing about, any automatic, summary, or interim suspension, to determine if there is a conviction for which the suspension is appropriate. These suspensions take effect unless the licensee requests a hearing, but the only issues at these hearings concern the existence of the conviction and whether it is the type of conviction that allows the Board to take the action it took. Certain crimes are conclusively presumed to be substantially related to the practice of pharmacy, including murder and controlled substances convictions (§4311(c)(4)). The Board will also need to seek a permanent disciplinary order against the licensee; in some circumstances the matter of interim and final penalties may be combined. The Board has authorized its executive officer to issue an automatic, summary, or interim suspension order (§1703).

1996)).[12] The preponderance standard also applies if a licensee who is on probation is charged with violations of probation or if the case involves an applicant for initial licensure.

Disciplinary cases are often settled without going to hearing. The Board may settle a case on any terms that are not contrary to public policy, and with a disposition from dismissal of all charges (a rare settlement result) to outright revocation (*Rich Vision Centers, Inc. v. Board of Medical Examiners*, 144 Cal. App. 3d 110, 115-116 (2d Dist. 1983)). Once a settlement between the accused and the Board's executive officer is final, both are bound by it and it goes before the Board for review and acceptance or (in rare cases) rejection (*Frankel v. Board of Dental Examiners*, 46 Cal. App. 4th 534, 546-547 (3d Dist. 1996)).

The Board has adopted disciplinary guidelines (§1760) to consider when reaching disciplinary decisions. It also has model disciplinary terms to govern settlements and decisions following hearing. Those terms include the standard provisions the Board wants in every decision and provisions that may or may not be imposed, depending on the facts of the particular case. These documents are available at www.pharmacy.ca.gov/laws_regs/1760_guidelines.pdf.

Cases are heard before a hearing officer known as an administrative law judge (ALJ). The ALJ prepares a written "proposed" decision. The Board reviews that decision and can accept ("adopt") it or reject ("non-adopt") it. If it wishes to reduce the proposed penalty without changing the findings, it may do so. Otherwise, it must either ask the ALJ to take further evidence and issue a new proposed decision or, more commonly, decide the case itself, after obtaining and reviewing the transcript of the hearing and any exhibits and giving both sides the opportunity to make written and/or oral arguments. Then the Board adopts its own decision.

The final decision may be appealed to the superior court (and in rare cases the court may issue a stay to delay the decision from going into effect until the appeal has been heard). The court's review is generally based upon the transcript, exhibits, and the decision of the Board, plus the arguments of the parties. An unsatisfied petitioner may then appeal to California's appellate courts.

Either in settlement, or as part of a decision in its favor following hearing, the Board can seek to recover its costs of investigation and prosecution of a disciplinary case, up to the time of hearing, from the accused (B&PC §125.3; *Angelier v. California State Board of Pharmacy*, 58 Cal. App. 4th 592, 601 (2d Dist. 1997)).

**Mental or Physical Impairment Actions.** Whenever it appears that a pharmacist (or any other healing arts practitioner licensed under the same division of the Business and Professions Code) may be unable to practice his or her profession safely because of impairment due to mental illness or physical illness affecting competence, the Board has two options: it may order the licensee to be examined by one or more physicians or psychologists it designates (B&PC §820) or it may take action against the licensee on the grounds of his or her impairment (B&PC §822).

If the Board determines, after receiving the report of such an examination, that there is insufficient evidence of impairment, all Board records, including the order for examination, are confidential and not subject to discovery or subpoena. If no further proceedings are conducted to determine the licensee's fitness within five years, the records must be purged and destroyed. If new proceedings are instituted during the five years, the prior records may be used in the proceedings and shall be available through discovery to the licensee (B&PC §828).

---

[12] While pharmacy technicians and exemptees/designated representatives must meet training requirements, they are not "professionals" in the same sense as are pharmacists. No case has determined which standard must be met in respect to either category of licensee.

If the Board determines the licensee's ability to practice is impaired, it may suspend or revoke the license (B&PC §822); the proceedings are to be conducted in accordance with the APA (B&PC §826). The Board has the option of proceeding under Business and Professions Code section 820, section 822, or both (B&PC §824). If it acts under section 822, it may not reinstate a revoked or suspended licensee until it has received competent evidence the condition causing the discipline is absent or controlled and it is satisfied the person may be reinstated safely with due regard for public health and safety (B&PC §822).

A licensee disciplined under section 822 may be conditionally reinstated on appropriate terms, including: obtaining additional professional training; passing an examination (oral, written, practical, or clinical, or any combination) to determine present fitness to practice the profession; submitting to a complete diagnostic physical or mental examination by physicians or psychologists selected by the Board (in which case the Board also must consider any similar report submitted by the licensee's physician or psychologist); continuing treatment; or restricting or limiting the extent, scope, or type of practice (B&PC §823).

**Pharmacists Recovery Program.** In response to a legislative mandate to "seek ways and means to identify and rehabilitate pharmacists whose competency may be impaired due to abuse of alcohol and other drugs, or due to mental illness, so that pharmacists so afflicted may be treated and returned to the practice of pharmacy in a manner that will not endanger the public health and safety" (§4360), the Board created the Pharmacists Recovery Program.

This program functions both as a diversion program, an alternative to traditional disciplinary action when an investigation suggests there is an abuse problem, and as a program to which pharmacists can turn voluntarily for confidential assistance when they recognize their own problems of substance abuse or mental impairment (§4362). A pharmacist may be required to participate in the program as part of a disciplinary order, either after hearing or by settlement.

When a pharmacist agrees to enter the program in lieu of discipline,[13] either when under investigation or as part of a disciplinary order or settlement, his or her participation will be known to the Board. The pharmacist is evaluated to determine whether he or she needs and is suitable for a diversion contract and is willing to sign and comply with it. If so, a contract is drafted, and the pharmacist is expected to sign it and comply with it fully (§4369(b)). If the pharmacist is not found to be suitable for participation or refuses to participate, disciplinary proceedings will go forward.

When pharmacists seek the services of the program on their own, their names and all identifying information pertaining to them are not disclosed to the Board except under specific circumstances (§4363). First, the Board must be informed of a pharmacist's noncompliance with the treatment program if the administrator determines that the pharmacist's resuming the practice of pharmacy would pose a threat to the health and safety of the public (§4370(b)). Second, when monitoring by the Board of the program reveals misdiagnosis, case mismanagement, or

---

[13] If the licensee agrees to enter the Pharmacists Recovery Program when disciplinary charges are pending, the circumstances of the particular case will determine whether participation in the program will substitute for, or become part of, a disciplinary order. If it substitutes for a disciplinary order, the pharmacist's participation in the program will not become a matter of public record. The decision will depend upon whether allegations of drug abuse are the only significant charges, or whether there also are allegations of drug shortages, filling illegitimate prescriptions, or other such behavior.

noncompliance by the participant, the names of the affected participants also may be revealed to the Board (§4371).[14]

When a pharmacist participating by referral from the Board has been terminated from the program, the Board must be notified both of the termination and the reason for it (§4369). Notice that a voluntary participant has been terminated is only given to the Board when it is determined that the pharmacist's resuming the practice of pharmacy would pose a threat to the public; that notice must include the basis for the determination that the pharmacist's practice of pharmacy would be a threat (§4370). Records of the program may be disclosed, and testimony provided in connection with a participant, only when they are relevant to the conduct for which the pharmacist was terminated from the program (§4372). Additional information about the program is available at www.pharmacy.ca.gov/licensing/pharmacist_recovery.htm.

**Suppose a pharmacist admits to herself she has a substance abuse problem, enters the Pharmacists Recovery Program, is evaluated, signs a contract, and begins treatment. After she starts treatment, the Board learns she has stolen drugs to support her drug use. May the Board commence disciplinary action?**

Yes, it may do so.

**Suppose the employee assistance program (EAP) learns of this pharmacist's drug theft and terminates her from the program for noncompliance. Must the EAP notify the Board?**

It must notify the Board only if it concludes that she is likely to pose a threat to public health and safety if she continues to practice pharmacy (§4370(b)). One would suspect that drug theft, presumably from pharmaceutical sources, would constitute such a threat in most circumstances.

The activities of the EAP are to be evaluated by the Board quarterly. As part of this evaluation, the Board is mandated to review files of all participants in the diversion program. The names of pharmacists who entered the program voluntarily without the knowledge of the Board remain confidential except as noted above (§4371).

All records of the Board and the EAP pertaining to the treatment of a participating pharmacist are confidential and not subject to discovery or subpoena (§4372). There also are very strict rules governing disclosure of information from federally funded drug treatment programs (42 CFR Part 2). No member of the Board or the contracting professional association or any volunteer intervenor shall be liable for any civil damages because of acts or omissions that may occur while acting in good faith under this program (§4373).

**Criminal, civil, or other actions.** The Board may refer cases to state or federal criminal prosecutors for the filing of criminal charges if it uncovers criminal conduct by either a licensee or

---

[14] The Pharmacists Recovery Program is designed and administered by an employee assistance program (EAP) with which the Board contracts to provide confidential assessments and referral services (§4365). The EAP's functions are to evaluate those pharmacists who request participation in the program according to the guidelines and criteria prescribed by the Board under section 4364, to review and designate those treatment facilities and services to which pharmacists in the program may be referred, to receive and review information concerning a pharmacist's participation in the program, and to assist pharmacists' professional associations in publicizing the program (§4366).

Whether a pharmacist is referred to the EAP as part of a Board action or voluntarily participates in the impairment program, he or she must be informed in writing of the procedures followed in the program, the rights and responsibilities of the participating pharmacist, and the possible consequences of noncompliance.

nonlicensee. Although most violations of the Pharmacy Law can be prosecuted as crimes, referral to criminal prosecutors generally is reserved for serious legal violations. The Board may also file civil actions against both licensees and nonlicensees seeking injunctions against continuing or threatened violations of the law and/or civil penalties, as noted above. In unusual cases, licensee conduct may give rise to cases seeking asset forfeiture and even to complaints for criminal or civil violations of the tax laws.

# Other Agencies Relevant to Board Licensees

A variety of California, federal, and even local agencies may have at least some authority over and impact on pharmacies, pharmacists, and other licensees of the Board. Address, telephone number, and website information for the California and federal agencies listed below are found in Appendix C. In some cases a person, or especially a business entity such as a manufacturer, wholesaler, or specialized pharmacy, may be licensed, registered, or otherwise regulated and monitored by one or more of these other agencies. The person or entity must know and be in compliance with all applicable laws and regulations of those agencies.

Each of these agencies has fairly broad authority to inspect premises, including pharmacies, and to examine and take or copy records (for example, see 21 CFR §1316.03). In some cases you may withhold consent to inspect or examine or take records in the absence of a warrant or subpoena, but the exceptions to this right of refusal are generally quite broad (21 CFR §1306.17). Failure to comply with a warrant is usually a violation of law. At least in the case of the Drug Enforcement Administration, the licensee served with a warrant is warned and, if entry and cooperation are still refused, arrested. The inspection then proceeds (21 CFR §1316.12). The Food and Drug Administration has authority to make inspections of places, including pharmacies, where drugs are held either before or after their introduction into interstate commerce (21 USC §374). However, in enforcing the laws concerning adulteration and misbranding, the FDA does not have authority to inspect records, files, papers, processes, controls, or facilities of a pharmacy that only engages in traditional pharmacy practice (21 USC §374(a)(2)).[15] In general, federal agencies defer to the Board when a pharmacy issue arises, even though they may have authority to take action.

Whenever a representative of a regulatory agency contacts you or appears at your premises, it is important to understand who that person is (staff member? investigator? peace officer?), what branch of which agency he or she represents (licensing? enforcement?), and the scope of the agency's concern with, and authority over, your practice. Your appropriate response, and your level of concern, should depend upon the nature and level of the contact. This text only introduces these various agencies; the details of their enforcement authority, types of personnel, and powers of inspection are beyond its scope.

**California's Department of Consumer Affairs** is the umbrella agency of which the Pharmacy Board (and Medical Board, among others) is a part. The Medical Board of California performs the same function for allopathic physicians as the Board does for pharmacies and

---

[15] Note that refusal of entry is itself a violation of the law (21 USC §§331(f), 333(a); *U.S. v. Jamieson-McKames Pharmaceuticals, Inc.*, 651 F.2d 532, 539 (8th Cir. 1981)). The Fifth Amendment privilege against self-incrimination does not allow a person required by law to keep pharmacy records to withhold them from government inspection, even when criminal, as opposed to regulatory, charges are being brought (*In re Grand Jury Proceedings*, 801 F.2d 1164, 1167-1168 (9th Cir. 1986)).

The Board's inspectors clearly have the right to inspect pharmacy stock and drug records without either a subpoena or a warrant (*People v. Doss*, 4 Cal. App. 4th 1585, 1598 (2d Dist. 1992)), and to take prescription records for investigative purposes, leaving a receipt for controlled substances prescriptions (H&SC §11195)).

pharmacists; the Osteopathic Medical Board performs that function for osteopaths.  Other boards with similar functions are the Board of Registered Nursing, the Dental Board, and the Veterinary Medical Board; there are dozens more.

Other California agencies with which a pharmacist or pharmacy may have to deal are the **Department of Managed Health Care**, the **Department of Health Services,** and the **California Department of Justice.**

The Department of Managed Health Care deals with health care plan issues, including issues involving prescription drug benefits.

The Department of Health Services has a number of sub-units that impact pharmacy.  Its Medical Services Branch operates Medi-Cal; pharmacies must register to be Medi-Cal providers.  Its Audits and Investigations Division is concerned with Medi-Cal fraud and overpayment, among other things.  The Food and Drug Branch is responsible for enforcement of California's food and drug laws.  Its Licensing and Certification Branch licenses and oversees hospitals and other health facilities such as LTCs, ICFs, SNFs, and home health agencies.

The California Department of Justice is made up of several branches, one of which is the Office of the Attorney General, including the Licensing Section whose attorneys handle the disciplinary cases of the Board of Pharmacy, and the Bureau of Medi-Cal Fraud and Elder Abuse.  The Department also includes the Division of Law Enforcement, including  the Bureau of Narcotic Enforcement (BNE), which administers the CURES system and investigates cases involving criminal violations of the California Uniform Controlled Substances Act.

Federal agencies of relevance to the pharmacy profession include the **United States Department of Justice,** particularly the Drug Enforcement Administration, the **Department of Health and Human Services** (HHS), and the **Nuclear Regulatory Commission**.

The HHS units of most importance to pharmacy are the Food and Drug Administration, the Centers for Medicare & Medicaid Services (CMS), and the Substance Abuse and Mental Health Services Administration (SAMHSA).  The Nuclear Regulatory Commission has an impact on pharmacy because it has authority over all use of nuclear byproducts, including radiopharmaceuticals.

Of these agencies, the most likely to impact pharmacy practice are the Drug Enforcement Administration of the U.S. Department of Justice and the federal and state agencies that regulate Medi-Cal and Medicare.  DEA is critical because a pharmacy cannot dispense, obtain, or handle controlled substances without a DEA registration.

## *Dealing with DEA*

Pharmacies, as opposed to pharmacists, must register with the DEA to dispense controlled substances.[16]  To register, an applicant entity must be authorized to dispense controlled substances under the laws of its home state.  The application may be denied if the Attorney General of the United States determines that registration would be inconsistent with the public interest.  The factors to be considered in making this decision are:

---

[16] A pharmacist would only need to register as an individual if he or she qualified as a mid-level practitioner (see Chap. IX: Prescriptions: Receipt to Labeling), and thus was being treated as a type of prescriber.  Every prescriber who either issues prescriptions or order for or handles controlled substances also must be registered with the DEA.

- the recommendation of the appropriate state licensing board or professional disciplinary authority;
- the applicant's experience in dispensing controlled substances;
- the applicant's conviction record under federal or state laws relating to the manufacture, distribution, or dispensing of controlled substances;
- compliance with applicable state, federal, or local laws relating to controlled substances; and
- other conduct that may threaten the public health and safety (21 USC §823(f)).

Once granted, DEA registration may be suspended or revoked upon a finding that the registrant:

- has materially falsified any application filed with the DEA;
- has been convicted of a felony relating to any substance defined as a controlled substance;
- has had his state license or registration suspended, revoked, or denied by competent state authority and is no longer authorized by state law to engage in the manufacturing, distribution, or dispensing of controlled substances or has had the suspension, revocation, or denial of his registration recommended by competent state authority;
- has committed such acts as would render his registration inconsistent with the public interest; or
- has been excluded, or directed to be excluded, from participation in federally-funded health care programs (21 USC §824(a); DEA Pharmacist's Manual, p. 9).

The DEA may investigate anyone, registrant or not, involved with controlled substances; it may impose fines, restrict or revoke registrations, file civil and criminal actions, or seek asset forfeiture. While civil or criminal prosecutions resulting from DEA investigations are usually filed in federal court, sometimes DEA refers cases to local or state prosecutors for filing in state court, often because it has pursued a case in cooperation with state officials. The potential risks from engaging in controlled substance violations that the DEA considers to be illicit sale, possession for illicit sale, or trafficking are substantial. The fact that the pharmacist or pharmacy engages in legitimate use of controlled substances as well as the uses challenged as illegitimate is no defense against the forfeiture of property used for both legal and illegal transactions (see Chap. XII: Practice Pitfalls).

The DEA disciplinary charge filing is called an "order to show cause" (why the registration should not be restricted or revoked). Where contested, the charges are heard by one of DEA's own administrative law judges, subject to the review of the Administrator of the DEA, its chief officer. An adverse decision may be appealed to the federal courts.

The DEA regularly works closely with the Board of Pharmacy and DEA's parallel state agency, BNE. It can call upon the cooperation and resources of the Federal Bureau of Investigation, Customs, the Coast Guard, or other branches of the federal government with a role in drug law enforcement. When international activity is suspected, DEA also can seek the cooperation of foreign enforcement and regulatory authorities. Overall, its enforcement capabilities are quite extensive.

## *Monitoring Systems*

Some of these agencies have monitoring systems that contain individually identifiable information. Medi-Cal maintains a database for all visits and prescriptions provided for beneficiaries and billed to Medi-Cal. All providers are required to submit billings for services on standard forms, using patient- and provider-specific identifiers. The data, including the name of the provider, the name of the beneficiary, the date of service, the type of service, and the cost of service, is entered into a database. The most recent data (from the preceding 30 days and usually substantially longer) is available to state and federal medical assistance investigators and other law enforcement and regulatory personnel.  More comprehensive data for a longer time period is available to appropriate law enforcement officials on request from Sacramento.  The data is usually current to within 30 days of the date of the request.

This database allows monitoring of comprehensive information about providers and beneficiaries.  The information in the system covers all prescription drug services billed to Medi-Cal.  Although the system only records data from Medi-Cal patients, if an examination of this data suggests misconduct, further investigation is certainly warranted.  Because relatively few practitioners entirely refuse to treat Medi-Cal patients, this database allows a cross-check of a practitioner about whom there is other evidence of violative conduct involving dispensing practices.

The DEA maintains a system called ARCOS (Automation of Reports and Consolidated Orders System), which tracks the sale of certain controlled substances, particularly Schedule IIs down to the retail level (physicians, clinics, hospitals, pharmacies).  It does not track the individual dispensing to patients.

Of singular importance to all California practitioners is CURES (Controlled Substance Utilization Review and Evaluation System), which receives reports from all pharmacies of the orders for Schedule II and III controlled substances they dispense and from physicians and other practitioners of the same drugs when dispensed from their offices.  CURES is described more fully in Chapter IX: Prescriptions: Receipt to Labeling.

The United States Supreme Court has upheld the constitutionality of statewide monitoring systems against claims they invade a patient's privacy rights, as long as the system has adequate safeguards to protect the security and confidentiality of the information (*Whalen v. Roe*, 429 U.S. 589 (1977) (upholding New York monitoring system)).

There are also data banks of disciplinary actions maintained by the associations of different professional boards, including the National Association of Boards of Pharmacy.  The federal government also maintains the National Practitioner Data Bank;  all covered boards, including pharmacy boards, are required to report disciplinary actions to it.

**What you should think about after reading this chapter:**

1.  If you had the power of appointment, what qualities would you seek in appointing pharmacist and nonpharmacist members to the Board of Pharmacy?

2.  How much authority does the Board of Pharmacy have over the practice of pharmacy and the enforcement of pharmacy laws in California?

3.  How might you change the authority of the Board?  How might you change how the Board functions?

4.  What additional publications ought the Board provide?  What additional information ought the Board make available on its website?

5.  What issues not yet on its agenda do you think the Board ought to be considering at this time?

6.  Under what circumstances would you want to review the records and information the Board maintains about you?

7.  How does the Board inspect or investigate its licensees?

8.  What kinds of actions might the Board take when it finds violations?

9.  What are the most important agencies, other than the Board, with which a pharmacy or pharmacist might have to deal?

10. What monitoring systems might affect a pharmacy's practice, and how?

# Chapter XIV

# Other Law Relevant to Pharmacy

---

**What you should know after reading this chapter:**

1. What local, state, or federal laws may affect the operation of a drug-related business?

2. What types of business conduct, in general, do antitrust laws forbid?

3. What are the legal bases for the right to privacy?

4. What is HIPAA? What is personal health information? What is a covered entity?

5. Under what circumstances may a pharmacist release a patient's records? To whom?

6. Under what circumstances may a pharmacy share patient records electronically with another pharmacy? With a health insurance company? With a drug manufacturer?

7. What are a pharmacist's workplace rights?

---

A pharmacist employed by others in a community pharmacy, and not involved in management, may well have few encounters with legal issues during his or her career, other than those discussed in the preceding chapters. In contrast, a pharmacy manager or owner, or a pharmacist involved in our increasingly complex health care institutions and their management, is likely to have many such encounters. The intent of this chapter is to familiarize pharmacists with the general nature of various other areas of the law that are the most likely to be encountered in the course of a career in pharmacy. While no substitute for obtaining legal advice, and certainly not a detailed description or discussion of such laws, it may sensitize you to situations in which legal advice may be important to obtain.

## Setting Up a Business

Many aspects of starting a business in the field of pharmacy will involve decisions with legal ramifications for which the advice of qualified lawyers may be necessary. For example, if you choose to open a pharmacy you will need to do much more than get a pharmacy permit from the Board.

**Business Structure.** You will need to determine whether you should operate the business as a corporation, limited liability company, or a partnership, rather than just as a sole proprietorship under your name. Setting up and operating certain entities can be complex; tax and liability considerations will be part of your decision for which professional accounting as well as legal assistance will almost certainly be required.

**Registrations.** Even what you call your business is subject to legal control; you need to register to protect the "fictitious name" of your business (B&PC §§17900-17930). Of course, you will also need DEA registration and, almost certainly, registration as a Medi-Cal provider.

**Zoning and Other General Requirements.** Locating your business will require consideration of local zoning rules; modifying the premises is likely to require local building permits. In some circumstances environmental protection rules of various levels of government may have an impact on your plans. Your local community also may impose business taxes or registration requirements with which you must comply.

**Sales and Other Tax Issues.** Getting started requires taking steps to comply with all state taxation requirements. As an employer you will need to withhold and pay the appropriate employment taxes (federal Social Security and Medicare taxes, federal and state unemployment taxes, and state disability insurance premiums) on your employees' earnings and secure workers' compensation insurance or an exemption (as well as other insurance to protect your own interests). Plus, of course, there are state and federal taxes on the income of corporations and partnerships as well as on individuals.

As a retailer you will have to register with the Franchise Tax Board to collect sales taxes, which apply to retail sales of drugs, medicines, and other items by a pharmacist except for sales of medicine legally dispensed on a prescription for treatment of a human being (but not of an animal) (18 CCR §1591(d)). Other dispensers of prescription medication are similarly excepted from collection of sales taxes. For purposes of this sales tax exemption, "medicine" includes, among other things, various orthotic devices, and "prescription" is defined largely as it is defined in the Pharmacy Law (18 CCR §1591(a)(7),(b)). Insulin and insulin syringes furnished by a pharmacist for a diabetic as directed by a physician are deemed to be dispensed on prescription (18 CCR §1591.1(b)(5)).

**Labor Laws.** Compliance with worker safety and other labor-protective laws (such as those governing minimum wages and maximum hours) also is necessary. California law even includes a specific section on maximum hours for pharmacy employees (Lab. Code §850).

**Contract, Commercial Transaction, and Property Laws.** As discussed in Chapter XII: Practice Pitfalls, buying or leasing a building, purchasing equipment, fixtures, and supplies, and making agreements for the purchase of necessary stock (prescription drugs and devices, OTC products, non-pharmacy sundries, and the like) require knowledge of a variety of business laws.

# Antitrust Issues

Many of the pitfalls for a pharmacist operating a business have been discussed in Chapter XII: Practice Pitfalls. Another that is worthy of some consideration is antitrust law.

Antitrust law, to reduce phenomenal complexity to a few words, prohibits the use of monopoly power in the marketplace to displace free and fair competition. The Sherman Act (15 USC §1), primarily enforced by the United States Department of Justice, forbids contracts, combinations, and conspiracies in restraint of trade or commerce. The Robinson-Patman Act, 15 USC § 13, which is enforced by the Federal Trade Commission (FTC), prohibits price discrimination; its intent is to prevent larger businesses from gaining unfair preferences in connection with the sale of goods over smaller businesses.

These provisions sound very simple, but they are anything but simple. Antitrust law is an arcane specialty. It has become an increasing concern in the pharmacy world, especially with upheavals in the businesses of providing health care and making and selling pharmaceuticals.

Antitrust issues have come up for pharmacy, and its customers, in various ways.[1] What joint marketing or purchasing arrangements may independent pharmacists legally make with their competitors to help them compete against multistore chains? What are the antitrust implications of health care providers purchasing generic drug companies, creating formularies that encourage or require the use of the drug company's products without the prescriber's approval? May manufacturers give big discounts to large buyers like hospitals, health maintenance organizations, and mail order drug companies?[2] May brand-name pharmaceutical companies pay generic drug makers to keep their

---

[1] A number of antitrust and unfair trade practices cases have been filed in recent years against the biggest PBMs. The Prescription Access Litigation Project and the nation's second-largest trade union alleged that through undisclosed rebates and discounts, and fraudulent use of average wholesale prices (advantages gained through their control of 80 percent of the PBM market), the four defendant PBMs generated revenues that they did not pass on to their client health plans, in violation of their fiduciary duties (*In Brief/Pharmaceuticals; Suit Filed Against Prescription Managers*, LOS ANGELES TIMES, Mar. 19, 2003, p. C4; see www.prescriptionaccesslitigation.org/pbms.htm). The federal government brought fraud charges against one of the same large PBMs, alleging it paid sizeable kickbacks to win a contract to provide pharmacy services to federal employees and Medicare beneficiaries (*In Brief/Pharmaceuticals; Medco Defends Itself Against Federal Charge*, LOS ANGELES TIMES, Dec. 11, 2003, p. C3). Medco, the largest PBM, settled for almost $30 million charges that it encouraged physicians to switch patients to different drugs, but without always passing on the savings to patients or their health care plans. Medco agreed that it would no longer switch drugs if the cost of the proposed drug is greater than the cost of the one prescribed, notify patients and prescribers of a switch in advance (and include information about the cost savings), disclose any incentives it has received to make the switch, and monitor the health effects of drug switches (Julie Appleby, *Medco settles benefits charges*, USA TODAY, Apr. 27, 2004, p. 1B). New York State brought suit against PBM Express Scripts, charging it engaged in various schemes that inflated drug costs for New York employees. Among the allegations were deceiving doctors into switching patients to drugs for which the company received bigger rebates, pocketing rebates, lying about discounts, and inflating the costs of some generic drugs (Mary Jo Feldstein, *Suit accuses Express Scripts of fraud*, ST. LOUIS POST-DISPATCH, Aug. 5, 2004, p. A01).

A group of California pharmacies has sued more than a dozen pharmaceutical manufacturers, claiming that they conspired to keep prices in the United States much higher than those for their same drugs in Canada and elsewhere. The pharmacies claimed they were put at a competitive disadvantage to other sellers of the same drugs, especially those on the Internet (James F. Peltz, *Drug Makers Sued on Pricing; Fourteen pharmacies accuse the companies of charging more for medicines in the U.S.*, LOS ANGELES TIMES, Aug. 27, 2004, p. C1).

[2] In 1994, a class of nearly 40,000 retail pharmacies, representing 45 percent of the pharmacy business, charged drug manufacturers and wholesalers with antitrust violations for conspiring to deny retailers the same discount prices they offered to hospitals, health maintenance organizations, and nursing homes. Many defendants entered into settlements with the class of plaintiffs. In 1996, eleven major drug makers agreed to pay $351 million, not to deny discounts to drug sellers merely because they are retailers, and to allow retail pharmacies and buying groups that are able to demonstrate an ability to affect market share the same type of discounts enjoyed by the favored buyers. Another company settled for $22 million in November 1997, and four more settled for $345 million in August 1998. The remaining defendants went to trial; the trial judge dismissed the suit against them, declaring that the discounts to hospitals and HMOs are in the nature of the business and not a use of their market power in violation of the law. The wholesaler defendants entirely prevailed on appeal; one issue remained in the case against the manufacturers. The decision of the United States Court of Appeals is an interesting, but complex, primer on antitrust law as it applies to the pharmaceutical industry (*In re Brand Name Prescription Drugs Antitrust Litigation*, 186 F.3d 781 (7th Cir. 1999)). Skirmishes in this lengthy battle (involving many dozen court appearances and hundreds of attorneys) continued for a number of years (and included such matters as divvying up the settlement proceeds among class members). Since the filing of the original lawsuit in this matter, the Federal Trade Commission initiated an investigation of pricing practices in the drug industry.

competitive products off the market?[3]  When will a merger of two large drug manufacturers or wholesalers constitute a possible antitrust violation?

These types of issues are most likely to be encountered by pharmacists in the context of their work for large companies or chain drug stores or as involved members in pharmacy organizations. However, the basic notions should be kept in mind so that advice can be sought when it might be needed.  Actions of businesses, particularly businesses working with their competitors, that have the intent or effect of making it more difficult for others to compete with them may have antitrust implications.[4]

# Protecting the Patient's Right to Privacy

Most of pharmacy law is directed toward protecting the health and safety of the consumer of pharmacy services.  Elsewhere we have discussed the need also to protect the patient's right to be free from discrimination and sexual misconduct.  Another important right discussed in brief in earlier chapters (Chap. X: Dispensing and Beyond and Chap. XI: Record-Keeping) is the patient's right to privacy.  Privacy is protected in various ways by state and federal law.

## *Nature of the Right*

The information received by a pharmacy or pharmacist or stored in a patient profile is extremely private.  The pharmacist (in every setting where he or she works) is obliged to protect a patient's privacy and the confidentiality of all medical information, both by Board regulations (§§1717.2, 1717.4(h)) and by state and federal law that applies to health care providers generally, as well as to others, as discussed below.

The pharmacist's obligation to protect patient privacy covers records, both written and electronic.  Computerized systems, like paper-based systems, must be constructed and operated to avoid violation of patient confidentiality.  It is the pharmacist's responsibility to ensure that no one in the pharmacy is disseminating information improperly, and that the pharmacy record-keeping system

---

[3]  Because of the huge financial implications of avoiding generic competition, pharmaceutical companies have taken a variety of approaches to protecting their brand name drugs, some of them arguably illegal.  The Federal Trade Commission filed actions in 2000 and 2001 charging that three brand name drug companies and their generic rivals teamed up to protect the brand name drugs' markets.  In one case, Hoechst Marion Roussel, Inc. was alleged to have paid a small drug company, Andrx Corp., $10 million per calendar quarter from the time it received marketing approval from FDA for its generic version of Hoechst's Cardizem CD, a popular heart medication.  Hoechst had filed a patent infringement lawsuit against Andrx, and the payments were claimed to result from, but not settle, that suit.  The arrangement prohibited marketing of the generic drug pending the end of the lawsuit and provided that Andrx would receive an additional $15 million per quarter year retroactive to July 1998 if it prevailed.  In the resolution of the complaint, Hoechst and Andrx did not admit any wrongdoing and were not fined, but both were barred from entering into future arrangements to delay the introduction of generic drugs (David Ranii, *Generic Drug Companies Complain about Brand-Name Pharmaceutical Firms*, THE NEWS & OBSERVER, Sept. 29, 2001, p. D1).

Hoechst (now called Aventis) was not the only pharmaceutical company to think of this type of strategy.  Patent infringement lawsuits involving high blood pressure drugs made by Abbott Laboratories and the antibiotic Cipro, made by Bayer, were settled several years ago with agreements by the brand name drug's owner to pay the generic drug maker not to market the generic drug.  The potential impacts on competition and drug prices are a matter of concern (Susan R. Miller, *No product, nice profit; agreeing to shelve a low-cost heart drug, Andrx is finally in the black.  Is it a savvy deal or simply a bribe to limit competition?* BROWARD DAILY BUSINESS REVIEW, Nov. 11, 1998, p. A1).

[4]  The Sherman Act's basic provision is deemed to outlaw agreements about prices or other important terms of trade.  California has its own parallel antitrust laws (B&PC §§16600-16700, 17200 (unfair competition)).

(both paper and electronic) has adequate security to deter access by unauthorized persons or access by authorized persons to information they should not have.

The pharmacy may use any means of security to accomplish this result, but it must be done, and done adequately. A pharmacy may violate privacy rights by allowing computer access by unauthorized persons, by leaving a terminal where unauthorized persons can see it (such as where it is visible to the public), by leaving paper records accessible to unauthorized persons, by allowing unnecessarily broad access to authorized persons, or by failing to properly dispose of records. Privacy protections are likely to be considered of increasing importance by the public as information is collected, maintained, transmitted, and shared through a complex medical system with the use of electronic tools. Instead of carrying paper records from provider to provider, patients are increasingly likely to have their records transmitted by computer, and ultimately on "smart cards," complete medical histories on a credit card-sized disk, or even implanted under the skin.

### May you disclose patient information to the patient's spouse, child, or parent?

The answer once may have seemed fairly obvious if the patient and the person requesting the information and their relationship were known to the pharmacist. If the request seemed reasonable, such as for billing records for tax purposes or for information about side effects or noncompliance involving the caller's family member, the pharmacist would have been likely to provide the information. But it is clear that this is not what the law authorizes; disclosure requires consent of the patient. Breaches of medical privacy can have serious consequences for patients and lead to significant liability, including fines, for the health care provider. In *Wise v. Thrifty Payless, Inc.*, 83 Cal. App. 4th 1296 (3d Dist. 2000), an unauthorized disclosure to a husband of a wife's prescriptions resulted in a $100,000 judgment against the pharmacy. The husband and wife were estranged; the wife had specifically cautioned the pharmacy not to release information about her prescriptions to her husband. The husband used the information in the divorce proceedings, to seek custody of their children.

The only exception to the rule that you not disclose without patient consent may be for information about prescription medication for a minor child where there is no reason to believe the parent does not know of the underlying condition. Special care must be taken even when parents and minors are involved. California law allows minors under a number of circumstances to consent without parental involvement to various types of medical care (including for birth control, treatment of pregnancy, communicable diseases, and the effects of rape or assault and to obtain drug and alcohol and mental health treatment; Fam. Code §§6920-6929). When that law applies to the child's circumstances, only the child may consent to disclosure. In addition, an emancipated[5] minor who can consent to medical treatment (Fam. Code §7050) also should be assumed to have privacy rights equivalent to those of an adult. In addition, if the pharmacy knows the minor is not residing with the requesting parent or is under the guardianship of another adult, disclosure may be neither appropriate nor legal.

### Suppose an adult child asks for prescription information about his mother; she is not taking her medication, and he wants to know what she is supposed to be taking because he is concerned about the effects of her noncompliance.

You might well wonder why he doesn't look at the prescription container or call his mother's physician. In any case, the information about the mother's prescriptions is private; you may not

---

[5] A minor is emancipated when he or she marries or goes on active duty in the Armed Forces, or by obtaining an order of emancipation from a court (Fam. Code §7002).

disclose it without her consent unless the son is her legal guardian or has power of attorney. You cannot be sure that he will not use the information he receives in a way that is contrary to his mother's interests; she or her representatives could sue you for unauthorized disclosure.

**May you tell a mother about her daughter's prescriptions for birth control drugs or devices? Or treatment for sexually transmitted diseases? What if the child is taking zidovudine (AZT, Retrovir®) or some other drug for treatment of HIV or AIDS? Or received drugs after an abortion?**

You might think that a parent would be entitled to information about a minor child. However, if the patient has the right to obtain such treatments without parental consent (and, as noted above, she generally does), she surely has the right to keep prescription or patient profile information private as well, even from her parents.

**May you provide prescription information to the family member preparing tax returns?**

No, not without consent from those whose records are involved. Obviously, where the records involve children, discretion will need to be exercised to distinguish records that must be kept private in the absence of the child-patient's consent from those that can be safely disclosed for tax purposes without consent.

The obligation to protect a patient's privacy extends also to conversation. Pharmacists must avoid providing consultation, or otherwise talking to a patient about his or her medical condition or information, in a location or in a manner where others (including members of the pharmacy staff who have no need for the information) may overhear private information or see, or otherwise access, such information. In addition, pharmacists should exercise discretion when asking the patient questions about the legitimacy of a prescription under the same circumstances. The pharmacist in a clinical or other setting should take the same care. Although the legal concern is for privacy, pharmacists ought to consider methods of obtaining information necessary to validate prescriptions that would avoid unnecessary embarrassment to patients.

**What do you do about telephone orders for refills?**

It makes no sense to conclude that privacy rights mean that no oral order may ever be honored. It will depend upon how well you know the patient and the caller and their relationship. In some cases you might want to confirm the caller's authority. In most cases you would be safe if the caller can provide you with all the pertinent information from the prescription, because in that case you would not be providing any information unknown to the caller.

## *Privacy Protection Under California Law*

In California, the right of privacy is express and constitutional (CAL. CONST. art. I, §1). There is no express federal constitutional right of privacy, but such a right has been found by the United States Supreme Court to emanate from the "penumbra" of the Bill of Rights. The California right to privacy, added to our Constitution in 1974 in the wake of Watergate and other perceived invasions of privacy by government, has been interpreted broadly to cover business and individual as well as government invasions of privacy (*White v. Davis,* 13 Cal. 3d 757, 772-775 (1975)) and to give rise to a suit for damages for its violation.

In addition, a state statute generally prohibits disclosure of medical information by health care providers (Civ. Code §56.10); it applies to pharmacies and pharmacy records and information.

Essentially, except where the law specifically permits or mandates disclosure without patient consent, no medical provider (including pharmacists and pharmacies) with access to protected information may disclose it without patient permission. The law makes adequate provision for disclosure of information to other health care practitioners in connection with the patient's care, to insurers and others when needed to evaluate claims or make payments, and to investigators such as those working for the Pharmacy Board. In each case the information is only to be used for the authorized purpose for which it was disclosed.

This law has been substantially strengthened so that it now covers all licensed health care professionals, virtually all providers of health care services, including health plans and their contractors, and pharmaceutical companies and their agents and representatives[6] (Civ. Code §56.05(b)-(d),(h)), as well as corporations and their affiliates and subsidiaries. "Identifiable medical information" is defined to include any information which is sufficient to allow identification of an individual, alone or in combination with other information that is publicly available (Civ. Code §56.05(f)). Provisions barring disclosure without patient consent have been strengthened, and penalties for violation of the law have been enhanced. There are substantial civil penalties and administrative fines for its violation, and consumers who prevail in civil suits may now collect nominal damages of $1,000 even without proof of actual damages (Civ. Code §56.36(b)).

## *Federal Privacy Protection*

Under the authority of a federal statute,[7] the Department of Health and Human Services adopted detailed regulations (called the HIPAA rule) in 2002 to govern the creation, maintenance, and use of personal medical information records (both on paper and electronic). The regulations and explanatory material fill hundreds of pages of the Federal Register (see www.access.gpo.gov/nara/ cfr/waisidx_02/ 45cfr164_02.html). The regulations were highly controversial and the process of adoption took a long time, in part because there were over 50,000 comments from the public to which HHS had to respond. The regulations were adopted in December 2000 by the Clinton Administration and then were revised in 2002 by the Bush Administration before they had gone into effect. Most of the provisions took effect in April 2003.

It is important to keep in mind that HIPAA does not supersede state medical privacy laws that are even more protective of patient privacy (45 CFR §160.203(a)(2)).

The key provisions of the HIPAA privacy rule, especially for pharmacists and pharmacies, are:[8]

---

[6] "Pharmaceutical company" is defined to include any business that "manufactures, sells, or distributes pharmaceuticals, but not pharmacy benefit managers (Civ. Code §56.10(h)).

[7] The statute is the Health Insurance Portability and Accountability Act of 1996, or HIPAA (P. L. 104-191 (1996)). A major purpose of the Act was to enable persons with employer-paid health insurance to carry it from one employer to another. Another purpose was to enable establishment of a comprehensive electronic data base for processing health care information, while protecting medical information from inappropriate use and disclosure (see 42 USC §1320d-6, for penalties for wrongful disclosure). Although HIPAA generally preempts state law, it does not preempt (substitute for) state medical privacy laws that are more protective of patient privacy (42 USC §1320d-7, 45 CFR §160.203(a)(2)). California's medical privacy law, described above, is more protective than HIPAA; for example, pharmaceutical companies are not covered entities under HIPAA, but must comply with California law. Thus California entities that have been in compliance with California law should have little difficulty complying with HIPAA.

[8] This is a great deal of literature available explaining the requirements of this complicated rule, including the following:

• The President's Advisory Commission on Consumer Protection and Quality in the Health Care Industry has developed a

- The HIPAA privacy rules apply to covered entities, which include health care information clearinghouses, health plans, health care providers, all providers of health services, and anyone who furnishes, bills, or is paid for health care (45 CFR §160.103).
- The rules cover protected health information (PHI), which includes all medical records and other individually identifiable health information used or disclosed by a covered entity in any form, written, oral, or electronic.
- Each covered entity must have and enforce privacy procedures and ensure patient education about privacy rights.
- Each covered entity must designate a privacy officer to be responsible for compliance; all employees who may come in contact with PHI must be trained to understand the entity's privacy procedures (45 CFR §§164.530(a),(b)).[9]
- In general only the minimum necessary information is to be disclosed for payment purposes; disclosures to other health care practitioners for treatment purposes are not so limited (45 CFR §§164.406, 164.502(b), 164.514(d)).
- Patients must be provided with a clear, written notice, separate from any patient treatment consent forms, of the covered entity's privacy practices (45 CFR §164.520); patients must generally have ready access to their own medical information.
- The covered entity must be able to account for any disclosures of PHI, with some exceptions, such as disclosures for treatment purposes (45 CFR §164.528(a)).
- The covered entity must include in contracts with any business that operates on the entity's behalf, such as claims processors, assurances regarding the proper use of PHI.
- There are civil money penalties for violations of the law and criminal penalties for more serious violations.
- All covered entities had to be in compliance with HIPAA by April 2003, except for small health plans, which had until April 2004 to come into compliance.

HIPAA is not intended to inhibit sharing of information among health care providers for treatment purposes,[10] although it does require taking care that others do not overhear conversations or see PHI (such as through written material or on a computer screen). HIPAA does recognize and allow what it calls "incidental disclosures" (45 CFR §164.502(a)(1)(iii)), such as a patient's being called in a waiting room. However, identifying the patient's condition or some other information or, in a pharmacy, the drug or drugs the patient is getting ("Mr. Doan, your herpes prescription is ready"), would be improper.

---

HIPAA "Consumer Bill of Rights and Responsibilities" (www.opm.gov/insure/health/cbrr.htm), a 51-page booklet;
- www.hhs.gov/ocr/hipaa, rom the Office of Civil Rights, HHS;
- www.ama-assn.org/go/hipaa, from the American Medical Association;
- www.cms.gov/hipaa/hipaa2/support/tools/decisionsupport/default.asp, Centers for Medicare & Medicaid Services, HHS;
- many articles on aspects of HIPAA from a pharmacy/pharmacist perspective at the Drug Topics website,
- www.drugtopics.com; use HIPAA as the search term (and the advanced search function for older material);
- and the Board included questions and answers about HIPAA in the October 2003 issue of *The Script*, www.pharmacy.ca.gov/publications/03_oct_script.pdf, p. 5.

[9] It is unclear whether all employees, regardless of whether they may come into contact with PHI, have to be trained, but the training requirement would certainly apply at least to pharmacists, pharmacy technicians, interns, pharmacy and front-end staff who handle prescriptions or prescription payments, pharmacy billing staff, marketing staff who use patient lists, lawyers working on lawsuits, investigations, or other matters that involve PHI, any other people at the pharmacy who could access or see PHI, and personnel at a pharmacy's or pharmacy chain's headquarters who oversee pharmacy operations.

[10] One of the August 2002 revisions to the rule allowed such disclosures. The original rule approved in 2000 would not have allowed disclosures, even for treatment purposes, without prior patient consent. The earlier version would also have required patient consent before disclosure for payment purposes or health care operations.

Although a full discussion of HIPAA is beyond the scope of this text, some other issues of importance to pharmacists and pharmacies are:

- A family member or friend may pick up prescriptions, but the pharmacist must exercise his or her professional judgment whether to release prescriptions to others (45 CFR §164.510(b)).
- A pharmacist may obtain and use PHI to fill an oral prescription for a new patient for whom the pharmacy does not yet have a written consent on file (but the pharmacy must then obtain that consent from the new patient).
- A pharmacy does not need to have a private room for consultation, but must take reasonable steps to protect privacy (for example, by assuring other customers are a few feet away from the area where consultation is taking place).
- A pharmacist may leave a message for a patient at home, either with a family member or on an answering machine, to inform the patient a prescription is ready to pick up or leave a reminder that it is time to refill a prescription (45 CFR §164.510(b)(3)), unless the patient requests greater confidentiality (45 CFR §164.522(b)).
- Physical security standards adopted in 2003 go into effect on April 21, 2005 (68 FR 8334, Feb. 20, 2003).

Access to PHI for marketing purposes was a major concern. In general, if the communication to a patient encourages the patient to purchase or use a product or service, it is marketing (45 CFR §164.501) and requires prior consumer authorization, as well as the disclosure of the fact of any remuneration to the entity from which the PHI is to be obtained (45 CFR §§164.508). Patient refill reminders from a pharmacy are not subject to the prior consumer authorization requirement even if the mailing costs of the refill reminder program are being paid for by a third party, such as the manufacturer of the drug. The situation where a covered entity discloses PHI, whether for direct or indirect remuneration, so that the party receiving the PHI can contact the patient to encourage the purchase of goods or services, is covered by the rule and requires prior authorization. So is a transaction whereby a drug manufacturer obtains patient lists, for remuneration, to send patients discount coupons for a new medication.

Communications for the purpose of case management or case coordination or to direct or recommend alternative treatment, health care provider, or health care setting, or to recommend disease management, health promotion, preventive care, or wellness programs are also not considered marketing covered by HIPAA. A covered entity may communicate with a patient to describe a health-related product or service that is provided by, or included in, a plan of benefits of the covered entity. A pharmacy may contact its patients to recommend an alternative medication even when the contact program is funded by a drug manufacturer. On the other hand, the pharmacy does need patient authorization to sell PHI to a third party, such as a pharmaceutical manufacturer, for that company's marketing purposes. Although it falls within the regulation's definition of "marketing," patient authorization is not required for a face-to-face communication by a covered entity with the patient or to make a promotional gift of nominal value provided by the covered entity (45 CFR §164.508(a)(3)).

HIPAA also recognizes, and allows, disclosures of PHI without patient authorization for public health activities, research, and workers' compensation purposes.

The National Association of Chain Drug Stores published a practical checklist for HIPAA compliance in July 2003, which included the following useful questions:

- Is your notice of privacy practice in a prominent position in the pharmacy?
- Do you have copies of your notices of privacy practice available for distribution?
- Do employees understand the procedure for acknowledgment signature capture?

- Are your employees aware of your disposal procedures for PHI, including appropriate measures for discarding patients' used prescription vials?
- Are employees familiar with procedures in case patients exercise their rights to request a copy of their PHI, to make an amendment to their PHI, or to restrict use of their PHI?
- Do pharmacy managers understand company procedures should they be presented with a subpoena to release PHI or make an accounting disclosure?
- Do employees know the procedures for reporting privacy violations?
- Is the public area of the pharmacy counter free of PHI? For instance, are "will call" scripts out of the view of the consumer?
- Do employees understand the concept of "minimum necessary" when it comes to verbal conversation, both in person or via telephone?
- Do employees know who the privacy officer at your company is?
(*Chain Pharmacist Practice Memo*, Vol. 7, No. 11 (mid-July 2003), www.nacds.org/user-assets/PDF_files/070203cppm.pdf.)

## *Common Law Privacy Protection*

Even in the absence of a specific state or federal law, the common law has protected privacy by the development of a common law right. It is a tort (a civil wrong) to invade someone's privacy. The aspect of that common law protection most relevant to pharmacy practice is its allowance of a lawsuit for the public disclosure of private facts (DAN B. DOBBS, THE LAW OF TORTS (West Group 2000), pp. 1200-1208).

## *Disclosure Issues*

**Government Agencies.** Disclosure of medical information to government agencies is permitted when and to the extent authorized by law (*Whalen v. Roe,* 429 U.S. 589 (1977), see Chap. XIII: Board of Pharmacy ("Monitoring Systems")). California courts have upheld warrantless searches of pharmacy records, including prescription records, because pharmacies are considered pervasively regulated (*People v. Doss,* 4 Cal. App. 4th 1585, 1597 (2d Dist. 1992); see §4332).

It is less certain whether nonprescription information, such as a patient profile, is subject to disclosure to the Board without subpoena or warrant. Generally, a patient release or a subpoena is required before the disclosure of protected personal health and financial information. However, as discussed in Chapter XI: Record-Keeping ("Patient Profiles"), Board inspectors have the right to demand some disclosures without a release or a subpoena, because of pharmacy's closely-regulated status. Whether, under HIPAA and state privacy law, patient profiles are included is not clear, so a pharmacy should probably insist upon receiving a subpoena before disclosing patient profile information in the absence of patient consent (unless the inspector needs to view profiles generally to confirm they are being kept as required).

The Board now requires its inspectors to provide licensees with a list of prescription records accessed even during a routine inspection. This policy of providing a receipt for the information will enable the pharmacy to meet its obligation under HIPAA to account to patients, if they request it, even for the disclosure of their PHI to government officials. When doing an investigation, the inspector will provide a medical release, a subpoena, or an "investigative demand." In the latter case, a statement of facts would be included about why the information is relevant to the investigation and why information with PHI redacted would not suffice.

**Shared Access Databases.** It is particularly important to be cautious about the privacy of patient information in this computer age. It is now common for pharmacy chains or multilevel health providers to share information or allow access to it via computer. Ordinarily, patient-specific information may not be maintained in a file accessible to other pharmacies or facilities without consent of the patient (Civ. Code §56.10; §§1717.1-1717.2, 1717.4(h)). The patient must be notified that his or her information will be in such a shared system, told the purposes for which the information will be used, and given the opportunity to demand its exclusion from the system (§1717.2). The information should be maintained in such a way that only those with a need for it have access to it and only to the extent necessary, unless the patient has given clear consent to broader use. It probably does not matter what the law is in another state in which a computer terminal is maintained if a California resident is involved; California's constitutional right to privacy should protect Californians in any case.

The information that may be accessed may include the patient's name, telephone number, address, and medical history or at least drug information history. Release of any of that information constitutes an invasion of the patient's privacy. There is some reason to believe there is often inadequate control over who may access such information in linked systems. If there is inadequate control, the person who accesses the information may be liable for invasion of privacy if access is achieved without patient permission or for a purpose beyond that for which permission was granted. The person responsible for the inadequacy of control also may be liable for invasion of privacy. Needless to say, however tempting it may be, a pharmacist has no right to "cruise" a personally-identifiable database even within his or her own store or chain without a proper purpose.

Information may be "individually identifiable" even if no name, address, social security number, or driver's license number is included. Patient confidentiality is violated if the pharmacy shares enough information with a third party that the recipient of the information readily and easily can identify the patient. And keep in mind that a patient's privacy may be violated by your carelessness in your use of computerized systems as well as by intentional entries into the database.

**Patient Consent.** Records always may be disclosed with the consent of the patient. Upon the request of the patient, you may obtain her prescription from another pharmacy and refill it, as discussed in Chapter X: The Prescription Process: Dispensing and Beyond. A pharmacy or pharmacist would be wise to document patient consent to records disclosure and to disclose only to such persons and in such detail as the consent clearly authorizes. This caution should arise both from respect for the patient's right to keep personal and medical information private and from the financial and professional consequences of violating the right of privacy. The Board takes quite seriously allegations of abuse by its licensees of private medical information.

**Other Requests for Data Access.** Some pharmacy information must be shared with a pharmacy's accounting or corporate offices or with third parties for purposes of billing or similar functions. However, persons to whom pharmacy information is provided may only use it for the purposes for which it is needed. Using that information for promotional or other purposes without the consent of the patient is a violation of privacy laws (Civ. Code §§56.10, 56.13). That prohibition against use for other purposes includes even beneficial programs. For example, programs in which patients are contacted to check on compliance with a drug regimen or to encourage appropriate and timely renewal of a prescription are a violation of privacy rights if the information is used to promote other products or to encourage switching to a replacement drug product, if the information is being used by an unlicensed person, or if the information has been transmitted for use outside the licensed premises (even to the corporate office). Recently, a pharmacy chain and numerous major drug manufacturers were sued for using customers' prescription drug information to contact them by letter or telephone to renew or extend prescriptions and, in some cases, to change medications (Terri Somers, *Albertsons sued over Rx practices; Firms said to pay for data on its customers*, SAN DIEGO UNION-TRIBUNE, Sept. 10, 2004, p. C-1).

A third party who asks for information that is not needed for actual care or billing must be refused access. Unless the patient is not individually identifiable, no information may be shared except for medical or billing purposes (Civ. Code §56.10(c)). Third party payors and others frequently ask for pharmacy data about prescriptions in general, certain classes of drugs, or certain individual drugs. It may not be adequate in terms of protecting patients' privacy rights simply to excise names, addresses, and telephone numbers if the remaining information is such that the recipient may use it to identify any one or some patients. Third parties requesting access to prescription records generally do so for statistical analysis to promote their financial interests, much more rarely for true medical research. Risks to patient privacy (and perhaps to one's own professional interests) should be weighed against the benefits of disclosing data in any form.

**Disposal or Destruction of Records.** Disposal or destruction of records must be accomplished so as to protect against disclosure of private information. Every provider of health care (which includes pharmacies) that has records must maintain, store, discard, and destroy them so as to preserve the confidentiality of the information in them; their negligent disposal, abandonment, or destruction is a violation of the law (Civ. Code 56.101). Another law requires every business (which includes all entities licensed by the Board) to take reasonable steps to destroy or arrange for destruction of records (electronic or written) containing personal identifying information by shredding, erasing, or otherwise modifying the information so that it is unreadable or undecipherable (Civ. Code §1798.81)). In other words, the business cannot just throw away written records, magnetic tapes, disks, or hard drives that contain such information. Any person injured by a violation of this new law may sue for damages. A business that violates, or proposes to violate, the law may be enjoined from doing so (Civ. Code §1798.82).

No contract, no demand from another person – even a superior, pharmacy owner, parent company, insurer, or third party payor – justifies violating these standards. The misuse of personal patient information, even the mere identity of the patient, violates the law and is a basis for civil liability and, in some circumstances, criminal action. Disciplinary action for unprofessional conduct is another risk. Furthermore, patients are unlikely to patronize a pharmacy or other health care provider known to lack respect for patient privacy. The pharmacist particularly must be alert to avoid breaches of privacy in the context of filling prescriptions.

# The Americans with Disabilities Act

The Americans with Disabilities Act (42 USC Chapter 126) was adopted by Congress in 1992 to assist people with disabilities to play a productive role in society, including in the work force, and to eliminate impediments to their full participation in society. The ADA is enforced at the federal, state, and local levels. In addition to the protections it offers patients and customers (see Chapter XII: Practice Pitfalls), the ADA provides the disabled protections in respect to hiring, employment conditions, and termination. The employment provisions apply to the government and to private employers of 15 or more people.

Basically, the law forbids discrimination in employment against a disabled person who is otherwise qualified for a job, who can perform its essential functions. It is forbidden to ask people protected under the ADA about their disabilities, although they can be asked if they are able to perform specific functions if all applicants are asked the same questions. Similarly, they can only be subjected to evaluations and examinations required of all employees or applicants in their class. In addition, an employer cannot simply reject or terminate a disabled person, but must make a reasonable effort to accommodate his or her special needs. A disabled person may be rejected for employment or laid off if the employee cannot meet the job requirements even after reasonable accommodation. Reasonable accommodation requires the employer to consider adjustments to the employee's environment and work schedule, other jobs within the organization that the disabled employee could handle, removal of impediments to access, and the like.

A person is considered disabled if he or she has a mental or physical impairment that substantially limits his or her ability to perform one or more of life's major activities, has a record of that impairment, or is regarded as having such an impairment. The protection extends to discrimination against those with a known association or relationship with a disabled person (for example, a partner, spouse, or family member of someone who is HIV+ or who has AIDS). The protection has been broadly interpreted. Court decisions have concluded that an HIV+ person is disabled within the meaning of the ADA, even if he or she is asymptomatic; also included in its protections are people with epilepsy, paralysis, AIDS, substantial hearing or visual loss, mental retardation, and specific learning disabilities. The language regarding a person with a "record" of a disability covers people who have recovered from cancer, alcoholism, or mental illness. On the other hand, a person diagnosed with diabetes but asymptomatic is not protected under the ADA (*Orr v. Wal-Mart Stores, Inc.*, 297 F. 3d 720 (8th Cir. 2002)(diabetic pharmacist fired for failing to keep a single-pharmacist store open during his half-hour lunch break, as required by his employer, was not covered by the ADA, even though he alleged he needed an uninterrupted break to manage his diet and take his insulin).[11]

Familiarity with the ADA is important to those who own, operate, or manage a business or supervise employees, who must comply with its terms. If you are an employee and are or become disabled, the ADA provides important protections. And, as noted in Chapter XII: Practice Pitfalls, businesses open to the public must ensure access in compliance with the ADA.

# Working Conditions

**Hours and Breaks.** For a long time pharmacists had relatively little protection under California's labor laws. The law has long provided that other pharmacy employees may not work "in any store, dispensary, pharmacy, laboratory, or office for more than an average of nine hours per day, or for more than 108 hours in any two consecutive weeks or for more than 12 days in any two consecutive weeks." But the same law adds that "any registered pharmacist may be so employed and may perform such work for the full period of time permitted by this section" (Lab. Code §850). Although hardly a model of clarity, this last clause appeared to mean that the pharmacist did not share these protections.

In response to concerns about adverse working conditions creating stress and resulting in errors by pharmacists, the Labor Code was amended, effective in 2000, so that pharmacists, except those in an executive or administrative position, are now covered by limitations on hours and protections assuring breaks and meal time (Lab. Code §1186). An employer must provide an employee who works over five hours in a day a minimum 30 minute meal break; the employer and the employee may "mutually consent" to waive the meal break as long as the total work period during a given day does not exceed six hours (Lab. Code §512).

The law that demanded the continuous presence of a pharmacist for a pharmacy to remain open was amended to enable the Board to adopt regulations (§1714.1) to provide for the temporary absence of a pharmacist to accommodate breaks and lunch periods (§4116(b)(2)). The regulations

---

[11] Physical disability is defined more broadly under the California Fair Employment and Housing Act, the state equivalent of the ADA, than it is under the ADA. A claimant under the California law need only show a physiological disease or condition affecting a body system that limits (rather than "substantially" limits) the person's ability to participate in a major life activity (not "activities") (*Colmenares v. Braemer Country Club, Inc.,* 29 Cal.4th 1019, 1027-1028 (2003)).

allowing for the temporary absence of a pharmacist apply only to pharmacies staffed by a single pharmacist. The pharmacist may leave the pharmacy temporarily for breaks and meals without either closing the pharmacy or removing ancillary staff, as long as the pharmacist reasonably believes the pharmacy, including all its stock of drugs, will be secure during his or her absence (§1714.1(a)). If, in the opinion of the pharmacist, the pharmacy would not be secure, he or she must close it and remove its ancillary staff during that absence (§1714.1(a)). For purposes of this section, ancillary staff includes any intern, pharmacy technician, or technician trainee as well as nonlicensed personnel (§1714.1(g)).

During the absence only refill medications may be physically provided to a patient or his or her agent and only if the pharmacist has checked the refill medication, released it for furnishing to the patient, and determined the refill does not require consultation (§1714.1(b)). During the pharmacist's absence, ancillary staff may continue to perform nondiscretionary acts, but their work must be checked by the pharmacist upon his or her return to the pharmacy (§1714.1(c)). During such an absence the intern may not perform any discretionary act and may not otherwise act as a pharmacist (§1714.1(d)).

The temporary absence authorized by section 1714.1 is limited to the minimum period (30 minutes) authorized by the Labor Code; during that time the pharmacist who is on break shall not be required to remain in the pharmacy area (§1714.1(e)). The pharmacy must have written policies and procedures regarding pharmacy operation during such absences; these policies must cover the authorized duties of ancillary staff, the pharmacist's responsibility for checking work done in his or her absence, and the pharmacist's responsibility for maintaining pharmacy security (§1714.1(f)).

The decision whether the pharmacy may remain open under section 1714.1 is left to the professional judgment of the pharmacist; it is not a decision for the employer. The law does not allow a waiver of the 30 minute meal break for a work day exceeding six hours in length. The law reflects public policy that no employee should work more than six hours without a meal break, and is quite clear that meal and other break periods are to be free of duties. That is, the pharmacist may not be required to be nearby, or available for any urgent situation, during such breaks.

A pharmacist, like other pharmacy employees, is entitled to at least one complete day of rest per week (Lab. Code §852) and to consecutive working hours on any day's shift, except for up to one hour for meal time and excepting Sundays and holidays (Lab. Code §851.5). Excepted from the requirement of providing consecutive hours is a hospital that employs only one person who compounds prescriptions (Lab. Code §851.5).

The Labor Code provisions concerning work hours do not apply in case of emergencies, defined in the statute as accident, death, sickness, or epidemic (Lab. Code §854). Otherwise, violation of these protections is a misdemeanor (Lab. Code §853). Neither the Labor Code nor the Pharmacy Law currently contains other restrictions on a pharmacist's workload; some states (notably North Carolina) have adopted such provisions.

**Management Interference with Professional Judgment.** As discussed in the section entitled "Special Concerns for Employee Pharmacists" in Chapter XII: Practice Pitfalls, and elsewhere in this text, working conditions for employee pharmacists may be adversely affected by management interference with the pharmacist's exercise of his or her professional judgment. Such interference may take the form of instructions to do something the pharmacist thinks is wrong or not to do something the pharmacist believes is required. More difficult situations arise when pharmacy staffing is insufficient to provide adequate attention to the requirements of the law and regulations and the needs of proper patient care.

Unless the pharmacist has a contract, a union, or other job protection, he or she may be fired at the discretion of management.[12]  If the termination can be proven to be for a reason deemed improper by law (such as illegal discrimination), there may be recourse.  However, it is not improper for a pharmacy to fire a pharmacist based upon management's disagreement with the way the pharmacist exercises his or her professional discretion.  That is, if the pharmacy disagrees with the pharmacist's conclusions – for example, about which prescriptions are not for a legitimate medical purpose or for how extensive consultation must be to comply with the law – it may terminate the pharmacist's employment.  While California law protects from retaliation employees who report their employer's violations of law to a government agency (Lab. Code §1102.5), there is a vast area for potential disagreement about sound professional practices within the bounds of the legal conduct of a pharmacy.

**Workplace Violence.**  Of increasing concern in the workplace is violence, whether committed by fellow workers, customers, or intruders.  Not only is an employer entitled to seek a protective restraining order on behalf of an employee against another employee (Civ. Pro. Code §527.8), the employer is required to use means that are reasonably adequate to furnish safe and healthful employment conditions (Lab. Code §§6400-6401, 6402).  Section 601 of the Penal Code provides protection from non-employees who threaten workplace violence.  California's Division of Occupational Safety and Health (Cal-OSHA) is responsible for workplace security.  One important aspect of providing a secure workplace is providing timely, adequate notice to an employee known to the employer to face potential danger, so that the employee can take precautions.

**Discrimination and Harassment.**  Both state (Civ. Code §51.9) and federal law (42 USC §2000e-2, Title VII of the Civil Rights Act) make it unlawful for an employer to engage in discriminatory conduct based on gender, to engage in sexual harassment, or to punish or discriminate against an employee because he or she has opposed any unlawful employment practice or has participated in an investigation, proceeding, or hearing under Title VII or similar state laws.

One issue is whether such laws bar any "sexist" utterance or only more pervasive, abusive conduct.  California courts, like many others, have tended to interpret terms such as "sexual harassment" very broadly.  However, the United States Supreme Court, in *Clark County School District v. Breeden*, 532 U.S. 268 (2001), held that a single inappropriate comment could not constitute sexual harassment.  The Court held that the conduct, to be actionable, must be so severe or pervasive as to alter the conditions of the victim's employment and create an abusive working environment. The Court indicated it would look to factors such as frequency and severity of the conduct, whether it was physically threatening or humiliating, and whether it unreasonably interferes with an employee's work performance.

# Filling Prescriptions for Experimental Drugs

Both federal and state laws and regulations provide that patients must be given the opportunity to give their informed consent before they are involved in any medical experimentation (see, for example, 21 CFR §50.25, Elements of Informed Consent (FDA)).  However, the pharmacist is exempt from the requirements concerning the assurance of informed consent if he or she merely fills a prescription for an experimental drug (H&SC §24179).  Nevertheless, it is obviously very important that patients receive adequate information upon which to make a judgment whether or not to follow an experimental drug regimen.  The pharmacist may play an important role in ensuring that this

---

[12] In *Ryan v. Dan's Food Store*, 972 P.2d 395 (Utah 1998), the fired pharmacist was properly notified of his at-will employment status by the employee handbook.  The court held that his firing did not violate public policy because the pharmacist could not show by a preponderance of the evidence that his questioning of prescriptions, as required by 21 CFR §1306.04 (corresponding responsibility), was a substantial factor in his termination.

298 Other Law Relevant to Pharmacy

information is adequately communicated.  Of course, in a blind study the pharmacist cannot provide information to the patient without defeating the study's purpose.

As discussed in Chapter II: Drug Classifications, physicians may choose to prescribe drugs "off-label," for uses for which they have not been approved.  Quite often a drug is well accepted for uses far broader than those in their labeling.  The drug's sponsor, which is responsible for the collection and transmission of data to the FDA to support new labeled uses, often lags behind clinical judgment in getting these changes accomplished.  Such prescriptions may come to the pharmacist's attention in the course of patient counseling.  It would seem wise for a physician prescribing a drug beyond its labeled uses to have discussed his or her intention and reasons with the patient.  The pharmacist ought to have no liability for filling such a prescription under Health and Safety Code section 24179, because the physician essentially is using the drug experimentally.  Good communication with physicians whose prescriptions you are filling will be helpful in assuring that patients receive proper information about their drugs.

---

**What you should think about after reading this chapter:**

1.  What types of policies and procedures would be beneficial to protect the privacy of patient records?

2.  What legal and practical considerations should you think about when establishing, owning, or managing a pharmacy or other drug-related business?

3.  Ought there be additional workplace protections for pharmacists?

4.  What should a pharmacist consider when deciding whether the pharmacy could safely remain open while he or she is on break?

5.  How might a pharmacy pose access problems for a disabled employee or customer?

---

# Chapter XV

# Ethics and Law

**What you should know after reading this chapter:**

1.  What is the Code of Ethics for Pharmacists?

2.  What is a conscience clause?

3.  Does California law or regulation recognize or protect a pharmacist who chooses not to fill particular prescriptions?

Ethics basically refers to the duty of a person to respect the fundamental mores of society and his or her own tenets as to how he or she acts, especially where those acts may affect others, from family and friends to society in general. Ethics ranges from treatment of another person – patient or otherwise – to the handling of one's own and others' property, to honesty in dealing with other persons, entities, and the government.

Generally we both hope and expect that what the law requires, and what we are asked or directed to do, conforms to our sense of what is ethical, what is right. However, from time to time, one's sense of what is ethical – whether religiously, culturally, philosophically, or personally based – may come into conflict with, or appear to be in conflict with, what a law, regulation, agency, employer, or supervisor requires (or prohibits).

This book is about law, so its first purpose is to tell you what the law demands or allows. But even apparently strict requirements of the law are touched with humanity; at least in some cases, situations arise where resistance to or disobedience of law may be necessary and justified. The difficulty is that when one engages in an "ethical" violation of a law there is a very real risk that some agency will disbelieve or disagree with your rationale for your conduct or feel it did not justify your violation, and you will be subject to the penalties applicable to that violation. Your good intention may, in some cases, moderate the choice of the penalty imposed.

The defense, "I had to violate the law," rarely works, but there are exceptions. For example, criminal prosecutions of individuals for operating clean needle exchange programs, which were clearly in violation of California law until 2000, consistently resulted in acquittals, starting in the 1990s. Defendants put forth a defense of medical necessity, the need to stem the spread of HIV and AIDS (see Chap. V: Other Board Licensees), and juries refused to convict, regardless of the law. The same argument might be made by one who supplies or directs a patient to a source of marijuana for pain when no other relief is effective or available. But it is risky, at best, to place one's faith or trust in the sympathy or agreement of a judge and/or jury.

In addition to situations where one may be asked to choose between what one believes is right for the patient and what the law dictates, there are situations where one's own beliefs may place a pharmacist in conflict with what a patient wants and the law allows him or her to have, as discussed below under "Conscience Clause."

# The Code of Ethics for Pharmacists

No specific code of principles or ethical behavior governs the practice of pharmacy.[1] However, the major national professional pharmacists' associations have adopted the "Code of Ethics for Pharmacists." The American Pharmacists Association (APhA) adopted this code in 1994; it was endorsed by the American Society of Health System Pharmacists in 1996. There are eight basic principles:[2]

I.     A pharmacist respects the covenantal relationship between the patient and pharmacist.
II.    A pharmacist promotes the good of every patient in a caring, compassionate, and confidential manner.
III.   A pharmacist respects the autonomy and dignity of each patient.
IV.    A pharmacist acts with honesty and integrity in professional relationships.
V.     A pharmacist maintains professional competence.
VI.    A pharmacist respects the values and abilities of colleagues and other health professionals.
VII.   A pharmacist serves individual, community, and societal needs.
VIII.  A pharmacist seeks justice in the distribution of health resources.

In 1994, an oath was created[3] that is taken by students entering pharmacy schools throughout the United States:

## Oath of a Pharmacist

- At this time, I vow to devote my professional life to the service of all humankind through the profession of pharmacy.
- I will consider the welfare of humanity and relief of human suffering my primary concerns.
- I will apply my knowledge, experience, and skills to the best of my ability to assure optimal drug therapy outcomes for the patients I serve.
- I will keep abreast of developments and maintain professional competency in my profession of pharmacy.
- I will maintain the highest principles of moral, ethical, and legal conduct.
- I will embrace and advocate change in the profession of pharmacy that improves patient care. I take these vows voluntarily with the full realization of the responsibility with which I am entrusted by the public.

In other words, the oath's message is that in carrying out professional responsibilities as a pharmacist, the pharmacist should not only respect a patient's dignity, privacy, and autonomy and look out for his or her best interests, but keep his or her knowledge current and look to improve the profession of pharmacy itself.

---

[1]  That is, there is no general code of ethics in a statute in California (and the authors know of none in any other state). The California Board does have regulations governing professional conduct (§§1760-1766).

[2]  Each principle has accompanying interpretative comments, some of which are noted in the text.

[3]  This oath was developed by the American Pharmacists Association Academy of Students of Pharmacy and the American Association of Colleges of Pharmacy Council of Deans (APhA-ASP/AACP-COD) Task Force on Professionalism, June 26, 1994 (available at the AACP website, www.aacp.org/site/tertiary.asp?CID=290&DID=4339).

# Conscience Clause

In addition to the above eight principles, the APhA has adopted a "conscience clause," a concept largely driven by the organized opposition of some pharmacists to the use of abortifacients and drugs for assisted suicide. In 1998, APhA recognized a pharmacist's right to exercise conscientious refusal to fill certain types of prescriptions. It simultaneously supported the establishment of systems to ensure patient access to legally prescribed therapy without the need to compromise the pharmacist's right of conscientious refusal. A 1998 policy adopted by the California Pharmacists Association is similar, but more aggressively recognizes the obligation of a pharmacist who objects to filling a particular prescription to help the patient obtain pharmaceutical care from another pharmacy in a timely and appropriate manner.

Although efforts have been made in multiple states to enact conscience clauses for pharmacists, very few have done so (Alan Meisel, *Pharmacists, Physicians, Assisted Suicide, and Pain Control*, 2 JOURNAL OF HEALTH CARE LAW AND POLICY 211 (1999)). South Dakota is one of the few states that has. It adopted, in 1998, a very powerful conscience clause that bars lawsuits, discrimination, or recriminations against, or dismissal of, a pharmacist who refuses to dispense drugs if there is even reason to believe the medication would be used to cause an abortion, destroy an unborn child, or cause death through assisted suicide, euthanasia, or mercy killing (South Dakota Code §36-11-70). Arkansas has such a law, as does Mississippi, whose statute allows all health care providers to refuse to participate in procedures to which they have moral objections. Similar legislation was introduced (but not passed) in ten other states in 2004 (Charisse Jones, *Druggists refuse to give out pill*, USA TODAY, Nov. 9, 2004, p. 3A). No such proposal has yet been introduced in the California Legislature.

In the absence of a "conscience clause" statute, numerous pharmacies mandate that their pharmacists fill all valid, legal prescriptions regardless of personal belief. One chain with such a policy, however, simply does not stock so-called emergency contraception (so-called "morning-after") drugs.

There is no California statute that mandates that a pharmacy or pharmacist fill every valid prescription. However, the Board's recently-adopted regulation on emergency contraception specifically provides, "If emergency contraception services are not immediately available at the pharmacy or the pharmacist declines to furnish pursuant to conscience clause, the pharmacist will refer the patient to another emergency contraception provider" (§1746). While this regulation recognizes that some pharmacists might not wish to make emergency contraception available, it requires them to refer patients seeking emergency contraception to another pharmacist or pharmacy; failure to comply is grounds for discipline. There is no other law or regulation that contains similar language applicable to other drugs. But nothing in California law prohibits an employer from requiring a pharmacist either to fill all lawful prescriptions or, if he or she cannot as a matter of conscience do so, ensure that the patient has an alternative. That alternative could be another pharmacist in the same pharmacy or a referral to another, convenient pharmacy, consistent with the APhA and CPhA conscience clauses.

In a variety of cases in different states, individual pharmacists have refused to fill some prescriptions, without offering the patient an alternative. For example, in Wisconsin a pharmacist who refused to refill a prescription for an oral contraceptive faced discipline for refusing to tell the patient where she might go to have her prescription refilled and for refusing to transfer the prescription to the pharmacy where the patient went for the refill (Anita Weier, *Rx License is on the Line in Abortion Fight; Pharmacist Refused Pill Order Due to Faith*, CAPITAL TIMES, Oct. 12, 2004, p. 1A). In Texas, a pharmacist was fired by a pharmacy chain for refusing to fill prescriptions for emergency contraception. The chain's employment manual states that its pharmacists may not decline to fill a prescription based on religious, moral or ethical grounds (*Pharmacist denies woman's request for morning-after pill*, UNION LEADER, Sept. 27, 2004, p. C7).

# Specific Ethical Dilemmas

We address a few examples of ethical dilemmas below, to point out some potential conflicts between law and ethics and how one might analyze them and reconcile them. This short discussion is not intended to be a substitute for a course in ethics.

**What if you receive a prescription for an abortifacient (and you oppose abortion)? For AIDS drugs for a homosexual (and you believe homosexuality is a sin)? Assuming it were legal in California, for drugs to aid a terminal patient to commit suicide (and you believe suicide is morally wrong)?**

As noted above, a pharmacy is not obligated to fill every prescription it receives; no California law requires it to do so. That is the law in virtually every state. At the same time, if the refusal to fill a legitimate prescription denies a patient his or her legally-ordered care, the refusal might be grounds for a lawsuit (if it could be considered malpractice) or discipline (if it could be considered unprofessional conduct). If a pharmacist were engaging in forbidden discrimination (by race, gender, or national origin, for example) in refusing to fill certain types of prescriptions, that might also be a matter for discipline. That is why the APhA policy, and the policy of the California Pharmacists Association more strongly, recognizes that when a pharmacist refuses to fill such a prescription, a system to ensure the patient can still get the prescription filled should exist.[4]

**What if your employer has policies requiring you to fill the above prescriptions (or not to refuse any prescription unless it appears to violate the law)?**

If you violate an employment policy that has been clearly conveyed to you in advance, you risk sanction by your employer, possibly including termination, for failure to fill the valid prescription. Pharmacists have been fired on that basis, not only in the Texas case mentioned above, but also in California. The only exception would be in a state where the conscience clause precludes the termination, making a contrary clause in an employment policy unenforceable.

**If you refuse to fill a prescription for ethical reasons, must you refer the patient to another pharmacy that will fill the prescription?**

California law does not require you to fill the prescription in the first place. However, given the fact that you are not challenging the legitimacy or legality of the prescription, and considering the patient's rights, it would seem most ethical to refer him or her to a pharmacy and pharmacist who will fill the prescription (and that is certainly consistent with the thrust of APhA's policy and the specific language of CPhA's policy). At the same time, if you firmly believe the prescription is immoral, enabling the patient to do what you morally oppose by making the referral would not seem to solve your moral dilemma (as the pharmacist's decision in the Wisconsin situation cited above demonstrates).

The authors believe that the intent of the Pharmacy Law is that you fill every legitimate prescription you receive, even though the law does not expressly require you to do so; Principle II of

---

[4]  The note to Principle III of the Code of Ethics refers to the patient's right of self-determination. Respecting that right would require meeting the obligation to fill, or assure the filling of, a legal prescription the patient wants, rather than imposing one's own beliefs so as to deprive the patient of the medication.

the Code of Ethics appears to be in agreement.  At this time there appears to be no significant threat to public health or individual patients' rights from pharmacists' refusals based on conscience to fill certain prescriptions, but such a problem could arise.  Although the numbers of such refusals have been small, if they were to increase significantly, or if such refusals were to occur in isolated areas where alternative pharmacy services were not easily available, the issues of public health and patients' rights would need to be addressed by regulators.

**If you refuse to fill a prescription for ethical reasons, may you explain those reasons to the patient?  Ought you explain those reasons to the patient?  May you attempt to convince the patient not to fill the particular prescription, for example for an abortifacient?**

There is no law barring you from explaining your actions to a patient, and if you are refusing to fill a prescription for reasons of conscience it is surely more appropriate to give the patient your reasons rather than simply to refuse to fill the prescription (as if there were some legal flaw in it).  However, there is a difference between explaining your reasons and proselytizing – attempting to impose your values on others.  Your role as a practicing pharmacist is to prepare and dispense medication, to provide clinical advice to other health care professionals, and to counsel patients about the medications they have been prescribed.  It is often appropriate for a pharmacist to suggest to a patient that he or she consider not filling a particular prescription – for medical reasons.  For the pharmacist to use his or her counseling role to raise other than medical issues seems inappropriate and unprofessional, as well as intruding on the physician-patient relationship.

Of course, if one can anticipate such problems and discuss them with one's employer in advance, some ethical conflicts can be avoided; another pharmacist, for example, could fill all prescriptions for a certain drug or of a certain type.  Your employer might well be willing to take your ethical concern into account, if it is presented in a professional manner prior to causing any discomfort or problem for a customer.

If you are the pharmacy owner, there is no law requiring you to stock all drugs.  If a prescription for a drug you stock is being used for a purpose of which you do not approve, and patients have reasonable access to alternative pharmacy services, your refusal to fill certain prescriptions is probably not unprofessional conduct.  However, if your pharmacy is in a rural or isolated area, and patients cannot easily find an alternative pharmacy, it might well be unprofessional conduct to impose your personal views on the patients whom you have been licensed to serve.

**A patient is prescribed a new medication; it is essential for treatment of a serious condition and there are no comparably-effective alternatives available.  The drug has a fairly rare, but serious, side effect.  You are concerned that if the patient knows about the side effect she might not take the medication.  You withhold the information about the side effect because you decide the risk of her not taking the medication outweighs her right to the information.**

Your withholding the information about a serious side effect violates both the patient consultation regulation and drug warning statute.  In addition, you have violated your ethical obligation to respect the autonomy and dignity of each patient, as it is presented in the APhA's Code of Ethics.  The patient's right to self-determination includes the right to participate in decisions about his or her own health.

**While you are providing consultation to a regular patient, he tells you he plans to commit suicide.  You believe he may well be serious.  Should you tell someone?  Who?**

The law does not require you to report the patient's comment to anyone, and your obligation to respect the patient's dignity and autonomy (as well as his right to privacy) would also seem to militate against disclosure. This conclusion is consistent with the first principle of the Code of Ethics, which is accompanied by a note about maintaining the patient's trust. Yet that same note also says a pharmacist promises to be committed to the patient's welfare. The comments to the second principle mention both the obligation to serve the patient in a private and confidential manner and to place concern for the well-being of the patient at the center of professional practice.

In other words, the Code of Ethics pulls a pharmacist in conflicting directions in this situation. It would certainly seem both reasonable and humane for the pharmacist to take some appropriate steps to ensure that the patient gets help that might intervene before he has the chance to commit suicide. The patient's disclosure of his intentions to the pharmacist, after all, probably signals a request for help.

**You receive prescriptions for a terminally ill patient for a combination of large amounts of morphine and Nembutal®. You are aware that such large amounts of those drugs, in combination, can be fatal. Can you fill the prescriptions if you believe the patient intends to kill himself by taking all the drugs at one time?**

Assuming the prescriptions are otherwise legitimate and could be used for a medical purpose other than for the patient to kill himself, ordinarily you would go ahead and fill them. But if you believed the patient intended to use the drugs to kill himself, you would be aiding the commission of a suicide, which is illegal in every state. (Even in Oregon, it is only legal to dispense prescriptions for assisted suicide when done according to the provisions of that state's laws). If you merely suspected a suicidal intent, you would at least want to talk with the patient about the intended use of the drugs and possible effects if taken all at once. You also might well be obligated to talk to his prescriber. Although principle III of the Code of Ethics calls for respect for a patient's dignity and autonomy, you might be subject to criminal prosecution were you to fill these prescriptions *believing* the patient intended to use them to kill himself, were he to do so.

**What if you are the pharmacist-in-charge and observe illegal activities in the pharmacy?**

You have a legal obligation as pharmacist-in-charge to ensure the pharmacy is in compliance with laws and regulations governing pharmacy. In addition, you have a personal ethical obligation to see that the law is not violated in your workplace. Not all violations of laws and regulations are of equal risk to the public. While no violation of law is "acceptable," neither does every violation of law, no matter how insignificant and unintentional, justify a confrontation with your employer at the risk of your employment. However, when the violation does pose a significant risk, your ethical obligation is to take action even if your employment might be jeopardized.

The note to principle VII of the Code of Ethics mentions that the pharmacist has obligations to the community and society. The pharmacist also has an obligation to act with honesty and integrity in professional relationships, and to tell the truth (principle IV and its note). Together these principles suggest that the pharmacist-in-charge should not ignore known illegality.

**What if the illegality has nothing to do with the practice of pharmacy? What if it involves failure to properly report sales for sales tax purposes? What if it is entirely unrelated to the practice or business of pharmacy, such as your employer illegally hooking up the store to a cable television system?**

As an ethical issue, the type of illegality is irrelevant: if you know it's wrong, it's wrong. But that conclusion does not address what, if anything, you ought to do about it. As the pharmacist-in-charge, you will almost certainly be held culpable for sales tax violations or fraud, if you know of them or participate in them (and perhaps even without knowledge or involvement). If you are one of multiple pharmacists at the store, and not the pharmacist-in-charge, you would have no direct culpability; nevertheless, you should not countenance fraud.

The pharmacist-in-charge would have no direct, legal obligation to stop the illegal cable television hookup or report it to the cable company, but is it ethical simply to ignore it? If the act is wrong, it is wrong.

**You observe a fellow employee pharmacist who frequently smells of alcohol and exhibits other signs of alcohol or drug abuse while on duty. You decide it is none of your business.**

Aside from any legal reporting obligations or any obligation your employer may impose, you certainly have a duty to customers of the pharmacy not to ignore conduct that may make the pharmacist unsafe to practice pharmacy (after all, that pharmacist's conduct is grounds for discipline (§4301(h)).

**Suppose you know the pharmacist is in treatment for the alcohol or drug problem?**

This knowledge makes the decision more difficult. Treatment and rehabilitation of highly-skilled professionals is both sensible and official policy (see Pharmacists Recovery Program discussion in Chap. XIII: Board of Pharmacy). However, one's obligation to patients receiving prescriptions at the pharmacy would outweigh other factors if the pharmacist, despite receiving treatment for the problem, appears to be unable to practice safely at present.

**A patient without prescription coverage brings in a prescription for a very expensive drug that is essential to the patient's continued health. When you tell her the price, the patient tells you not to fill the prescription, because she simply cannot afford it. You provide it free of charge, without prior permission from the pharmacy owner, and you do not tell the owner about it afterward. Is this legal?**

The patient had a prescription, so furnishing the drugs was legal. However, your conduct was unethical, because, although motivated by your concern for the patient, you committed a fraud on your employer, first by giving the drug away without permission and then by failing to notify the owner you had done so. Surely you are free to pay for the prescription out of your own pocket (something you likely could not afford to do on a regular basis). While your motivation was humanitarian, the problem with your actions is where and when does one draw the line? How much loss of profit by your owner would you deem "proper?" Principle II of the Code of Ethics instructs pharmacists to promote the good of every patient in a caring, compassionate manner; principle VIII instructs pharmacists to seek justice in the distribution of health resources. These principles could be read as urging such actions as giving patients drugs for free. But Principle IV requires that the pharmacist act with honesty and integrity in professional relationships. Defrauding one's employer, even with the best of motivation, does not meet this standard.

**Suppose you widely advertised the availability of flu shots, for $20 apiece. At the time of your advertisements, your cost for a dose of vaccine was expected to be $8, and you had been promised 500 doses. Because of the 2004 flu vaccine shortage, your usual supplier could not provide the vaccine. Another distributor has contacted you and offered vaccine, for $80 a dose. Should you buy the vaccine and offer flu shots? At what price? Should you consider charging more than the advertised $20, but less than your actual cost? Public health officials have mandated that flu shots be given only to infants, the elderly, and the chronically ill. Will you screen the people seeking flu shots? How?**

Because the shortage of flu vaccine was beyond your control, you are likely not to be in violation of false advertising laws if you were to cancel your plans to offer flu shots, or to offer the shots but raise the price to reflect, in a reasonable way, your added costs. But what would be reasonable? If you expected to make $12 beyond the cost of the vaccine, could you now reasonably charge $92? (After all, you still need to pay your staff and overhead, and make a profit.) If people call and offer $200 to get a flu shot without standing on line, should you agree? Is the ethical thing to charge more than the advertised $20, but less than your actual cost? Or is the ethical thing to tell the distributor charging ten times the usual cost, "no, thank you," and not offer flu shots at all?

In fact, during the late fall of 2004 pharmacies reported offers to supply flu vaccine at prices from four to ten times the usual cost. While some reported this price gouging to government officials, and refused the purchases, surely some pharmacies and physicians wished to provide their patients protection, even at an unreasonably high price (Debora Vrana and Denise Gellene, *Prices Inflated for Scarce Flu Vaccine; Some drug distributors are demanding four to 10 times the usual cost, a hospital survey shows*, LOS ANGELES TIMES, Oct. 14, 2004, p. A1).

While a pharmacy could determine which of the people seeking flu shots were infants by observation and which were over 65 by asking for identification, it is not possible to determine, at a glance, whether or not someone has a chronic illness. While of course you could ask each patient (taking care to do so privately, to protect that personal health information), could you ethically turn some people down on the basis of your disbelief after your conversation? Could you ethically *not* turn some people down? (Could you suggest to those you disbelieve that you would be willing to consult with their physicians?) To deal with the shortage in 2004, some pharmacists counseled healthy patients about health maintenance measures as alternatives to flu shots.

**You are helping to establish or revise a drug formulary for an entity that pays for prescription drug benefits. One of the expensive new antibiotics that is under consideration for inclusion in the formulary is made by a drug company in which you have a substantial financial interest. May you vote for including that antibiotic without revealing your investment?**

You have a serious potential conflict of interest, because your personal financial interest may conflict with your obligation to make a professional judgment for the benefit of patients. It certainly would appear to the ordinary person that you would have a difficult time making an ethical, independent decision, even if you are confident that you would never let the possible effect on your own income or net worth influence your judgment. Participating in the decision, at least without revealing the investment, seems to violate a pharmacist's obligation to act with integrity (Principle IV). It may also be contrary to the pharmacist's obligation to seek justice in the distribution of health resources, because your self-interest threatens your making a choice that would lead to delivery of quality, reasonable-cost pharmaceutical care.

**As the pharmacist-in-charge, you discover a thousand doses of penicillin are missing. You believe they have been shipped, free of charge, to people overseas who have no access to life-saving drugs. How do you balance your concern about diversion and your impulse toward humanitarianism? If you are leaning toward the humanitarian, where would you draw the line?**

There is no line to draw here. One doesn't balance humanitarian concerns in this situation. A prescription is required for provision of penicillin. Any furnishing of drugs to anyone for general use, here or abroad, is illegal unless you have authority – which is generally a prescription – to furnish the drugs and the recipient is authorized to receive them. As the pharmacist-in-charge, you are responsible for drug shortages, regardless of the intentions of those who misappropriated the drugs. Several of the principles of the Code of Ethics, and their notes, may suggest a balancing, because of the obligations to patient care and the fair distribution of health resources. However, diversion, even of antibiotics, is a significant violation of a clear legal standard. Sometimes, as noted below, the only way to resolve such an apparent conflict between ethics and the law is to seek to change the law, but to comply with it until it is changed. Another way to resolve the conflict is to become involved with organizations that provide medical supplies and volunteers to needy overseas communities.

Ultimately, of course, we each must live with our own judgments of right and wrong, and our own decisions about what, if anything, to do in any given situation. Some violations of law might be worth the risk of the penalty for the conduct, including the risk of loss of license, financial consequences, or loss of liberty, while others might not be, in your judgment.

The law reflects what society has determined to be right and wrong; one also has to consider the readings of one's own moral compass. Acting ethically and humanely are important to a healthy society, at times perhaps even worthy of greater respect than law itself. Nevertheless, if you choose a course that violates the law, or threatens your employment, because of your ethical views or the ethical standards of your profession, you must recognize that there may well be adverse legal and practical consequences. If you are making what seems to you to be the proper choice (or, in your view, the only choice), you must be ready to accept those consequences. Similarly, ignoring violations of law by others may sometimes be legally and even socially acceptable, but a complete violation of one's own principles. Ironically, following one's moral compass and attempting to correct the legal violations of others may also have adverse consequences of a practical sort.

Despite the somewhat simplistic answers suggested here to several ethical dilemmas, there are no "answers" to ethical questions, because ethics, although often reflective of what we have learned from family, religion, society, and educators, ultimately is a very personal matter. It is important to consider ethical questions, and discuss them with your peers, in the workplace, and through professional and trade associations. When regulatory change appears to you to be necessary, bring these issues to the Board of Pharmacy, the Legislature, or other government entities. The more often concerned pharmacists call attention to the ethical issues or dilemmas of pharmacy practice, the more likely the ethical dimensions of practice issues will be taken into account in the continuing evolution of the profession and the laws governing it.

---

**What you should think about after reading this chapter:**

1.  What is the relationship of ethics to the law?

2.  May I refuse to do what the law requires because it violates my ethical beliefs? What might the consequences be of doing so?

3.  How can I minimize the possibility that ethical conflicts will interfere with my obligation to the patient? To my employment?

4.  What should I do when I observe a violation of law in my place of employment?

5.  How can I remain an ethical pharmacist in a practical world?

6.  What is my obligation to maintain and raise the ethics of my profession?

---

*Appendix A*

# Study Guide for the
# California Pharmacist Jurisprudence Exam (CPJE)

The California State Board of Pharmacy has published a detailed content outline for the California Pharmacist Jurisprudence Examination (CPJE) in its examination handbook, which is posted at www.pharmacy.ca.gov/forms/exam_outline.pdf. The primary focus of the exam is pharmacy law, covered in this text, but it also includes clinical aspects of the practice of pharmacy. While there are many potential sources of study material on clinical pharmacy, the Board specifically refers in the exam handbook to the materials published by the Board in *Health Notes* and *The Script*. The chart below therefore lists issues of those publications, as well as pages in this book, as suggested material for study. However, candidates are well-advised to review those publications themselves (available at www.pharmacy.ca.gov/publications/publications.htm) and decide which materials might be helpful for each item of the examination. In addition, candidates should review Board publications issued after the date of this text (January 2005) for relevance to the stated CJPE content. The chart was based upon the content outline in the March 1, 2004, version of the *CJPE Handbook*; the Board may, of course, modify the content outline at its discretion.

An excellent source of study material that is *not* included in the chart below is the column titled *Rx for Good Practice* that appeared in every issue of *The Script* published from 2000-2003. Each column addressed several pharmacy practice issues of relevance to a jurisprudence examination. All of these columns (about 30) are available online. They are an excellent source for study and to test your understanding of important legal and practice issues, and worth your printing and reading.

In reviewing legal materials included in *The Script*, it is advisable to read the most recent publications first, and work backwards. Material in earlier articles may have been superseded by changes in laws and regulations.

*Guide to the Chart*: The left-hand column is the content item from the Board's detailed content outline. The second column details the parts of this text that provide information relevant to that content item; listed are chapter numbers (without the word "chapter") and page numbers (without the word "page"). Where a chapter is noted without specific page numbers, the entire chapter is relevant to the subject being tested.

The third column (headed "*HN*") refers to articles in the Board's *Health Notes* series. *Health Notes* issues are abbreviated as follows: Alternative Medicine (Alt. Med., Care of Children & Adults with Developmental Disabilities (Devel. Dis.), Drug Therapy Considerations in Older Adults (Older Adults), Pharmacist Involvement in Anticoagulant Therapy (Anticoag.), Quality Assurance (QA), and Women's Health (WH). Sections are also abbreviated. Where no sections are noted, much of the issue is relevant. The *Health Notes* issues are likely to be relevant to many more parts of the examination content outline than those for which they are cited in the table; they are cited where they are most directly relevant. A prudent examinee is well-advised to review all the *Health Notes* to determine their relevance to particular aspects of the examination.

The fourth column (headed "*TS*") refers to issues of *The Script* by issue date and, in parentheses, page number.

| CONTENT ITEM | TEXT PAGES | *HN* | *TS* |
|---|---|---|---|
| **1. Provide Medication to Patients in Compliance with California Law (29% of exam)** | VI (98-103, 105-109), IX, and X | Alt. Med.(Legal Cons, Dietary Supps.) | ----- |
| **A. Organize and Evaluate Information as Communicated by the Prescriber, Prescriber's Authorized Agent, or Patient/Patient's Representative** | VI (100-101), IX, X (especially 186-190) | ----- | ----- |
| (1) Assess prescription/medication order for completeness, correctness, authenticity, and legality | VI (98-100), IX, XII (231-238) | ----- | 3/04[1] (3-9), 3/03 (12), 7/01 (3), 1/01 (1, 7-9), 7/00 (10), 4/00 (6-7), 1/00 (3 [AB 1545], 4 [SB 816]), 4/99 (10), 1/99 (11-13) |
| (2) Assess prescription/medication order for reimbursement eligibility | X (200-204) | Older Adults (Reimb.), Anticoag. (Est. Services) | 3/03 (5 [SB 1278]), 1/02 (3 [AB 207]), 4/00 (16) |
| (3) Evaluate the pharmaceutical information needs of the patient/patient's representative | VI (100-101), X (186-190, 191-193, 197-198) | Devel. Dis. (Parts 2 & 3) | ----- |
| **B. Dispense Medications in Compliance with California Law** | VI (99-100), VIII, IX, X | ----- | ----- |
| (1) Enter prescription information into patient profile | X (186), XI (216-217), XIV (286-294) | ----- | 1/01 (7 [SB 1903]) |
| (2) Document preparation of medication in various dosage forms | IV (69-77), VIII, XI | ----- | ----- |
| (3) Prepare label(s) for prescription containers | VIII (140-142, IX (181-183), X (186-190) | ----- | ----- |
| (4) Select auxiliary label(s) for container(s) | IX (181-183, X (186-190) | ----- | ----- |

---

[1] Material in the March 2004 edition of *The Script* appears in the Board's index of articles as January 2004; there does not appear to be a January 2004 edition.

| | | | |
|---|---|---|---|
| (5) Prior to dispensing, perform the final check of the medication (e.g., correct drug, dose, route, directions) | III (46-48), IV (63-65), IX (183), X (185) | ----- | ----- |
| **2. Monitor, Communicate and Manage Patient Outcomes (31% of exam)** | VI (100-105), X (186) | Devel. Dis. (Psychotropic Med. Use), Older Adults, Anticoag., WH | ----- |
| **A. Improve Patient Understanding, and Counsel Patient/Patient's Representative in Compliance with California Law** | VI (100-105), X (186) | Older Adults (Part III), Anticoag., QA | ----- |
| (1) Assess the patient's knowledge of the disease and treatment | X (186-190) | ----- | ----- |
| (2) Determine the need for a referral | ----- | Anticoag. (Part 3) | ----- |
| (3) Counsel patient/patient's representative regarding prescription medication therapy | X (186-190, 197-198) | Devel. Dis. (Parts 2 & 3), Older Adults (Management of Diseases, Geriatric Self-Care), Anticoag. (Patient Ed.), WH | 3/03 (14), 11/00 (3), 4/00 (2-5) |
| (4) Counsel patient/patient's representative regarding herbal/alternative therapies | II (30-31), X (186-190) | Alt. Med., Older Adults (Geriatric Self-Care) | ----- |
| (5) Verify the patient's/patient representative's understanding of the information presented | VI (99-101), X (186-190) | Devel. Dis. (Selected Tips) | ----- |
| **B. Monitor, Communicate, and Manage Patient Outcomes** | VI (100-105), IX (174-175), X (186, 193-195), XII (231-244) | Older Adults (Prescribing Challenges), Anticoag., WH | ----- |
| (1) Communicate results of monitoring to patient/patient's representative, prescriber and/or other health care professionals | VI (100-105) | Anticoag. (Imp. of Monitoring) | 10/03 (5, 13) |
| (2) Adjust patient's drug therapy according to written protocols developed with prescriber(s) | VI (100-105), X (186-190) | Anticoag. | ----- |

312

| | | | |
|---|---|---|---|
| **3. Manage Operations in Accordance with California Law (40% of exam)** | II-XI, esp. IV, VI, VII, VIII, IX, X, XI; III (42-44), XIV (295-297) | ----- | ----- |
| **A. Obtain and Document Pharmaceuticals, Devices and Supplies** | II, VII, VIII | ----- | 10/03 (4, 12), 1/02 (3 [SB 293], 4 [SB 724]), 7/01 (1, 12), 1/00 (3 [SB 188]) |
| (1) Maintain a borrow/loan system in compliance with legal requirements | VII (115-118), XI (210-211) | ----- | ----- |
| (2) Maintain a record-keeping system of items purchased/received/returned in compliance with legal requirements and professional standards | VII, XI | ----- | ----- |
| **B. Perform Quality Assurance/ Improvement to Enhance Patient Safety and Meet Legal Requirements** | IV (57-58) | Anticoag. (Improving Outcomes), QA | 3/03 (4-5), 10/01 (3-5, 10-11), 11/00 (1) |
| (1) Measure, assess and improve the accuracy of medication dispensing by pharmacy staff | III (43-44, 47-48), IV (57-58) | QA | ----- |
| (2) Measure, assess and improve patient compliance/adherence with medication regimens | X (186-190, 193-195) | Older Adults (Management of Diseases, Prescribing Challenges), QA (Using * * * to Reduce Error) | ----- |
| (3) Measure, assess and improve the disease-management outcomes of patient populations | ----- | Older Adults, Anticoag. (What Are * * *?, Improving Safety), WH (Part 2) | 10/01 (1, 7) |
| **C. Manage Operations, Human Resources and Information Systems** | III (37-39, 42-51), IV, VI (100-101), X (186-190, 197-198), XI | ----- | ----- |
| (1) Monitor the practice site and/or service areas for compliance with federal, state and local laws, regulations and professional standards | III (42-44), IV, VI (98-99, 105-109), VII - XII, XIV (295-297) | ----- | 3/03 (4-5), 7/01 (7), 4/01 (4), 4/99 (1,3,6), 1/99 (1,7) |

| | | | |
|---|---|---|---|
| (2) Develop and implement policies and procedures for pharmacy technicians | III (45-51), IV (58) | ----- | ----- |
| (3) Supervise the work of pharmacists, pharmacy technicians and/or other pharmacy staff | III (37-39, 42-51), IV (58, 105-109) | ----- | 3/04 (13), 3/03 (14), 10/01 (11), 4/99 (2), 1/99 (6) |
| (4) Ensure the availability of patient-related information (e.g., patient profiles, medication administration records) | VI (100-105), X (186-190, 195-198), XI (216-217) | ----- | ----- |
| **D. Establish and Manage Medication Use Systems in Accordance with Patient Safety Guidelines and California Law** | VII-IX, X (186, 195-197) | Anticoag. | 4/99 (4-5) |
| (1) Apply therapeutic interchange (i.e., formulary substitution) guidelines | II (19-20), IX (178-180) | ----- | ----- |
| (2) Establish and maintain a system by which adverse drug reactions are documented, analyzed, evaluated and reported | IV (57-58) | Older Adults (Eval. the Risks), QA | ----- |
| (3) Establish and maintain a system for medication error reporting including root cause analysis | IV (57-58) | QA | 1/01 (7 [SB 1875]), 4/99 (1,3) |

314

## *Appendix B*

# Definitions of Various Health Facilities

The California Health and Safety Code defines the various types of health care facilities in the state and establishes requirements for their licensure or operation. Other provisions of law, including pharmacy law, rely upon these definitions of the various facilities.

**Clinics.** Under section 1200 of the Health and Safety Code, a clinic is "an organized outpatient health facility which provides direct medical, surgical, dental, optometric, or podiatric advice, services, or treatment to patients who remain less than 24 hours, and which may also provide diagnostic or therapeutic services to patients in the home as an incident to care provided at the clinic facility."

The various types of clinic provided for under this section of the Code include:

- psychological clinics (§§1200.1, 1204.1)
- nonprofit speech and hearing centers (§1201.5)
- special service clinics, as defined by the Department of Health Services, including birth services clinics (§1203)
- community clinics (§1204(a)(1)(A))
- free clinics (§1204(a)(1)(B))
- surgical clinics (§1204(b)(1))
- chronic dialysis clinics (§1204(b)(2))
- rehabilitation clinics (§1204(b)(3))
- alternative birth centers (§1204(b)(4))

The clinics defined in section 1204(a) are considered primary care clinics; those defined in section 1204(b) are considered specialty clinics.

The law explicitly exempts certain types of clinics from licensure, including nonprofit multi-specialty clinics (§1206(l)).

**Health Facilities.** Under section 1250 of the Health and Safety Code, a health facility is "any facility, place, or building that is organized, maintained, and operated for the diagnosis, care, prevention, and treatment of human illness, physical or mental, including convalescence and rehabilitation and including care during and after pregnancy, or for one or more of these purposes, for one or more persons, to which the persons are admitted for a 24-hour stay or longer."

The various facilities provided for under this section of the Code include:

- general acute care hospitals (§1250(a))
- acute psychiatric hospitals (§1250(b))
- skilled nursing facilities (§1250(c))
- intermediate care facilities (§1250(d))
- intermediate care facilities/ developmentally disabled habilitative (§1250(e))
- special hospitals (dentistry or maternity) (§1250(f))
- intermediate care facilities/ developmentally disabled facility (§1250(g))
- intermediate care facilities/ developmentally disabled—nursing (§1250(h))
- congregate living health facilities (§1250(I))
- correctional treatment centers (§1250(j))
- nursing facilities (skilled nursing facilities) (§1250(k))
- psychiatric health facilities (§1250.2)
- chemical dependency recovery hospitals (§1250.3)

**Health Care Service Plans.** Under section 1345(f) of the Health and Safety Code, a health care service plan is: "any person who undertakes to arrange for the provision of health care services to subscribers or enrollees, or to pay for or to reimburse any part of the cost for those services, in return for a prepaid or periodic charge paid by or on behalf of the subscribers or enrollees"; or "any person, whether located within or outside of this state, who solicits or contracts with a subscriber or enrollee in this state to pay for or reimburse any part of the cost of, or who undertakes to arrange or arranges for, the provision of health care services that are to be provided wholly or in part in a foreign country in return for a prepaid or periodic charge paid by or on behalf of the subscriber or enrollee."

**Home Health Agencies.** Under 1727(a) of the Health and Safety Code, a home health agency is "a private or public organization . . . which provides, or arranges for the provision of, skilled nursing services, to persons in their temporary or permanent place of residence."

*Appendix C*

# Other State and Federal Agencies

Following are the names, addresses, and telephone numbers of some key personnel at various state and federal agencies with authority that affects the practice of pharmacy. Some of these agencies also have home pages on the World Wide Web whose addresses are listed below. The DEA, FDA, and NRC home pages are extensive; the FDA also has a home page with current good manufacturing practices.

## California State Agencies

### *Licensing Boards*

**Dental Board of California**
1432 Howe Avenue, Suite 85
Sacramento, CA 95825
Executive Officer: Cynthia Gatlin
(916) 263-2300
*www.dbc.ca.gov*

**Medical Board of California**
1426 Howe Avenue, #54
Sacramento, CA 95825
Executive Director: Dave Thornton
(916) 263-2382
*www.medbd.ca.gov*

**California Board of Optometry**
400 R Street, Suite 4090
Sacramento, CA 95814
Executive Officer: Taryn Smith
(916) 323-8720
*www.optometry.ca.gov*

**Osteopathic Medical Board of California**
2720 Gateway Oaks Drive, Suite 350
Sacramento CA 95833
Executive Director: Linda Bergmann
(916) 263-3100
*www.dca.ca.gov/osteopathic/*

**Physician Assistant Committee**
1424 Howe Avenue, Suite 35
Sacramento CA 95825-3237
Executive Officer: Richard Wallinder
(916) 263-2670; (800) 555-8038
*www.physicianassistant.ca.gov*

**Board of Podiatric Medicine**
1420 Howe Avenue, Suite 8
Sacramento CA 95825
Executive Officer: James H. Rathlesberger
(916) 263-2647
*www.dca.ca.gov/bpm*

**Board of Registered Nursing**
400 R Street, Suite 4030
Sacramento CA 95814
Executive Officer: Ruth Ann Terry
(916) 322-3350
*www.rn.ca.gov*

## *Other State Agencies*

### Department of Health Services
For a complete organizational listing of branches within the Department of Health Services:
*www.dhs.ca.gov/home/organization*

*Food and Drug Branch,*
*Division of Food, Drug and Radiation*
*Safety*
*MS 7602*
1500 Capitol Avenue, Suite 72-436
Sacramento CA 95814
(916) 650-6500
*www.dhs.ca.gov/ps/fdb/default.htm*

*Licensing and Certification*
1501 Capitol Avenue
Sacramento CA 95814
(800) 236-9747
*www.dhs.ca.gov/lnc/default.htm*

*Medical Care Services*
1501 Capitol Avenue
P.O. Box 997419
Sacramento CA 95899-7419
(916) 654-0391
*www.dhs.ca.gov/mcs*

*Medi-Cal Managed Care Division*
1501 Capitol Avenue
P.O. Box 997419
Sacramento CA 95899-7419
(916) 449-5000
*www.dhs.ca.gov/mcs/mcmcd/index.html*

### Department of Justice
*Bureau of Narcotic Enforcement*
California Department of Justice
4949 Broadway
Sacramento, CA 95820
(916) 227-4044
*www.caag.state.ca.us/bne/index.htm*

### Department of Consumer Affairs
400 R Street
Sacramento, CA 95814
Director: Charlene Zettel
(800) 952-5210; (916) 445-1254
*www.dca.ca.gov*

### Department of Managed Health Care
980 9th Street, Suite 500
Sacramento, CA 95814
(916) 322-2078
*www.dmhc.ca.gov*

320 West 4th Street, Suite 880
Los Angeles, CA 90013-2344
(323) 576-5773

### Secretary of State
Business Filings Division
1500 11th Street
Sacramento CA 95814
(916) 657-5448
Special Filings email: SFTM@ss.ca.gov
*www.ss.ca.gov/business*

### Senate Business and Professions Committee
Room 2053, The Capitol
Sacramento CA 95814
(916) 445-3435
*www.senate.ca.gov/ftp/sen/committee/*
*standing/business/_home1/profile.htm*

# Federal Agencies

## Drug Enforcement Administration
### Liaison and Policy Section
600 Army-Navy Drive
Arlington, VA 22202
Liaison Chief: Patricia Good
(202) 307-7297
*www.usdoj.gov/dea/*

### Office of Diversion Control
Registration & Program Support Section
Chief: Richard Boyd
(800) 882-9539; (202) 307-4925
*www.deadiversion.usdoj.gov*

### San Francisco Field Division
450 Golden Gate Avenue, 14th Floor
San Francisco, CA 94102
(415) 436-7463

### Los Angeles Field Division
255 East Temple Street, 20th Floor
Los Angeles, CA 90012
(213) 621-6711

### San Diego Field Division
4560 Viewridge Avenue
San Diego, CA 92123-1637
(858) 616-4100

## Department of Health and Human Services
### Health Resources and Services Administration
Administrator: Elizabeth M. Duke, Ph.D.
*www.hrsa.gov*

### Food and Drug Administration
(888) 463-6332
*www.fda.gov*

## Pacific Regional Office/Office of Criminal Investigations
1301 Clay Street, Suite 1180-N
Oakland CA 94612-5217
(510) 637-3960

## Los Angeles District
19701 Fairchild
Irvine, CA 92612
(949) 608-2900

## San Francisco District
1431 Harbor Bay Parkway,
Alameda, CA 94502
(510) 337-6700

## Medwatch
To report adverse reaction and drug product defects:
(800) 332-1088
*www.fda.gov/medwatch*

## Office of Pharmacy Affairs
Asst. Director for Pharmacy Affairs: Thomas J. McGinnis
Parklawn Building HFP-1
5600 Fishers Lane
Rockville, Maryland 20857
(800) 628-6297
*www.bphc.hrsa.gov/opa*

## Nuclear Regulatory Commission
One White Flint North
11555 Rockville Pike,
Rockville, MD 20852
(301) 415-7000
*www.nrc.gov*

### Office of Public Affairs (OPA)
(800) 368-5642

### Office of Nuclear Material Safety and Safeguards
Industrial and Medical Nuclear Safety Division
Director: Charles L. Miller
(301) 415-7197

# Index

322

## Prescriptions